POLAROGRAPHIC TECHNIQUES

POLAROGRAPHIC TECHNIQUES

SECOND EDITION

LOUIS MEITES

Professor of Analytical Chemistry
Polytechnic Institute of Brooklyn
Brooklyn, New York

WITH A FOREWORD BY I. M. KOLTHOFF

Interscience Publishers

A DIVISION OF JOHN WILEY & SONS
New York • London • Sydney

FOREWORD TO THE SECOND EDITION

As had been anticipated, the first edition of Dr. Meites' book has met with a warm reception not only by electroanalytical chemists but also by all other chemists who use polarography in their research and as a technique in their analyses. The present edition has been greatly expanded and extended over the original one because of the tremendous advances in the techniques and interpretation of polarography and voltammetry in general, and because of the development of related techniques.

Not only the analytical, but also the inorganic, organic, physical, biochemical, and industrial literature is replete with applications of polarography and related techniques to specific research problems and also as a routine method of analysis. The present up-to-date revision by Dr. Meites, who is a recognized leader in the field and who has enriched the literature with many original contributions on several phases of polarography, will serve as a welcome guide to all chemists who use polarography, voltammetry, amperometry, chronopotentiometry, coulometry, and stripping analysis in their work. Not only the experienced polarographer but also the technician who is being initiated in the art and the science will have frequent occasion to consult this book as a reliable source of information and interpretation.

I. M. Kolthoff

PREFACE TO THE SECOND EDITION

Very substantial advances have been made in polarographic theory, instrumentation, and methodology since the first edition of this book was published in 1955, and these advances in polarography itself have been accompanied by the appearance and development of a host of other electroanalytical techniques intimately related to polarography. It has therefore seemed desirable to prepare a second edition that would take these recent developments into account.

To do so it has been necessary to expand the book considerably: it is now almost exactly three times its former length. Very little that seemed fundamental to polarographic theory and practice in 1955 seems any less fundamental today, although the topics considered in the first edition have been further illuminated by more recent work to such an extent that not a single paragraph has survived without change. Other topics whose omission seemed justified in 1955 because they were only beginning to be explored have since been found to be far too important to be ignored even by the beginner, and still others whose study was not begun until after 1955 have also already attained this status.

For two reasons, however, I have striven to keep this expansion to a minimum. The first edition was said to be "intended to serve as an introduction to the field for students, practical analysts, and research chemists generally," and the reception accorded it has seemed to indicate that others share my feeling that such an introduction is needed. Indeed, the need now seems even more pressing that it did in 1955: the more complex a subject becomes, the more difficult it is for the beginner to gain entry to it and for the worker experienced in one corner of it to keep abreast of the concepts and techniques regarded as elementary by his colleagues in other areas.

In addition, the literature of polarography has also grown markedly since 1955. G. W. C. Milner's *The Principles and Applications of Polarography and Other Electroanalytical Processes* is an excellent one-volume treatment of the field, and it includes much detailed information on the behaviors and determinations of organic, inorganic, and biological materials. The several authors of *Advances in Polarography*, edited by I. S. Longmuir, of *Progress in Polarography*, edited by P. Zuman and I. M. Kolthoff, and of the chapters on electroanalytical subjects in Volume 4 of Part I of the *Treatise on Analytical Chemistry*, edited by I. M. Kolthoff and P. J. Elving, have given valuable summaries of up-to-date information on a wealth of topics important to the beginner as well as to the more advanced worker. The forthcoming third edition of *Polarography*, by I. M. Kolthoff and J. J. Lingane and their collaborators, can be expected to be a *sine qua non* in every polarographic laboratory. A number of monographs have also appeared, and others are in preparation, on various advanced topics. *Alternating Current Polarography and Tensammetry*, by B. Breyer and H. H. Bauer, is a thorough and authoritative review of its field. *Modern Polarographic Methods*, by H. Schmidt and M. v. Stackelberg, is a lucid brief introduction to matters more briefly discussed here in Chapter 10.IX, and *Controlled-Potential Analysis*, by G. A. Rechnitz, is a valuable introduction to the applications of controlled-potential electrolysis and coulometry in inorganic analysis. Of great value to the organic analyst is the authoritative *Organic Polarographic Analysis*, by P. Zuman, and much valuable practical information can also be found in *Polarography in Medicine, Biochemistry and Pharmacy*, by M. Březina and P. Zuman. Amperometric titrations are comprehensively reviewed by J. Doležal and J. Zýka, though their book is unfortunately available only in Czech. The existence of these works has made it possible to omit or greatly condense discussions of many subjects. Reference to them and to individual review articles are given at many points to guide the reader's further study.

Within this framework, however, very substantial changes have been made. The section on polarographic instrumentation has been rewritten to include descriptions and recommendations of the various polarographs available in this country. Much fuller accounts are given of the theory of kinetic, catalytic, and adsorption waves, and a fairly comprehensive description of modern diffusion-current theory and its limitations has been added as well. So much progress has been made in the understanding of irreversible waves that an extensive account of their behavior and interpretation has been added, together with a description of the role played by the structure of the double layer. The treatment of half-wave potentials has been supplemented by an outline of the correlations that have been drawn between the half-wave potentials of organic compounds and their structures, and also by an explicit description of the difficulties of qualitative polarographic analysis. The prevalent theory of maxima is described at some length, and a short section has been added on adsorption analysis and electrochemical masking. Much discussion of the problems and techniques peculiar to organic analysis has been added in Chapter 7 and elsewhere, and the problems of wave order and wave separation are discussed at some length to lay the groundwork for the discussions in Chapter 10 of other techniques developed to deal with them. A new chapter has been added on voltammetric indicator electrodes other than the dropping electrode. The theory of amperometric titration curves is discussed much more fully than in the first edition, with special reference to the problems that arise when the reaction is far from complete; techniques of amperometric titrations with EDTA and similar reagents are described in some detail; and an account is given of dual-electrode amperometric titrations. Chapter 10 is almost wholly new, and represents an attempt to relate the techniques it describes to the conceptual foundations of classical polarography and thus to show why and how they are likely to be useful, as well as to provide some indications of their limitations, rather than to give comprehensive accounts of them in a necessarily restricted space.

Most of the chapters in the first edition were accompanied by directions for illustrative experiments. It has seemed necessary to sacrifice these to prevent the growth of the book from exceeding reasonable bounds. However, Appendix A has been revised to include the salient features of a number of separate experiments in the first edition and to assist the lone worker in diagnosing and correcting sources of trouble and error in his execution of the manipulations and measurements most often encountered in polarographic work.

Appendix B in the first edition was a comprehensive tabulation of virtually all of the inorganic polarographic data that were available when it was published, and it included a bibliography of several hundred references. To have included an equally complete table and its supporting references in this edition would have increased the length and price of the book so much that it could not be considered.

Hence the present Appendix B is far less complete than its predecessor, but it does contain considerably more information in a much more compact typographical arrangement. The data now included are those believed likely to be most generally interesting and useful. Literature references were sacrificed with regret, but the space saved by omitting them has made it possible to include a fairly extensive compilation of organic polarographic data in a new Appendix C.

I am glad to have this opportunity to acknowledge my gratitude to Dr. Petr Zuman for his generous help in pointing out a number of passages in the first edition that were erroneous or open to misinterpretation.

Louis Meites

Brooklyn, New York
October, 1964

From the Preface to the First Edition

Polarography is a complex science; it is complex experimentally as well as theoretically, and our knowledge of it is not yet so complete that there is not often much art to it as well. This volume is intended to serve as an introduction to the field for students, practical analysts, and research chemists generally. It began as a manual of purely experimental techniques, but it soon became evident that these could only be explained rationally by reference to the theory which guides all of our experimental manipulations.

Consequently this book contains a considerable amount of theoretical material; enough, I hope, to enable the beginner both to understand those well-established techniques for which explicit directions could be given and to cope with unexpected situations which may force him to modify a conventional technique or even devise a new one. In addition, I have attempted to give sufficiently complete and detailed directions for the common manipulations involved in polarographic work to make it possible for the tyro to carry them out with a minimum of trial and error of his own.

That the entire field of polarography could be adequately covered in a small book is quite impossible, and so I have regretfully had to omit discussions of many topics and to greatly curtail the expositions of many others. No doubt the beginner will wish to continue his education in polarography by consulting other works on the subject. Far and away the most comprehensive of these is the second edition of *Polarography*, by I. M. Kolthoff and J. J. Lingane: this monumental monograph is not only the most complete compilation of the data available as late as 1951, but also provides the best presentation of the whole of polarographic theory available anywhere. No one interested in the polarography of organic compounds can afford to be without O. H. Müller's chapter on this subject in Weissberger's *Technique of Organic Chemistry*. Lingane's *Electroanalytical Chemistry* contains the best exposition I know of the fundamental theory common to polarography and all other electrical methods of analysis, and in addition it is a veritable bible of the new field of controlled-potential electrolysis in which its author has done so much invaluable pioneer work. A great deal of information concerning new techniques related to polarography will be found in P. Delahay's *New Instrumental Methods in Electrochemistry*.

In addition to these general references, I have tried to select for inclusion in the bibliography those papers which would best serve to extend the student's knowledge of matters which limitations of space forbade me to discuss in greater detail. My omission of literature references which would only have served to substantiate numerical values and the like quoted in the text reflects, not a lack of appreciation of the labor which was expended in measuring those values, but simply a desire to provide the beginner with a list of those papers whose study I thought most essential to the furtherance of his knowledge.

I am deeply indebted to Professor I. M. Kolthoff, who first suggested the writing of this book and who offered a large number of most helpful suggestions while it was in preparation. He is to a considerable extent responsible for any merit the book may have; it is scarcely necessary to add that its faults are my responsibility alone. It is no less a pleasure to acknowledge my indebtedness to Professor James J. Lingane, who in guiding my early education in electro-analytical chemistry did for me what I hope that, in some small measure at least, this book may do for its readers. Not only have my wife's advice, suggestions, and criticisms been of immense assistance to me in the preparation of this manuscript, but her collaboration and help over the years have long been an invaluable aid and stimulus.

Louis Meites

New Haven, Connecticut
February, 1955

CONTENTS

CHAPTER 1

THE NATURE AND APPLICATIONS OF POLAROGRAPHY

Voltammetry is the branch of electroanalytical chemistry that deals with the effect of the potential of an electrode in an electrolysis cell on the current that flows through it. The electrode whose potential is varied is called the indicator electrode. Voltammetric indicator electrodes may be made from any of a large number of materials, including mercury, platinum, gold, graphite, and many others; they may have almost any size, shape, and construction; they may be stationary or in motion; and the solutions in which they are used may be stirred or quiet. Polarography is the branch of voltammetry in which a dropping mercury electrode is used as the indicator electrode.

The dropping mercury electrode consists of a capillary that has a very small internal diameter and that is nearly always made of glass. One end of the capillary is connected to a reservoir of mercury and the other end is immersed in the solution being investigated. The hydrostatic pressure of the mercury column causes mercury to flow through the capillary and form a droplet at the capillary tip. The droplet grows until it reaches a certain size, which depends on the geometry of the capillary tip and on the interfacial tension between the mercury and the solution, and then it falls, stirring the solution as it goes. At the same instant another droplet begins to form; this repeats the life cycle of its predecessor, and so on. Typically the lifetime of each droplet may be a few seconds.

Polarography was the first of the voltammetric techniques to gain prominence, and it is still the most widely used, because there are several advantages peculiar to the dropping mercury electrode. Probably the most important of these is that, except under certain very unusual circumstances, each drop exactly duplicates the behavior of the one that preceded it. This is because successive drops are born into solutions of identical composition, grow at the same rate, and reach the same maximum size. Consequently the currents are accurately reproducible from one drop to the next, and independent of the previous history of the experiment. Solid products cannot accumulate

1

on the electrode surface, changing its properties, as is possible with solid electrodes. The duration of the experiment is practically without effect, leaving only three important variables (electrode potential, solution composition, and current) to be considered. Another advantage inherent in the periodic nature of the dropping electrode is that it is much less sensitive to mechanical disturbances than stationary electrodes are. With a dropping electrode, a momentary jar or shock will cause one drop to behave erratically, but will have no effect on the following one, whereas with a stationary electrode it would vitiate the entire measurement by changing the structure of the diffusion layer which is slowly growing away from the electrode surface. Still another advantage of the dropping electrode is that the high overpotential for the reduction of hydrogen ion or water on a mercury surface makes it possible to investigate processes that can occur only under extremely strongly reducing conditions. These include the reductions of alkali and alkaline earth metal ions, and also of many difficultly reducible organic compounds like acetone, acrylonitrile, bromobenzene, and naphthalene.

There are, however, also some disadvantages associated with the dropping mercury electrode. One is that mercury is rather easily oxidized, so that very positive (i.e., strongly oxidizing) potentials cannot be secured. Another is that the continuous variation of electrode area gives rise to significant currents even in the absence of a reducible or oxidizable substance. These and other problems are responsible for the interest that has been shown in the use of other materials and configurations in the design of voltammetric indicator electrodes. The principles and techniques that underlie the use of these other electrodes are so closely related to those of polarography that the latter will be discussed first in this book. A separate chapter is devoted to other indicator electrodes.

The essential features of current-potential curves obtained with dropping mercury electrodes are shown in Fig. 1.1. Curve b is the polarogram of a dilute solution of hydrochloric acid; curve a was obtained under exactly the same conditions after the addition of a small concentration of cadmium ion. Each oscillation represents the life cycle of one drop. It is the difference between the currents on the two curves that is of interest. At potentials less negative than about −0.5 v., no detectable change of current results from the addition of cadmium ion, because these potentials are insufficiently negative to

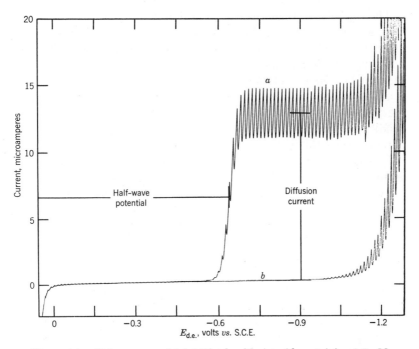

Figure 1.1.   Polarograms of (a) $1F$ hydrochloric acid containing 0.5mM cadmium ion, and (b) $1F$ hydrochloric acid alone.

bring about the reduction of any appreciable fraction of the cadmium ions at the surface of the drop. At potentials more negative than this, however, a wave appears: the reduction of cadmium ion proceeds more and more rapidly as the potential becomes more negative until eventually, at potentials more negative than about −0.7 v., it is so fast that cadmium ions are reduced as rapidly as they can diffuse from the bulk of the solution up to the surface of the electrode. The rate of this diffusion depends on a number of factors, among which the concentration of cadmium ion in the bulk of the solution is of special importance: the more concentrated the solution, the greater the rate at which cadmium ions reach the electrode surface, and the greater the diffusion current that results from their reduction. The proportionality between the diffusion current and the concentration of the substance responsible for the wave is the basis for nearly all quantitative polarographic analysis.

The ease of reduction or oxidation differs for different substances, and is reflected by the position of the wave with respect to the potential axis. This is expressed by a parameter called the half-wave potential, which is defined as the potential at which the current due to the reduction or oxidation of the substance responsible for the wave is half as large as on the plateau. The half-wave potential of cadmium ion is shown in Fig. 1.1(a). Under any defined set of experimental conditions, each substance has its own characteristic half-wave potential, and this is the basis of qualitative polarographic analysis.

Many other kinds of information can also be obtained from polarographic experiments. The diffusion current depends on the number of electrons consumed by each ion or molecule of the substance responsible for the wave, and so the product of the electrode reaction can often be inferred from diffusion-current data. It also depends on the diffusion coefficient of that substance, so that information regarding the size and solvation of the diffusing species can often be obtained. Side reactions may contribute to the current, and these can then be studied in considerable detail. The electrode reaction may be so rapid that equilibrium is closely approached at every potential in a time much shorter than the drop life; in this case the wave is said to be reversible, and studying the effects of potential and solution composition on the currents along the rising part of the wave then provides information on the thermodynamics of the half-reaction. Or the electrode reaction may involve a step having a large activation overpotential; then the variations of current with potential and solution composition are due to kinetic rather than thermodynamic effects, and in this case detailed information on the mechanism of the rate-determining step can be secured.

Polarographic analysis can be applied to volumes of solution as small as one or two drops. It is best suited to the determination of concentrations between about 1×10^{-5} and $2 \times 10^{-3}M$ (0.01 to 2mM). In this range, relative errors of the order of ± 2 or 3% can usually be attained by a moderately experienced technician in a routine laboratory; with more experience and with special equipment, relative errors as small as ± 1 or even 0.5% are often possible. The relative error rises rapidly as the concentration falls below about 0.01mM, for the current that flows in the absence of the substance of interest then becomes a substantial fraction of the total current on the plateau, from which it must be subtracted in order to evaluate the diffusion current. This correction naturally becomes increasingly uncertain as the diffusion current becomes smaller. Nevertheless, analyses of $0.001mM$ solutions can often be performed with relative errors no worse than about $\pm 10\%$ if interfering substances are absent or can be removed, and in some exceptional cases even $10^{-4}mM$ solutions can be analyzed. This lower limit can be considerably extended by other voltammetric techniques. With solutions more concentrated than about $2mM$, various difficulties may arise, including adsorption and also convection caused by density gradients in the layer of solution surrounding the mercury drop; the polarograms become distorted, the currents fluctuate irregularly, and exact proportionality between diffusion current and concentration becomes less likely.

Polarographic analysis can be used directly for the determination of any substance—solid, liquid, or gaseous, organic or inorganic, ionic or molecular—that can be dissolved in a solvent of reasonable dielectric constant and either reduced or oxidized at a mercury electrode. This includes the ions of nearly all metals and many nonmetals, and also organic compounds containing conjugated double or triple bonds, including polynuclear aromatic ring systems, as well as compounds like oximes, imines, ketones, aldehydes, peroxides, nitro, nitroso, hydroxylamino, and diazo compounds, and halosubstituted compounds. Many substances not included in this list can be determined by relatively simple expedients: typical examples are the determinations of sulfate (by precipitation with excess lead ion and determination of the excess) and of mononuclear aromatics (by nitration and determination of the resulting nitro derivative). To the practical analyst one of the most important advantages of polarography and the other voltammetric techniques is that they often enable him to determine two or even more substances by obtaining a single current-potential curve. For example, the simultaneous determination of cadmium and zinc is easy and usually even trivial, and so is that of naphthalene and anthracene. A single polarogram suffices even for the analysis of a solution containing all three of the isomeric nitrobenzoic acids if their concentrations are not too widely disparate. By many other techniques such analyses as these can be performed only after excessively laborious separations.

Another important analytical technique closely related to polarography is that of amperometric titration. Here polarographic or other voltammetric measurements are used to follow the concentration of one or more of the reactants or products during a titration with a suitable reagent. When the stoichiometry of the titration reaction is sufficiently reproducible and when the solution being analyzed is not too dilute, results accurate and precise to a few tenths of a per cent can often be obtained.

In addition to these analytical uses, polarography is one of the most fruitful techniques of research in physical, inorganic, and organic chemistry, and is coming to be more and more widely used in such subsidiary fields as biochemistry, pharmaceutical chemistry, and others. It has been used to study such diverse topics as hydrolysis, solubility, complex formation, adsorption, the stoichiometry and kinetics of chemical reactions, the mechanisms of electrode reactions and of chemical reactions accompanying them, standard and formal potentials, molecular dimensions, the effects of structure on reactivity, and many others of interest and importance. Polarography and the techniques related to it are among the most useful and versatile at the chemist's disposal.

CHAPTER 2

POLAROGRAPHS AND OTHER APPARATUS

I. Polarographic Circuits

In polarography as in most other instrumental techniques of analysis and research, little work is done nowadays with any but commercial instruments. Descriptions of the currently available polarographs are therefore given in some detail in the next section of this chapter. Most of these serve essentially the same purposes in essentially the same ways; they do differ in precision, convenience, and versatility, but their differences are much less striking than their similarities. This is a reflection of the inherent simplicity of polarographic circuits. This section is intended to describe the common principles underlying the design and operation of the majority of commercial polarographs, to provide the reader with a sound basis for understanding their features and limitations and evaluating the relevance of these to his own work, and to furnish guidance to the prospective user who does not need or cannot afford a commercial instrument.

Although the ability to perform other operations is usually desirable and often necessary, there are only two simple functions that a polarographic circuit must fulfill. One is the application across the electrolysis cell of any desired d.-c. voltage up to about 3 v. The other is the measurement of the current flowing through the cell, which may have any value up to perhaps 100 μamp.; for trace analysis and other work with very dilute solutions, it must be possible to detect and measure currents of the order of a few thousandths of a microampere.

There are two kinds of polarographs: manual and recording. With a manual instrument, the potential applied to the cell is adjusted to some desired value and the current is measured. A single point on the polarogram is thus obtained; if the whole curve is wanted, the procedure must be repeated many times. This is so tedious, especially if the polarogram consists of several waves or is otherwise complex, that manual polarographs cannot be recommended for this purpose in

7

routine work, although they can yield current-potential data much more precise than can be obtained with a recording instrument. Moreover, manual polarographs are not at a disadvantage when the shape of the curve is known and all that is wanted is a measurement of the height of a wave. This is the case in much routine analysis, in amperometric titrations, in studies of the rates of chemical reactions, and in many other applications. Diffusion-current measurements can be made more precisely and more quickly with manual than with recording polarographs, and serious consideration should therefore be given to the acquisition of a manual polarograph in either of two circumstances: in laboratories where very little polarographic work is done and the much higher cost of a recording instrument cannot be justified, and in laboratories where both routine and nonroutine work are done and where the manual instrument would free a recording one for research and nonroutine analytical work.

In a recording polarograph, on the other hand, the potential applied to the cell is obtained from a motor-driven voltage divider. Two procedures have been most frequently employed for recording the current. In one, the current is passed through a galvanometer, and the deflections of the galvanometer are recorded photographically on a piece of photographic paper moving at a known rate past a slit. In the other, which is now by far the more common in this country and most others, the current is passed through a standard resistor in series with the cell, and the resulting iR drop is presented to a strip-chart recording potentiometer, which plots the iR drop against time. Correlating the rates of motion of the chart and the voltage divider makes it possible to interpret the curve as a plot of current against applied potential. Usually a recording polarograph employs a rate of change of potential of about 0.2 volt per minute and furnishes a complete polarogram in about 10 minutes. The time required for the recording is, of course, smaller if only a portion of the curve need be examined.

The essential elements of a very simple manual polarograph are shown in Fig. 2.1. The required d.-c. voltage can be most economically secured from dry cells or from a lead storage battery, either of which should be partially discharged before use to ensure maximum stability. Laboratory d.-c. supplies are not usually stable enough for the purpose. The potentiometer R_{11} serves to adjust the voltage applied to the cell circuit to the desired value, which is indicated by the

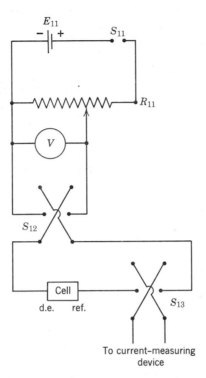

Figure 2.1. Schematic diagram of a simple manual polarograph. E_{11}: 2–4-v. d.-c. source; R_{11}: voltage divider (rheostat or radio potentiometer); S_{11}: SPST on–off switch; S_{12}: DPDT reversing switch for applying positive or negative potentials to the dropping electrode; S_{13}: DPDT reversing switch for presenting positive or negative currents to the current-measuring device; V: 0–3-v. d.-c. voltmeter. Throughout this chapter, the first digit in the number of an electrical component (or the first two digits when there are three in all) identifies the figure in which the component appears. Thus S_{12} and S_{211} appear in Figs. 2.1 and 2.21, respectively.

voltmeter V. This should have a 0–3-v. range and its readability and accuracy should be no worse than ± 0.02 v. The linearities of inexpensive panel voltmeters are usually such ($\pm 2\%$ of full scale, or ± 0.06 v. for an 0–3-v. meter) that calibration is necessary to ensure that the potential actually applied to the cell circuit is sufficiently close to that desired. The reversing switches S_{12} and S_{13} are included because the dropping electrode may have to be either the positive or

the negative electrode of the cell and because the current may be
either positive or negative. By convention a positive current corresponds to reduction at the indicator electrode. In much routine work,
however, it can be foreseen that only one or two of the quadrants of
the complete current-potential diagram will be of interest, and one
or both of these switches can then be omitted. The current-measuring
device may be a microammeter such as the Triplett Model 726 (The
Triplett Electrical Instrument Co., Bluffton, Ohio), which has a
6.4-in. scale and a 0–50-μamp. range. The period of a microammeter
is so short that the excursions resulting from the periodic growth and
fall of the mercury drops are too wide for convenience unless the
meter is damped, and an electrolytic capacitor of about 1000 μf.
should, therefore, be connected across its terminals.

Although circuitry as simple as this would often suffice for such
purposes as routine checking of the concentration of a major constituent of an electroplating solution, both the sensitivity and the
precision of a microammeter are too limited for most polarographic

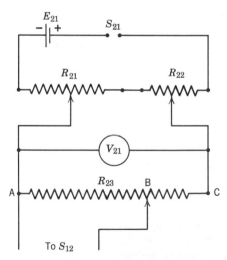

Figure 2.2. Schematic diagram of a more precise applied-potential module.
E_{21}: 2–4-v. d.-c. source; R_{21}: 100-ohm linear taper single-turn potentiometer for
coarse adjustment of bridge voltage; R_{22}: 10-ohm linear taper single-turn potentiometer for fine adjustment of bridge voltage; R_{23}: bridge (see text); S_{21}: SPST
on-off switch; V_{21}: 0–3-v. d.-c. voltmeter.

work, and other current-measuring devices are therefore generally preferable. Two will be discussed here: galvanometers and precision potentiometers. At the same time, the applied-potential circuit shown in Fig. 2.1 is always replaced by a more accurate one like that shown in Fig. 2.2.

Here the coarse and fine potentiometers R_{21} and R_{22} are used to adjust the potential across the bridge R_{23} to some convenient value, such as 1.00 or 3.00 v. Any error in the voltmeter V is thus minimized, for only a fraction of its absolute error appears in the potential applied to the cell. In any work except that in which values of the current alone are wanted, however, it is desirable to calibrate the voltmeter against a precision potentiometer. Alternatively, one may employ the module shown in Fig. 2.3, which permits standardization of the bridge against the Weston cell E_{31}. With the cell circuit disconnected by throwing S_{31} to the center off position, the slider B of R_{23} is set to provide a nominal output of 1.018 v., and R_{21} and R_{22} are then adjusted so that no deflection of the microammeter M (which may be an inexpensive panel meter of the center zero type) is obtained when the circuit through it is closed momentarily by means of S_{31}.

The bridge R_{23} is used to apply a known fraction of the voltage across it to the portion of the circuit containing the cell and the current-measuring device. So that R_{23} will function as an accurately linear voltage divider, its resistance must be very much smaller than the effective resistance of the cell circuit. Values up to about 100 ohms are satisfactory in polarographic work; lower values might be needed in some stirred-electrode voltammetry with moderately concentrated solutions (cf. Chap. 8). A ten-turn helical potentiometer,

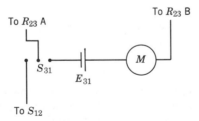

Figure 2.3. Schematic diagram of a simple module for standardizing the bridge R_{23} to eliminate errors in voltmeter reading and calibration. E_{31}: Weston cell; M: 50–0–50 microampere d.-c. meter or pointer-type galvanometer; S_{31}: SPDT switch with center off and (on right-hand side) momentary on positions.

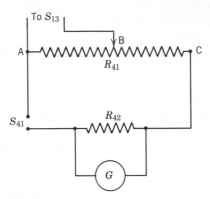

Figure 2.4. Schematic diagram of a module employing a galvanometer for measurements of current. G: galvanometer; R_{41}: Ayrton-type shunt (see text); R_{42}: resistor for damping and adjustment of sensitivity (see text); S_{41}: SPST on–off switch (which may be omitted if S_{13} has a center off position).

such as a Helipot or Borg Micropot with an accompanying dial, is suitable. Its linearity should be at least as good as $\pm 0.1\%$. In especially careful work, such as the measurement of half-wave potentials with a precision better than a few millivolts, the mean potential drop across the cell at each point on the current-voltage curve should be measured directly with a precision potentiometer.

A typical circuit module employing a galvanometer is shown in Fig. 2.4. Here the linear voltage divider R_{41} serves as an Ayrton-type shunt to adjust the effective sensitivity of the galvanometer so that easily and precisely measurable deflections can be obtained throughout the expected range of currents. If s^0 is the maximum effective sensitivity of the galvanometer (which is dependent on both its rated sensitivity and the value of the damping resistor R_{42}), its sensitivity s at any setting of R_{41} will be given by

$$s = (R_{AC}/R_{AB})\, s^0 \qquad (2.1)$$

To facilitate the comparison of deflections obtained at different shunt settings, it is convenient to have R_{AC}, which is the total resistance of R_{41}, equal to some even value such as 1000 ohms. One may use two decade resistance boxes, subtracting from one box the same resistance that is added to the other so that the sum of their resistances is always 1000 ohms. Three ganged back-to-back pairs of decade resistance units (e.g., Types 510 C-E, General Radio Co., West Concord, Massachusetts) will perform the subtraction and addition simultaneously and save much time and trouble in the long run. A 1000-ohm ten-turn helical potentiometer with a linearity of $\pm 0.1\%$ or better is more economical, compact, and convenient, although its accuracy is inferior at high currents (low shunt settings) because the linearity error then becomes relatively large. Each of these arrangements gives a much wider choice of settings than any commercially available Ayrton shunt. This is advantageous because the full width of the galvanometer scale can then be employed for measuring all but the very smallest currents. Shunts whose successive settings differ by factors of ten, though readily available commercially, are unsuitable for polarographic use.

The damping resistance R_{42} governs the widths of the oscillations resulting from the growth and fall of the drops, and also affects the maximum effective sensitivity. Its resistance must be very much smaller than that of the shunt R_{41}, for otherwise the effect of the latter will not be linear. However, this is of no importance if measurement and calibration are always performed at identical shunt settings. If the apparatus is to be used for studying the mechanisms of irreversible electrode processes, R_{42} should equal or just barely exceed the critical damping resistance of the galvanometer and the critically damped galvanometer should have a period no longer than one second. As was indicated above, however, manual polarographs are rarely used for such purposes, for there is too little use for the greater precision they can provide to justify the additional labor needed to operate them. For diffusion-current measurements it is better to choose a value of R_{42} that gives a galvanometer period between 15 and 20 sec.; longer periods make the instrument undesirably sluggish, while shorter ones yield average currents differing appreciably from the truth. Galvanometers with critically damped periods as long as this are not easily secured, and therefore it is almost always necessary to overdamp the galvanometer considerably. This involves so much sacrifice of sensitivity that care should be taken to select a galvanometer whose critically damped sensitivity is great enough to permit severe overdamping without reducing the sensitivity to a figure any larger than 0.003–0.005 μamp./mm. at a distance of one meter. Excellent performance can be secured with Leeds and Northrup Type HS or Rubicon Type 3514 taut suspension galvanometers.

Very sensitive galvanometers like these are inherently very susceptible to vibration and shock; this is one reason why strip-chart recording instruments are so widely preferred over photographic ones. The problem of contriving adequately vibration-proof mountings for a galvanometer and a dropping-electrode assembly, especially in industrial or metropolitan surroundings, is often extremely vexing. It is mentioned briefly in Sec. V below, but for the most part it must be left to the ingenuity of the individual experimenter. Because the zero position and sensitivity of a galvanometer are affected by changes of temperature, care should be taken to place the galvanometer in a location well protected from drafts, and it should be enclosed in a case lined with asbestos, Fiberglas, or some other insulating material.

A galvanometer should be recalibrated at frequent intervals, and this is best done with the aid of the circuit module shown in Fig. 2.5. To evaluate the sensitivity s at any setting of the shunt R_{41}, the switch S_{51} is thrown to the "calibrate" position and the potentiometer R_{51} is adjusted (preferably by decreasing its resistance from an initially high value) to give a conveniently measurable deflection. Deviations of the galvanometer response from linearity become less important as this deflection becomes more nearly equal to that produced by a current measured just before the calibration at the same shunt setting. The voltage drop E across the precision 10,000-ohm resistor R_{52} is measured with a precision potentiometer, and the sensitivity is computed from the equation $s = 100E/d$; s will be given

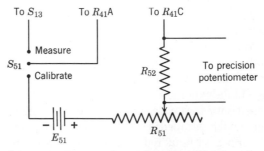

Figure 2.5.   Schematic diagram of a module for calibration of a galvanometer with the aid of a precision potentiometer. E_{51}: 22.5 volts d.c.; R_{51}: 2-megohm linear taper single-turn potentiometer for adjustment of current; R_{52}: 10,000-ohm precision ($\pm 0.1\%$) resistor; S_{51}: SPDT switch.

in microamperes/millimeter if E is expressed in volts and the deflection d in millimeters. This procedure eliminates the effects of any errors in the calibration of the shunt R_{41}.

If a precision potentiometer is not available, one may employ the following procedure, which is also suitable for calibrating the current scale of a recording polarograph. The electrolysis cell is replaced by a precision resistor having a value of, say, 1000 ohms. This should be so chosen as to yield a current in the range of interest. Then a potential of about 1 v. is applied by suitable adjustment of R_{23}, and the setting of the shunt R_{41} is increased from an initially small value until an easily measurable galvanometer deflection results. If E_1 is the total voltage across the precision resistor and the galvanometer and its shunts, and if R is the effective resistance of R_{41}, R_{42}, and the galvanometer (which varies with the shunt setting and is a maximum when R_{AB} is approximately half of the total resistance of R_{41}),

$$E_1 = i(1000 + R) \qquad (2.2)$$

Next the 1000-ohm precision resistor is replaced by a 2000-ohm one and, without changing the shunt setting, the applied potential is increased until the galvanometer deflection (and hence the current flowing through it) is restored to exactly the same value. Now the applied voltage E_2 is given by

$$E_2 = i(2000 + R) \qquad (2.3)$$

Since R is the same for the two measurements, eqs. (2.2) and (2.3) may be combined to give

$$E_2 - E_1 = 1000i \qquad (2.4)$$

If d is the galvanometer deflection and s the sensitivity,

$$i = sd \qquad (2.5)$$

Combining eqs. (2.4) and (2.5) and changing the units of i from amperes to microamperes,

$$s = 1000(E_2 - E_1)/d \qquad (2.6)$$

where s will be given in microamperes/millimeter if E is expressed in volts and d in millimeters. The sensitivity at any other shunt setting $f \ (= R_{AB}/R_{AC})$ is obtained by rewriting eq. (2.1):

$$s = s^0/f \qquad (2.7)$$

from which it follows that the product sf is constant if the shunt is accurately linear.

Another calibration technique, which is recommended by the manufacturers of some commercial polarographs, both manual and recording, consists of replacing the electrolysis cell with a precision resistor whose resistance R_s is comparatively high, typically 250,000 ohms. A potential E of about 1 v. is applied to the cell circuit by means of the bridge, and the galvanometer or recorder deflection d is measured at an appropriate setting of the shunt. The sensitivity at that shunt setting is computed from the equation

$$s = 10^6 \, E/d \, R_s \qquad (2.8)$$

and will be given in microamperes/millimeter if E is expressed in volts, d in millimeters, and R_s in ohms. Though this is less accurate than either of the above techniques because it neglects the resistance of the galvanometer and its shunts (or of the recorder and the resistance across which the iR drop is recorded), with the instruments for which it is recommended these resistances are small enough that the error is unlikely ever to be significant.

Galvanometer deflections may be measured with either a lamp and scale or telescope and scale. The former is usually preferable because it permits a more compact arrangement. In setting up a galvanometer, the experimenter should be aware of the "tangent error." This arises from the fact that the deflection d observed on a linear scale is proportional to the tangent of the angular deflection θ of the galvanometer, whereas it is θ itself that is proportional to the current. The values of θ and $\tan \theta$ diverge more and more widely as they increase; when $\theta = 9.8°$ the difference between them reaches 1%. If the error is not to exceed this value, the distance from the galvanometer to the scale must be at least six times the scale width, which in turn should be at least 40 or 50 cm. Except in laboratories of substantial dimensions, this is hardly possible unless several reflections are included in the optical path, which is sufficiently difficult to arrange that it is usually better to employ a curved scale whose radius of curvature is approximately equal to its distance from the galvanometer. The galvanometer should be so adjusted that the zero-current position lies 1–2 cm. away from one end of the scale. Provision must be made for the measurement of currents that oscillate between small positive and small negative values, but substantial currents of either sign should be brought on scale by manipulation of the switch S_{13} rather than by means of a center zero setting of the galvanometer.

Measuring the oscillating current obtained from a dropping electrode is often troublesome for the beginner, but it rapidly becomes less so with practice. What is usually wanted is the mean of the maximum and minimum scale readings during the drop life. Under normal conditions these are extremely reproducible from drop to drop. It is easiest to concentrate on the maximum readings for several drops, then on the minimum ones for several more. This is still easier to do if the oscillations are made very narrow by temporarily connecting a small auxiliary resistor or a large electrolytic capacitor in parallel with R_{42}. The galvanometer will then be so sluggish that it will be necessary to wait for a minute or two before beginning the readings. When experience and confidence have been gained, the circuit may be restored to normal operation by removing the resistor or capacitor. The oscillations are of great value, despite the confusion they cause the beginner, because their reproducibility (or lack of it) indicates whether the capillary is functioning properly or not.

Two alternative circuit modules in which a precision potentiometer is used for measuring the current are shown in Figs. 2.6 and 2.7. That in Fig. 2.6 is the more closely allied to the circuits of recording

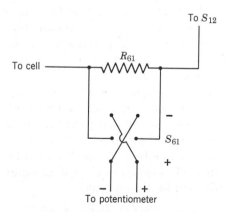

Figure 2.6. Schematic diagram of a module employing a precision potentiometer for measurements of current. R_{61}: precision ($\pm 0.1\%$) resistor chosen to yield a suitable iR drop, typically 10,000 ohms; S_{61}: DPDT reversing switch to permit presentation to the potentiometer of an iR drop having the same sign regardless of the sign of the current.

polarographs employing recording potentiometers, while that in Fig. 2.7 is intended to provide the greatest possible precision in measurements of the voltage across the cell.

In the circuit of Fig. 2.6, the precision resistor R_{61} in series with the cell develops an iR drop that is measured with the precision potentiometer; the switch S_{61} permits the measurement of currents of either sign, as did S_{13}. Different values of R_{61} should be available so that currents of different magnitudes can be measured, and can be most conveniently provided by connecting several precision resistors to a selector switch. The iR drop across R_{61} should be a sufficiently large fraction of the full range of the potentiometer to permit convenient and precise measurement. The potentiometer should be capable of measuring voltages no larger than a few hundredths of a volt with a precision at least as good as $\pm 0.5\%$.

The maximum current during the drop life can be measured by critically damping the galvanometer employed as the null detector in the potentiometric circuit and finding the setting of the potentiometer that produces no galvanometer deflection at the instant when the drop attains its maximum age. It must again be emphasized, however, that this is a special purpose; for diffusion-current measurements and in nearly all other work the galvanometer should instead be severely overdamped by connecting a small resistance across its terminals. The damped period should be so long that the oscillations during the drop life are no wider than 1 or 2 cm. It is probably not necessary to state that the tapping key of the potentiometer must be held down continuously during the measurements, and not just depressed momentarily in the usual manner.

In any of these polarographic circuits, the voltage obtained from the applied potential circuit (e.g., from the bridge R_{23}) appears partly as a voltage drop across the cell and partly as an iR drop across the current-measuring device. In the galvanometric circuit of Fig. 2.4, the resistance of R_{42} is usually much smaller than that of the galvanometer, and so the resistance R_g of the galvanometer and its shunts is closely approximated by the equation

$$R_g = f(1 - f) R_{41} + R_{42} \tag{2.9}$$

where f is the setting of R_{41} as defined above (p. 15). Combining this with eqs. (2.5) and (2.7) yields an expression for the iR drop across R_g:

$$iR_g = [(1 - f) R_{41} + R_{42}/f] s^0 d \tag{2.10}$$

where the value of iR_g will be given in microvolts if the other quantities have their customary units. If the deflection d is constant, there is no maximum value of iR_g, but even under rather extreme conditions it is unlikely to exceed 2 or 3 mv. with typical values of the circuit parameters. Corrections for the iR drop across a galvanometer and its shunts are, therefore, necessary only when the ultimate accuracy must be attained in the values of the voltage across the cell; they are ignored in all analytical and most other work.

The situation is quite different, however, when a resistance-potentiometer arrangement is employed, for then the iR drop that is measured by the potentiometer is unlikely to be much smaller than 10 mv. and may often be as large as a tenth of a volt. In an instrument constructed by inserting the module shown in Fig. 2.6 into the circuit shown in Fig. 2.2, the easiest way to apply the correction is provided by the equation

$$E_{cc} = E_{cell} + E_R \qquad (2.11)$$

where E_{cc} is the voltage applied to the cell circuit and is evaluated from the setting of the bridge R_{23} and the voltage across it, E_{cell} is the voltage drop across the cell, and E_R is the voltage drop across the resistor R_{61}, which is, of course, equal to the reading of the potentiometer when it is balanced. Here as elsewhere in electrochemical work, signs can cause much confusion. The following conventions must be observed: E_{cc} has the same sign as the terminal of the d.-c. supply to which the dropping electrode is connected (all of the circuit diagrams in this chapter are drawn to correspond to negative values of E_{cc}), E_{cell} has the same sign as the potential of the dropping electrode with respect to the other electrode of the cell (so that E_{cell} is negative when the dropping electrode is the negative electrode), and E_R has the sign opposite to that of the current (which is indicated by the direction in which S_{61} must be thrown to obtain balance, as shown in Fig. 2.6). Thus E_R is negative if the current is cathodic, and positive if it is anodic. This source of confusion is, unfortunately, usually overlooked until a case is encountered in which E_{cc} and E_{cell} have opposite signs. It may be mentioned that E_{cell} includes the iR drop through the cell as well as the desired difference between the potentials of the two electrodes. Correction for this is discussed in Sec. IV below.

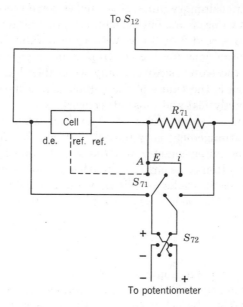

Figure 2.7. Schematic diagram of a module employing a precision potentiometer for measurements of both the current and the potential of the dropping electrode. R_{71}: precision resistor (see R_{61} in Fig. 2.6); S_{71}: DPDT switch to present either the cell potential or the iR drop across R_{71} to the potentiometer; S_{72}: DPDT reversing switch permitting access to all four quadrants of the current–potential diagram. Errors resulting from iR drop through the cell can be minimized by using a three-electrode cell, with S_{71} connected to a second reference electrode, which does not carry the electrolysis current, as shown by the dashed line rather than to point A as shown by the solid line.

The arrangement in Fig. 2.7 permits the potentiometer to be used for measuring E_{cell} directly; it is used for measuring the current in the same way as in the module of Fig. 2.6, but now the range of the potentiometer must be wide enough to accommodate the largest expected value of E_{cell}. In work with difficultly reducible substances this may have to be as large as 2.7 v. As potentiometers are rarely provided with ranges this wide, and as it is not convenient to connect a voltage divider in parallel with the cell, this circuit is less widely useful than that of Fig. 2.6, and in addition it virtually doubles the time that must be expended on each point. But as long as E_{cell} is not too large the circuit of Fig. 2.7 can yield current–potential data suitable for the most refined theoretical studies. Another special advantage of this circuit arises in work with three-electrode cells and is mentioned in Sec. IV below.

The above circuit modules form the basis of recording as well as manual polarographs. In recording instruments, however, some modifications and additions are necessitated by the nature of the recording process, while others become desirable for the sake of greater versatility, convenience, or accuracy.

Recording instruments based on the modules of Figs. 2.1, 2.2, and 2.4 have been constructed by a number of authors; those of Figs. 2.3 and 2.5 are easily added if their functions are wanted. It now becomes necessary to provide for scanning the potential range, which is readily done by means of a motor attached to the shaft of R_{23}, and also for recording the deflections of the galvanometer. This has usually been done by wrapping a sheet of photographic bromide paper around a cylindrical drum that rotates in an enclosure that has a slit accurately parallel to the axis of the drum but is otherwise light-tight. The image of the galvanometer lamp, which must be perpendicular to the slit and as narrow as possible, is focused on the paper. A dot is produced on the paper; its position along the axis of the slit depends on the current, while its position along the axis perpendicular to the slit varies at a known rate as the drum turns, so that a photographic record of the current–voltage curve is obtained as the bridge and drum rotate. Unless the apparatus is light-tight it must be operated in a darkroom to prevent the intrusion of stray light. The bridge and drum should have a common shaft and be turned by the same motor, so that the position of the dot can be exactly correlated with the setting of the bridge. This was the principle of the original Heyrovský-Shikata instrument, and an instrument essentially identical with this is still available as the Model XII Polarograph from E. H. Sargent & Co.

A darkroom is a vital adjunct to a photographically recording polarograph, for the loading and processing operations can hardly be carried out in the light. This is one reason why such instruments are becoming less popular. Another is that the photographic processing is somewhat time-consuming. A third is that galvanometers are much more sensitive to vibration than strip-chart recorders, which may occasionally necessitate the construction of a vibration-proof mounting (1) for a photographically recording instrument. A fourth is that the beginner often finds it hard to visualize the appearance of the curve from the galvanometer deflections he can observe on the scale provided, and so must wait until the paper is developed to feel sure of what he has obtained; this problem, however, vanishes rapidly with practice. Similar instruments are still very widely used in Europe, and in the writer's opinion the Sargent Model XII is well worth considering when automatic recording is desired but when only occasional polarographic work is contemplated and the higher cost of a visible-recording instrument cannot be justified. On the other hand, if darkroom facilities are not already available it is usually more economical to buy a potentiometrically recording instrument.

Because the dimensions of a piece of photographic paper may change appreciably during processing and drying, and may continue to vary slightly with changing humidity thereafter, it is necessary to define the voltage and current scales on each polarogram. To mark the voltage scale, the galvanometer is adjusted so that the image of the filament falls just above the lower (left-hand) edge of the paper; then the bridge is set to zero and the slit is opened for a few seconds. This is repeated at a number of points along the bridge, giving a series of dots at known values of the applied potential. The galvanometer zero is then set at the desired position (near the left-hand edge of the paper for a cathodic wave, near the right-hand edge for an anodic one, or near the center if both anodic and cathodic currents must be recorded on the same curve) and this position is marked by placing a dot on the paper at each extreme of the rotation of the bridge. The "paper sensitivity" of the galvanometer is recorded in the same way by placing a dot on the paper that corresponds to the deflection used in the calibration procedure (p. 15); this will not be the same as the deflection observed on the visual scale because the distances from the galvanometer to the paper and to the visual scale are unequal.

Provision must be made for recording both anodic and cathodic currents, as mentioned in the preceding paragraph. This, of course, is the function of S_{13}, but although this arrangement is perfectly satisfactory in a manual instrument no one would want to interrupt and distort a continuous curve by changing its direction while it was being recorded. The zero-current position of the light spot in a photographically recording instrument could be varied by rotating the galvanometer suspension, while that of the pen of a recording potentiometer could be varied by changing its point of attachment to its linkage, but these are crude expedients, and a compensation circuit like the one shown in Fig. 2.8 is always used instead. The points of attachment of this module and the values of the circuit parameters are suitable for use with a recording potentiometer having a full-scale range of 10 mv.; if its range were, say, 1 mv., both R_{83} and R_{84} should have ten times the values shown. A slightly different arrangement is needed for use with a galvanometer. Moving the slider of either R_{81} or R_{82} away from their junction point A adds a voltage to the iR drop across the measuring resistor R_{61}. It is the sum of these that is presented to the recorder input, and so the recorder zero moves upscale if the slider of R_{81} is moved away from A. If the recorder zero is set near the upper end of the chart, most of the chart width is available for recording anodic currents; if it is set to a point near the center of the chart, both an anodic and a cathodic wave can be recorded on the same polarogram. The polarity of the voltage drop across R_{82} is opposite to that across R_{81}, and so the recorder zero moves downscale as the slider of R_{82} is moved away from A. If R_{83} and R_{84} have different values, one potentiometer will serve for coarse and the other for fine adjustment. The module also serves for compensating the diffusion current of a wave preceding the one of interest, as discussed in Chap. 3 V. Multiple cathodic waves are so much more common than multiple anodic ones that it is convenient for the downscale control R_{82} to have the wider range, which is achieved by making R_{84} smaller than R_{83}. The usual ranges are such that the upscale control can displace the recorder zero by about two chart widths from its null position, while the downscale control has a range of about ten chart widths.

It is necessary to allow for both positive and negative potentials. It must also be possible to expand a selected narrow range of potentials to cover the full length of the chart; to examine the wave of, say, phenylacetylene, whose half-wave potential is about -2.4 v., it would be a waste of time to begin the polarogram at 0 v. One might certainly apply 3 v. across the bridge and begin the recording with a bridge setting that yielded 2.1 v. across the cell, but then the wave would occur in so small a fraction of the bridge rotation that it would be compressed into an undesirably small length. For these reasons it is desirable to be able to choose different initial and span potentials by means of separate circuits. The span potential is that across the bridge, and is the difference between the applied potentials at the end

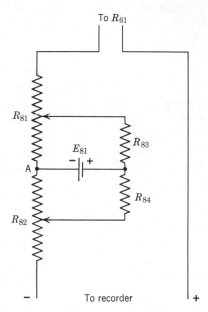

Figure 2.8. Schematic diagram of a module for shifting the null-current position of the recorder in a recording polarograph. E_{81}: 1.5-v. dry cell; R_{81} and R_{82}: 25-ohm linear taper potentiometers; R_{83}: 2000-ohm $\frac{1}{2}$-w. carbon resistor; R_{84}: 400-ohm $\frac{1}{2}$-w. carbon resistor.

and at the beginning of the polarogram; the initial potential is that applied to the cell circuit at the start of the polarogram.

The number of choices necessary or desirable depends, of course, on what is to be done with the instrument. If one is interested in the detailed shape of a wave occurring around -1.0 v., it is extremely convenient to be able to spread the region from, say, -0.75 to -1.25 v. over the whole length of the chart; if an initial potential near -0.75 v. is not available, some precision of measurement must be sacrificed. Maximum versatility is obtained by employing the module shown in Fig. 2.9 in conjunction with the span-potential module of Fig. 2.2. The reversing switch S_{91} permits changing the sign of the span potential E_s, so that the potential of the dropping electrode can be made to become either more negative or more positive as the recording proceeds. Polarization toward increasingly negative potentials ($E_s < 0$) is almost universally employed in work with the dropping electrode. Some experimenters use polarization toward increasingly positive potentials ($E_s > 0$) when the rate of polarization (which is proportional to the value of E_s) is so high, or when the recorder is so slow or so excessively damped, that a faithful reproduction of the rapidly increasing current on the rising part of a wave cannot be obtained. If the polarogram is recorded once with the potential becoming increasingly negative and then again with the potential becoming increasingly positive, each of the two half-wave potentials will differ from the truth, but the deviations will be in opposite directions, and the mean of their values will often be nearly correct. Despite the frequency with which this is recommended, the writer thinks it better to use an instrument correctly once than wrongly twice; if one is interested in the half-wave potential, he should simply not use a damping or a span potential so high that an erroneous value is obtained. Moreover, the theoretical justification for the procedure, such as it is, depends on the symmetry of the polarographic wave; although most waves are symmetrical around the half-wave potential there are some that are not, and the procedure cannot in principle yield correct values for the half-wave potentials of asymmetrical waves. A valid reason for making provision for polarization toward increasingly positive potentials arises in work with solid electrodes such as platinum, where the nature of the electrode depends on its history. Because of the existence and characteristics of oxide and other films, an electrode whose potential is becoming more positive may have a surface quite different from that of another whose potential is becoming more negative even at the instant when their potentials are the same. It may also be mentioned that the ability to effect polarization toward increasingly positive potentials is absolutely indispensable in anodic voltammetry with stationary electrodes. These matters are discussed in Chap. 8.

The circuitry around S_{92} and S_{93} provides the initial potential. The reversing switch S_{92} allows this to have either sign, while S_{93} both disconnects the battery E_{91} and shorts out the whole module when the polarogram is to be begun from 0 v. Since any error in the voltmeter V_{91}, on which the initial potential is indicated, results in an exactly equal error in every potential on the polarogram (which is not true of any error in the span-potential voltmeter V_{21}), V_{91} must be capable of being read to ± 2 mv. or better and should be carefully calibrated. It is still better in very precise measurements of half-wave

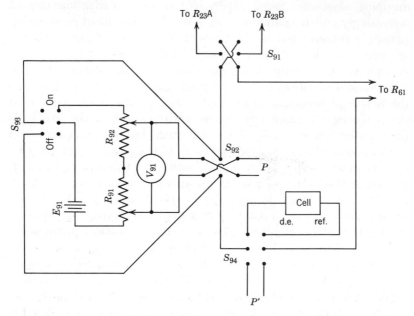

Figure 2.9. Schematic diagram of a module for providing any desired initial potential in a recording polarograph. E_{91}: 1.5- (or, rarely, 3-) v. d.-c. source; R_{91}: 100-ohm linear taper potentiometer for coarse adjustment of initial potential; R_{92}: 10-ohm linear taper potentiometer for fine adjustment; S_{91}: DPDT reversing switch providing polarization in either direction; S_{92}: DPDT reversing switch providing initial potentials of either sign; S_{93}: DPDT on-off switch; S_{94}: optional DPDT switch for direct measurement of the potential applied to the cell when a precision potentiometer is connected at P'. Connection at P provides a value of the initial potential only if the mechanical and electrical zero points of the bridge R_{23} coincide.

potentials to use a precision potentiometer to measure the initial potential directly. This can be done by connecting the potentiometer at P (in which case S_{94} is unnecessary) or by substituting it for the cell at P' by means of S_{94}. The latter is better because any zero-point error in the bridge R_{23} is then taken into account by making the measurement with S_{21} on, V_{21} set to the desired value of E_s, and R_{23} set to zero as for starting the polarogram.

One advantage of this arrangement is illustrated by the curves shown in Fig. 2.10. These were obtained under exactly identical conditions except for the difference between their initial potentials. In

each case the anodic current flowing at potentials more positive than
+0.05 v. is due to the oxidation of mercury according to the half-
reaction $2 \text{ Hg} + 2 \text{ Cl}^- = \text{Hg}_2\text{Cl}_2 + 2 e$. Figure 2.10($a$) contains no
more information than Fig. 2.10(b). The only difference is that in
recording Fig. 2.10(a) a large current flowed for some time before the
potential reached a value at which the pen departed from the edge

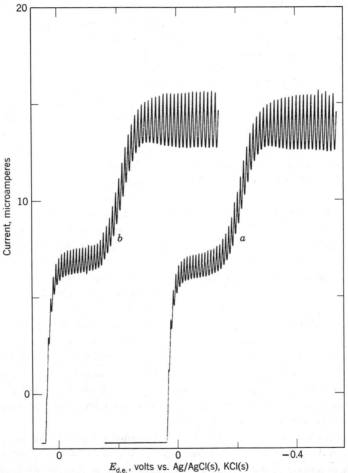

Figure 2.10. Polarograms of 1.2mM copper(II) in 1.5F potassium chloride
containing 0.0015% Triton X-100, begun from (a) +0.26 v. and (b) +0.06 v. vs.
a silver–silver chloride–saturated potassium chloride reference electrode.

of the chart. Some of the mercurous chloride that forms inside the capillary tip during such an interval remains there, and the capillary deteriorates more rapidly than if the recording is begun at a potential where mercury is less rapidly oxidized.

There are commercial instruments that provide for internal standardization of the initial potential against a standard cell, which appears at first glance to permit very high precision to be obtained in measurements of half-wave and other potentials from recorded polarograms. To make such standardization feasible, however, the number of initial potentials available must be rather small. The user of the resulting instrument, confronted by the solution of Fig. 2.10, may proceed in either of two ways. He can begin the polarogram at whichever of the accurately standardized initial potentials is next more positive than the potential at which information begins to become available. If the initial potentials provided are $+1$ and 0 v., he must choose the former to avoid losing part of the wave in which he is interested. On this basis he might set the initial potential to $+1$ v. and start the recording with the bridge set at zero so that the initial potential will be accurately known (which is, however, less certain than it may seem, for the electrical and mechanical zeros of the bridge may not coincide quite exactly). By the time the applied potential reaches the value where the interesting portion of the curve begins, his capillary may be well along the road to ruin. Alternatively, he might begin the recording with the bridge set to some other point; if the initial and span potentials are set to $+1$ and -2 v., respectively, to obtain a range (from $+1$ to -1 v.) that includes the desired wave, the bridge might be set to 47% of its total rotation, giving an actual starting potential of $+0.06$ v. $[= +1.00 - (0.47)(2.00)]$. He will then obtain the curve of Fig. 2.10(b). But in this case the actual starting potential will depend on the linearity of the bridge, on the linearity, readability, and parallactic error of the dial, and on the amount of backlash in the bridge drive mechanism; the advantage of the internal standardization has vanished. These considerations lead the writer to prefer the arrangement of Fig. 2.9.

For recording current–time curves at constant potential, as is done when a dropping electrode is used in studies of chemical kinetics, the span-potential circuit must be disengaged. It is usually desirable to include a limit switch to stop or disengage the bridge and chart motors at the end of a polarogram, and when this is done it is a simple matter to record a current–time curve for the duration of an ordinary polarogram by setting the initial-potential circuit to give the desired potential, opening S_{21} to give a span potential of zero, and recording in the ordinary way. With strip-chart instruments (though not with photographically recording ones or those that provide pen-and-ink recordings on single sheets of paper), the current can be followed for a much longer time by disengaging the clutch or gear train in the drive of R_{23}. It is often very convenient in work of this sort to use a recorder provided with a logarithmic scale, such as the Linear/log Model 43 Varicord (Photovolt Corp., New York). Provision for disengaging the bridge drive also allows the experimenter to scan the potential range manually before beginning a recording. This is desirable because it permits him to choose the best settings of the various controls.

With a recording potentiometer of fixed range, provision for recording currents of different magnitudes is most easily made by changing the value of R_{61} in the basic potentiometric module. Increasing the number of values available increases the precision that can be secured in measuring the heights of recorded waves, for maximum precision is obtained when the wave can be made to occupy nearly the full width of the chart. A precision resistance box can be used, or one can connect four decade resistance units in series. With a 10-mv. recorder the resistances should cover the range from 10 to 20,000 ohms to provide full-scale sensitivities from 0.5 to 1000 μamp. Sensitivities between 100 and 1000 μamp. full-scale are useless in polarography, but are occasionally needed in voltammetry with electrodes of large area (e.g., the stirred mercury pool). Few recorders have input impedances large enough to tolerate resistances above 20,000 ohms, but sensitivities better than 0.5 μamp. full-scale (which is equivalent to 0.002 microampere/millimeter for a 10-in. chart width) are not often useful.

For work with solutions so dilute—perhaps micromolar or even less—that very high sensitivities are essential, yet another module is desirable and is found on a few commercial instruments. It is intended to deal with the problem illustrated by Fig. 2.11. Curve a is an ordinary polarogram of a hydrochloric acid solution containing a trace of bismuth. The residual current, which flows in the hydrochloric acid alone and whose causes are discussed in Chap. 3 I, is substantial and increases almost linearly with potential in the range shown here.

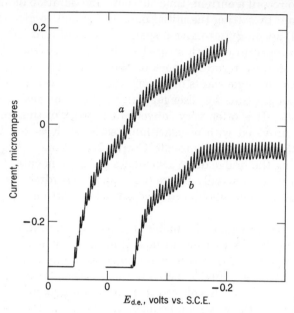

Figure 2.11.   Polarograms of 0.002mM bismuth(III) in 1.5F hydrochloric acid containing 0.001% Triton X-100: (*a*) ordinary polarogram, (*b*) with linear compensation of the residual current. The recorder sensitivities are the same for the two curves, but the action of the linear-compensation circuit is such that absolute values of the currents on curve *b* cannot be obtained directly from the ordinate scale. This is a somewhat unfavorable case because the bismuth wave begins before the initial current rise has quite ended.

At worst, the increasing residual current may lead the operator to overlook a wave altogether or to dismiss it as a mere irregularity of the curve (or, conversely, to mistake an irregularity for a wave); at best, it will cost him some trouble and uncertainty in measuring the wave height. If one adds to the recorder input a voltage that varies linearly with the applied potential but in the opposite direction from the iR drop corresponding to the residual current, the variation of the latter can be almost completely cancelled out, as shown in Fig. 2.11(*b*). This linear current compensation (which is often called condenser-current compensation, although what is compensated is not the condenser current but its variation with potential) is obviously quite unrelated to the constant current compensation provided by the

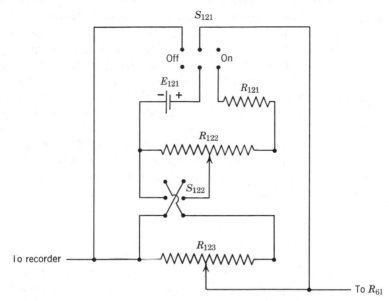

Figure 2.12.   Schematic diagram of a module providing linear compensation. E_{121}: 1.5-v. dry cell; R_{121}: 2000-ohm ½-w. carbon resistor; R_{122}: 10-ohm linear taper single-turn potentiometer; R_{123}: 100-ohm linear taper potentiometer (see text); S_{121}: DPDT on–off switch; S_{122}: DPDT reversing switch (see text).

module of Fig. 2.8. It then becomes feasible to use very high sensitivities, although to do so it is usually necessary to employ a cathode-follower circuit or some other device for matching the input impedance of the recorder to the necessary high value of the measuring resistor used as R_{61}. This is the principle of the Microrange Extender (S-29315) available from E. H. Sargent & Co.

A circuit module providing linear compensation is shown in Fig. 2.12. The potentiometer R_{123} must have the same number of turns as the bridge R_{23} and, like R_{23}, it must be driven at a constant rate. It is simplest to use two identical, ganged, ten-turn potentiometers. As the rotation of R_{23} changes the potential being applied to the cell, that of R_{123} produces a proportional change of the potential being added to the iR drop across R_{61}, and thus a proportional shift of the recorder zero. The magnitude of the compensation thus provided is varied by adjusting the setting of R_{122}, which should be so chosen that the portion of the residual-current curve preceding the wave of interest has a slope very close to zero. This is done by alternately setting the polarograph to two potentials as widely spaced as possible on this portion of the curve, and adjusting R_{122} so that the average deflection of the pen is the same at each of these potentials. In some cases, of course, two potentials on the plateau of the wave may be used instead, as was done in obtaining Fig. 2.11. It is most convenient to gang S_{122} to S_{91} so as to obtain compensation in the proper direction regardless of the direction of polarization; the sign of the variation of residual current with potential is, of course, unaffected by the direction in which the potential is being changed. The on-off switch S_{121} also serves to short the module out when it is not being used. With the aid of this circuit it is occasionally possible under optimum conditions to obtain useful data even at concentrations of the order of a tenth of a micromole per liter.

It may be emphasized that this circuit can compensate only for a current that varies linearly with potential. It cannot compensate for the nonlinear variations that occur near the beginning and end of the useful range of potentials, as illustrated by Fig. 2.11; for waves due to impurities in the supporting electrolyte or in the mercury; or for the change in the slope of the condenser-current curve at the potential of the electrocapillary maximum (2). Instrumental compensation for these is possible (3) but requires far more complex circuitry.

It is often necessary to vary the period of the recorder over a considerable range: one may want to measure the maximum current during a drop life, or one may want to measure the limiting current on the plateau of a wave. Erroneous values of the maximum current are obtained unless the recorder period is considerably shorter than the drop life. For this reason the undamped period of the recorder should be no longer than 1 sec., but little is gained if it is shorter than this. A recorder with a full-scale response time of 1 sec. does not accurately reproduce the whole current–time curve during the drop life, but the rate of change of current is so much smaller near the end of the drop life than near its beginning that the error in the maximum current is inappreciable. In measurements of the limiting current, however, the narrower oscillations that result from damping are not only convenient but actually essential, for the average current during the life of a drop may be very different from that corresponding to the average of the maximum and minimum excursions of the pen of an undamped recorder. This is discussed further in Chap. 3 III; here it need only be said that with an extremely fast recorder the average deflection would correspond to a current that may be as little as three fifths of the true average current. This is also the reason for the long periods recommended for a galvanometer used for measurements of the average current.

A recorder may be most easily damped by connecting an electrolytic capacitor across its terminals. Because the time constant depends on the value of the measuring resistor R_{61} as well as on that of the capacitor, a large number of capacitors (at least a dozen) must be provided for use at different sensitivity settings, and care must be taken to match the damping capacitor to the measuring resistor before each recording is begun. As this is somewhat troublesome, damping is usually achieved in commercial instruments by altering the time constant of the amplifier in the recorder, and only a few settings are then needed or desirable. Periods of 1, 5, 15, and 45 sec. suffice for every purpose. The shortest is needed only for measuring maximum currents; the longest should be used only for measuring wave heights in routine analysis. The intermediate values are used for measuring half-wave potentials, evaluating reversibilities, and other purposes where the shape of the rising part of the wave is important. Though there is no reason to have a wide variety of choices available in this range, it is convenient to have at least two so that accurate curves can be obtained at any polarization rate. Much more efficient damping modules have been devised; by their use it is possible to obtain accurate values of the average current, even on the rising part of a wave, even though the oscillations are nearly completely suppressed. These are of great value in differential and derivative polarography, where the oscillations are a nuisance. But in ordinary polarography irregularities in the oscillations are a sign of trouble far too valuable to be sacrificed for a minor gain in convenience of measuring wave heights.

In kinetic work and in monitoring flowing solutions, it is sometimes convenient to be able to follow the concentrations of two substances simultaneously. This can be done by inserting the module of Fig. 2.13 into the span-potential circuit. The lever-type microswitch S_{131} is alternately opened and closed by the action of the motor-driven cam C_{131}. When it is open, only the initial potential is applied to the cell; if this has a value on the plateau of the first of the two waves on the

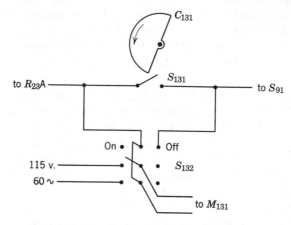

Figure 2.13.   Schematic diagram of a module providing alternation between two potentials. C_{131}: motor-driven cam (0.5–2 r.p.m.); M_{131}: a.-c. motor with suitable gear train, or small synchronous motor, driving C_{131}; S_{131}: lever-type SPST microswitch; S_{132}: 3PDT on–off switch.

polarogram, only the first limiting current is recorded during this interval. When it is closed, an increment of potential is added by the span-potential circuit; if this is set so that the sum of the two potentials has a value on the plateau of the second wave, the second limiting current is recorded during this interval. Changes in the output of the span-potential circuit during the recording must be prevented by disengaging the bridge drive. The difference between the two limiting currents is, of course, the height of the second wave. The speed of the motor and the design of the cam are conveniently such that the cycle consumes about 30 sec. If this simple technique is combined with compensation of the limiting current of the first wave, it becomes possible to obtain an accurate record of the variations of the concentration of a minor constituent in the presence of a fairly large, but not necessarily exactly constant, excess of a more easily reducible major one (4).

Recorders of several different kinds have been used in polarographs. For most purposes, a recorder that plots curves on individual sheets of graph paper is extremely convenient. In kinetic work, however, strip-chart recorders have the advantage of permitting the current–time curve to be followed for much longer periods, as was mentioned above, and this advantage becomes a necessity if the polarograph is to be used for monitoring the concentration of a process stream or the effluent from an ion-exchange or chromatographic column over a long interval. For maximum flexibility, the full-scale response time of the recorder should be about 1 sec., though slower responses can be tolerated if it is quite certain that the polarograph will be used only for analytical work. The usable chart width (that is, the maximum pen deflection) affects the precision of measurement, and so it is advantageous for the chart to be as wide as possible. The linearity and dead-zone width of the recorder are so unlikely to be a significant fraction of the probable error of measuring the height of a recorded wave that they are hardly worth inquiring into except with extremely inexpensive recorders. Those who contemplate the publication of their polarograms should be aware that they can be most satisfactorily reproduced if the coordinate background on the chart is printed in blue or, better still, if unlined paper is used; that ball-point pens do not usually draw lines sufficiently heavy to survive the reduction employed by the journals; and that red ink is more photogenic than black. Because one often wants to record two or more polarograms on the same coordinate axes, especially when publication is planned, it is very convenient for the chart-drive motor to be electrically reversible, for this saves the labor of rewinding the chart by hand.

These are the elements of the circuits found in the majority of commercial polarographs, which are described in the following section. Although it naturally costs considerably more to buy an assembled instrument than to buy the component parts of one that is equal or even superior to any on the market, and although home-made polarographs are used in a number of laboratories including his own, the writer's opinion is that the construction of a polarograph is justified only under extraordinary circumstances, for the machine shop charges and the value of the chemist's time can hardly be expected to total appreciably less than the additional cost of the commercial instrument.

II. Commercially Available Polarographs

A summary of the characteristics of a number of commercially available polarographs is given in Table 2.1 to guide the prospective purchaser of an instrument. With polarographs as with most other

TABLE 2.1.

Characteristics of Commercially Available Polarographs

Group 1

	American Optical Company, Instrument Division, Buffalo, New York, 14215	Atlas-Mess-und-Analysentechnik Gesellschaft mit beschränkter Haftung, Woltmershauser Strasse 442–448a, 28 Bremen, Germany	Electrochem Company, P.O. Box 245, Olympia, Washington
Manufacturer's name and address			
Designation of instrument	Recording Electro-Polarizer	Tastpolarograph Selector D	Auto-Scan polarograph
I. Measurements of current			
A. Current-measuring device			
1. Type	Varian strip-chart recording potentiometer	D.-c. amplifier and 1-v. compensation recorder	Integral microammeter for manual operation; connections to external recorder are provided.
2. Voltage drop for full-scale deflection, mv.	10	—	Depends on recorder employed: specify whether 1, 5, or 10 mv. full-scale.
3. Usable chart width, mm.	127	200	100 on microammeter scale; chart width depends on recorder employed.
B. Sensitivities			
1. Highest, μamp./mm.	0.004	0.00025	25
2. Number of steps	11	22	3
3. Lowest, μamp./mm.	0.8	0.375	125
4. Calibration procedure	Recording c.-v. curve for precision resistor supplied	Standardization of recorder against integral standard cell	Full-scale sensitivity = $1/($attenuator setting$)$ microamps.
5. Accuracies of shunt or measuring resistors	±0.1%	±0.5%	±0.25% relative; ±5% absolute. Calibration of attenuator is recommended for higher accuracy.

For the Electrochem Company column, items B.1–B.3 (25, 3, 125) are bracketed together with the note: on microammeter; sensitivity of recorder can be varied from 1 to over 250 μamps. full-scale by 10-turn 0.25%-linearity helical potentiometer used as attenuator.

C. Periods			
1. Period with minimum available damping, sec.	2.5 full-scale	1.0 full-scale	With Heath EUW-20 recorder, 0.9-2.5 (for 90% deflection), depending on attenuator setting
2. Type of damping	RC, applied to recorder input signal	RC, in recorder amplifier	RC
3. Number of steps	4	6	7
4. Period with maximum available damping, sec.	5.0 full-scale	30 (for 90% deflection)	15
D. Compensation			
1. Maximum upscale, scale widths	Provided, but information not available	7	Not provided
2. Maximum downscale, scale widths	Provided, but information not available	7	
3. Maximum compensation of a linearly varying current, μamps./v.	Not provided	10	
II. Measurements of cell voltage			
A. Initial potential			
1. How established	Output of 10-turn 0.1% linearity helical potentiometer used as voltage divider and calibrated against integral standard cell. Voltage across this potentiometer is indicated on a voltmeter.	Reference voltage (8 v.) stabilized by Zener diodes	Microammeter and series resistor may be connected across bridge output at start of scan. Smallest division on meter represents 0.05 v.
2. Values available	Continuously variable, 0 to ±3 v.	Continuously variable from 0 to ±2.0 v.; −2.0 to −4.0 v. in 0.5-v. steps	Continuously variable, 0 to ±2.5 v.
B. Span potential			
1. How established	Calibration of bridge voltage against integral standard cell or (for values below 1 v.) against previously calibrated potentiometer in initial-potential circuit. Bridge voltage is indicated on a separate voltmeter.	See II A1	See II A1. Meter is calibrated to ±1% at 1 v.
2. Values available	Continuously variable, 0 to ±3 v.	2 v.	Continuously variable, 0 to ± 2.5 v.
3. Direction of polarization	Either	Either	Either

(Table 2.1, *Group 1, continued*)

TABLE 2.1 (continued)

Group 1 (continued)

	American Optical Company	Atlas-Mess-und-Analysentechnik Gesellschaft mit beschrankter Haftung	Electrochem Company
	Recording Electro-Polarizer	Tastpolarograph Selector D	Auto-Scan polarograph
C. Bridge			
1. Type	10-turn helical potentiometer with integrating dial, driven by solenoid-operated friction clutch	10-turn helical potentiometer	10-turn helical potentiometer driven by reversible synchronous motor
2. Resistance, ohms	100	200	100
3. Linearity, %	0.1	0.1	0.25
4. Total turns if wire-wound			
5. Automatic stop at end of bridge traverse	Chart and bridge motors are turned off automatically when full-scale deflection is reached.	Yes	No, but clutch slippage prevents mechanical damage.
6. Time for full traverse of bridge, minutes	10	6 or 12[a]; 76 or 152 sec.[a] when used for rapid polarography	10
D. Chart			
1. Rate of motion, mm./min.	50.8	100, 200, or 400[a] for full traverse of bridge (see II C6); 8.3–67[a] mm./min.	Depends on recorder employed
2. Synchronization of chart and bridge drives	Simultaneous actuation of motors	Both are driven by the same synchronous motor.	By simultaneous operation of switches on polarizing unit and recorder. Bridge drive starts within 10 msec.
3. Maximum chart length available for recording current–time curves	80 ft.	10 m.	
4. Colors of grids available on chart paper	Black	Green	
5. Type of pen	Leroy 3233–00	Ink pen with reservoir	

III. Other characteristics			
A. Size (width × depth × height, in.)	25.5 × 16.25 × 8.25	30.7 × 17.3 × 14.1	10 × 7 × 6
B. Batteries required	1 Mallory 2-RM-12-R mercury cell, 4 Burgess 4FH dry cells	None; Zener diode d.-c. supply	2 mercury cells
C. Provision for external checking of standard cell	No	No	—
D. Other features		Switch-operated solenoid to disengage pen from chart; fast chart reverse; provision for tast polarography (b)[b], derivative tast polarography, and rapid polarography	A higher priced model employs a taut band meter calibrated to an accuracy of ±0.5% at any point on the scale and contains a Zener-diode-regulated d.-c. supply.
IV. Price	$1195.00	$4140.00	$210.00
V. Available in the United States from	Manufacturer	Applied Physics Corporation, 2724 South Peck Road, Monrovia, California	Manufacturer

[a] These values pertain to operation at 50 c.p.s. and are affected by line frequency.

[b] See Chap. 10 IX.

(Table 2.1, *continued*)

TABLE 2.1 (continued)
Group 2

	Fisher Scientific Company, Instrument Division, 711 Forbes Avenue, Pittsburgh, Pennsylvania 15219	Fisher Scientific Company, Instrument Division, 711 Forbes Avenue, Pittsburgh, Pennsylvania 15219	Laboratorní Přístroje N.P., Prague, Czechoslovakia
Manufacturer's name and address			
Designation of instrument	Electrodropode Model 65	Electrodropode Model 65 with Recorder Model 66	LP 60 Polarograph with EZ 2 Recorder
I. Measurements of current			
A. Current-measuring device			
1. Type	Galvanometer	Strip-chart recording potentiometer	Strip-chart recording potentiometer
2. Voltage drop for full-scale deflection, mv.	—	2.2	0.1, 0.2, 0.5, 1, 2, or 5, selected by connection at terminal block
3. Usable chart width, mm.	254-mm. scale	254	280
B. Sensitivities			
1. Highest, μamp./mm.	0.01	0.004	0.000036
2. Number of steps	9	9	20 (25 by changing recorder sensitivity)
3. Lowest, μamp./mm.	4.0	1.6	0.36 (18 by changing recorder sensitivity)
4. Calibration procedure	Standardization against integral mercury cell ±0.5%	Standardization of recorder against integral mercury cell ±0.5%	Recorder has Zener-diode-stabilized power supply. ±0.02%
5. Accuracies of shunt or measuring resistors			
C. Periods			
1. Period with minimum available damping, sec.	1 (for 66% deflection)	1.5 (for 66% deflection)	3 (for full-scale deflection)
2. Type of damping	RC	RC	RC π-T filter
3. Number of steps	Continuous with off position	Continuous with off position	4
4. Period with maximum available damping, sec.	2.5 (for 66% deflection)	4.0 (for 66% deflection)	35 (for 99.9% deflection)
D. Compensation			
1. Maximum upscale, scale widths	1.25	2	5
2. Maximum downscale, scale widths	1.25	2	6
3. Maximum compensation of a linearly varying current, μamps./v.	Not provided	Not provided	1.1

II. Measurements of cell voltage	Applied potential is standardized against mercury cell.		
A. Initial potential			
1. How established		Standardization against mercury cell	Standardization against integral Weston cell[c]
2. Values available		+2[a], 0, −1, −2[b] and −3[b] v.	+2, +1, 0, −1, and −2 v.
B. Span potential			
1. How established		Standardization against mercury cell	Standardization against integral Weston cell[c] (simultaneous with standardization of initial potential)
2. Values available		2 v.	2 or 4 v.
3. Direction of polarization		Either	Either
C. Bridge			
1. Type	Single-turn potentiometer, manually operated	Single-turn potentiometer	10-turn wire-wound potentiometer
2. Resistance, ohms	100	100	16
3. Linearity, %	0.15	0.15	0.025
4. Total turns if wire-wound			
5. Automatic stop at end of bridge traverse		No	Yes, or at any desired point during traverse of bridge
6. Time for full traverse of bridge, minutes		10	10 or 20, selected by switch
D. Chart	None		
1. Rate of motion, mm./min.		2.54, 5.08, 10.16, 15.24, 30.48, or 40.64	1/6, 1/3, 2/3, 4/3, 2, 8/3, 4, 5, 6, 10, 20, 40, 60, 80, 120, or 180
2. Synchronization of chart and bridge drives		Simultaneous actuation of motors	Simultaneous actuation of motors (by single switch and relay)
3. Maximum chart length available for recording current–time curves		40 yards	16–18 m.
4. Colors of grids available on chart paper		Black	Any desired
5. Type of pen		Reservoir	Capillary ink pen

(Table 2.1, *Group 2, continued*)

TABLE 2.1 (*continued*)

Group 2 (*continued*)

	Fisher Scientific Company Electropode Model 65	Fisher Scientific Company Electropode Model 65 with Recorder Model 66	Laboratorní Přístroje N.P. LP 60 Polarograph with EZ 2 Recorder
III. Other characteristics			
A. Size (width × depth × height, in.)	21.75 × 15.25 × 12.88	Polarizing unit: 21.75 × 15.25 × 12.88 Recording unit: 21.75 × 15.25 × 19.88	Polarizing unit: 16.5 × 11.8 × 11.0 Recording unit: 20.0 × 13.8 × 16.5
B. Batteries required	None: Zener diode d.-c. supply	None: Zener diode d.-c. supply	Lead storage battery (6 v., 14 amp.-hr.), continuously recharged by germanium rectifier
C. Provision for external checking standard cell			No
D. Other features			220-v. 50-cycle a.-c. is required. One setting of the damping network provides derivative polarograms.
IV. Price	$615.00	$1665.00	$3123.00
V. Available in the United States from	Manufacturer	Manufacturer	

a For polarization toward increasingly negative potentials only.
b For polarization toward increasingly positive potentials only.
c Automatic (at 2-hr. intervals) or manual

		Group 3	
Manufacturer's name and address	Leeds & Northrup Company, 4901 Stenton Avenue, Philadelphia 44, Pennsylvahnia	Metrohm Ltd., 9100 Herisau, Switzerland	Numec Instruments and Controls Corp., Apollo, Pennsylvania
Designation of instrument	Electrochemograph, Type E	Metrohm Polarecord E 261 R	Numec Polaroscan (controlled-potential and derivative polarograph)
I. Measurements of current			
A. Current-measuring device			
1. Type	Strip-chart current-balancing recorder	Strip-chart recording potentiometer	Strip-chart recording potentiometer
2. Voltage drop for full-scale deflection, mv.	0	10	10
3. Usable chart width, mm.	250.8	250	250
B. Sensitivities			
1. Highest, μamp./mm.	0.00398	0.0001	0.00002
2. Number of steps	11	14	22
3. Lowest, μamp./mm.	0.398	2	2
4. Calibration procedure	Standardization of recorder against integral Eppley cell	Standardization against integral Weston cell	Standardization against constant voltage source
5. Accuracies of shunt or measuring resistors	±0.05%	±0.5%	
C. Periods			
1. Period with minimum available damping, sec.	1.0 ± 0.2 (for 99.5% of full-scale deflection)	<1 (for full-scale deflection)	0.25. Maximum currents can be recorded without distortion due to damping by means of a peak-follower.
2. Type of damping	RC	RC, applied to recorder input signal	Parallel-T RC filter for recording average currents or derivative curves
3. Number of steps	4	Continuously variable	Continuously variable
4. Period with maximum available damping, sec.	19 ± 5 (for 63% of full-scale deflection)	15 (for 90% deflection)	
D. Compensation			
1. Maximum upscale, scale widths	2	5	Compensation up to 100 μamps. is available from a 10-turn helical potentiometer.
2. Maximum downscale, scale widths	2	5	
3. Maximum compensation of a linearly varying current, μamps./v.	Not provided	1.25	Electronic compensation circuit provides up to 0.125 μamp./min. (see II C6).

(Table 2.1, *Group 3, continued*)

TABLE 2.1 (*continued*)

Group 3 (*continued*)

	Leeds & Northrup Company Electrochemograph, Type E	Metrohm Ltd. Metrohm Polarecord E 261 R	Numec Instruments and Controls Corp. Numec Polaroscan (controlled-potential and derivative polarograph)
II. Measurements of cell voltage			
A. Initial potential			
1. How established	Standardization against integral Eppley cell	Standardization against integral Weston cell	Internal test function
2. Values available	+1[a], 0[a], −1, −2[b], and −3[b]	+2 to −2 v. in 0.25-v. steps	Continuously variable, 0 to ±3 v.
B. Span potential			
1. How established	Standardization against integral Eppley cell	Standardization against integral Weston cell	Internal test function
2. Values available	2 v.	−3, −2, −1, −0.5 v. (polarization toward increasingly negative potentials); +1, +2 v. (polarization toward increasingly positive potentials)	2 v.
3. Direction of polarization	Either	Either; see II B2.	Either
C. Bridge			
1. Type	Motor-driven single-turn slidewire with indicating dial	Linear-taper potentiometer, 250 mm. long, wound with gold wire	Electronic scan circuit. Scan potential is derived from the output of an integrator supplied with a constant potential of suitable magnitude. Scan rate is adjusted by selecting a resistor in series with the integrator input; standard rates are 20, 50, and 100 mv./min., but others may be obtained by changing resistors.
2. Resistance, ohms	40 (shunted) ±0.05%	60	
3. Linearity, %	0.1	0.2	
4. Total turns if wire-wound	Approximately 1300	1000	
5. Automatic stop at end of bridge traverse	Yes. A slip clutch is provided for manual rotation of the bridge.	Friction clutch	
6. Time for full traverse of bridge, minutes	10	1 or 6	20, 40, or 100 (standard; see preceding entry and II B2)

D. Chart			
1. Rate of motion, mm./min.	50.8	250 *for full traverse of bridge*	25 standard; other values available by changing gears
2. Synchronization of chart and bridge drives	Both are driven by synchronous motors.	Simultaneous actuation of motors and automatic markings on chart (see III D)	
3. Maximum chart length available for recording current–time curves	40 yards	16.5 in. (sheets) or 24 m. (rolls)	40 yards
4. Colors of grids available on chart paper	Green, black, blue, or unlined	Brown (sheets) or gray (rolls)	Red
5. Type of pen	Capillary pen with reservoir	Ball-point pen	Reservoir
III. Other characteristics			
A. Size (width × depth × height, in.)	22 × 18 × 34.5	17 × 18 × 10	17 × 18 × 10
B. Batteries required	2 lead storage batteries, or Regulated Power Supply	None: Zener diode d.-c. supply	None: Zener diode d.-c. supply
C. Provision for external checking of standard cell	No	No	
D. Other features		Voltage-marking pen marks each 20% of span or may be controlled by external signal; 6 calibrated mv. ranges from 10 to 2000 mv. full-scale; derivative network; accessories available for a.-c. polarography, rapid polarography (premature detachment of drop synchronized with a.-c. line frequency f at any of 5 frequencies between $f/16$ and $f/8$), automatic compensation of iR drop in cell, and anodic stripping voltammetry; input voltage selector (110, 125, 145, 220, or 250 v. at 50 or 60 c.p.s.) available on request without extra cost	Controlled-potential circuitry (permits use of fiber-type reference electrodes); derivative network

(Table 2.1, *Group 3, continued*)

TABLE 2.1 (*Continued*)

Group 3 (*Continued*)

	Leeds & Northrup Company Electrochemograph, Type E	Metrohm Ltd. Metrohm Polarecord E 261 R	Numec Instruments and Controls Corp. Numec Polaroscan (controlled-potential and derivative polarograph)
IV. Price	$2445.00 (not including d.-c. supply). The lead storage batteries are available for $94.50, or the Regulated Power Supply ($200.00) may be used instead.	From $2650 without accessories	$4990.00 (without recorder, $4200.00)
V. Available in the United States from	Manufacturer	Brinkmann Instruments, Inc. Cantiague Road, Westbury, L.I., New York 11590	Manufacturer

a For polarization toward increasingly negative potentials only.

b For polarization toward increasingly positive potentials only.

Group 4

	Radiometer, Emdrupvej 72, Copenhagen NV, Denmark P03	Radiometer, Emdrupvej 72, Copenhagen NV, Denmark P04	E. H. Sargent & Co., 4647 W. Foster Avenue, Chicago, Illinois 60630 Model III Polarograph
Manufacturer's name and address			
Designation of instrument			
I. Measurements of current			
A. Current-measuring device			
1. Type	Strip-chart recording potentiometer	Strip-chart recording potentiometer	Enclosed lamp-and-scale galvanometer
2. Voltage drop for full-scale deflection, mv.	3–6	<0.005	—
3. Usable chart width, mm.	100	250	315 (scale width)
B. Sensitivities			
1. Highest, μamp./mm.	0.0003	0.00008	0.006
2. Number of steps	24	25	10
3. Lowest, μamp./mm.	6	0.8	6
4. Calibration procedure	Voltmeter and test resistor	Standardization of recorder against integral Weston cell	Measurement of deflection produced by known current
5. Accuracies of shunt or measuring resistors	±0.2% (13 low current ranges) or ±0.5% (9 high current ranges)	±0.3% from 0.00008 to 0.0006 and from 0.08 to 0.8 μamps./mm.; ±0.1% from 0.0008 to 0.06 μamps./mm.	±0.1%
C. Periods			
1. Period with minimum available damping, sec.	9.25 (for 99% of full-scale deflection)	2.25 (for 99% of full-scale deflection)	Approximately 4 sec. response time
2. Type of damping	Double RC filter	Double or (on 2 positions giving least damping) single RC filter	—
3. Number of steps	10	9	—
4. Period with maximum available damping, sec.	15.25 (for 90% of full-scale deflection)	20 (for 90% of full-scale deflection)	—
D. Compensation			
1. Maximum upscale, scale widths	1.5–2.5	20 μamp.	1
2. Maximum downscale, scale widths	7.5–13	100 μamp.	9
3. Maximum compensation of a linearly varying current, μamps./v.	1.2 or 3, depending on amplifier sensitivity	0.5	Not provided

(Table 2.1, *Group 4, continued*)

TABLE 2.1 (*continued*)
Group 4 (continued)

	Radiometer PO3	Radiometer PO4	E. H. Sargent & Co. Model III Polarograph
II. Measurements of cell voltage			
A. Initial potential			
1. How established	Voltmeter	Standardization against integral Weston cell	Voltage across bridge is indicated on 0–3-v. meter (±1% accuracy).
2. Values available	Continuously variable, 0 to ±1.0 v. (adjustable to ±1.5 v.)	Continuously variable from +0.5 to −3.0 v.	—
B. Span potential			
1. How established	Voltmeter	Standardization against integral Weston cell	
2. Values available	2 v. (adjustable to 1 or 3)	Continuously variable from +0.5 to −3.0 v.	
3. Direction of polarization	Increasingly negative only	Either	
C. Bridge			
1. Type	Two parallel potentiometers	Single-turn potentiometer	10-turn helical potentiometer with integrating dial, manually operated
2. Resistance, ohms	15–35	15–45	200
3. Linearity, %	±0.2	±0.1	0.1
4. Total turns if wire-wound	700 ± 200	1350 ± 100	—
5. Automatic stop at end of bridge traverse	Yes	Yes	—
6. Time for full traverse of bridge, minutes	5	4.33, 8.67, 17.3, or 34.7	
D. Chart			
1. Rate of motion, mm./min.	40	20, 40, or 80	—
2. Synchronization of chart and bridge drives	Both are driven by the same motor.	Both are driven by the same motor.	
3. Maximum chart length available for recording current–time curves	30 m.	30 m.	
4. Color of grids available on chart paper	Gray	Gray	
5. Type of pen	Reservoir	Reservoir	

III. Other characteristics			
A. Size (width × depth × height, in.)	25 × 12 × 19.7	28 × 14 × 10.5	16.75 × 17 × 10
B. Batteries required	4–6-v. storage battery, 6-v. dry cell	No	3 Burgess 6F dry cells
C. Provision for external checking of standard cell		No	
D. Other features	Accessories available include dropping-electrode, hanging mercury drop, and rotating platinum electrode assemblies, as well as apparatus for enforced mechanical detachment of the mercury drops (for rapid polarography).	Accessories available include dropping-electrode, hanging mercury drop, and rotating platinum electrode assemblies, as well as apparatus for enforced mechanical detachment of the mercury drops (for rapid polarography). Provision is made for recording peak currents, thereby eliminating oscillations due to growth and fall of the drops.	Galvanometer has reversing switch; transformer is required for 220-v. 50- or 60-cycle operation.
IV. Price	$1,750.00	$3,215.00	$615.00
V. Available in the United States from	The London Company, 811 Sharon Drive, Westlake, Ohio 44091	The London Company, 811 Sharon Drive, Westlake, Ohio 44091	Manufacturer

(Table 2.1, *continued*)

TABLE 2.1 *(continued)*
Group 5

	E. H. Sargent & Co., 4647 W. Foster Avenue, Chicago, Illinois 60630	E. H. Sargent & Co., 4647 W. Foster Avenue, Chicago, Illinois 60630	Shimadzu Seisakusho Ltd., Nishioji Sanjo, Nakagyoku, Kyoto, Japan
Manufacturer's name and address			
Designation of instrument	Model XV Polarograph with Micro-range extender	Model FS Polarograph	Shimadzu Polarographic Analyzer Type RP-2
I. Measurements of current			
A. Current-measuring device			
1. Type	Strip-chart recording potentiometer. Current-measuring accuracy is ±0.1%	Strip-chart recording potentiometer	Strip-chart current-balancing reorder
2. Voltage drop for full-scale deflection, mv.	2.5	2.5	0
3. Usable chart width, mm.	250	250	200
B. Sensitivities			
1. Highest, μamp./mm.	0.0001	0.0004	0.0025
2. Number of steps	26	19	10
3. Lowest, μamp./mm.	1	0.4	2.5
4. Calibration procedure	Standardization against integral standard cell and calibration with external precision potentiometer	Standardization against integral standard cell	Standardization against integral Weston cell
5. Accuracies of shunt or measuring resistors	±0.1%	±0.1%	±0.1%
C. Periods			
1. Period with minimum available damping, sec.	10 (for full-scale deflection)	1 (for full-scale deflection)	3.5 (for full-scale deflection)
2. Type of damping	RC	None	RC
3. Number of steps	4		4
4. Period with maximum available damping, sec.			120 (for full-scale deflection)
D. Compensation			
1. Maximum upscale, scale widths	6	6	2
2. Maximum downscale, scale widths	6	6	6
3. Maximum compensation of a linearly varying current, μamps./v.	20 chart widths *for full traverse of bridge*	Not provided	Not provided

II. Measurements of cell voltage — Voltage accuracy is ±0.25%.

A. Initial potential			
1. How established	Standardization against integral standard cell	Standardization against integral standard cell	Standardization against integral Weston cell
2. Values available	See II B2.	Continuously variable, 0 to ±3 v.	0, ±0.5, ±1.0, and ±1.5 v.
B. Span potential			
1. How established	Standardization against integral standard cell	Standardization against integral standard cell	Standardization against integral Weston cell
2. Values available	10 fixed ranges: 0 to −1, 0 to −2, 0 to −3, −1 to −2, −2 to −3, −3 to −4, −2 to −4, +0.5 to −0.5, +1 to −1, and +1.5 to −1.5. A reversing switch provides 10 additional ranges of opposite signs: 0 to +1, 0 to +2, 0 to +3, +1 to +2, etc.	1.0, 1.5, 2.0, 2.5, and 3.0 v.	1, 2, and 3 v.
3. Direction of polarization	Either	Either	Either
C. Bridge			
1. Type	Single-turn potentiometer with 100 divisions	Single-turn potentiometer	Single-turn potentiometer with integrating dial
2. Resistance, ohms	200	200	50
3. Linearity, %	0.1	0.1	0.1
4. Total turns if wire-wound	1200	1200	2000
5. Automatic stop at end of bridge traverse	No; continuous rotation	No; continuous rotation	Yes
6. Time for full traverse of bridge, minutes	10	1.0	10
D. Chart			
1. Rate of motion, mm./min.	25.4	254	10, 20, 40, 80, or 160
2. Synchronization of chart and bridge drives	Simultaneous actuation of synchronous motors	Simultaneous actuation of synchronous motors	Simultaneous actuation of synchronous motors
3. Maximum chart length available for recording current–time curves	40 yards	40 yards	17 m.
4. Colors of grids available on chart paper	Blue	Blue	Silver gray
5. Type of pen	Ball point; ink pens are available as accessories	Ball point; ink pens are available as accessories	Reservoir

(Table 2.1, *Group 5, continued*)

TABLE 2.1 (continued)
Group 5 (continued)

	E. H. Sargent & Co. Model XV Polarograph with Micro-range extender	E. H. Sargent & Co. Model FS Polarograph	Shimadzu Seisakusho Ltd. Shimadzu Polarographic Analyzer Type RP-2
III. Other characteristics			
A. Size (width × depth × height, in.)	Polarograph: 23.5 × 16 × 10 Micro-range extender: 10 × 9.5 × 6.5	23.5 × 16 × 10	20 × 24 × 24
B. Batteries required	6 dry cells, 2 mercury cells	6 dry cells, 2 mercury cells	6-v. storage battery
C. Provision for external checking of standard cell	No	No	No
D. Other features	Units for 220-v. 50- or 60-cycle operation available from stock; switch selection permits use of recorder separately		At each side of chart a switch-operated solenoid lifts the pen from the paper. Units for 220-v. operation are supplied on request.
IV. Price	Polarograph: $1650.00 Micro-range extender: $310.00	$1800.00	$1420.00[a]
V. Available in the United States from	Manufacturer	Manufacturer	Ataka New York Inc., 633 Third Avenue, New York, New York 10017

[a] At official rate of exchange.

Group 6

Manufacturer's name and address	Yokogawa Electric Works, Ltd., 2–9 Nakacho, Musashino-shi, Tokyo, Japan	Yokogawa Electric Works, Ltd., 2–9 Nakacho, Musashino-shi, Tokyo, Japan
Designation of instrument	DC Polarocorder (Type POL-11)	High-Sensitivity Polarocorder (Type POL-12)
I. Measurements of current		
A. Current-measuring device		
1. Type	Strip-chart current-balancing recorder	Strip-chart current-balancing recorder
2. Voltage drop for full-scale deflection, mv.		(10)
3. Usable chart width, mm.		180
B. Sensitivities		
1. Highest, μamp./mm.	1 *full-scale*	0.0005
2. Number of steps	11	13
3. Lowest, μamp./mm.	100 *full-scale*	0.5
4. Calibration procedure	Recorder has Zener diode-stabilized power supply.	Recorder has Zener diode-stabilized power supply.
5. Accuracies of shunt or measuring resistors	±0.5% (of full-scale) overall accuracy	±0.1%
C. Periods		
1. Period with minimum available damping, sec.	4 full-scale	2.5 full-scale
2. Type of damping	RC, applied to recorder input signal	RC, in feedback circuit
3. Number of steps	5	5
4. Period with maximum available damping, sec.		25 (for 90% of full-scale deflection)

(Table 2.1, *Group 6, continued*)

TABLE 2.1 *(continued)*
Group 6 (continued)

	Yokogawa Electric Works, Ltd. DC Polarocorder (Type POL-11)	Yokogawa Electric Works, Ltd. High-Sensitivity Polarocorder (Type POL-12)
D. Compensation		
1. Maximum upscale, scale widths	1	1
2. Maximum downscale, scale widths	1	1
3. Maximum compensation of a linearly varying current, μamps./volt	40% of full-scale deflection per volt	40% of full-scale deflection per volt
II. Measurements of cell voltage		
A. Initial potential		
1. How established	Reference voltage stabilized by Zener diodes	Reference voltage stabilized by Zener diodes
2. Values available	0, ±0.5, ±1.0, and ±2.5 v. (±0.2% precision, ±0.5% accuracy)	0, ±0.5, ±1.0, and ±2.5 v. (±0.2% precision, ±0.5% accuracy)
B. Span potential		
1. How established	See II A1	See II A1
2. Values available	0, ±1.25, and ±2.5 v. (±0.2% precision, ±0.5% accuracy)	0, ±1.25, and ±2.5 v. (±0.2% precision, ±0.5% accuracy)
3. Direction of polarization	Either	Either
C. Bridge		
1. Type		Single-turn potentiometer
2. Resistance, ohms		100
3. Linearity, %		0.1
4. Total turns if wire-wound		750
5. Automatic stop at end of bridge traverse	Yes, or at any desired point during traverse of bridge	Yes, or at any desired point during traverse of bridge
6. Time for full traverse of bridge, minutes	12.5	12.5

D. Chart		
1. Rate of motion, mm./min.	12.5, 25, 50, 75, 150, or 300	12.5, 25, 50, 75, 150, or 300
2. Synchronization of chart and bridge drives	Simultaneous actuation of motors	Simultaneous actuation of motors
3. Maximum chart length available for recording current-time curves	20 m.	20 m.
4. Colors of grids available on chart paper	Red or green	Red or green
5. Type of pen	Ink pen with reservoir	Ink pen with reservoir
III. Other characteristics		
A. Size (width × depth × height, in.)	14.2 × 14.6 × 27.0	14.2 × 14.6 × 27.0
B. Batteries required	None	None
C. Provision for external checking of standard cell	No	No
D. Other features	Pen lifter	Pen lifter; a.-c. polarography (with superimposed 20-mv. a.-c. obtained from the power line).
IV. Price		
V. Available in the United States from	Yokogawa Electric Works, Inc. 40 Worth Street, New York, New York 10013	Yokogawa Electric Works, Inc., 40 Worth Street, New York, New York 10013

instruments, increased flexibility is obtained at the expense of simplicity of operation. Most designers in the United States have striven to keep their polarographs reasonably simple for the sake of the technician who spends only a fraction of his time in making polarographic analyses, who has little if any use for an extremely versatile instrument, and who would more probably be dismayed than reassured by a wide assortment of functions and controls. A striking example of this philosophy is apparent in the Leeds and Northrup Type E Electrochemograph (the variety of names borne by commercial instruments reflects the fact that the term "Polarograph" is a registered trademark of E. H. Sargent & Co.), whose control panel provides instructions sufficiently complete to permit its operation even by one who has had little or no previous experience with the technique. Partly because polarography is more widely used for routine analytical work abroad than in this country, however, the majority of designers in other countries have striven for greater versatility instead. For example, several polarographs manufactured abroad, including the Japanese Shimadzu RP-2 and the Czechoslovakian LP 60, provide a selection of different chart speeds; this is useful for such diverse purposes as studies of chemical reaction rates and voltammetry with hanging mercury drop electrodes, but is not available on any commercial American instrument. This is one reason why a number of polarographs manufactured abroad have been included in Table 2.1.

The information in Table 2.1 has been furnished by the manufacturers of the respective instruments, to whom the writer is indebted for making it available and for giving permission to publish it in this form. The significances and desirable values or ranges of most of the tabulated characteristics are given in the preceding section. Other characteristics can be evaluated by combining tabulated values; for example, with an instrument having a minimum span potential of 1 v., a fixed time of 10 min. for full rotation of the bridge, and a fixed chart speed of 25 mm./min., a precision of ±1 mm. in locating the half-wave potential on the recorded polarogram would correspond to an uncertainty of ±4 mv. A few characteristics, such as the size and d.-c. input requirements, are matters of convenience; others, such as the total number of turns on a wire-wound bridge (which affects the resolution attainable and may, if small, lead to significant distortions of voltammograms obtained with solid or stationary electrodes, though its effect on an ordinary polarogram is masked by the oscillations resulting from the growth and fall of the drops) are of vital importance only in special applications and are discussed in subsequent sections.

There is no one "best" polarograph; a rational selection can be made only by taking into account one's budget, the conditions under which the instrument is to be used, the experience of its least skilled user, and the purposes to which it may be put. On the basis of the information in Table 2.1 and personal experience with many of these instruments, however, the writer feels that the following recommendations may reasonably be made to prospective purchasers in the United States:

1. If economy is a major concern:

   a. Manual and photographically recording instruments: Sargent Models III and XII

   b. Pen-and-ink recording instruments: American Optical Co. Electro-Polarizer, Sargent Model XV

2. If routine analysis will be the principal use: Leeds and Northrup Type E Electrochemograph, Sargent Model XV

3. If extreme simplicity of operation is important: Leeds and Northrup Type E Electrochemograph

4. If flexibility, accuracy, and precision are the principal desiderata: Metrohm E261 R Polarecord, Numec, Radiometer PO 4, Shimadzu RP-2.

Several instruments not included in the above list have special features that are uniquely advantageous in special circumstances, but these can easily be gleaned from Table 2.1 and an exhaustive list of recommendations would be too lengthy to deserve inclusion here.

III. Polarographic Cells

The cell is that portion of the apparatus that contains the solution being studied. It also includes a nonpolarizable electrode to which the potential of the dropping electrode is referred. Because oxygen is reducible at the dropping electrode over most of the range of potentials that is important in polarography, and can also have various other undesirable effects, it must usually be removed by bubbling an inert gas through the solution before the measurements, then passing this over the surface of the solution during the measurements to prevent re-solution of air.

The specific details of cell construction are so much a matter of individual taste that an immense number of cells have been described in the literature. Only a few of these can be mentioned here. Those that are mentioned are the ones that are most readily available or most easily constructed, most convenient, and most versatile and widely used.

The most important part of a cell is its reference electrode. The polarograph applies a voltage across the cell; even neglecting for the moment the iR drop included in this (which will be discussed below), it is plain that any error or variation in the potential of the reference electrode leads to a corresponding uncertainty in the potential of the dropping electrode. Except in analytical work of the most routine kind, where exact definition of the potential axis of the polarogram is of little importance, it is vital that the potential of the reference electrode be not only known but also essentially independent of the current flowing through it. Two kinds of reference electrodes, "internal" and "external," are in general use. An internal electrode is in direct contact with the solution being studied, while an external electrode is separated from it by a salt bridge or porous membrane. Internal electrodes are chiefly valuable in routine analyses, in which their sometimes limited constancy of potential is unimportant. They are also often used in work (e.g., at very negative potentials) where contamination by alkali metal ions or other constituents of a salt bridge would be harmful; in cells containing only one or two drops of solution, because of the mechanical difficulty of bringing an external electrode into contact with so small a volume of sample; and in continuous polarographic analysis, where the slow contamination of an external electrode would eventually render its potential as uncertain as that of an internal one.

What is probably the best, although it is not the most widely used, internal reference electrode is made by coiling about 15–20 cm. of 14-gauge silver wire into a helix; it is often convenient to coil it around the dropping electrode. In a solution containing an ion X^- that forms an insoluble silver salt, the potential of this electrode depends only on the activity of X^- in the solution, provided, of course, that the solution is saturated with AgX. If its solubility is very small, enough AgX to satisfy this requirement will be formed by reaction with dissolved oxygen when an air-saturated solution is placed in contact with the electrode before deaeration. This, however, involves the danger of partial hydrolytic precipitation of heavy metal ions if the solution is neutral and unbuffered, as is mentioned below. The electrode should not be used unless a precipitate results when a drop of a solution containing $0.01M$ silver ion is added to 10 ml. of the sample solution. Otherwise the concentration of dissolved silver ion, and hence the potential of the silver electrode, may change considerably during the recording of the polarogram, and in addition the concentration of silver ion may become high enough to give rise to a substantial current at the dropping electrode. The silver electrode is useless in solutions containing ammonia, cyanide, thiosulfate, and high concentrations of halides, as well as in solutions containing only nitrate, acetate, perchlorate, and other ions whose silver salts are appreciably soluble. The coating of insoluble salts that forms on the electrode when it is used as the anode of the cell should be removed occasionally by treatment with ammonia, thiosulfate, or cyanide, followed by thorough rinsing with distilled water. If the electrode is wound around the capillary tip during use, it should be removed for cleaning.

The mercury pool reference electrode has been widely used since the earliest days of polarography (8). It is simply a pool of pure mercury on the bottom of the cell, connected to the polarograph via a platinum wire sealed through the wall of the cell. The area of a mercury pool electrode should not be too small but need not exceed several square centimeters, and may have to be much less than this in a micro cell intended for use with small volumes of solution. Heyrovský cells of various sizes can be procured from E. H. Sargent & Co. (S-29370, S-29373, S-29376, and S-29380); the one shown in Fig. 2.14(a) is typical. That in Fig. 2.14(b) serves the same purposes; by sliding it up and down through a small cylinder of Teflon, the same glass tube can be used to bubble inert gas through the solution to deaerate it and then over the solution to keep it deaerated. The one in Fig. 2.14(c) keeps the mercury that has fallen from the capillary tip separate from the annular ring of mercury that constitutes the pool electrode, and can be used for determining the value of m for the capillary.

Mercury pool electrodes should be used only in solutions that contain ions giving insoluble mercurous or mercuric salts. A list of

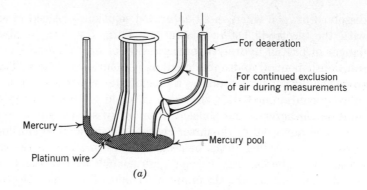

For deaeration

For continued exclusion
of air during measurements

Mercury

Mercury pool

Platinum wire

(a)

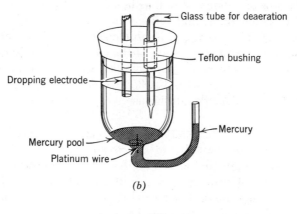

Glass tube for deaeration

Teflon bushing

Dropping electrode

Mercury

Mercury pool

Platinum wire

(b)

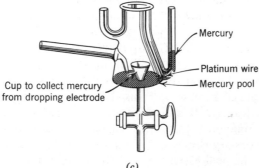

Mercury

Platinum wire

Mercury pool

Cup to collect mercury
from dropping electrode

(c)

Figure 2.14.　Typical Heyrovský cells. Cells a and c are shown by permission
of E. H. Sargent & Co., from whom they are available as catalog numbers S-29370
and S-29380, respectively.

solutions in which they should not be used would practically duplicate the list given above for silver electrodes. As is also true of a silver electrode that is initially clean, the potential of a mercury pool is not truly constant while the polarogram is being recorded, but may drift as much as 20 mv.; although a silver electrode may be poised by preanodizing it in a solution similar to the one being studied, this is hardly possible with a mercury pool. Though a drift of this magnitude would be relatively unimportant in purely analytical work, it would preclude the accurate measurement of a half-wave potential, an assessment of reversibility, or the evaluation of the electrochemical kinetic parameters that characterize a half-reaction at the dropping electrode.

The uncertainties in their potentials, together with the troubles that may arise when these rather readily oxidizable metals are brought into contact with solutions containing strong oxidizing agents (which are described in Chap. 7 II-B), incline the writer to the view that the simplicity of internal reference electrodes is more than counterbalanced by the troubles they may cause. Even their simplicity is largely illusory in work that is to be published because of the long-standing custom of referring all polarographic potentials to the saturated calomel electrode. This is done to permit comparison of half-wave potentials measured in different media. Since the potential of an internal reference electrode varies from one medium to another, such comparisons can be made only if the potential of the internal electrode is measured against an external saturated calomel electrode. This should of course be done with a precision potentiometer, and it is prudent to do it twice: once before the polarogram is recorded and again after it is completed so that changes during the experiment will not escape notice. Internal reference electrodes cannot be used in solutions containing oxidizing agents powerful enough to oxidize the electrode metal, or reducing agents powerful enough to reduce the poising salt (AgX, Hg_2X_2, etc.). Nor are they as useful when the dropping electrode is the anode as when it is the cathode; in the former case the solution is usually capable of reducing the poising salt chemically, and even if this reaction were slow the poising salt would be reduced at the reference electrode as the polarogram was recorded. If the quantity of electricity flowing through the cell is large enough, the potential of the reference electrode will necessarily undergo a large drift toward more negative values.

External reference electrodes, on the other hand, have potentials that are either accurately known or can be measured once and for all (usually, indeed, the S.C.E. itself is used) and that are independent of the composition of the sample solution, so that only very infrequent checking is needed to ensure that no contamination has occurred. When properly used they rarely need renewing; they may be used with solutions containing strong oxidizing or reducing agents; and they render the presence of a depolarizing anion in the sample unnecessary, thereby permitting the range of the dropping electrode to be extended to somewhat more positive potentials.

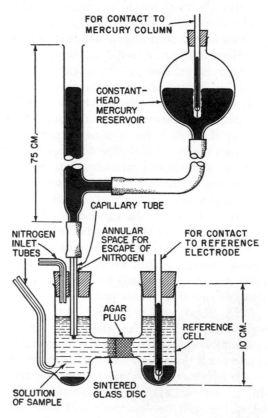

Figure 2.15.   H-cell and stand tube according to Lingane and Laitinen (9).

The most widely used cell with an external reference electrode is the H-cell (9), one form of which is shown in Fig. 2.15. It consists of two compartments, one containing the solution being studied and the other containing the reference electrode. To avert polarization of the reference electrode, the compartment containing it should be made from tubing of at least 20 mm. i.d., but the dimensions of the solution compartment can be varied widely to accommodate any desired volume of solution. In the Lingane–Laitinen cell of Fig. 2.15, these compartments are separated by a cross-member filled with a 4% agar–saturated potassium chloride gel, which is held in place by a medium-porosity sintered-Pyrex disc. To facilitate rapid and complete deaeration of the solution, the disc should be placed as near to the solution compartment as the glassblower's skill will permit, and for the same reason the side tube through which the inert gas is passed through the solution should be as near to the bottom of the cell as possible.

The agar gel is prepared by warming a small flask containing 4 g. of agar and 90 ml. of water in a large beaker filled with boiling water, or on a steam bath, until solution is complete, then adding 30 g. of potassium chloride and stirring thoroughly. Heating over a flame, or even on many hot plates, causes scorching and must be avoided. The solidified gel must be white, for a yellow or brownish gel will contaminate solutions that come in contact with it. It is essential to use a good grade of agar, such as the Bacto agar sold by the Difco Laboratories (Detroit, Michigan) and several supply houses. When the salt has dissolved, the clean dry cell is clamped with the cross-member vertical and the solution compartment down, and gel is pipetted into the cross-member until it is almost completely filled; then the cell is allowed to stand undisturbed until the gel has solidified. The unused gel may be stored in a tightly stoppered flask and reliquefied by heating in the same way when it is needed.

After the gel has solidified, the cell is turned upright and enough pure mercury is added to the reference-electrode compartment to give a layer 1 to 2 cm. deep. This is covered with an equally thick layer of a paste made by stirring equal weights of mercurous and potassium chlorides with a little saturated potassium chloride, and the compartment is filled with saturated potassium chloride solution containing a large excess of the solid salt. Electrical connection to the mercury is made by means of a glass tube through which a small platinum wire is sealed so as to project into the mercury for a few millimeters; this tube is filled with mercury and inserted into a rubber stopper which serves to seal the reference-electrode compartment tightly. The wire leading to the reference-electrode terminal of the polarograph is simply dipped into the mercury in this tube. Creeping of the potassium chloride can be prevented by a liberal coat of silicone grease on each of the stopper-glass boundaries.

The solution compartment of the cell should finally be filled with saturated potassium chloride solution, and a day or two should be allowed for the S.C.E. to reach its equilibrium potential.

In use, the solution compartment is emptied, washed with water, and either dried (preferably by aspirating air through it) or rinsed with several portions of the sample; then at least enough solution is added to cover the entire fritted disc. Dissolved air is removed by passing nitrogen or some other gas (see Sec. V below) into the side tube so that it bubbles through the solution. The length of time required for complete deaeration may vary considerably from one solution to another; some solutions foam so badly that only a very slow stream of gas can be used, while others permit the use of a very rapid stream. In general, it is prudent to allow half an hour, which implies that it is convenient to have two cells available in routine work so that a solution can be deaerated in one while another solution is being examined in the other. An estimate of the time that should be allowed for deaeration can be obtained by measuring the current at a dropping-electrode potential of -0.7 v. vs. S.C.E. at intervals during the deaeration of a dilute solution of potassium chloride.

When deaeration is judged to be complete, a two-way stopcock in the gas stream is used to divert the gas over the surface of the solution through a tube passing through the stopper of the solution compartment. Measurements should not be attempted with gas bubbling through the solution, for the stirring causes high and erratic currents. Finally the dropping electrode is inserted through another hole in the stopper, which must be large enough for easy insertion and removal of the capillary (thereby providing an annulus for the escape of the gas stream), and the measurements are carried out.

Insertion of the dropping electrode should be deferred until the last possible instant because this minimizes the difficulties that may sometimes arise on prolonged contact between mercury and the solution. If it is inserted before deaeration is complete, a substantial concentration of mercurous or mercuric ion may be formed by the reaction

$$4 \text{ Hg} + O_2 + 4 \text{ H}^+ = 2 \text{ Hg}_2^{++} + 2 \text{ H}_2O$$

if the solution is acidic and contains no ion yielding an insoluble mercury salt. Or an appreciable fraction of a heavy metal ion may be lost by a reaction like

$$\text{Pb}^{++} + 2 \text{ Hg} + 2 \text{ Cl}^- + \tfrac{1}{2} O_2 + \text{H}_2O = \text{Hg}_2\text{Cl}_2 + \text{Pb(OH)}_2$$

if the solution is neutral and unbuffered. Oxidation of the mercury which accumulates at the bottom of the cell also occurs in solutions containing strong oxidants like silver and ferric ions or, in acidic media, quinones and polynitroaromatics, and may lead to substantial changes in the currents measured, as discussed in Chap. 7 II-B.

After the measurements have been completed, the solution is removed by suction, by opening a stopcock sealed to the bottom of the solution compartment, or by simply turning the cell upside down and pouring it out; the first of these is the most convenient, especially if the cell is thermostatted. A trap in the suction line will serve to collect the mercury for repurification. The cell must be promptly and thoroughly washed as described below.

The solution compartment of an H-cell should never be allowed to stand empty for more than a few minutes at a time, for the agar bridge will dry out and shrink, permitting bulk flow of liquid between the two compartments of the cell. On the contrary, it should always be kept filled with either water or, for overnight or longer periods, saturated potassium chloride. Mercury must be scrupulously removed before the cell is allowed to stand even overnight, for the mercurous salts formed by air-oxidation will accumulate on the cell walls and contaminate subsequent samples.

The length of time required for complete deaeration may be greatly reduced by replacing the capillary side-tube with a medium- or coarse-porosity fritted gas-dispersion cylinder ring-sealed through the cell wall as shown in Fig. 2.16 (10). This breaks up the gas stream into a large number of tiny bubbles so that a moderately rapid flow of gas effects complete deaeration within a minute or two. These cells are available from E. H. Sargent & Co. (S-29438). A microcell of similar design, which can be used with as little as 0.1 ml. of solution,

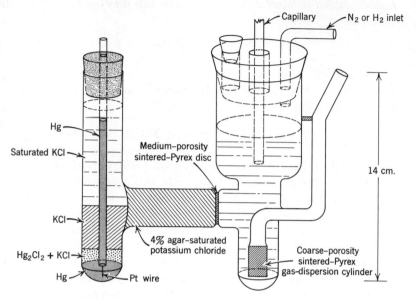

Figure 2.16. H-cell modified to permit rapid deaeration.

is available from the Macalaster Bicknell Company of Connecticut, Inc. (New Haven, Connecticut) as catalog number 12065.

When using an H-cell, care must be taken to avoid contamination with constituents of the preceding solution that remain in one or both of the frits by washing these thoroughly after removing a solution from the cell. It is convenient to carry out the major part of the washing with gas bubbling through the side-tube or gas-dispersion cylinder, but this should also be flushed out. The best way to do this is to partly fill the solution compartment of the cell with water or some other efficient solvent (e.g., acid or ethanol) for the constituents of the preceding sample, divert the gas stream through the tube that would normally lead it over the surface of the solution, and squeeze the tubing connecting the side tube to the gas train so that gas is forced out into the bulk of the solution. On releasing the pressure the solvent is sucked back into the side tube, whence it is forced into the body of the solution compartment when pressure is again applied to the side tube. Repeating this with two or three portions of the solvent decreases cross-contamination to a wholly negligible level.

Contamination of samples by agar or by constituents of the salt bridge occasionally causes trouble. The circumstances in which this is especially to be feared are discussed in Chap. 7 II-A. Here it may be said that, except in extremely prolonged experiments, trouble due to the use of agar is practically never encountered in work with solutions that do not attack agar chemically, despite the fears that have been expressed by many authors. Solutions containing high concentrations of acids, alkalies, or non-aqueous solvents do often cause trouble, however, and then there is nothing to do but remove the agar from any possible contact with the sample.

This can be accomplished in either of two ways, of which the currently more popular one is to use an "outflow" cell like the Kalousek cell shown in Fig. 2.17. Here a saturated calomel electrode is connected to a reservoir of saturated potassium chloride solution and also, through an ungreased stopcock in its cross-member, to the solution compartment. Electrolytic contact is made through the ground portion of the stopcock. At the end of an experiment the solution compartment is thoroughly cleaned and a small volume of

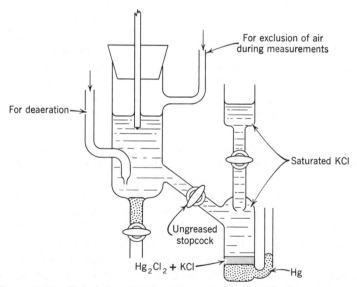

Figure 2.17.   Kalousek cell (*11*) with saturated calomel reference electrode.

saturated potassium chloride solution is allowed to flow out of the reservoir and through the stopcock to remove the preceding solution. The solution compartment is rinsed again to remove the potassium chloride, and the cell is then ready for another experiment. The constituents of the reference electrode can of course be changed at will: sodium chloride may be used instead of potassium chloride in work with perchlorate solutions, unsaturated solutions of potassium chloride may be used instead of saturated ones, or a mercury— mercurous sulfate–potassium sulfate electrode may be used if halides must be excluded.

The user of the Kalousek cell avoids two problems—contamination by the constituents of a preceding solution, and contamination by agar—associated with the use of H-cells of the Lingane–Laitinen and related types by incurring two others. Deaeration of the portion of the sample in the tube leading from the solution compartment to the stopcock is not easily achieved in the Kalousek cell. This is of little consequence in ordinary work, since only a negligible trace of oxygen could diffuse from this part of the solution to the vicinity of the capillary tip in the few minutes needed to record a polarogram, but might become important in more prolonged experiments or in work with very powerful reducing agents. A related difficulty arises in work in which a concentrated solution of a sample is added to the previously deaerated supporting electrolyte in the cell; because efficient mixing of the entire solution is not easily achieved, the capillary may be surrounded by a solution whose concentration is appreciably higher than it should be. Careful design and construction of the connecting tube will help to minimize both of these problems. It is especially advantageous to place the stopcock as close to the solution compartment as possible.

Another solution to the problem of contamination by agar consists of using a silver–silver chloride electrode of the type shown in Fig. 2.18. The glass components of this electrode are available from the Macalaster Bicknell Company of Connecticut, Inc. (New Haven, Connecticut) as catalog number 12066. The tip of the electrode is inserted directly into the solution being studied, as close to the tip of the capillary as possible. A small lipless beaker or a test tube may be used as the cell; if its diameter is sufficiently large, a sintered-glass gas-dispersion cylinder may be mounted in the stopper so that it nearly touches the bottom of the cell. Complete deaeration can then

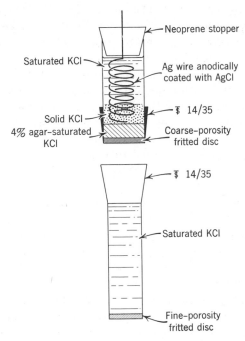

Figure 2.18.   Silver–silver chloride–saturated potassium chloride reference electrode and bridge according to Meites and Moros (*12*).

be achieved in a minute or two. The long bridge compartment of this electrode effectively separates the solution being studied from the substances in the reference electrode itself, even though the experiment may be prolonged for many hours. The solution in the bridge compartment should be changed daily, or after each experiment if the conditions are extreme. Between experiments the electrode-bridge assembly should be allowed to stand in a vessel containing the same solution as the bridge to prevent crystallization in the pores of the fritted disc. An assembled cell is shown in Fig. 7.4.

This arrangement also practically eliminates any possibility of contaminating the reference electrode and changing its potential, which is a real danger with both H-cells and Kalousek cells. In the latter case the danger is especially great if the solution being investigated is much denser than the solution in the reference electrode, in which event the cross member should have the opposite inclination from that shown in Fig. 2.17. The potential of any reference electrode used for polarographic work should be checked at regular intervals, using another electrode specifically reserved for the purpose. Such checks revealed no significant variation of the potential of an electrode like that shown in Fig. 2.18 during many months of work with concentrated cyanide solutions. On the basis of this and other similar experience, and in view of the known superiorities of silver–silver chloride over calomel electrodes, the writer feels that this arrangement deserves widespread adoption in polarographic laboratories. Half-wave potentials measured against this electrode may be converted to the usual S.C.E. by adding -0.042 v. If a silver–silver chloride electrode is made with saturated sodium rather than potassium chloride, which is useful in work with concentrated perchlorate solutions, the correction is -0.047 v.

Other methods of separating the solution from the reference electrode have been proposed (13–17) but are less often used. In any event, the electrolytic resistance of the cell should preferably not exceed about 1000 ohms, for then the iR drop through it becomes appreciable and gives rise to a substantial error in the potential of the dropping electrode unless it is eliminated or corrected for. The resistance of a cell may be determined by measurement with a conductance bridge, using a small platinum electrode in place of the dropping electrode, or by comparing the half-wave potentials obtained with different concentrations of the same reducible substance in the same supporting electrolyte, provided that one is chosen for which the true half-wave potential is known to be independent of concentration. The latter method is easier and is quite accurate enough for most purposes.

If, for example, $0.1mM$ cadmium ion in $1F$ potassium nitrate gives $i_d = 0.8$ μamp. and $E_{1/2} = -0.579$ v., while $2mM$ cadmium ion in the same supporting electrolyte gives $i_d = 16.0$ μamp. and $E_{1/2} = -0.594$ v., then

$$R = \Delta E_{1/2}/0.5\Delta i_d = 0.015/(0.5)(15.2 \times 10^{-6}) = 2000 \text{ ohms}$$

Note that the iR drop causes the half-wave potential of a cathodic wave to be more negative than the true value, while it causes the half-wave potential of an anodic wave to be more positive than the true value.

A resistance higher than about 1000 ohms in a polarographic cell can arise in any of several ways. Some of these are purely mechanical and easily avoided or cured. The plug and shell of the central stopcock in a Kalousek cell should not be too finely ground. Commercial saturated calomel and other reference electrode sold for use with pH meters must not be used in polarographic work, for their potentials vary considerably with current and in addition their resistances are far too high. Crystallization or precipitation should not be allowed to occur in the pores of any fritted disc or in the plug of the central stopcock in a Kalousek cell.

Of much more serious concern than any of these, however, is the high resistance that accompanies the use of many non-aqueous solvents. The uses of such solvents in polarography are discussed briefly in Chap. 7 I; here it will suffice to say that, because both the dielectric constants of most non-aqueous solvents and the solvation energies of ions dissolved in them are much smaller than the corresponding values for water, the solubilities of most inorganic salts in these media are rather small. Hence it is often impossible to prepare solutions of low specific resistance, so that correction or compensation for the iR drop through the cell becomes vital, not only in measuring half-wave potentials and in other operations in which precise knowledge of the potential of the dropping electrode is needed, but even in obtaining a curve with a recognizable shape.

Numerous expedients have been proposed for dealing with high cell resistances. Algebraic correction of the potential at each point can, in principle, be made in the manner illustrated by the example above. However, it is tedious, and in addition its accuracy is limited by the difficulties of measuring the cell resistance accurately, keeping it constant throughout the experiment (which is especially relevant to the use of mercury pool electrodes because the cell resistance is then critically dependent on the distance between the capillary tip and the pool, which may vary significantly during a prolonged experiment), and reproducing it from one experiment to the next. It is not ordinarily feasible to deal with the iR drop by working with more dilute solutions to decrease the currents that flow, for then the correction for the residual current becomes increasingly important while the form of the wave may deteriorate as well. Three much more satisfactory approaches are available.

One is to make electrical or electronic compensation for the iR drop across an ordinary polarographic cell (18–20), but this becomes less and less satisfactory as the cell resistance increases above perhaps

20,000 ohms. Another is to employ a cell containing a second reference electrode, which is connected to one of the X-input terminals of an X–Y recorder while the dropping electrode is connected to the other. Meanwhile the iR drop derived from the passage of the cell current through a standard resistor in series with the cell is applied to the Y-input terminals, and the recorder then furnishes a plot of the cell current against the potential difference between the dropping electrode and the second reference electrode, through which the cell current does not flow (20–22). Amplification is advantageous to decrease the current drawn by the X-input circuit of the recorder (23). The pen traces a complex curve during the life of each drop, for the voltage V applied across the cell, which is described by the equation

$$V = E_a - E_c + iR \tag{2.12}$$

where E_a and E_c are the potentials of the anode and cathode, respectively, is nearly constant over the short life of the drop. At the beginning of the drop life, when the current i is small, the potential difference $E_a - E_c$ must be large, but as the drop grows i increases and the potential difference becomes smaller. As the applied voltage is varied one obtains a number of overlapping traces representing these variations for the different drops, and the envelope of these traces is similar in shape to an ordinary polarogram. Its significance is shrouded, however, by uncertainty about the effects of the wide swings of the potential of the dropping electrode; different half-reactions must occur during different stages of the drop life (24), but it is not certainly known how seriously this affects the curves obtained. By appropriate modification of the circuit it is possible to use a conventional polarograph instead of an X–Y recorder and also to provide an electronic correction to V to eliminate the wide swings of potential (25–27). A device serving this purpose and a three-electrode cell for use with it are available from E. H. Sargent & Co. A more direct and better approach is to replace the polarizing circuit of the polarograph by operational-amplifier circuitry that continuously readjusts the value of V during the life of each drop so that the difference between the potentials of the dropping electrode and a reference electrode is always kept equal to the desired value (6,7,28, 29). A three-electrode cell is again used so that the reference electrode does not carry the electrolysis current, and the potential of the dropping electrode is slowly varied in the same fashion as by an ordinary polarograph in ordinary circumstances. Such a controlled-potential polarograph is commercially available from the Nuclear Materials and Equipment Corp. (Apollo, Pennsylvania), and its characteristics are summarized in Table 2.1.

It is convenient to divide the resistance of a polarographic cell into two parts (30). Imagine a stationary spherical surface that coincides with the surface of the drop at the instant just before it falls. The "external" resistance is the resistance through the bulk of the solution between this surface and the reference electrode; even though the specific conductance of the solution may be very low, this resistance can be made very small by appropriate placement of the reference electrode. The "internal" resistance is the resistance between this surface and the drop at a preceding instant during the drop life; this varies with the drop age, decreasing as the drop grows, and has a finite average value even if the tip of the reference-electrode probe is right at the surface of the imaginary sphere. For these reasons it is immune to instrumental compensation (31). It appears as an iR drop included in the potential sensed by the external circuit. It may be appreciable in a solvent of low dielectric constant even though the distances involved are very small, and it constitutes the principal deterrent to polarographic work in such solvents.

Other additions to polarographic cells—including electrodes for coulometric titrations (Chap. 10 VI) with amperometric end points, glass electrodes for pH measurements in situ, and the like—can of course be made at will.

Many other polarographic cells have been designed to serve special purposes. These cannot be described in detail, but the following references may be consulted by those interested:

1. For determinations of oxygen in body fluids: 32.
2. For continuous analyses of flowing solutions: 32a, 33–41.
3. For analyses of gases: 42–45.
4. For studies of two-phase systems: 46.
5. For deaeration during measurements of current (e.g., in rapid amperometric titrations): 47.
6. For work at high or low pressures: 48,49.

IV. Dropping Electrodes

The dropping electrode assembly comprises the capillary, the column of mercury above it, and the connection between the mercury and the wire leading to the polarograph. The capillary must have a length and an internal diameter such that a droplet of mercury falls from its tip every 3–6 seconds when it is in use. Although the length of this interval, which is known as the drop time, varies with the composition of the solution and the potential applied by the polarograph, its reproducibility under fixed conditions is crucial to the success of polarographic measurements.

Capillaries satisfactory for most polarographic work are easily made from marine barometer tubing, which is available on special order from the Corning Glass Works (Corning, New York), and which can also be procured in 21-cm. lengths from E. H. Sargent & Co. Its external and internal diameters are about 6–7 and 0.06–0.08 mm., respectively. A 5- to 10-cm. length usually gives a drop time in the desired range. The stock of tubing must be tightly sealed to prevent access of dust, and it is also wise to cut off and discard about 1 cm. from a length of tubing before cutting the capillary. Short lengths of tubing are most easily cut by scratching the tubing with a very sharp file, then breaking it with the aid of a cork borer just large enough to admit it. A suitable length is then cut from the remainder of the piece. A 10-cm. piece usually gives a drop time in the desired range when the column of mercury above its tip is roughly 50 cm. high. Care must be taken that the last break is accurately perpendicular to the axis of the tubing, for the current decreases and becomes less reproducible if it is not (50–52). For the same reason, the plane of the capillary tip must be horizontal within two or three degrees when it is in use. The capillary tip must not be ground or polished, and it should be connected to the mercury column without delay.

As will be shown in Chap. 3 IV-B, the drop time is very nearly directly proportional to the length of the capillary and inversely proportional to the height of the column of mercury above the capillary tip. Consequently a capillary that gives too long a drop time can sometimes be used by simply raising the mercury reservoir, and the long capillaries that must be used in cells having very large solution compartments require correspondingly high mercury pressures.

Sometimes, as when a microcell is to be used, it is desirable to have a capillary of very small external diameter. To make such a capillary, a length of 0.25 to 0.5-mm. i.d. capillary tubing or, better, thermometer tubing is allowed to soften in a rather cool flame, then it is drawn out very slowly and evenly while the tubing is held vertically. The aim is to secure a wall thickness as great as possible to minimize breakage, and this is facilitated by prolonging the preliminary softening as much as possible. The i.d. should be fairly uniform for at least 2 cm. above the tip, for a continuously tapering capillary gives less reproducible drop times. Much practice is necessary before useful and stable capillaries can be secured consistently, and few experimenters now draw their own capillaries except for this one special purpose.

Many other types of capillaries have been described in the literature, including capillaries with flared orifices, multiple capillaries connected to a single mercury column, vibrating capillaries, capillaries with mechanical premature dislodgment of the drop, and rotating capillaries. Some of these are certainly advantageous in special circumstances, as is the vibrating electrode, for example, in solutions that must be efficiently stirred while the measurements are being made. But none of them can be recommended for ordinary polarographic purposes. Capillaries bent through 90° so that the mercury issues horizontally into the drop have been said to be advantageous (53), but the writer's experience with them (54) did not seem to justify this claim.

Nevertheless, capillaries of constant internal diameter do not give perfectly regular residual-current curves. More or less random, but often definitely periodic, variations of slope occur, and become larger as the potential becomes more negative, more frequent as the rate of flow of mercury through the capillary increases, and relatively more important as the concentration of the solution decreases. In much polarographic work they can be neglected, but they become important in work with solutions much more dilute than about 0.05mM and also in work at very negative potentials, as in investigations or determinations of difficultly reducible organic compounds, where regular drop formation often gives way to the production of an almost continuous stream of very tiny drops. Moreover, they are ultimately responsible for the lower limit of utility of polarographic analyses. Close inspection of Fig. 2.11 will reveal a few irregularities typical of what is observed even under optimum conditions.

This "capillary noise" (55–57) has been attributed to the formation and dislodgment of pockets of solution a millimeter or two above the orifice of the capillary. When the drop falls, the mercury thread does not break at the orifice, but some distance above it (58), permitting entry of the solution into the capillary. The phenomenon can be

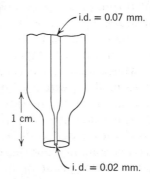

i.d. = 0.07 mm.

1 cm.

i.d. = 0.02 mm.

Figure 2.19.   Modified capillary for minimization of capillary noise, according to
Cooke, Kelley, and Fisher (56).

minimized by drawing out a conventional capillary slightly, as shown
in Fig. 2.19. This decreases the rate of flow of mercury through the
capillary and thus, as will be apparent from Chap. 3 III, decreases
the diffusion current. It also decreases the residual current, but these
effects are of very little importance; what is important is the considerable improvement that is effected in the ratio of the diffusion
current to the "noise" in the residual current, for it is this ratio that
determines the limit of detection and the precision that can be
attained in work with very dilute solutions. In the writer's hands a
capillary like that of Fig. 2.19 has seemed to exhibit less tendency
toward streaming at very negative potentials than an ordinary
capillary, but it cannot be said whether this will always be the case.

It is convenient to be able to judge quickly whether a capillary will
have characteristics suitable for polarographic work, particularly if it
has been hand-drawn. For this purpose the capillary tip must be
immersed in liquid; the drop time in air is meaningless because the
drop adheres to a dry capillary tip and grows to a size much larger
than it attains in actual use. The most rapid and convenient technique
consists of raising the height of the mercury column to about the
desired value (about 50 cm. represents a reasonable compromise
between a height so great that it is awkward to measure and one so
small that it is troublesome to reproduce), and then, with the mercury
flowing, immersing the capillary tip in pure water. If the drop time is
reproducible and between 4 and 8 sec., the capillary may be deemed
to be satisfactory. Because the drop time varies with potential, it may

be much shorter in use than during this test; the more negative the potential at which the capillary is to be used, the longer its drop time under these conditions should be.

A capillary should last almost indefinitely if it is properly cared for. It is absolutely essential that no solid matter of any kind ever be allowed to reach the inside of the capillary. As was mentioned in connection with Fig. 2.10, dropping electrodes must not be subjected to large positive potentials. An electrolyte solution must never be allowed to dry on the capillary. A capillary must never be immersed in a solution before the flow of mercury starts nor be left in one while the flow is stopped. Capillaries used in solutions containing precipitates, as in amperometric precipitation titrations, cannot be expected to last as long as those used only in homogeneous solutions. No particular harm seems to result from long exposure to fairly concentrated solutions of ammonia or alkalies, but strongly acidic fluoride solutions do cause rapid deterioration. Capillaries fabricated from Teflon (59) may be used in these and other media that attack glass.

With the dry, newly cut capillary standing in air, the height of the mercury column at which the flow of mercury just stops should be noted, and the pressure of mercury should then always be kept greater than this unless the capillary is perfectly clean and dry.

The capillary is best safeguarded by rigid adherence to the following procedure. The sample solution is first deaerated; then, with the dry capillary tip in the air, the mercury pressure is raised to at least 10 cm. above the equilibrium value previously noted. After mercury drops have started to form, the capillary is inserted into the cell, and finally the mercury level is adjusted to the desired value, which should never be less than 10 cm. above the equilibrium value. After the measurements are complete, the capillary is raised out of the solution and immediately washed very thoroughly with a suitable solvent. Ammonia, dilute acids, ethanol, or other solvents may be used to remove the constituents of the sample solution, but in any case the final washing should be made with not less than 100 ml. of distilled water. Finally the mercury pressure is lowered to 1–2 cm. above the equilibrium value and the capillary is left to dry with mercury still flowing very slowly through it. If a stand tube with a stopcock is used (see below), closing the stopcock at this point will permit the mercury to continue flowing until the equilibrium height is reached, by which time the residual water on the capillary tip will have evaporated so that flow ceases with the capillary filled with mercury. Nothing is gained by washing the capillary with acetone or drying it with absorbent paper to hasten the drying process, for the risk of introducing grease or paper fibers into the tip outweighs any possible advantage. Leaving the capillary tip immersed in mercury when it is not in use is sometimes recommended to ensure that dust and dirt cannot enter the capillary tip, but the writer cannot join in the recommendation: one must then either allow mercury to flow through the capillary continuously or close off the reservoir by means of a stopcock. The former is wasteful because there are few laboratories in which mercury exposed for long periods will not pick up enough grease and dirt to prevent its reuse unless it is purified, while the latter empties the capillary completely and leaves it open to anything that may fall into it.

A capillary which, in the absence of any mechanical vibration, gives an irregular drop time had better be discarded without further ado. Very rarely a capillary may be saved by alternately immersing its tip *with the mercury flowing* in 1:1 nitric acid for a minute or two and rinsing very thoroughly with distilled water. Organic solvents may of course be used first if contamination by organic material is suspected. Treatment with aqua regia usually only makes matters worse. Attempts to clean a capillary by sucking acids or other liquids through it usually only waste time: it is better to change the capillary and take better care of the new one. The trouble of changing the capillary can occasionally be avoided by simply cutting 5–10 mm. off its tip with the aid of a cork borer as described above. Care should be taken that the break is square for the reasons previously mentioned.

The simplest possible dropping electrode assembly is made by attaching the capillary to a length of Tygon tubing leading to a leveling bulb partially filled with mercury. Electrical connection to the mercury is made through a connector that consists of a short piece of platinum or tungsten wire sealed through the end of a length of glass tubing. This is inserted into one hole of a two-hole rubber stopper in the leveling bulb; the wire makes a connection between the mercury in the leveling bulb and a column of mercury inside the tube, into which the lead from the polarograph is dipped. The other hole of the stopper carries a short inverted U-tube loosely plugged with cotton or glass wool to permit pressure equalization while preventing excessive ingress of dust. There have been occasional reports of peculiarities caused by the use of Tygon, apparently due to plasticizer that forms a film on the surface of the mercury emerging from the capillary. To avoid this, it may be better to use rubber or neoprene tubing; polyethylene is unsatisfactory because it is too inflexible. Rubber tubing should be freed from sulfur by boiling it for 30–60 min. in 2F sodium hydroxide, then washing it very thoroughly with distilled water and drying it. All connections in the mercury line should be secured with stout wire, for obvious reasons.

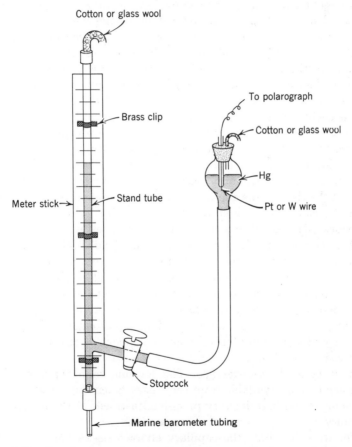

Figure 2.20.   Stand tube and mercury reservoir assembly for use with dropping mercury electrodes.

A better and more convenient arrangement involves the use of a stand tube. That shown in Fig. 2.20 is modified from the one in Fig. 2.15, and is considerably easier and more convenient to use. A 2-mm. stopcock is sealed to a 1-m. length of 7- or 8-mm. i.d. glass tubing about 10 cm. from one of its ends. To ensure that air bubbles will not be trapped in the plug of the stopcock, it should be inclined slightly as shown in the figure. A small inverted U-tube loosely packed with cotton or glass wool is attached to the other end of the tubing to keep dust out of it, and the finished stand tube is attached to a meter stick with several narrow brass strips secured with screws. A short length of Tygon or rubber tubing around the stand tube under each brass clip will prevent breakage when the screws are tightened. The lower end of the stand tube should project about 2 cm. below the bottom of the meter stick so that the tubing connecting the stand tube to the capillary can be securely wired in place. The capillary is placed inside the stand tube for a distance of 1–2 cm. (failure to do this necessitates checking the vertical alignment of the capillary every time it is used) and securely wired in place. A leveling bulb is connected to the stopcock by a length of Tygon tubing; the writer has never encountered any difficulties arising from the use of Tygon in this apparatus, presumably because any plasticizer that enters the stand tube rises to the top of the mercury column instead of flowing into the capillary. The stopcock can be very lightly greased with stopcock grease or silicone lubricant, but it is better to use a stopcock with a Teflon plug. In any case, a spring-loaded stopcock retainer should be attached to the plug to prevent its coming loose; mercury is too expensive and too toxic to be showered all over the laboratory. The meter stick should be held in two three-finger clamps attached to the same support rod and locked together by a vertical cross-brace. It can then be raised and lowered without danger of tilting the capillary. The leveling bulb should be supported from a second support rod, parallel to the one carrying the stand tube and far enough from it to avoid interference. The leveling bulb support (catalog number 14-753) available from the Fisher Scientific Co. is extremely convenient and permits very precise adjustment of the height of the mercury column.

For work in which the capillary characteristics must be checked frequently (measurement of diffusion current constants, much practical analytical work of a non-routine nature, etc.), the stand tube

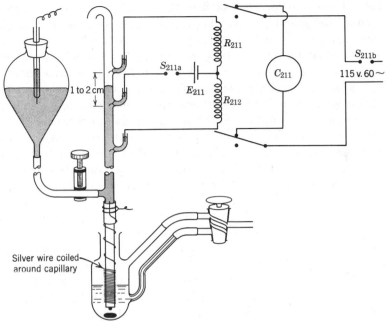

Figure 2.21. Automatic device for the determination of m according to Lingane (60), shown with cell employing internal silver-wire reference electrode. E_{211}: low voltage d.-c. source sufficient to actuate relays; R_{211} and R_{212}: d.-c. relays, normally open; S_{211a} and S_{211b}: DPDT on–off switch; C_{211}: electric stop clock.

shown in Fig. 2.21 is extremely convenient. It permits the automatic determination of the rate of flow of mercury through the capillary (which is expressed in milligrams per second and denoted by the symbol m). The level of mercury in the stand tube is raised so that the mercury touches the highest of the three pointed tungsten contacts, then the switch S_{211} is closed and the stand tube is cut off from the mercury reservoir by closing the stopcock, which should preferably have a Teflon plug. At the instant when the mercury level falls below the tip of this contact, the relay R_{211} opens and the electric stop clock C_{211} starts. It continues to run until the mercury falls below the tip of the middle contact, when R_{212} also opens and stops the clock. Hence the clock runs for a time that is equal to the weight of mercury contained between these contacts divided by the average rate of flow of mercury; if the contacts are not too far apart, this is essentially equal to the constant rate of flow that would be obtained with a mercury level exactly halfway between the two contacts. The weight of mercury required in this calculation is determined once and for all by a manual determination of m for one capillary for which the outflow time is also measured. A precision of $\pm 0.1\%$ is easily obtained. The manual determination of m is discussed in the following section.

There are several dangers that accompany attempts to use impure mercury in polarographic work. Base metals can give rise to anodic waves that cause difficulties of interpretation and errors in analyses. Even quite small traces of noble metals affect the overpotential for hydrogen evolution, and may decrease it so much that the plateau of a wave becomes too short for convenient measurement, or may give rise to catalytic hydrogen waves. Oxides, grease, and dirt can render a capillary useless in a very short time, as can the oxidation of a base metal to an insoluble product inside the capillary tip.

Mercury quite pure enough for almost all polarographic work can be obtained as Vacumetal mercury from Metalsalts, Inc. (Hawthorne, New Jersey). In the writer's opinion the much more expensive "instrument grade" mercury available from various suppliers is not worth its extra cost. Four or five pounds of mercury suffice for occasional polarographic work, but if the polarograph is to be used almost continuously it is better to have about ten pounds of mercury reserved for use with it.

Many procedures for the purification of mercury have been proposed. Those appropriate for use in polarographic laboratories are relatively simple and consume very little time, but the experimenter has first to determine whether they are worth adopting. If a single capillary is used for six hours during every working day and if there are 250 working days in a year, the total consumption of mercury will be roughly 25 pounds per year, essentially all of which can be recovered with very little trouble. It costs only about $15 to exchange this for an equal weight of pure mercury. Nevertheless, it may still be necessary or desirable to purify one's own mercury for trace polarographic analysis, for hanging-drop voltammetry, and for various other purposes, while laboratories engaged in much voltammetry or controlled-potential electrolysis at large stirred mercury-pool electrodes may find it to be financially essential.

The following very simple procedure may be recommended for the small-scale purification of mercury for polarographic purposes. The used mercury is collected in a polyethylene beaker half filled with $3F$ nitric acid and stirred periodically. When enough mercury has accumulated, two or three weeks are allowed to elapse to ensure the oxidation of any base metals in the last portion of mercury added, then the acid is sucked off, the mercury is washed very thoroughly with dilute nitric acid and then with water and dried. It is then pinholed twice and stored in a tightly stoppered bottle. It is not worth trying to recover the mercurous nitrate formed.

The above procedure is not well suited to the purification of large amounts of mercury. A more complex, but also more rapid and in the long run more economical, one is the following, which has been used for some years in the writer's laboratory. Used mercury in 25-lb. batches is subjected to the action of an Oxifier (Bethlehem Apparatus Co., Inc., Hellertown, Pennsylvania) for 72 hr., left to stand for 24 hr. more in a large separatory funnel to permit the finely divided oxides to rise to the surface, and then drawn off into a 2-l. suction flask containing about 500 ml. of $1F$ perchloric acid. Air is aspirated from the room through the Oxifier and thence into the flask through a sintered-glass gas-dispersion cylinder which is completely covered by the mercury. After several days the mercury is washed with distilled water, dried by blotting with absorbent paper, and pinholed twice into a clean dry bottle. Mercury thus purified contains at most only a fraction of a part per billion of zinc, which is often present at much higher concentrations in commercial distilled mercury, and is also free from any detectable trace of any other base metal. However, metals as noble as platinum and gold can hardly be affected by this procedure, and even silver is probably removed only in part. When contamination by these metals may occur, it is wise either to distill the mercury or to exchange it for mercury that has been distilled.

V. Auxiliary Equipment and Laboratory Design

The first consideration in setting up a polarographic laboratory is the sensitivity of a dropping electrode to vibration. Really satisfactory results are hard to obtain in a laboratory that has shaky floors and walls, that is located near heavy machinery, or that serves as a traffic artery. Expecially in metropolitan areas, air conditioning is highly desirable, not only because it simplifies the problem of controlling the temperature of the cell and eliminates undesirable large gradients of temperature along the mercury column, but also because it protects the capillary from airborne dust and dirt. Usually it is advantageous to place the polarographic apparatus in a room by itself in a corner of the building, because outside walls are generally more sturdy and free from vibration than inner partitions.

Another important consideration is that temperature control is necessary in almost all polarographic measurements. The temperature coefficient of the diffusion current is usually about $+1.3\%$ per degree. Even in routine work, therefore, the temperature of the solution should be controlled within half a degree at most. In careful measurements of the diffusion current, and especially in work with kinetic and catalytic currents, whose temperature coefficients may be very much larger, control to within even a few hundredths of a degree is not unreasonably exacting. Some authors have devised water-jacketed cells through which water is circulated from a thermostat, but such cells are both expensive and fragile, and therefore it seems better simply to immerse the cell in a water bath unless this is impossible for some reason. A cell holder convenient for this purpose is available from E. H. Sargent & Co. (S-29353). A large shallow aquarium serves very well as a constant-temperature bath, is inexpensive, and can be obtained from an aquarium manufacturer in any desired shape and size.

Few experimenters have the opportunity to design a polarographic laboratory starting with a bare room. The arrangement is usually dictated to a very large extent by the furniture and facilities already in the room as well as by its size and shape. It would, therefore, serve no purpose to describe what seems to the writer to be the ideal arrangement of a laboratory. Instead it is hoped that the following general discussion will enable the reader to select the better of any two alternatives available.

It is usually best to plan the laboratory around the thermostat and the dropping-electrode assemblies surrounding it. These should be placed on a sturdy vibration-free bench unit or table that is used for no other purpose and that should preferably be firmly attached to two stoutly built walls. The length and width of this working surface should not exceed those of the thermostat by more than 16 in.; otherwise the temptation to use it for other purposes while polarograms are being recorded may prove to be irresistible. The stirrer, the polarograph, and anything else that will run or be handled while a polarogram is being recorded should be placed on separate tables that do not touch the one holding the thermostat. The only exception to this arises when the polarograph is of the photographically recording type, in which case it will benefit from the solidity of the thermostat table. A common error is to provide room for making notes beside the thermostat. If the floor of the room is sufficiently solid, advantage may be taken of an open space in the center of the laboratory by placing two tables that do not touch each other in it: one for the thermostat and dropping-electrode assemblies, and the other for the stirrer, polarograph, notebook, and the like.

Two vertical support rods, each preferably 5–6 feet high so that they can be joined at the top without restricting the working space, are needed for each dropping-electrode assembly. One is for the stand tube and the other for the mercury reservoir. Tripods, ring stands, and the like are not very satisfactory, and a support frame rigidly attached to the surface supporting the thermostat should be con-structed instead. Enough sturdiness is gained by using stainless steel instead of aluminum alloy rods to justify the extra cost. Ordinary iron or japanned rods should not be used; it is not worth saving a few pennies by incurring the risk of a slow shower of rust into the cell. The support rods for the stand tube and reservoir should be 6–8 in. apart; the one for the stand tube should be almost at the corner of the thermostat, that for the reservoir almost at the corner of the table. This permits swinging the stand tube back and forth between two cells, one on each side of the thermostat near the corner. Addi-tional support rods may be added for other dropping-electrode assemblies, for rotating platinum electrodes, or for any other appa-ratus that may be used. A horizontal support rod extending around the thermostat a few inches below its top is convenient for mounting stopcocks used in deaerating solutions, a suction line and trap for emptying cells after use, and similar accessories. All the vertical support rods should be very thoroughly cross-braced, not only by attaching them to each other, but also by connecting the whole assembly to the walls of the room at several points.

When a dropping-electrode assembly is mounted on the completed frame, the surface of the mercury in the reservoir should be perfectly quiet. Satisfactory results are unlikely to be obtained if any standing waves can be observed. A more stringent test may be performed by adjusting the level of the mercury in the stand tube to a convenient height, immersing the capillary tip in a dilute aqueous solution of some electrolyte (such as perchloric or sulfuric acid), and measuring the time required for ten or twenty drops to fall. This is essentially the procedure used for measuring the drop time t, although in an actual polarographic experiment this must always be done with the capillary tip immersed in the solution being studied and with the polarograph set to provide the potential at which a wave height or some other quantity is to be measured. An electric stop clock with 0.1-sec. divisions is more suitable for the purpose than a stop watch. The clock should be started just at the instant of fall of a drop, and stopped at the instant when the tenth or twentieth drop thereafter falls. If replicate measurements under these conditions differ by more than a few milliseconds per drop, either the capillary is dirty or the vibration is excessive. When using a commercial water bath provided with an integral stirrer, it is advisable to turn the stirrer off before applying this test; if the results indicate that the apparatus is satisfactorily free from vibration, the stirrer should be turned on and the test should be repeated. If turning the stirrer on affects either the mean value of t or its mean deviation, it must be turned off whenever a polarogram is to be recorded or any other polarographic measurement is to be made. In studies of adsorption onto dropping electrodes much time may be saved by employing an automatic device to record the variation of t with potential (61,62).

To avoid undesirable phenomena resulting from stray a.c. in the dropping-electrode circuit, it is advisable to ground the thermostat. This can be done by filling it with a dilute solution (about 0.2 g./l.) of sodium chromate, and connecting the shells of the stirrer and heater to each other and to a good ground by a heavy copper wire. The sodium chromate serves to minimize corrosion of the thermoregulator shell, cooling coil, and other metallic parts of the thermostat. The stirrer and heater must not be grounded separately for fear of producing a ground loop that will make the a.-c. pickup worse. It may be desirable to use a twisted pair of wires or a shielded cable for attaching the cell to the polarograph, and it is usually advisable to ground the dropping-electrode terminal of the polarograph.

Except for such special purposes as measuring temperature coefficients, all polarographic work should be performed at 25° so that the data will be comparable with those obtained in other laboratories.

Dissolved oxygen must usually be removed from solutions that are to be investigated polarographically, both because it is reducible at the dropping electrode over most of the attainable range of potentials and because it reacts chemically with many solutions. It can be removed from most alkaline solutions by the addition of sulfite or hydrazine, and sulfite can also be used in many neutral unbuffered solutions. Neither is useful in even weakly acidic media nor in all alkaline ones. For example, traces of lead greatly decrease the rate of the reaction between oxygen and sulfite in alkaline solutions. Deaeration is therefore usually accomplished by passing an oxygen-free gas stream through the solution before its polarogram is recorded, then over its surface throughout the measurements to ensure the continued exclusion of air. Very roughly 200 ml. of gas is needed per minute for each cell. However, deaeration is usually unnecessary in voltammetric work that is confined to potentials more positive than about $+0.1$ v. vs. S.C.E.

The gas used for deaeration must not react chemically with the sample solution and must not be reducible or oxidizable at the dropping electrode. For a long time hydrogen was the best choice because it could be obtained with a smaller oxygen content than any other commercially available gas, but nitrogen is now much more widely used. This should be of the "Seaford" or "prepurified" grade. It is advantageous to use a gas denser than air to form a blanket over the solution, though the advantage is a minor one. Argon is used by those who can afford it, carbon dioxide is convenient in work with acidic solutions, and propane has been recommended.

In an air-saturated solution the total diffusion current of oxygen is typically of the order of 5 μamp. To decrease this to a value that will be essentially undetectable at the highest sensitivity of a representative commercial polarograph, which implies a diffusion current of 0.0005 μamp. or less, the solution must be equilibrated with a gas stream containing no more than 20 parts per million of oxygen. This, however, is the upper limit of the oxygen content that can be tolerated. Suppose that one wishes to examine the polarogram of 10 ml. of a solution containing 0.04mM chromous ion. Even if the solution absorbed only half of the oxygen passing into it, "deaeration" at the above rate with a gas containing 20 p.p.m. of oxygen would oxidize the chromous ion quantitatively in a single minute. In such circumstances one would hardly want to use even prepurified nitrogen containing 5 parts per million of oxygen. Though tank gas can be used without further purification for much polarographic work, it is very much better to take the not very complicated steps required to obtain a stream of gas that is virtually completely free from oxygen. These steps are also essential to the success of work with more sensitive techniques, such as mercury-pool voltammetry and controlled-potential coulometry.

The classical method of removing oxygen from a gas stream consists of passing it through a tube filled with sulfur-free copper wire heated to 450–500°. In a stream of hydrogen, any oxygen is converted to water vapor and the tube can be used indefinitely. In streams of nitrogen and most other gases, the oxygen is converted to cupric oxide, which must be re-reduced by passing hydrogen through the tube for a few minutes at occasional intervals to maintain the activity of the copper surface. A copper heater is easily prepared by placing a loose plug of copper gauze several inches from one end of a 20-in. long silica or Vycor tube having an internal diameter of about 1 inch. Short lengths of fine copper wire are added to form a column about 12 in. long, and should be packed as tightly as possible without impeding the flow of gas. Proper packing is facilitated by bending the wires slightly as they are added. Finally another loose plug of copper gauze is added to keep the wires in place. The wire packing can be heated in an electric combustion furnace having a 12-in. heating chamber. Or the tube can be wound with a single layer of asbestos paper, then with a coil of resistance wire, and finally with several additional layers of asbestos paper, and an autotransformer can be used for temperature control; this is less expensive than the furnace but has the disadvantage that the condition of the packing cannot be inspected. In any case, the tube should be so inclined that any water vapor condensing beyond it cannot trickle back into it. A small copper heater is available from E. H. Sargent & Co. (S-36517 and S-36518).

Though a properly operating copper heater doubtless removes oxygen from a gas stream more completely and surely than any other device, it has the disadvantage of requiring a considerable length of time to reach its operating temperature each time it is turned on, and many substitutes for it have therefore been proposed. Hydrogen may be purified by passing it through a finely divided palladium catalyst at room temperature, but other gases must be scrubbed with solutions that absorb oxygen. Alkaline pyrogallol or dithionite, Fieser's solution, and various other reagents are used for this purpose in Orsat analysis and elsewhere but are useless for polarography because of their limited efficiency. Solutions of chromous or vanadous chloride are much more suitable. Chromous solutions are appreciably more efficient, but are also more troublesome to prepare and much more difficult to regenerate, and vanadous solutions are therefore preferable for most work. They are prepared by boiling 2 g. of ammonium meta-vanadate with 25 ml. of concentrated hydrochloric acid, diluting to 200 ml., and shaking with a few grams of heavily amalgamated zinc, adding a little more acid if a precipitate or turbidity forms. Reduction will not be complete because the solution reacts so avidly with oxygen. The partly reduced solution is divided between two 250-ml. gas-washing bottles with coarse-porosity sintered-glass gas-dispersion cylinders or discs, each containing about 25 g. of heavily amalgamated zinc to re-reduce the vanadium(III) formed as oxygen is absorbed. The bottles are tightly stoppered, using heavy coats of silicone grease on their ground joints to keep them from freezing and wires or springs to keep the joints in place. The reduction of the vanadium will become complete when a slow stream of gas is passed into the bottles for a few minutes, and the solutions will then be clear deep violet in color. The gas emerging from the second bottle is washed with water in a third similar one to remove any acid or vanadium carried over in the gas stream. It is wise to place this last bottle in the thermostat so that the gas emerging from it will be in equilibrium with water vapor at the temperature of the thermostat. This avoids the danger of evaporation from or condensation into the solution in the cell. Should the solution contain a volatile constituent like ammonia, dioxane, or pyridine, another gas-washing bottle filled with the solution and immersed in the thermostat should be used to prevent differential evaporation of the volatile material. After the train has been used for some time, the vanadium solutions will lose their violet color and some precipitate will form in them, but they may be rapidly restored to their original condition by adding a little concentrated hydrochloric acid. Although vanadous sulfate solutions were originally recommended (63), they evolve hydrogen sulfide slowly, and chloride solutions are therefore much to be preferred.

Chromous solutions are prepared in much the same way. An $0.5F$ solution of chromic chloride in concentrated hydrochloric acid is the most convenient starting material. It should be prepared a day or two before use to allow complete conversion of the chromium into the easily reducible green chlorochromic complex, and can then be stored indefinitely. About 20 ml. of it is added to each of two 250-ml. gas-washing bottles containing about 25 g. of heavily amalgamated zinc and 80 ml. of water, and the train is assembled as for use with vanadous solutions. When the acid concentration decreases so far that precipitation begins, it is better to replace the solutions with fresh ones prepared in the same way than to try to regenerate them by adding acid.

Air diffuses through rubber tubing at an appreciable rate, and the gas line should therefore be constructed entirely of Tygon, glass, and metal. In a laboratory doing much polarographic and other electro-analytical work it is very convenient to have a gas line fed by a single tank and providing needle-valve outlets every few feet along the bench top and around the thermostat. It then becomes feasible to use a single purification train for the whole laboratory instead of a sepa-rate one for each station. Appropriate traps must of course be pro-vided so that the whole line will not be contaminated with air if one outlet is carelessly left open. There should be a two-way all-glass stopcock near each cell to facilitate passing the gas stream through and then over the solution.

Another necessary facility is a suction line, which should also have an outlet near each cell. If a polyethylene medicine dropper with a slightly drawn out tip is attached to each outlet, even the most com-plex cell can be easily cleaned. A trap should be provided to collect mercury drawn into the line.

Deionized water is now provided in so many laboratories that special mention must be made of the difficulties that have been found to result from its use. Traces of organic materials are extracted from the resin bed and may be adsorbed at the interface between the dropping electrode and the solution or may remove traces of metal ions from the solution (64). Some idea of the possible effects of adsorbed organic materials can be gleaned from Chap. 6 III and V, while the removal of dissolved metal ions leads to very large errors in analyses of dilute solutions. These problems are best avoided by using only distilled water in polarographic work.

An automatic device for the determination of m was shown in Fig. 2.21 above. To calibrate it, or for occasional measurements or those of the highest accuracy, one may simply collect the mercury that flows through the capillary in a measured length of time. For this purpose a fairly large bubble is blown on the end of a length of 1-mm. i.d. capillary tubing, and one side of the bubble is removed to form a cup over which the tip of the capillary may be positioned. The tubing is bent through 90° so that its end projects up through the stopper of the cell and serves as a handle for raising and lowering the cup. In use, the dropping electrode is immersed in the solution of interest (m-values in air differ from those in solutions, though not by as large a factor as the corresponding drop times), and a stop clock is started just as a drop falls. The cup is swung under the capillary tip before the next drop falls, and is allowed to remain there for 10–20 min. At the end of this time the stop clock is stopped, again just as a drop falls, and the cup is swung away from the capillary tip before the next drop falls. The mercury is then poured into a small weighing bottle, washed twice with distilled water and once or twice with reagent-grade acetone, allowed to stand at room temperature for a minute or two to permit the acetone to evaporate, and weighed. If the solution contains a surface-active agent like gelatin, the droplets falling from the capillary tip may not coalesce in the cup, and great care is then necessary to guard against losing some of the mercury while transferring it to the weighing bottle. Values of m reproducible to $\pm 0.05\%$ or better can easily be secured by this technique. Because the value of m depends on the potential of the electrode, it should, whenever possible, be measured at the same potential used for measuring the other quantities (wave height, drop time, etc.) with which it is to be combined.

One often wishes to add a number of successive aliquots of one solution to a known volume of another, as in amperometric titrations or studies of the relation between wave height and concentration or half-wave potential and pH. For this purpose it is very convenient to use a buret having a three-way stopcock at its bottom and a bulb at its top. The solution in the buret can then be deaerated by passing a slow stream of gas up through the stopcock while the original solution in the cell is being deaerated. This eliminates the necessity of repeating the deaeration after the addition of each aliquot.

The polarographer must be constantly alert to the cumulative nature and serious consequences of mercury poisoning. Good practice demands that every glass vessel containing mercury be kept in an enamel or stainless steel pan which will catch the mercury if the glass should break. All operations involved in the purification of mercury should be carried out over a similar tray. The capillary must always be kept over the thermostat vessel so that mercury will not drop onto the bench top or floor. Even with the most assiduous attention to reducing spillage and to cleaning up any mercury that is spilled by accident, some hazard is inevitably connected with the continuous handling of mercury in quantities as large as those found in the average polarographic laboratory. There is no excuse for tolerating inadequate ventilation in laboratories where polarographic work is done. The use of a mercury-vapor detector for the routine monitoring of the air may be strongly recommended. In the last analysis, however, the matter is one of enlightened self-interest and mature responsibility; anyone who fails to exert the most scrupulous and unremitting care in handling mercury is thereby endangering not only himself but all of his colleagues as well.

References

(1) G. E. Philbrook and H. M. Grubb, *Anal. Chem.*, **19**, 7 (1947).

(2) A. Bresle, *Science Tools*, **3**, 9 (1956); **4**, 33 (1957).

(3) M. T. Kelley and H. H. Miller, *Anal. Chem.*, **24**, 1895 (1952).

(4) L. Meites and R. H. Schlossel, *J. Phys. Chem.*, **67**, 2397 (1963).

(5) K. Kronenberger, H. Strehlow, and A. W. Elbel, *Leybolds Polarogr. Ber.*, **5**, 62 (1957).

(6) M. T. Kelley, H. C. Jones, and D. J. Fisher, *Anal. Chem.*, **31**, 1475 (1959).

(7) M. T. Kelley, D. J. Fisher, and H. C. Jones, *Anal. Chem.*, **32**, 1262 (1960).

(8) J. Heyrovský, in *Die physikalische Methoden der chemischen Analyse*, W. Böttger, ed., Leipzig, 1936, Vol. II, p. 260.

(9) J. J. Lingane and H. A. Laitinen, *Ind. Eng. Chem., Anal. Ed.*, **11**, 504 (1939).

(10) L. Meites and T. Meites, *Anal. Chem.*, **23**, 1194 (1951).

(11) J. Heyrovský and M. Kalousek, *Collection Czechoslov. Chem. Communs.*, **11**, 464 (1939).

(12) L. Meites and S. A. Moros, *Anal. Chem.*, **31**, 23 (1959).

(13) O. Gawron, *Anal. Chem.*, **22**, 614 (1950).

(14) L. Serak, *Chem. Listy*, **17**, 86 (1953).

(15) G. Maassen, *Angew. Chem.*, **50**, 375 (1937).

(16) D. E. Carritt, Ph.D. Thesis, Harvard University, 1947.

(17) R. L. Pecsok and R. S. Juvet, Jr., *Anal. Chem.*, **27**, 165 (1955).

(18) M. M. Nicholson, *Anal. Chem.*, **27**, 1364 (1955).

(19) W. Jackson, Jr. and P. J. Elving, *Anal. Chem.*, **28**, 378 (1956).

(20) R. L. Pecsok and R. W. Farmer, *Anal. Chem.*, **28**, 985 (1956).

(21) K. Ezr, *Proc. 1st Intern. Polarogr. Congress*, Prague, 1951, Part III, p. 767.

(22) J. Peizker, *Collection Czechoslov. Chem. Communs.*, **24**, 2416 (1959).

(23) P. Arthur, P. A. Lewis, N. A. Lloyd, and R. H. Vanderkam, *Anal. Chem.*, **33**, 488 (1961).

(24) I. M. Kolthoff and Y. Okinaka, *J. Am. Chem. Soc.*, **80**, 4452 (1958).

(25) S. Oka, *Anal. Chem.*, **27**, 1364 (1955).

(26) P. Arthur and R. H. Vanderkam, *Anal. Chem.*, **33**, 765 (1961).

(27) R. Annino and K. J. Hagler, *Anal. Chem.*, **35**, 1555 (1963).

(28) C. G. Enke and R. A. Baxter, *J. Chem. Education*, **41**, 202 (1964).

(29) R. A. Durst, J. W. Ross, and D. N. Hume, *J. Electroanal. Chem.*, **7**, 245 (1964).

(30) I. M. Kolthoff, J. C. Marshall, and S. L. Gupta, *J. Electroanal. Chem.*, **3**, 209 (1962).

(31) W. B. Schaap and P. S. McKinney, *Anal. Chem.*, **36**, 29, 1251 (1964); L. Němec, *J. Electroanal. Chem.*, **8**, 166 (1964).

(32) H. K. Beecher, R. Follansbee, A. J. Murphy, and F. N. Craig, *J. Biol. Chem.*, **146**, 197 (1942).

(32a) W. J. Parker, *Metal Ind. (London)*, **100**, 105 (1962).

(33) L. D. Wilson and R. J. Smith, *Anal. Chem.*, **25**, 218, 334 (1953).

(34) W. Kemula, *Roczniki Chem.*, **26**, 281, 694, 696 (1952); **29**, 653, 1157 (1955).

(35) W. Kemula and A. Gorski, *Roczniki Chem.*, **26**, 639 (1952).

(36) W. Kemula and J. Witwicki, *Roczniki Chem.*, **29**, 1153 (1955).

(37) J. V. A. Novák, *Chem. Listy*, **49**, 227, 289, 1476 (1955); *Collection Czechoslov. Chem. Communs.*, **20**, 1076, 1090 (1955).

(38) J. Proszt and J. Kis, *Acta Chim. Acad. Sci. Hung.*, **9**, 191 (1956).

(39) W. J. Blaedel and J. W. Todd, *Anal. Chem.*, **20**, 1821 (1958).

(40) R. L. Rebertus, R. J. Cappell, and G. W. Bond, *Anal. Chem.*, **30**, 1825 (1958).

(41) W. J. Blaedel and J. H. Strohl, *Anal. Chem.*, **36**, 445 (1964).

(42) P. Beckmann, *Chem. & Ind. (London)*, 791 (1948).

(43) D. M. Miller, *Can. J. Chem.*, **33**, 1184 (1955).

(44) M. Nedorost, *Chem. Listy*, **50**, 317 (1956).

(45) K. H. Mancy and D. A. Okun, *Anal. Chem.*, **32**, 108 (1960).

(46) Z. P. Zagórski, in *Advances in Polarography*, I. S. Longmuir, ed., Pergamon, London, 1960, Vol. III, p. 1124.

(47) H. A. Laitinen and L. W. Burdett, *Anal. Chem.*, **22**, 833 (1950).

(48) W. B. Schaap, R. F. Conley, and F. C. Schmidt, *Anal. Chem.*, **33**, 498 (1961).

(49) H. Shimojima, *Bunseki Kagaku*, **8**, 320 (1959).

(50) I. M. Kolthoff and G. J. Kahan, *J. Am. Chem. Soc.*, **64**, 2553 (1942).

(51) O. H. Müller, *J. Am. Chem. Soc.*, **66**, 1019 (1944).

(52) B. A. Loveridge, Ph.D. Thesis, Harvard University, 1947.

(53) I. Smolér, *Chem. Listy*, **47**, 1667 (1953); *Collection Czechoslov. Chem. Communs.*, **19**, 238 (1954).

(54) L. Meites, *J. Am. Chem. Soc.*, **73**, 3724 (1951).

(55) G. C. Barker, *Anal. Chim. Acta*, **18**, 118 (1958).

(56) W. D. Cooke, M. T. Kelley, and D. J. Fisher, *Anal. Chem.*, **33**, 1209 (1961).

(57) B. C. Southworth, R. Osteryoung, K. D. Fleischer, and F. C. Nachod, *Anal. Chem.*, **33**, 209 (1961).

(58) D. W. Grant, L. Meites, and J. M. Sturtevant, paper presented at the 120th National Meeting of the American Chemical Society, New York, September, 1951.
(59) H. P. Raaen, *Anal. Chem.*, **34**, 1714 (1962); **36**, 2420 (1964).
(60) J. J. Lingane, *Ind. Eng. Chem., Anal. Ed.*, **16**, 329 (1944).
(61) J. Říha, in *Advances in Polarography*, I. S. Longmuir, ed., Pergamon, London, 1960, Vol. I, p. 210.
(62) A. J. Bard and H. B. Herman, *Anal. Chem.*, **37**, 317 (1965).
(63) L. Meites and T. Meites, *Anal. Chem.*, **20**, 984 (1948).
(64) R. C. Rooney, personal communication.

CHAPTER 3

THE LIMITING CURRENT

The total or limiting current that flows on the plateau of a wave includes contributions from several different processes. It includes the current that would flow under the same conditions but in the absence of the substance responsible for the wave: this is called the residual current. The wave height is defined as the difference between the total current and the residual current, and is the current due to the presence of the substance of interest.

If that substance is ionic, there will be an electrostatic force between its ions and the electrode. The force may be one of either attraction or repulsion: in either case it affects the rate at which the ions reach the electrode surface and undergo reduction or oxidation. The difference between the limiting current actually obtained and the limiting current that would be obtained in the absence of any electrostatic force is called the migration current. In all practical polarographic work the migration current is rendered negligible by the presence of a relatively large concentration of an indifferent electrolyte, whose ions serve to conduct current through the solution and thus dissipate the electrostatic force but are not reduced or oxidized over the range of potentials that is being studied.

The most important component of the wave height is the diffusion current, which reflects the rate at which the ions or molecules of the substance responsible for the wave reach the electrode surface under the sole influence of a diffusive force. On the plateau of the wave these ions or molecules are reduced (or oxidized) as rapidly as they reach the electrode surface, and their concentration in the layer of solution immediately adjacent to the electrode surface is therefore virtually zero. Hence there is a concentration gradient between the bulk of the solution and the layer at the electrode surface, and it is this concentration gradient that is responsible for the existence of the diffusive force. The diffusion current is of great importance in polarographic analysis because most practical methods are based on its measurement.

95

The rate at which electroactive material can reach the electrode surface may, however, be affected by many other phenomena. The original species or another electroactive one may be regenerated by a reaction between the product of the electrode reaction and some other constituent of the solution, and the current due to the reduction of the regenerated substance will then also be included in the wave height. If the solution contains a species that is not electroactive in slow equilibrium with one that is, the wave height will include not only the diffusion current of the electroactive species but also a current due to the reduction of additional electroactive material formed from the non-electroactive species as the equilibrium between them is displaced at the drop surface. Access of the electroactive substance to the electrode surface may be barred by a film of adsorbed material, or the electroactive substance or its reduction (or oxidation) product may undergo adsorption on the drop surface and the current may then be limited by the number of ions or molecules that can be adsorbed on each drop. Some voltammetric work is done with stirred solutions with a view to increasing the sensitivity by increasing the rate at which electroactive material reaches the electrode surface, and the current then depends on the rate of stirring and other hydro-dynamic variables.

The present chapter is devoted to the causes of the different components of the limiting current in polarographic work, to the ways in which they behave and the ways by which they can be recognized, and to the applications to which they have been put.

I. The Residual Current

The nature of the layer of an electrolyte solution immediately adjacent to the surface of a mercury drop depends on the potential applied to the drop. If a dropping electrode disconnected from the external circuit is immersed in a pure solution of potassium chloride, chloride ions will be preferentially adsorbed on the surface of the drop, and as a result the mercury in the reservoir will acquire a negative charge. This in turn will be imparted to the succeeding drops, which will, therefore, adsorb fewer and fewer chloride ions until equilibrium is attained. The negative charge accumulated by the mercury will then be just great enough to counterbalance the tendency for adsorption of excess chloride ions to occur on the drop surface. The potential of the mercury under this equilibrium condition is the potential of the electrocapillary maximum, and its value is, for example, -0.461 v. (vs. S.C.E.) in $0.1F$ potassium chloride, -0.535 v. in $0.1F$ potassium bromide, -0.589 v. in $0.1F$ potassium thiocyanate, and -0.693 v. in $0.1F$ potassium iodide. The differences among these values signify that bromide is more strongly adsorbed onto a mercury surface than chloride is, while thiocyanate is more strongly adsorbed than bromide, and so on. More negative potentials are required to overcome the greater tendencies for bromide, thiocyanate, and iodide ions to accumulate at the mercury-solution interface.

Now suppose that the same dropping electrode is immersed in $0.1F$ potassium chloride connected to an external S.C.E. by a salt bridge, and that a potential of exactly -0.461 v. is applied across the two electrodes from the polarograph. The minus sign signifies that the dropping electrode is made the negative electrode. At this potential the tendency for chloride ions to be preferentially adsorbed on the mercury surface is just counterbalanced by the potential applied, and so the layer of solution in immediate contact with the electrode will on the average contain exactly equal numbers of chloride and potassium ions, just as the bulk of the solution does. There is no separation of charge, no expenditure of energy is required, and no current will flow.

But if the applied potential is changed to a more negative value, say -1.0 v., chloride ions will be repelled from the electrode surface while potassium ions will be attracted to it. Very near the surface of the negatively charged electrode, there will be a layer of solution in which the concentration of potassium ion will be higher than that of chloride ion, and as the distance from the electrode increases the concentrations of the two ions will become more and more nearly equal. The layer of negative charge at the surface of the electrode and the layer of positively charged solution adjacent to it constitute the so-called electrical double layer. The separation of charges is tantamount to the charging of an electrical capacitor. To charge the double layer up to any potential E a certain quantity of electricity is required. For an electrode of constant area A (in cm.²) this is given by

$$q = \varkappa A (E_{\max} - E) \tag{3.1}$$

where q is the quantity of electricity in microcoulombs, $\varkappa$ is the differential capacity of the double layer in microfarads/square centimeter, and E_{max} is the potential of the electrocapillary maximum. The value of $\varkappa$ is not independent of potential; in dilute solutions of hydrochloric acid or alkali metal halides it is approximately 40 μf./cm.^{2} at potentials more positive than E_{max} but only about 18 μf./cm.^{2} at potentials more negative than E_{max}, and in each of these regions there are definite further variations with potential (1). Nevertheless, these two nearly constant values suffice to account for ordinary observations on the residual-current curve.

It is evident that the quantity of electricity described by eq. (3.1) is positive when E is more negative than E_{max}, zero when E and E_{max} are equal, and negative when E is more positive than E_{max}. The reversal of sign occurs because the polarity of the double layer is reversed in going from one side of the electrocapillary maximum to the other, and the signs are so chosen as to accord with the customary polarographic convention, in which the flow of electrons into the dropping electrode is taken to constitute a positive current. In other words, the current is taken to be positive when the dropping electrode is the cathode, negative when it is the anode.

During the life of any single mercury drop the variation of potential is so small that it may be neglected. The average value of the condenser or charging current i_c consumed in charging the double layer during the life of a drop at the constant potential E may be obtained by dividing the total quantity of electricity used for this purpose by the drop time:

$$\bar{i}_c = \frac{1}{t}\,\varkappa A_{max}(E_{max} - E) \tag{3.2}$$

where A_{max} is the maximum area of the drop, achieved when it is just t seconds old. The value of A_{max} is most conveniently expressed in terms of the parameters m and t. Because the product mt is equal to the mass of the drop when it is t seconds old, the volume V_{max} and the radius r_{max} of the drop at that instant are given by

$$V_{max} = 10^{-3}mt/d_{Hg} = \frac{4}{3}\,\pi r_{max}^3 \tag{3.3}$$

where d_{Hg} is the density of mercury; the factor 10^{-3} enters because the custom of expressing m in milligrams per second produces a value of mt having the units of milligrams rather than grams. The drop is assumed to be spherical; this is surely not exactly true, and in addition a small fraction of its area is shielded from the solution by the capillary lumen and the surrounding tip, but the error incurred by neglecting these facts is small. One can now write

$$A_{max} = 4\pi r^2{}_{max} = (4\pi)^{1/3}(3 \times 10^{-3}/d_{Hg})^{2/3}m^{2/3}t^{2/3} = 0.00853m^{2/3}t^{2/3}$$
(3.4)

whence

$$\bar{i}_c = 0.00853\varkappa(E_{max} - E) \, m^{2/3}t^{-1/3}$$
(3.5)

Equation (3.5) describes several important properties of the charging current. It is approximately linearly dependent on potential, both at potentials more positive than E_{max} and at potentials more negative than E_{max}. With a typical capillary, for which m and t might be 2 mg./sec. and 4 sec., respectively, the charging-current curve would have a slope of about 0.35 μamp./v. in the first of these regions and a slope of about 0.15 μamp./v. in the second. These values are different because the values of $\varkappa$ are different. The majority of practical polarographic analyses are performed by recording a polarogram of the solution being analyzed, linearly extrapolating the portion of the residual-current curve that precedes the wave of interest, and measuring the vertical distance from the plateau to the extrapolated line; the plateau may be extrapolated backwards and the height measured at the half-wave potential, but this does not affect the point in question here. Because neither $m^{2/3}t^{-1/3}$ nor $\varkappa$ is quite independent of potential, the linear extrapolation is not perfectly accurate no matter how it is done. However, the error that it introduces is negligibly small unless the solution being investigated is extremely dilute or unless the extrapolation crosses E_{max}.

Equation (3.5) may be written

$$\bar{i}_c = (kt^{-1/2}) \, m^{2/3}t^{1/6}$$
(3.6)

for a particular solution and a particular applied potential. It will be shown in a following section that the average diffusion current during the life of a drop, i_d, is approximately proportional to $m^{2/3}t^{1/6}$. Hence the ratio $i_d/\bar{i}_c$ is proportional to $t^{1/2}$. Decreasing the drop time (e.g., by increasing the height of the column of mercury above the capillary), therefore, decreases this ratio, because it causes the charging current to increase more rapidly than the diffusion current, and so the attainable sensitivity becomes poorer even though the diffusion current increases.

The variation of the charging current during the drop life (2) can also be deduced from eq. (3.1) by differentiating it with respect to the drop age τ:

$$\frac{dq}{d\tau} = i_c = \varkappa(E_{max} - E)\frac{dA}{d\tau} \qquad (3.7)$$

From an argument essentially identical with that embodied in eqs. (3.3) and (3.4), one can obtain an expression for $dA/d\tau$. Combining this with eq. (3.7) gives

$$i_c = 0.00569\varkappa(E_{max} - E)\ m^{2/3}\tau^{-1/3} \qquad (3.8)$$

As was mentioned in Chap. 2 IV, the mercury thread breaks inside the capillary when a drop falls; as the linear velocity of mercury through the capillary is only of the order of 5 cm./sec. under typical conditions, a few instants are required for the mercury to emerge from the capillary tip and a few more for the drop to achieve a spherical shape. Equation (3.8) is not valid during this interval, but this is of little interest in practical work because polarographic recorders are not fast enough to provide information about the early stages of the drop life. What is of interest is that the charging current decreases as the drop becomes older and jumps sharply as a new drop begins to form, and that the magnitude of its variation during the drop life decreases as E becomes more nearly equal to the electrocapillary maximum potential.

A typical residual-current curve is shown in Fig. 3.1 and is qualitatively in agreement with much of the above description. The value of E_{max} in $0.1F$ hydrochloric acid is -0.493 v. The curve is approximately linear at potentials between this value and about -0.1 v., where the initial current rise ends, and it is also approximately linear, though it has a distinctly smaller slope, at potentials between the electrocapillary maximum potential and about -1.0 v., where the final current rise begins. The significances of the initial and final current rises are described in subsequent paragraphs. The widths of the oscillations decrease to a minimum at a potential not very far

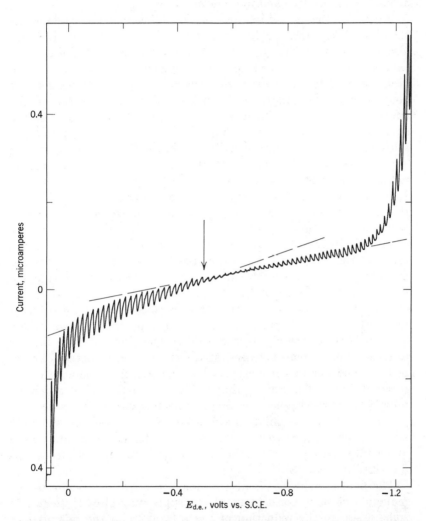

Figure 3.1.   Residual-current curve in $0.1F$ hydrochloric acid. The vertical arrow represents the potential of the electrocapillary maximum, and the dashed lines are drawn to emphasize the change of slope that occurs around this potential because of the variation of $\varkappa$.

from (but definitely a little more negative than) E_{max}, and are greater at both more positive and more negative potentials.

However, some of the features of Fig. 3.1 cannot be explained on the above basis: these include the initial and final current rises and also the fact that the current is not equal to zero at the electrocapillary maximum potential. These phenomena are due to the occurrence of faradaic processes, which are quite independent of double-layer charging. In most supporting electrolytes the anodic currents that flow at the most positive potentials are due to the oxidation of mercury. In perchlorate, nitrate, acetate, and similar solutions the oxidation proceeds to mercurous ion, and begins around $+0.3$ to $+0.4$ v. The potential at which it first becomes visible naturally depends on the sensitivity at which the curve is recorded. In solutions in which mercurous or mercuric mercury is stabilized by the formation of a precipitate or complex, the oxidation begins at more negative potentials: around $+0.1$ v. in chloride solutions, -0.2 v. in hydroxide solutions, or -0.7 v. in cyanide solutions, for example, though these values depend on the concentration of the ion in question. There are a few supporting electrolytes (such as alkaline and ammoniacal solutions containing hydrazine) in which the initial current rise reflects the oxidation of some constituent of the solution rather than of the mercury. At any rate, except in a few cases where a film of precipitate covers the drop surface and prevents further oxidation, the current increases rapidly on making the potential more positive, and usually becomes very large because large amounts of the reactants are available at the drop surface. The potential at which the initial current rise begins is for all practical purposes the most positive potential at which useful data can be secured. This fact has been the stimulus for much research on electrode materials that can be used at potentials too positive to be secured with mercury electrodes, as described in Chap. 8.

The final current rise is also faradaic in nature: it is due to the reduction of some constituent of the supporting electrolyte (or, in some cases, to the reduction of the solvent), and the potential at which it begins depends on the nature and concentration of that constituent. In solutions of strong acids it begins at about -1.0 v. and is due to the reduction of hydrogen ion; in neutral or alkaline solutions of alkali metal salts it begins at about -1.9 v. and is due to reduction of alkali metal ions to their amalgams; in similar solutions of certain tetraalkylammonium salts it does not begin until about -2.7 v. and is due to the reduction of water. It is because the last of these potentials is so negative that tetraalkylammonium salts are widely used in work with difficultly reducible organic substances. Although some small extension can be achieved by differential or derivative polarography, the potential at which the final current rise appears to begin is for all practical purposes the most negative potential at which useful data can be obtained.

In correlating polarographic residual currents with their equivalents in other techniques, it is important to be clear about the significance of the potential at which the final current rise appears to begin. More often than not the final current rise reflects the increasing rate of an irreversible electrode reaction, such as the reduction of hydrogen ion, the reduction of a weak acid (to hydrogen and the corresponding anion), or the reduction of water. The rate of such a process increases exponentially as the potential becomes more negative. Over a wide range of potentials it yields currents too small to be detected against the background of a substantial and continuously flowing charging current, but currents that are finite even though they cannot be seen. Eventually the potential becomes so negative that the exponentially increasing faradaic current becomes appreciable compared to the charging current, and this is the point where the final current rise seems to start. With an electrode of constant area the charging of the double layer takes place almost instantaneously and then the charging current vanishes unless the potential is varied. The faradaic component of the residual current thus becomes readily observable even under conditions where the presence of the large oscillating charging current would make it impossible to detect polarographically.

The fact that the current in Fig. 3.1 becomes zero at a potential more positive than the electrocapillary maximum potential also has a faradaic explanation. The hydrochloric acid solution used to obtain the curve could not have been wholly free from reducible impurities. It doubtless contained traces of oxygen, ferric iron, lead, arsenic, and other substances giving rise to waves too small to see on the scale of the figure. Astonishing numbers of heavy-metal impurities have been detected and determined in reagent-grade chemicals by square-wave polarography, anodic stripping voltammetry, and other sensitive techniques $(3,4)$. The reduction of these impurities produces a

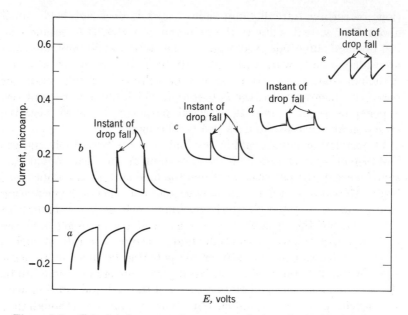

Figure 3.2. Calculated current–time curves during the lives of individual drops, drawn as they would appear on a recorded polarogram with time increasing from left to right. Curves *a* and *b* represent the variations of charging current with drop age at potentials where the average charging currents are −0.07 and +0.07 μamp., respectively; in each case there is a deflection away from the zero-current line as the drop falls. Curve *c* would be obtained under the same conditions as curve *b* if, in addition to the charging current, there were also a diffusion current of 0.12 μamp. due to some reducible impurity. Curves *d* and *e* would be obtained at potentials where the average diffusion currents were 0.24 and 0.48 μamp., respectively; note that on curve *e* there is a deflection toward the zero-current line as the drop falls. This change in the shape of the oscillation as the faradaic component of the current increases can be seen at potentials around the foot of the final current rise in Fig. 3.1.

cathodic (positive) faradaic current at the electrocapillary maximum potential, and the slope of the charging-current curve is so small that a considerably more positive potential is required to produce a charging current sufficiently negative to counterbalance the small positive faradaic current.

This same phenomenon is responsible for the fact that the width of the oscillations in Fig. 3.1 passes through a minimum at a potential more negative than the electrocapillary maximum potential (5).

Figure 3.2 shows why this is so. Curves a and b represent the variations of a pure charging current with drop age as they would appear on polarograms obtained with the customary polarization toward increasingly negative potentials: curve a at a potential more positive than the electrocapillary maximum potential, curve b at a potential more negative than this. Whereas the charging current decreases with increasing drop age, the faradaic component of the residual current increases; as a rough approximation one may say that the diffusion current at any instant during the drop life is proportional to $\tau^{1/6}$. Curves c–e show the effect of combining a diffusion current with a charging current. At every instant the current is the sum of these two components. If their average values over the drop life are roughly equal, the decrease of the charging current at small values of τ is approximately counterbalanced by the increase of the diffusion current, and therefore the total current varies less than either of its components. If the recorder is not too heavily overdamped, these variations in the shapes of the traces for individual drops are easily seen on original polarograms.

In practical analysis it is the average wave height during the drop life that is wanted, and this is obtained by subtracting the average residual current from the average limiting current. Average currents are easily obtained by suitably damping the recorder or galvanometer, as explained in Chap. 2 I, and by taking the midpoints of the oscillations. But in studies of irreversible electrode processes one wants the maximum wave height, corresponding to the instant just before the drop falls, and a fast recorder must be used to obtain this. Here it becomes important that the residual current at the instant of interest is the *minimum* current during the drop life if the supporting electrolyte is essentially free from reducible impurities.

II. The Migration Current

If a dropping electrode is immersed in a pure dilute solution of a salt like lead perchlorate, and if a potential on the plateau of the lead wave is applied to it, lead ions will be reduced as fast as they reach the surface of the drop. A current will therefore flow through the cell: some anodic reaction will occur at whatever reference electrode is being used, and ions will move through the solution to conduct the current from one electrode through the other. Lead ions will move toward the dropping electrode, and perchlorate ions will move toward the reference electrode. This motion of lead ions causes them to arrive at the drop surface more rapidly than they would if electrical migration did not occur, and this is the cause of the migration current.

The value of the migration current depends on the transference number of the ion being reduced (or oxidized) at the drop surface: the larger this transference number, the greater the fraction of the current carried by the motion of that ion. The transference number of the jth ion in a solution is given by

$$t_j = c_j\lambda_j / \sum_i c_i\lambda_i \tag{3.8}$$

where, as is usual in equations describing conductances, the c's are the concentrations in equivalents per liter and the λ's are the equivalent ionic conductances. The addition of a supporting electrolyte, whose ions contribute to the conductance but do not contribute to the current because they cannot be oxidized or reduced to any significant extent when they arrive at the drop surface, causes the transference number of the electroactive ion to decrease. If the concentration of the supporting electrolyte is very high, the transference number of the electroactive ion becomes practically zero. Current is then carried across the drop-solution interface by the reduction or oxidation of the electroactive ion, and is carried through the solution by the motion of the ions of the supporting electrolyte. Because its transference number is small, the electroactive ion in such a solution plays only a negligible part in the electrolytic conduction through the solution, and hence its motion is affected by the diffusive force alone.

The sign of the migration current depends on the sign of the charge on the electroactive ion. Cations are attracted to a cathode, and therefore the migration current increases the wave height when a cation is reduced at the dropping electrode. Anions migrate away from a cathode, and therefore the migration current decreases the wave height when an anion like iodate or chromate is reduced at the dropping electrode. These effects are shown in Fig. 3.3. The addition of supporting electrolyte decreases the wave height of cadmium ion, but increases that of iodate ion.

If it is assumed that the mechanism of diffusion is the same in a pure salt solution as in the presence of excess supporting electrolyte, so that the diffusion current is the same in the two cases, and that

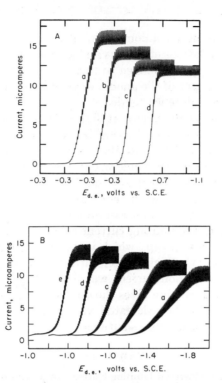

Figure 3.3. A: Polarograms of 1.0mF cadmium chloride containing 0.002% Triton X-100 and (a) 0, (b) 0.67, (c) 4.0, and (d) 30 mF potassium chloride, showing the decrease of the cathodic wave height of a cation as its migration current is suppressed. Each curve begins at −0.3 v. vs. S.C.E., and each interval along the potential axis corresponds to 0.2 v. B: Polarograms of 0.3mF potassium iodate containing 0.002% Triton X-100 and (a) 0, (b) 0.40, (c) 2.0, (d) 10, and (e) 100mF potassium chloride, showing the decrease of the cathodic wave height of an anion as its migration current is suppressed. Each curve begins at −1.0 v. vs. S.C.E., and each interval along the potential axis corresponds to 0.2 v.

the migration current is given by the product of the total limiting current by the transference number of the electroactive ion, one obtains (6,7)

$$i_l = i_d + i_m = i_d + i_l t_+ = i_d/(1 - t_+) \qquad (3.9)$$

for the reduction of a cation, and

$$i_l = i_d - i_m = i_d - i_l t_- = i_d/(1 + t_-) \qquad (3.10)$$

for the reduction of an anion. Equivalent expressions are easily written for the oxidations of cations and anions, for which the migration currents are opposite in sign to those for cathodic waves. Thus, for example, the height of the anodic wave of a cation would increase as supporting electrolyte was added.

The equivalent conductances at finite electrolyte concentrations that ought to be used in evaluating transference numbers from eq. (3.8) are rarely available, and the values at infinite dilution are generally used instead. In Table 3.1, the second column gives the transference numbers of lead ion thus calculated for a number of solutions containing a constant concentration of lead chloride and increasing concentrations of potassium nitrate (8). The third column gives the values of the limiting current calculated from eq. (3.9) by taking i_d equal to 8.45 μamp., which is the experimental value in the solution containing the highest concentration of supporting electrolyte, where the migration current was most nearly completely suppressed. The fourth column gives the observed values of the limiting current, with which the calculated values are in good agreement except in the two most dilute solutions.

TABLE 3.1.

Calculated and Observed Limiting Currents in Solutions Containing
Various Concentrations of Supporting Electrolyte

The solutions contained 0.95mF lead chloride and the stated concentrations of potassium nitrate, together with $4 \times 10^{-4}\%$ sodium methyl red as a maximum suppressor.

[KNO$_3$], F	$t_{Pb^{++}}$	Limiting current, μamp.	
		Calculated	Observed
0	0.477	16.2	17.6
0.0001	0.453	15.4	16.2
0.0002	0.430	14.8	15.0
0.0005	0.378	13.6	13.4
0.001	0.313	12.3	12.0
0.005	0.132	9.6	9.8
0.1	0.0089	8.51	8.45
1	0.00091	8.46	8.45

Corrections based on the fact that the electroactive ions are not free to diffuse independently of the counter ions in pure salt solutions, so that the diffusion current is not quite the same in such a solution as in the presence of a large excess of an indifferent electrolyte, have been advanced by Kolthoff and Lingane (8) and MacGillavry (9). The original literature must be consulted for details of these and other more recent amendments (10,11) to the simple theory described here.

All practical polarographic work is done under conditions that serve to render the migration current negligible. There are several reasons for this. The one of most importance in analytical work is that it would be very undesirable to have to try to calculate the concentration of the substance one was interested in from a wave height that depended not only on that concentration but also on the concentration and nature of every one of the other ions present. It is plain that the wave heights of lead ion would be quite different in solutions of lead chloride and lead perchlorate even though the concentrations of the two salts were the same, for the equivalent conductances of the chloride and perchlorate ions are sufficiently different to change the transference number of lead ion by about 3% even if complexation with chloride is neglected. Moreover, traces of sodium nitrate or potassium nitrate would affect the limiting current obtained with any given concentration of lead ion, and would do so to different extents because the equivalent conductances of these salts are not at all the same. One would need a great deal of information about the composition of the solution before it would be possible to calculate the concentration of lead ion, and then one would need a theory better than the best now available.

Another reason for using a considerable excess of supporting electrolyte in practical polarographic work is directly related to these considerations. It may be noted that the addition of supporting electrolyte produces smaller variations of the limiting currents in Fig. 3.3 than it should according to the above equations; this is because a few tenths of a millimole per liter of electrolyte entered the solution from the salt bridge during the preparation and deaeration of the solutions. This would be immaterial if a large excess of electrolyte were already present, but the problems of cell design be greatly exacerbated if foreign electrolytes could not be tolerated.

It may also be noted from Fig. 3.3 that the slopes of the waves increase and that the half-wave potentials become less negative as the electrolyte concentration rises. This is because the resistance of the solution is fairly high in the absence of added electrolyte, and so an appreciable fraction of the voltage applied by the polarograph is dissipated as iR drop through the cell. This could be compensated for, as described in Chap. 2 III, but it is certainly easier to decrease the resistance by adding electrolyte whenever it is possible.

In order to suppress the migration current so nearly completely that further variations of the electrolyte concentration will have no appreciable effect, a useful rule is that the concentration of the supporting electrolyte should be at least 50 times that of the electroactive ion. As this is based on the conductance equation (3.8), the concentrations must be expressed in equivalents per liter. This will usually decrease the transference number of the electroactive ion to about 0.01. A higher concentration of supporting electrolyte is needed if the electroactive ion has an unusually high equivalent conductance (as does hydrogen ion); a lower one will suffice if it has an unusually low equivalent conductance (as do large organic ions). Even the presence of a substantial further concentration of adventitious electrolyte will then have only a negligible effect on the migration current. This does not mean that the concentration of supporting electrolyte can be allowed to vary randomly in replicate experiments as long as it is large enough to suppress the migration current; see Sec. IV-D below.

The above rule indicates that quite dilute supporting electrolytes should be suitable for work with very small concentrations of electroactive ions. Their use may often be advantageous in trace analysis (12) because it decreases the faradaic component of the residual current due to impurities in the salts used. But, unless compensation is made for the iR drop through the cell, the concentration of supporting electrolyte should not be decreased so far as to cause the cell resistance to exceed a few thousand ohms at most. If the wave becomes drawn out because of a high cell resistance, more may be lost by having to extrapolate the residual current farther than is gained by the decrease in its faradaic component. Most polarographic work is carried out with supporting-electrolyte concentrations between about 0.1 and $1F$, and even much higher concentrations are often useful in inorganic polarography. Many metal ions are best determined, and some can only be determined, in strongly acidic media containing high concentrations of halide ions; these include tungsten (VI), tin(IV), antimony(V), and arsenic(V). In many other cases the use of a very concentrated medium may serve to mask an interfering ion; for example, thallous ion yields a wave in nearly every known supporting electrolyte but is masked in concentrated hydrochloric acid because of the formation of a chloro complex. It can be inferred that media of high ionic strengths may occasionally be useful in organic analysis, but there has been no practical demonstration of this, and in any case it is hardly feasible if solubility considerations dictate the use of a solvent of low dielectric constant.

Non-ionic substances should not give migration currents, but supporting electrolytes are still used in work with them for two reasons. One is to decrease the iR drop through the cell; the other is to buffer the solution. Hydrogen ions are consumed in the reductions (and liberated in the oxidations) of most organic compounds. In an unbuffered solution the pH at the electrode surface will increase as the cathodic current increases, and the variation of pH sometimes (but by no means always) causes pronounced changes in the characteristics of the polarogram. To avoid this, it is wise to buffer the solution unless it is found that buffering makes no difference. As a general rule, the (molar) concentration of the least concentrated component of the buffer system should be at least $20p$ times that of the compound being studied, where p is the number of hydrogen ions consumed or produced in the reduction or oxidation of each molecule of the compound. Thus an $0.1F$ acetate buffer of pH 5.7, containing $0.009M$ undissociated acetic acid (for which pK_a is 4.7 at this ionic strength), is too dilute for work with a $1mM$ solution of an organic compound, but would be satisfactory with $0.1mM$ solutions of all compounds except a few for which p is unusually large.

III. Theory of the Diffusion Current

Imagine a stationary electrode immersed in an initially homogeneous but unstirred solution containing an electroactive substance and subjected to a steady potential on the plateau of the wave, so that the ions or molecules of that substance are reduced or oxidized as rapidly as they reach the electrode surface. During the first instant after the potential is applied, the ions or molecules initially at the electrode surface will be consumed, and so their concentration will fall practically to zero in a very thin layer of solution in contact with the electrode. The resulting difference between their concentration in this layer and their as yet unaffected concentration in the adjacent layer a little farther away from the electrode causes ions or molecules to diffuse toward the electrode surface. They are reduced or oxidized on arriving there, and the result is the partial depletion of solution a little distance away from the electrode. As time goes on, the depletion extends farther and farther into the solution, and ions or molecules will reach the electrode surface more and more slowly. As the diffusion current is proportional to the rate at which the electroactive substance diffuses to the electrode surface, it decreases as the electrolysis is prolonged.

The necessity of taking this effect into explicit account is the fundamental experimental difference between voltammetry with stationary electrodes, such as the hanging mercury drop electrode, and polarography. With a dropping electrode the concentration gradient that forms around each successive drop is more or less completely destroyed as solution rushes in when the drop falls, and therefore the average current during the life of each drop is identical in all practical work with the average current during the life of the preceding one. One important consequence of this fact is that the plateau of a polarographic wave is essentially flat, and another is that its height is independent of the rate of polarization being provided by the polarograph that records it. In stationary-electrode voltammetry, however, the current decays with time on the plateau, and the rate of polarization affects the wave height because it influences the extent to which depletion has already taken place at the instant a current is recorded. This is discussed further in Chap. 8 I.

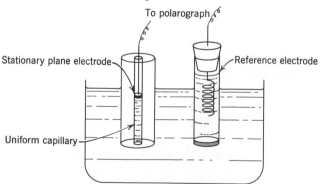

Figure 3.4.   Simple apparatus providing linear diffusion to a stationary plane electrode. See also Fig. 10.9.

It is convenient to begin by considering the simple case of linear diffusion to a stationary plane electrode, in which all of the diffusing ions or molecules move in the same direction. This is illustrated by Fig. 3.4, where the direction of motion is parallel to the axis of the capillary. The current at an instant τ seconds after the electrolysis is begun is given by (13)

$$i_\tau = nFAC(D/\pi\tau)^{1/2} \tag{3.11}$$

in which i_τ is the current (in microamperes) after correction for the residual current that would flow under the same conditions, n is the number of electrons consumed by each ion or molecule of the electro-active substance, F is the number of coulombs per faraday, A is the area (in cm.^{2}) of the electrode and of the column of solution in which diffusion is taking place, C is the concentration (in millimoles/1000 cm.^{3}) of the electroactive substance in the undepleted bulk of the solution, and D is its diffusion coefficient in square centimeters per second. Both i_τ and n are taken to be positive for cathodic processes and negative for anodic ones, in accordance with the sign convention mentioned in Sec. I.

Equation (3.11) was tested by Laitinen and Kolthoff (14) and has been used for the evaluation of diffusion coefficients under polarographic conditions (15,16).

By analogy with eq. (3.4), the electrode area τ seconds after a drop begins to form at a dropping electrode is given by

$$A = (4\pi)^{1/3}(3 \times 10^{-3}/d_{Hg})^{2/3}m^{2/3}\tau^{2/3} \tag{3.12}$$

Combining this with eq. (3.11), one obtains

$$i_\tau = 4^{1/3}\pi^{-1/6}(3 \times 10^{-3}/d_{Hg})^{2/3}\, nFD^{1/2}Cm^{2/3}\tau^{1/6} \tag{3.13}$$

A correction is needed, however, because the growth of the drop not only increases its area but also decreases the thickness of the layer of solution that has been depleted; more elaborate derivations (13,17, 18) indicate that the current given by eq. (3.13) should be multiplied by $(7/3)^{1/2}$ to take this into account. Introducing this factor along with the appropriate values of F and d_{Hg} (96487.2 coulombs/faraday and 13.534$_3$ g./cm.^{3} at 25°, respectively), eq. (3.13) can be rewritten in the form

$$i_\tau = 708.1nD^{1/2}Cm^{2/3}\tau^{1/6} \tag{3.14}$$

Integrating this over the drop life gives the total number of micro-coulombs per drop, and dividing the result by the drop life t in seconds gives the Ilkovič equation for the average diffusion current i_d during the drop life:

$$i_d = \frac{1}{t} \int_0^t i_\tau d\tau = 607.0 n D^{1/2} C m^{2/3} t^{1/6} \tag{3.15}$$

A theoretical difficulty of the Ilkovič equation arises from the fact that the dropping electrode is not planar but spherical, so that diffusion toward the electrode surface takes place along the radii of a sphere rather than linearly. In linear diffusion the cross-sectional area of the boundary between the bulk of the solution and the partly depleted diffusion layer remains constant and the boundary simply moves farther away from the electrode surface as the electrolysis continues. In spherical diffusion, however, the area of this boundary increases, and this in turn causes electroactive material to arrive at the surface of a spherical electrode more rapidly than linear diffusion would bring it to the surface of a plane electrode of the same area under otherwise identical conditions. The fundamental equation for spherical diffusion to a stationary electrode, which is analogous to eq. (3.11) for linear diffusion, is

$$i_\tau = nFAC \left[\left(\frac{D}{\pi\tau} \right)^{1/2} + \frac{D}{r_d} \right] \tag{3.16}$$

where r_d is the radius of the electrode (in centimeters) while the other symbols have the same significance as before. Equation (3.12) gives an expression for the area A, while an expression for r_d at any instant during the life of a drop at a dropping electrode can be obtained by analogy with equation (3.3):

$$r_d = \left(\frac{3 \times 10^{-3}}{4\pi d_{Hg}} \right)^{1/3} m^{1/3} \tau^{1/3} \tag{3.17}$$

Combining these expressions with eq. (3.16), introducing the factor $(7/3)^{1/2}$ as above to account for the decrease in the thickness of the diffusion layer that accompanies the growth of the drop, and using the appropriate values of the numerical factors gives the following equation for the instantaneous diffusion current:

$$i_\tau = 708.1 n D^{1/2} C m^{2/3} \tau^{1/6} (1 + 44.5 D^{1/2} \tau^{1/6} / m^{1/3}) \tag{3.18}$$

Integration as above yields

$$i_d = 607nD^{1/2}Cm^{2/3}t^{1/6}(1 + AD^{1/2}t^{1/6}/m^{1/3}) \qquad (3.19)$$

where the numerical constant A is 39 according to the above derivation; this is the Lingane–Loveridge equation (*19*). Strehlow and von Stackelberg (*20*) gave A = 17, as did Müller (*18*), and values intermediate between these extremes were deduced by others (*21,22*). The most sophisticated treatment (*23,24*) gives A = 34.7 and also provides another term:

$$i_d = 607nD^{1/2}Cm^{2/3}t^{1/6}[1 + 34.7D^{1/2}t^{1/6}/m^{1/3} + 100(D^{1/2}t^{1/6}/m^{1/3})^2]$$
$$(3.20)$$

which is the Koutecký equation.

Walkley (*25*) and Lingane (*26*) suggested rewriting eq. (3.15) in such a way as to separate its terms into two groups: one containing the terms whose values for any electroactive substance are completely defined by specifying the conditions of measurement (temperature, composition of the supporting electrolyte, potential of the dropping electrode, etc.), the other containing the terms that will still be free to vary from one measurement to another. The first group includes n, D, and the numerical constant 607; the second includes the diffusion current, the concentration C, and the capillary characteristics m and t. The diffusion current constant I is defined by the equation

$$I = i_d/Cm^{2/3}t^{1/6} \qquad (3.21)$$

According to the Ilkovič equation (3.15),

$$I = 607nD^{1/2} \qquad (3.22)$$

whereas the Koutecký equation (3.20) gives

$$I = 607nD^{1/2}[1 + 34.7D^{1/2}t^{1/6}/m^{1/3} + 100(D^{1/2}t^{1/6}/m^{1/3})^2] \qquad (3.23)$$

Thus the Ilkovič equation predicts that the diffusion current constant should actually be a constant under defined experimental conditions: it should be independent of the capillary characteristics, and reproducible in different laboratories or in the same laboratory with different capillaries (or with different pressures of mercury above the same capillary). The Koutecký equation, on the other hand, predicts that the diffusion current constant should not be a constant, but should vary with the capillary characteristics, so that different values will be obtained with different capillaries or even with the same capillary if the pressure of mercury above it is changed.

To put the difference between these predictions into practical terms, it may be said that the majority of electroactive substances have diffusion coefficients in the vicinity of 6×10^{-6} cm.^{2}/sec., though of course there are many exceptions. For a typical dropping electrode mt (the mass of each drop at the instant of fall) is around 8 mg., and the range of drop times used in most practical work is roughly 2–6 sec., so that m will ordinarily lie between about 4 and 1.3 mg./sec. while $t^{1/6}/m^{1/3}$ varies from about 0.7 to 1.2 sec.$^{1/2}$mg.$^{-1/3}$. Over this range of values of $t^{1/6}/m^{1/3}$ the value of the second term inside the square brackets on the right-hand side of eq. (3.23) will increase from about 0.07 to 0.12 if $D = 6 \times 10^{-6}$ cm.^{2}/sec. This represents a variation of roughly 5% in the value of I—or, what is perhaps more to the point, an average deviation of roughly 2.5% in the values of I obtained from measurements with different capillaries having characteristics in this range. The third term inside the square brackets, on the other hand, will have values only of the order of 0.0006, which is far too small to be detected experimentally.

Whether the difference between these equations is important or not depends on one's point of view. Most practical polarographic analyses are aimed at the determination of minor constituents, and in most such cases an average error of 2 to 3% is not very important. Indeed, it may easily be smaller than the associated chemical errors and errors of measurement. For these reasons it is often possible to ignore the difference between eqs. (3.15) and (3.20) altogether, even in analytical work. The same thing is true in many other applications, such as the evaluation of n from diffusion-current data (Sec. VI below).

In reporting the results of experimental measurements, it is always better to give values of the diffusion current constant, along with the values of m and t used to obtain them, than to follow the older custom of reporting simply the value of i_d/C. The value of m should be measured, and the value of t must be measured, under exactly the same conditions used in measuring the diffusion current; the important conditions include the composition of the solution, the temperature, and the potential of the dropping electrode. Reporting the value of the diffusion current constant makes it possible to compare results obtained in different laboratories and also facilitates chemical interpretation of the data. Literature values of the diffusion current constants of different substances under different conditions are valuable in analytical work because they permit concentrations to be estimated from measured values of i_d, m, and t by means of the equation

$$C = i_d / I m^{2/3} t^{1/6} \tag{3.24}$$

There are techniques of polarographic analysis, which are discussed in Chap. 7 IV-B, that obviate the whole question of how (and indeed whether) the diffusion current constant varies with capillary characteristics. In the present uncertain state of diffusion-current theory there is no doubt that the practical analyst is better off if he avoids

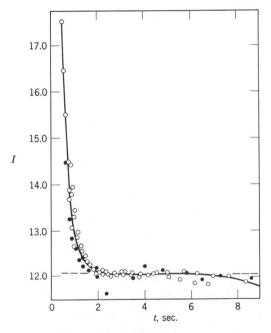

Figure 3.5. Effect of drop time on the diffusion current constants of iodate in 0.1F potassium chloride–0.1F hydrochloric acid [open circles (30)] and in 0.2F sodium phosphate at pH 7.0 [solid circles (29)]. Reproduced by permission of the *Journal of the American Chemical Society.*

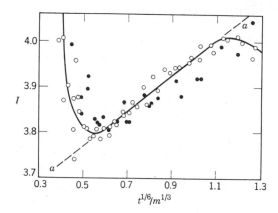

Figure 3.6.   Effect of $t^{1/6}/m^{1/3}$ on the diffusion current constants of lead ion in 0.1F potassium chloride–0.1F hydrochloric acid [open circles (*30*)] and in 1F potassium chloride [solid circles (*29*)], each containing 0.01% gelatin. Reproduced by permission of the *Journal of the American Chemical Society*.

this question, but avoiding it may entail more labor in preparing standard solutions and obtaining standard curves than the gain in accuracy is worth. Very extensive tables of diffusion current constants are available (*27*), and a few selected values are given in Appendix B and Appendix C.

It was said in the preceding paragraph that diffusion-current theory is in an uncertain state. The uncertainty seems to result from the fact that the theoretical equations are based on an oversimplified model. Several more or less important oversimplifications are involved, and they lead to a number of significant discrepancies between the theoretical predictions and experimental data.

Direct tests of the conflicting predictions of eqs. (3.22) and (3.23) regarding the effects of capillary characteristics on the diffusion current constant have been made by several authors (*20*,*28–34*) with the typical results shown in Figs. 3.5 and 3.6. The very rapid increase of I at drop times less than about 2 sec. is attributed to motion of solution near the capillary tip. Some turbulence is caused by the fall of a drop, and if the rate of flow of mercury into the drop is high some energy is transferred across the drop-solution interface to produce shearing in the diffusion layer. With any one capillary a decrease of t

is accompanied by an increase of m, and therefore both of these effects become increasingly important as t decreases. The most prominent feature of the current–time curve for a single drop, if t is very short, is the anomalously high current obtained during the first part of the drop life. Hence drop times shorter than about 2 sec. should never be used in practical work. The phenomenon is decreased by the addition of a maximum suppressor, such as gelatin, whose molecules are adsorbed onto the drop surface and decrease the rate of motion of solution past the drop surface.

At longer drop times, the diffusion current appears to obey the Ilkovič equation if gelatin is absent (Fig. 3.5), but the Koutecký equation if it is present (Fig. 3.6). It has indeed been asserted ([20],[33], [34]) that data obtained both in the presence and in the absence of gelatin obey the equation

$$I = 607nD^{1/2}(1 + 17D^{1/2}t^{1/6}/m^{1/3})$$ (3.25)

which might be regarded as an average of eqs. (3.22) and (3.23), and that they deviate from eq. (3.23) because of a combination of "depletion" and "enrichment" effects, but it has not been possible to confirm this in other laboratories. If the linear portion of Fig. 3.6 is fitted to the equation

$$I = k_1(1 + k_2t^{1/6}/m^{1/3})$$ (3.26)

by least-squares techniques, comparison with eq. (3.19) shows that

$$A = 607nk_2/k_1$$

so that the constant A can be evaluated experimentally. Its mean value, from data on many different electroactive species in different supporting electrolytes containing about 0.01% gelatin, is close to 31.5 ([31],[32]). The difference between this figure and the one appearing in eq. (3.23) corresponds to uncertainties of the order of tenths of a per cent in the experimental values of I. Whether or how the figure is affected by changes of gelatin concentration is unknown.

At very long drop times the values of I appear to fall off both in the presence and in the absence of gelatin. It has been suggested that this may be due to an increasing discrepancy between the averages of the galvanometer oscillations and the true average current. Data on this effect ([29]) indicate, however, that it should become perceptible only when the ratio of drop time to galvanometer period is larger than it is at the point where the decrease begins. What is even worse is that the decrease is not always observed (34) even at drop times so long that it should be very pronounced.

Many studies have been made of the instantaneous currents during the lives of individual drops (17,36–45). Typical data are shown in Fig. 3.7. Because the average current seems to obey an equation of the form of eq. (3.19) under these conditions, one might expect the instantaneous current to obey an equation of the form of eq. (3.18), according to which the ratio $i_\tau/\tau^{1/6}$ should increase linearly with $\tau^{1/6}$. This is not at all the behavior observed. On the contrary, the current is at least two orders of magnitude smaller than it should be at the beginning of the drop life, and it increases steadily to values well above those predicted from parameters that serve perfectly well to

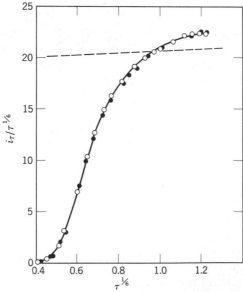

Figure 3.7.   Variation of $i_\tau/\tau^{1/6}$ with $\tau^{1/6}$ for the reduction of 3mM cadmium ion in 0.1F potassium chloride containing 0.01% gelatin. The open and solid circles represent the data obtained for two different drops by Taylor, Smith, and Cooter (36); the dashed line represents the variation predicted by an equation of the form of equation (3.19), using the values of D and A deduced from measurements of the average current by Strehlow and von Stackelberg (20). Reproduced by permission of the *Journal of the American Chemical Society* (37).

describe the average current. Grenier (44) confirmed this behavior in every one of a large number of other circumstances, as did Bresle (45), who further showed that the "constant" A in eq. (3.19) actually varies with drop age and also that changing the average value of m does not have the predicted effect. It appears that the Koutecký equation actually predicts too large a current near the start of the drop life and too small a current toward its end, and that it provides a reasonably accurate description of the average current obtained in the presence of gelatin merely because these opposing errors fortuitously involve nearly equal quantities of electricity. Nor does a plot of $i_\tau/\tau^{1/6}$ vs. $\tau^{1/6}$ consist of a horizontal straight line even under conditions where the Ilkovič equation appears to describe the average current; in the absence of gelatin such a plot differs in detail from that shown in Fig. 3.7 but has roughly the same general shape (44).

Numerous concordant data give the ratio i_d/i_{max} of the integrated average current to the maximum current during the drop life as 0.80 ± 0.01. According to the Ilkovič equation it should be 6/7 or 0.857, which is much larger than the experimental value. The Koutecký equation predicts

$$\frac{i_d}{i_{max}} = \frac{6}{7} \left(\frac{1 + 34.7D^{1/2}t^{1/6}/m^{1/3}}{1 + 39.7D^{1/2}t^{1/6}/m^{1/3}} \right) \qquad (3.28)$$

This is smaller than 6/7, but with typical values of D and $t^{1/6}/m^{1/3}$ (6 $\times$ 10^{-6} cm.^{2}/sec. and 1 sec.$^{1/2}$mg.$^{-1/3}$, respectively) it is still 0.848. This is not much of an improvement. It may be taken to mean that the current is smaller during the early stages of the drop life, but larger during its later stages, than either of the theoretical equations predicts, and this is of course in agreement with Fig. 3.7.

The assumptions made in deriving the Ilkovič and Koutecký equations are known to be false in several respects (46,47). It is assumed that the drop is accurately spherical, that its whole surface is exposed to the solution, and that the diffusion layer has the same thickness at every point. In fact, the electrode is not even approximately spherical until some little time after the mercury has emerged from the capillary tip, the area over which the drop is attached to the mercury thread inside the capillary is not exposed to the solution, and because the diffusion layer cannot extend up into the walls of the capillary it cannot become as thick at a point very near the capillary tip as it can at a point farther away. It is also assumed that the rate of flow of mercury is constant throughout the drop life; in fact m increases continuously during the drop life because the back pressure (Sec. IV-B) decreases as the drop grows.

Moreover, despite the turbulence that arises at the drop surface when t is short, the solution does not become completely homogeneous when a drop falls (41,47–51). Consequently, every drop after the first one emerges into a solution that has already been partly depleted of electroactive substance in the immediate vicinity of the capillary tip. The first drop, however, emerges into a solution that has not been depleted at all, and so it gives higher currents than any of the drops that follow it. The effect is greatest near the beginning of the drop life: at any small drop age the current obtained with the second drop is much smaller than it was for the first, but the difference between them becomes less and less as the drop becomes older. According to Kůta and Smoleř (50–52), the integrated average current is usually about 10 to 20% smaller for the second drop than for the first in the reduction of cadmium ion. However, each drop after the first gives essentially the same current: that is, the additional depletion that occurs during the life of the second drop is destroyed by stirring when it falls, so that the third drop is born into a solution indistinguishable from that which confronted the second.

On this basis it appears that the predictions of the Ilkovič and Koutecký equations should be compared, not with data on successive drops as has been done above, but with data on the first drop. For this purpose it is convenient to consider data obtained with cadmium ion in dilute chloride and nitrate solutions. The diffusion coefficients of cadmium ion in such media have been measured by a number of different techniques, including the Cottrell method (linear diffusion to a stationary plane electrode) (16), chronopotentiometry (53,54), and diaphragm-cell diffusion (55), with reasonably concordant results; one may take $D = 7.0 \times 10^{-6}$ cm.^{2}/sec. at 25° (56).

According to the Ilkovič equation this should correspond to a diffusion current constant of $(607)(2)(7.0 \times 10^{-6})^{1/2} = 3.21$, since n is 2 for the reduction of cadmium ion to cadmium amalgam. For the capillary characteristics cited by Kůta and Smoleř (52), which are $m = 2$ mg./sec. and $t = 3$ sec., the Koutecký equation predicts a diffusion current constant of $3.21(1 + 34.7D^{1/2}t^{1/6}/m^{1/3}) = 3.49$. Typical experimental values of the diffusion current constant, measured in the ordinary way with successive drops growing into partly depleted solutions, are 3.51 in 0.1F hydrochloric acid and 3.53 in 0.1F potassium nitrate. When the capillary characteristics have these values, according to Kůta and Smoleř, the average current is 20% higher for the first drop than for any later one, and this would correspond to a diffusion current constant of, say, $(3.52)(1.20) = 4.22$ for the first drop. This is not in acceptable agreement with either of the theoretical predictions.

The same result is obtained with other electroactive substances. In Sec. IV-E below it will be shown that the Koutecký equation predicts a diffusion current constant of 3.07 for thallous ion at infinite dilution with certain capillary characteristics; extrapolation of experimental data gives 3.04. For iodate ion the corresponding figures are 13.17 and 12.72. It is not possible to make such comparisons in very many cases, for there are few electroactive substances whose diffusion coefficients are known in the presence of the large excess of supporting electrolyte that is needed to suppress the migration current. But wherever comparison is possible it is always found that the Koutecký equation predicts a value that agrees, within a very few per cent, with the one found experimentally for successive drops. However, this equation cannot be valid for successive drops, because it assumes that the solution is completely homogeneous at the start of the drop life. One of two things must be true: either the solution around the capillary tip is not depleted by the prior drops, which is contrary to the results of several independent experimenters, or the Koutecký equation must be in error by 10 to 20% under ordinary polarographic conditions. In the latter case the error of the equation must be very nearly exactly compensated by the depletion of the solution (although evidence is presented in Sec. IV-E below to show that the compensation becomes very imperfect if the diffusion coefficient of the electroactive species is large). As yet there is no way to choose between these two unattractive alternatives.

Kůta and Smoleř found that a plot of log i_τ vs. log τ for the first drop in the reduction of cadmium ion was linear at drop ages above about 0.5 sec. and that the slope of its linear portion was 0.192 when the capillary characteristics had the above values. This is considerably different from the slope predicted by the Ilkovič equation; similar discrepancies have been observed by those who have worked with successive drops. Nor does it conform to the Koutecký equation:

Kůta and Smoleř found it possible to reconcile the observed slope with the calculated one only by assuming $D = 2 \times 10^{-5}$ cm.²/sec., which is nearly three times the correct value. The divergence arises from other phenomena that are not taken into account in the equations. One (57) is that m increases as the drop grows, instead of remaining constant and equal to its average value. Hence the drop is always a little smaller than it is taken to be. Los and Murray (57), who took this variation of m during the drop life into account, claimed to have obtained currents during the first drop that were in excellent accord with a suitably modified Koutecký equation when gelatin was present. Another fact that causes the current to increase more rapidly than theoretical equations predict is that the diffusion layer around the drop becomes thicker as the drop grows older; this gives rise to a density gradient, and at drop ages exceeding several seconds some turbulence can be detected by such techniques as microscopic observation of the motion of carbon particles (58) or schlieren photomicrography (59). This brings more of the electroactive substance to the drop surface than would reach it by diffusion alone, and so if t is sufficiently large the current becomes too high during the latter part of the drop life (57). On current–time curves the effect begins to become noticeable at drop ages even as small as 2 sec. This is probably the most important of the factors responsible for the difference between the average current predicted by the Koutecký equation and the one calculated for the first drop from experimental data.

A word may be added on the effects of gelatin and other maximum suppressors in connection with the difference between Figs. 3.5 and 3.6. Kůta and Smoleř (50–52) found that the addition of gelatin decreases the current during the life of the first drop, presumably because it hinders the motion of solution past the drop surface. On the other hand, they found that it increases the current during the first part of the life of each subsequent drop, and this is probably because the depleted solution very near the surface of a drop is trapped in the adsorbed film of the maximum suppressor and is carried away from the capillary tip when the drop falls. Hence each drop after the first is born into a solution that is more nearly homogeneous than it would be in the absence of a maximum suppressor. In addition, Gierst and Juliard (60) found chronopotentiometrically that both the apparent diffusion coefficient of cadmium ion and the kinetics of its reduction are markedly affected by even minute concentrations of gelatin (as little as $3 \times 10^{-6}\%$). All of these phenomena certainly affect diffusion currents measured in solutions containing gelatin (or any other maximum suppressor), but a quantitative interpretation is hardly possible.

IV. Factors Affecting the Diffusion Current

Despite their quantitative shortcomings, the theoretical equations for the diffusion current do provide useful qualitative descriptions of the effects of most of the important experimental variables. In the following discussion of these effects, the validity of the experimental evidence is of course independent of the defects of the theory. Frequent reference will be made to the theory, not because it predicts or accurately accounts for the experimental observations, but because it provides a convenient systematic frame of reference for the understanding and interpretation of the data. The Ilkovič equation will be invoked more often than the Koutecký equation, not because it is more accurate, but merely because it is simpler and serves the purpose with a minimum of algebraic complexity.

A. The Concentration of the Electroactive Substance

The rate at which the electroactive substance reaches the electrode surface, and consequently the current resulting from its reduction or oxidation as rapidly as it arrives there, is proportional to its concentration in the bulk of the solution. It does not matter whether the electrode is plane, spherical, cylindrical, or of some other shape; whether it is stationary or moving; whether its area is constant or increasing; or whether the mass transfer of the electroactive substance occurs by diffusion, laminar flow, or convection. There are only two requirements: one is that the supply of electroactive substance at the electrode surface must not be affected by any chemical or physical process (including some kinds of slow chemical reactions, adsorption on the electrode surface, etc.) whose rate or extent is not described by a first-order equation, and the other is that the hydrodynamics and mechanism of the mass-transfer process must be independent of the concentration of electroactive substance. This proportionality between the mass-transfer-controlled current and concentration is observed in all voltammetric techniques and is the basis of the vast majority of the practical analytical methods and physicochemical applications based on these techniques.

That the polarographic diffusion current is proportional to the concentration of electroactive substance has been repeatedly verified by many experimenters. Some typical data (*61*) illustrating this are shown in Table 3.2. The diffusion currents shown in the third column of this table were calculated by subtracting the residual current measured under the same conditions in the initially cadmium-free solution from the limiting currents measured after the successive additions of cadmium. The values of i_d/C listed in the fourth column are constant to better than $\pm 0.2\%$ over a 630-fold range of concentrations.

TABLE 3.2.
Constancy of i_d/C

Measured volumes of a standard cadmium solution were added to a known volume of $0.1F$ potassium chloride–$0.1F$ hydrochloric acid, and the total current at $E_{d.e.} = -1.00$ v. vs. S.C.E. was measured after each addition and deaeration with a capillary for which m was 3.299 mg./sec. and t was 2.47_0 sec.

$C_{Cd^{++}}$, mM	Total current, μamp.	i_d, μamp.	i_d/C
0	0.301 ($= i_r$)	—	—
0.01935	0.479	0.178	9.20
0.05538	0.808	0.507	9.15
0.1245	1.447	1.146	9.20
0.1847	2.001	1.700	9.20
0.2392	2.503	2.202	9.21
1.614	15.09	14.79	9.16
4.22_1	39.17	38.87	9.21
6.66_7	61.55	61.25	9.19
12.19	112.3	112.0	9.19
Mean...			*9.19 $\pm$ 0.01₅*

Some authors have asserted that i_d/C increases systematically with decreasing concentration of the electroactive substance, especially below about 0.5mM. This is quite different from the increasing uncertainty that is to be expected at low concentrations. In every chemically simple case in which such a claim has been carefully investigated it has been attributed to failure to apply the proper correction for the residual current or (which is really the same thing) to the injudicious use of an extrapolation method (Sec. V) for the measurement of the wave height.

There are, however, circumstances in which proportionality between the wave height and the concentration of electroactive substance actually is not secured. Some of these are apparent and some are real. Apparent variations of i_d/C can be produced by impurities that react with the electroactive substance: one may envision an attempt to measure the diffusion current of lead ion in a solution containing a trace of sulfate present as an impurity in the supporting electrolyte. A similar effect results if the solution contains two electroactive substances that can react with each other, or if an electroactive substance decomposes, is adsorbed onto the walls of the cell, or volatilizes during the preparation and deaeration of the solution. These are only apparent because it is actually C that is affected in each case, while the diffusion current may be quite accurately proportional to the concentration of the electroactive substance that remains. Cases of this sort are often much less trivial in the laboratory than they are on paper.

Real variations of i/C are observed for some catalytic waves (Sec. VIII), adsorption waves under certain conditions (Sec. IX), some waves representing electrode processes in which an intermediate can be consumed by a chemical side reaction (e.g., dimerization or reaction with the starting material to give an electrolytically inert product), and waves afflicted by anomalous capacity phenomena (Sec. XI). They are also observed in certain equilibrium mixtures of electroactive substances or when one electroactive substance in a solution can react with the product formed when another is reduced or oxidized (Sec. X). These exceptions are considered in the sections cited. For the moment it suffices to note that the proportionality cannot be taken for granted, but must always be checked in the development of any analytical procedure. Analyses are often feasible even when the wave height is not proportional to concentration, but special techniques are required (Chap. 7 I-C).

Even in cases that do not involve any of the above complications it may be found that the wave height is not proportional to concentration. There are two general circumstances. One arises at high concentrations of the electroactive substance. Its reduction or oxidation produces a layer of solution at the drop surface having a different density from the bulk of the solution a little distance away. The geometry of the resulting situation may be visualized with the aid of Fig. 3.8. The density gradient leads to convective mixing, and brings

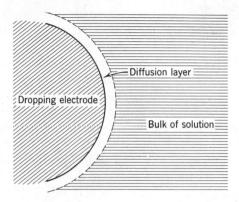

Figure 3.8.   The diffusion layer around a spherical microelectrode. Convective mixing will result from any difference between the densities of this layer and the bulk of the solution. The thickness of the layer is considerably exaggerated.

electroactive material to the drop surface more rapidly than it could get there by diffusion alone. At low concentrations of electroactive material the density gradients are small and there is little convection. As the concentration increases, so does the extent of convection, and the result is that the current increases more rapidly than the concentration does. A variation of i_d/C usually begins to become perceptible at a concentration around 3mM, and is often accompanied by irregularities in the oscillations on the plateau of a recorded polarogram even though these are perfectly regular at lower concentrations. However, there are cases in which i_d/C does remain constant up to much higher concentrations. One is shown in Table 3.2, and Schaap and McKinney (62) found that i_d/C remained constant up to concentrations of cadmium ion as high as 100mM in 5F sodium nitrate.

The other important general reason for deviations from proportionality between wave height and concentration is illustrated by Fig. 3.9. Curve a in this figure is a polarogram of lead ion alone. It is distorted by a maximum at about -0.5 v.; at potentials more negative than this the current decreases until a potential of about -0.7 v. is reached. Between -0.7 and -1.0 v. the wave height is proportional to the concentration of lead ion, but between -0.5 and -0.7 v. it is not. This is because the height of the maximum increases more rapidly than the concentration of lead ion, as may be seen by comparing curve a in Fig. 3.9 with curve a in Fig. 3.10, which was obtained

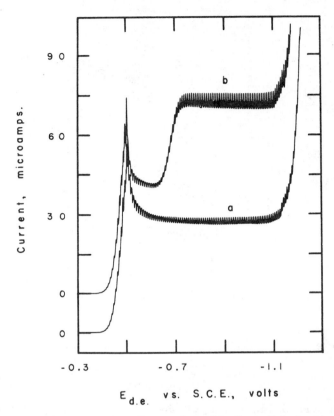

Figure 3.9. Polarograms of 1.0F potassium chloride–0.1F hydrochloric acid containing (a) 4mM lead ion, (b) 4mM lead ion and 4mM cadmium ion.

under exactly the same conditions but with a much smaller concentration of lead ion. Naturally it would be preferable to measure the wave height at a fairly negative potential, where it would be proportional to the concentration of lead ion, but in practical work this is not always possible, as may be seen from curves b of Figs. 3.9 and 3.10, which would be obtained in attempting to determine lead in the presence of cadmium. Here it is impossible to obtain any measure at all of the height of the lead wave except in just the region of potentials where it is not proportional to the concentration of lead ion. Situations like this can be recognized if close attention is paid to the slopes of the

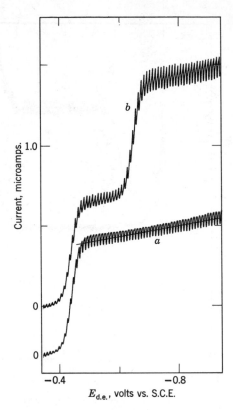

Figure 3.10.   Polarograms of $1.0F$ potassium chloride–$0.1F$ hydrochloric acid containing (*a*) 0.10 mM lead ion, (*b*) 0.10mM lead ion and 0.10mM cadmium ion. As the linear extrapolation of the plateau on curve *a* indicates, the currents around -0.5 v. are slightly too large even though a maximum cannot be perceived on casual inspection.

plateau and the residual-current curve over the range of potentials selected for the measurement of the wave height. If these are markedly different, regardless of whether or not a maximum can be seen, the measured wave height cannot be expected to be proportional to the concentration. This is most likely to be the case in the absence of a maximum suppressor, especially when the drop time is very short. A difference of slope in the absence of a visible maximum is especially insidious because the unwary analyst, employing an extrapolation method (Sec. V) for the measurement of the wave height, may succeed in confounding the shape and the height of the wave to such an extent that meaningful results become impossible to obtain (61,63). Wave heights measured under such conditions are, of course, abnormal in other respects as well: for example, increasing the height of the mercury column in the stand tube increases the wave height to a much larger than normal extent, for the height of a maximum increases rapidly when the drop time is decreased.

B. The Capillary Characteristics and the Factors Affecting Them

The diffusion current depends on the capillary characteristics m and t, and is therefore affected by their variations. Hence it is important to understand how they in turn are affected by the numerous factors that influence them.

In discussing the factors that influence the value of m, it is useful to refer to the Poiseuille equation, which may be written

$$m = \frac{125\pi r_c^4 d_{Hg}}{l\eta} \left(h_{Hg}d_{Hg}g - h_{soln}d_{soln}g - 43.1 \frac{d_{Hg}^{1/3}\sigma}{(mt)^{1/3}} \right) \quad (3.29)$$

where m is the average rate of flow of mercury (milligrams per second), r_c and l are the radius and length of the capillary (centimeters), d_{Hg} and η are the density and viscosity of mercury, h_{Hg} and h_{soln} are the heights (centimeters) of the mercury column and of the solution, respectively, above the capillary tip, d_{soln} is the density of the solution, σ is the interfacial tension (dynes/centimeter) between mercury and the solution, g is the gravitational constant, and t is the drop time (seconds). The variation of m during the life of a single drop has been discussed by Los and Murray (57). Combining the numerical constants, and taking an average value of $\sigma = 400$ dynes/ cm. for the interfacial tension between mercury and a dilute aqueous salt solution, one obtains at 25°

$$m = 4.64 \times 10^9 \frac{r_c^4}{l} \left(h_{Hg} - \frac{h_{soln}d_{soln}}{13.5} - \frac{3.1}{(mt)^{1/3}} \right) \quad (3.30)$$

The last term inside the parentheses on the right-hand side of this equation gives the back pressure due to the interfacial tension at the drop surface. The denominator of this term is the cube root of the drop weight; as this is usually about 8 mg., the back-pressure term corresponds to about 1.5 cm. of mercury. This is by no means negligible in comparison with the values of h_{Hg} ordinarily employed, which lie between about 30 and 100 cm. On the other hand, the second term, which reflects the back hydrostatic pressure of the solution, is rarely larger than 1 or 2 mm. of mercury, and can therefore be neglected in all but the most precise work. The algebraic sum of the terms within the parentheses is called the "net," "driving," "corrected," or "effective" pressure of mercury.

According to eq. (3.30), m is directly proportional to the net pressure on the mercury drop. At the same time, t is inversely proportional to this pressure, for although the drop weight mt varies with the interfacial tension and depends on the geometry of the capillary orifice, it is not affected by variations of the pressure. These relationships are demonstrated by Table 3.3 *(64)*.

TABLE 3.3.

Effects of Mercury Pressure on m and t

The data were secured at $E_{d.e.} = -1.00$ v. vs. S.C.E. in $0.10F$ potassium nitrate at 25°C. $h_{soln} = 3.0$ cm. ($= 0.22$ cm. of Hg).

h_{Hg}, cm.	m, mg./sec.	t, sec.	mt, mg.	$h_{corr.}$, cm.	$100m/h_{corr.}$	$h_{corr.}t$
108.0	4.2730	1.751	7.48	106.20	4.024	186.0
81.0	3.1837	2.346	7.47	79.20	4.020	185.8
58.0	2.2645	3.290	7.45	56.20	4.029	184.9
43.0	1.6625	4.505	7.49	41.20	4.035	185.7
32.0	1.2155	6.145	7.47	30.20	4.025	185.6
27.0	1.0118	7.372	7.46	25.20	4.015	185.8
Means....................			*7.47 ± 0.01*		*4.025 ± 0.005*	*185.6 ± 0.3*

Back pressure $= 3.1/(7.47)^{1/3}$
$= 1.58$ cm. of Hg

These effects of the corrected pressure h_{corr} on m and t are such that $m^{2/3}t^{1/6}$ is proportional to $h_{corr}^{1/2}$ while $t^{1/6}/m^{1/3}$ is proportional to $1/h_{corr}^{1/2}$. How the diffusion current will vary with h_{corr} will depend on which of the theoretical equations is more nearly obeyed. According to the Ilkovič equation one should have

$$i_d/h_{corr}^{1/2} = k_1 \tag{3.31}$$

where k_1 depends on a host of factors but is constant if nothing is varied except h_{corr}. The Koutecký equation predicts

$$i_d/h_{corr}^{1/2} = k_1 + \frac{k_2}{h_{corr}^{1/2}} \qquad (3.32)$$

where k_2 is also constant if only h_{corr} is varied. Because the term involving $t^{1/6}/m^{1/3}$ in the Koutecký equation usually amounts to only 5 to 10% of the diffusion current, the second term on the right-hand side of eq. (3.32) is much smaller than the first, and so the value of $i_d/h_{corr}^{1/2}$ should decrease a few per cent over a two- or threefold range of values of h_{corr}. Typical behavior in a case where the average current appears to obey the Koutecký equation is shown in Fig. 3.11.

This is the basis of a simple and widely used technique for ascertaining whether the height of a wave is diffusion-controlled. If $i_d/h_{corr}^{1/2}$ increases as $h_{corr}^{1/2}$ increases, or if it decreases much more rapidly than

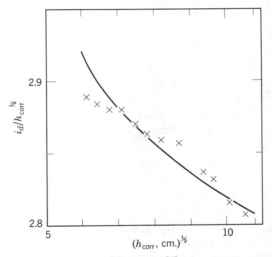

Figure 3.11. Variation of $i_d/h_{corr}^{1/2}$ with $h_{corr}^{1/2}$ for 4.1mM silver ion in 0.1F potassium nitrate containing 0.009% gelatin. These data conform to an equation of the form of eq. (3.19): a least-squares treatment gives A = 39.2 and $D = 1.40 \times 10^{-5}$ cm.²/sec. (*31*). Both of these values are larger than for any other substance on which precise data are available, so that the variation of $i_d/h_{corr}^{1/2}$ shown here is very nearly the largest that could be attributed to the operation of the Koutecký equation. The line represents the empirical equation $i_d/h_{corr}^{1/2} = 2.67 + 1.50/h_{corr}^{1/2}$ and its average deviation from the experimental points is ±0.23%.

in Fig. 3.11 (as the slope of such a plot is proportional to $D^{1/2}$, some variation from one electroactive substance to another is to be expected), the current must be partly or wholly governed by the rate of some process other than diffusion to the electrode surface (Secs. VII–X below). In applying this criterion it is important to avoid values of h_{corr} so high that the drop time falls below about 2.5 sec., because of the rapid increase of the wave height at shorter drop times; and it is also better to avoid values of h_{corr} so low that the drop time exceeds about 8 seconds, because of the uncertainty about how diffusion currents behave at such long drop times.

As the drop weight mt is quite closely proportional to the interfacial tension, the back-pressure term in eq. (3.29) actually involves only the two-thirds power of the interfacial tension. Because this term is not very large under any conditions, and because the interfacial tension between mercury and an aqueous solution is not grossly affected by the composition of the solution, there is but little difference among values of m measured under otherwise identical conditions but in different supporting electrolytes. In a typical case (64) values of 2.0640, 2.0653, and 2.0492 mg./sec. were obtained in $0.1F$ potassium nitrate, $0.1F$ potassium chloride–$0.1F$ hydrochloric acid, and $0.1F$ potassium chloride alone, respectively. The differences among these values are negligibly small for nearly all purposes. For the same reasons, the value of m is not appreciably affected by the addition of a surface-active agent (maximum suppressor). However, values of m measured in air are quite different from those secured in solutions, for the drops adhere to the glass around the orifice when the capillary tip is dry, and so they grow to a much larger size than they would in a solution. For example (29), a capillary that gave $mt = 6.25$ mg. in $1F$ potassium chloride gave $mt = 93.4$ mg. in air. This corresponds to a substantial change in the back pressure, and consequently to a substantial change in m, which under these conditions was 0.959 mg./sec. in $1F$ potassium chloride but 0.982 mg./sec. in air. Hence the value of m should always be measured in an electrolyte solution.

Because mt is proportional to the interfacial tension σ whereas m is nearly if not quite independent of it, the drop time t is evidently fairly closely proportional to σ. Consequently the value of t is considerably affected by changing the composition of the supporting electrolyte or by adding a maximum suppressor. Though only the sixth root of t appears in the Ilkovič equation, t is so sensitive to changes in the experimental conditions that much more attention has to be paid to its variations than to those of m. Drop times obtained in air are much longer than those in electrolyte solutions: in the example cited in the last paragraph, t was 6.52 sec. in $1F$ potassium chloride but 95.1 sec. in air.

TABLE 3.4.

Effects of Applied Potential on m and t

The data were secured at 25°C. in $0.1F$ potassium chloride. $h_{corr} = 30.1$ cm. of Hg.

$E_{d.e.}$ vs. S.C.E., v.	m, mg./sec.	t, sec.	$m^{2/3}t^{1/6}$
0.00	3.4042	2.700	2.6703
−0.20	3.3948	2.883	2.6947
−0.40	3.3831	2.925	2.6950
−0.60	3.3831	2.927	2.6953
−0.80	3.3872	2.882	2.6906
−1.00	3.3891	2.740	2.6690
−1.20	3.3915	2.551	2.6386
−1.40	3.4039	2.337	2.6068
−1.70	3.4218	1.933	2.5344
−2.00	3.4487	1.435	2.4243

The interfacial tension depends on the potential of the dropping electrode, and this affects m and t as shown in Table 3.4. In $0.1F$ potassium chloride the potential of the electrocapillary maximum is −0.461 v. vs. S.C.E., and the interfacial tension passes through a maximum at this potential. Consequently t passes through a maximum at the potential of the electrocapillary maximum, while m passes through a minimum because of the variation of the back-pressure term in eq. (3.29). The variation of t with potential has been used in evaluating the potential of the electrocapillary maximum in various electrolyte solutions (65). It may be noted that the percentage change in t between any two potentials is much larger than that in m. At −2.00 v. the value of t is about half as large as at the potential of the electrocapillary maximum (though the exact ratio differs from one supporting electrolyte to another), and it continues to decrease rapidly as the potential becomes still more negative, as in solutions of tetraalkylammonium salts. Measuring the drop time with the electrode disconnected from the polarizing circuit, as was suggested in Chap. 2 IV for evaluating the suitability of a new capillary, gives the value of t at the potential where the current is zero. If the solution were completely free from electroactive substances, this would be the potential of the electrocapillary maximum; in practice, however, as was mentioned in the discussion of Fig. 3.1, it is always a little more positive. Nevertheless, this test gives very nearly the maximum value of t. If one intends to use the capillary for measuring wave heights at very negative potentials, its drop time when disconnected from the polarograph should be long enough to ensure that a value in the desired range of 3 to 6 sec. will be obtained in use.

The variations of m and t with potential are reflected in variations of the product $m^{2/3}t^{1/6}$. This is constant to about $\pm 0.5\%$ from 0 to

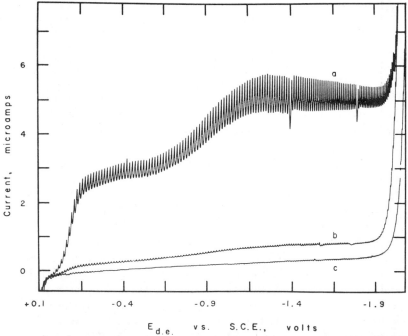

Figure 3.12.   Polarograms of $0.1F$ potassium chloride (a) saturated with air, showing the double wave of oxygen, (b) partially deaerated, and (c) after complete deaeration.

−1.0 v., but it decreases slightly at more negative potentials. So too does the diffusion current: the plateau of a wave has a smaller slope than the residual-current curve at potentials beyond about −1.0 v. Typical examples of this decrease are shown in Figs. 3.12 and 3.21.

This is of special importance when diffusion currents at widely different potentials must be compared. Suppose, for example, that the capillary of Table 3.4 were used to analyze a solution containing cadmium and manganous ions. The half-wave potentials of these ions are −0.6 and −1.5 v. vs. S.C.E., respectively, in 0.1F potassium chloride. If the diffusion current of cadmium ion at, say, −0.8 v. is 1.00 μamp., and if the total diffusion current on the plateau of the manganous-ion wave at −1.7 v. is 2.00 μamp., the diffusion current of manganous ion is not 1.00 μamp., but $2.00 - (2.534/2.691)(1.00) = 1.06$ μamp. The factor $(2.534/2.691)$ reflects the decrease of $m^{2/3}t^{1/6}$, and hence of the cadmium diffusion current, between −0.8 and −1.7 v. The error caused by neglecting this decrease would be 6% in the present example, and would increase as the ratio of cadmium to manganous-ion concentrations increased. Very nearly the same result is obtained if the Koutecký equation is used instead of the Ilkovič equation. Taking D as 7×10^{-6} cm.²/sec. for cadmium ion and writing

$$(i_d)_{-0.8 \text{ v.}} = 607nD^{1/2}C(m^{2/3}t^{1/6})_{-0.8 \text{ v.}}[1 + 34.7D^{1/2}(t^{1/6}/m^{1/3})_{-0.8 \text{ v.}}]$$

and

$$(i_d)_{-1.7 \text{ v.}} = 607nD^{1/2}C(m^{2/3}t^{1/6})_{-1.7 \text{ v.}}[1 + 34.7D^{1/2}(t^{1/6}/m^{1/3})_{-1.7 \text{ v.}}]$$

gives $(i_d)_{-1.7 \text{ v.}}/(i_d)_{-0.8 \text{ v.}} = (2.534/2.691) \times (1.0741/1.0863)$, instead of simply $(2.534/2.691)$ as obtained from the Ilkovič equation. This gives the diffusion current of cadmium ion as 0.93 (instead of 0.94) μamp. at −1.7 v., so that the diffusion current of manganous ion becomes 1.07 (instead of 1.06) μamp. The difference between the two results is so small that it will usually be comparable with the uncertainties in measuring the two diffusion currents. Even where the difference exceeds the estimated error of measurement, it does not seem advisable to use the more complicated Koutecký equation unless there is definite evidence (such as a variation of $i_d/h_{\text{corr}}^{1/2}$ with $h_{\text{corr}}^{1/2}$ like that shown in Fig. 3.11) to show that this equation agrees more closely with the data than the Ilkovič equation does.

Normally the height of the manganous-ion wave in such a situation would be estimated by extrapolating the plateau of the cadmium wave on a recorded polarogram (Sec. V below). It is true that the diffusion current of cadmium ion would not vary quite linearly with potential, because the slope of a plot of $m^{2/3}t^{1/6}$ versus potential decreases more and more as the potential becomes more negative, but the error thus introduced is inappreciable unless the extrapolation is longer than two or three tenths of a volt. The correction must be applied algebraically as described in the preceding paragraph if a manual polarograph is used to measure the current at just one potential on each plateau.

The density and viscosity of mercury and the interfacial tension between mercury and solution all change with temperature, and therefore m and t are also temperature-dependent. Unless the temperatures of the solution and the column of mercury above the capillary are the same, the temperature dependence of m is fairly complex because the linear rate of flow of mercury through the capillary is so high (typically 5 to 10 cm./sec.) that thermal equilibrium can hardly be attained inside the capillary. This not only causes the viscosity of mercury to vary along the length of the capillary, but also produces some variation of the capillary radius (to which m is extremely sensitive) as a result of thermal expansion of the glass. If the entire mercury column is at the same temperature, the temperature coefficient of m is about $+0.27\%$/deg., while that of t is about -0.22%/deg. Hence the temperature coefficient of $m^{2/3}t^{1/6}$ is about $+0.15\%$/deg.; this value is used in evaluating the temperature coefficient of the diffusion current in the following subsection.

As was mentioned in Chap. 2 IV, the plane of the capillary tip must be horizontal within two or three degrees. Both m and t are affected if the inclination is larger than this, and the values of t may become very imprecise. Capillaries whose tips are inclined at much larger angles (e.g., 90°) do give regular drop times but have no advantages in practical work.

C. Temperature

The effect of temperature on the diffusion current may be described by differentiating the Ilkovič equation with respect to temperature, which gives

$$\frac{1}{i_d}\frac{di_d}{dT} = \frac{1}{k}\frac{dk}{dT} + \frac{1}{2D}\frac{dD}{dT} + \frac{1}{C}\frac{dC}{dT} + \frac{1}{m^{2/3}t^{1/6}}\frac{d(m^{2/3}t^{1/6})}{dT} \qquad (3.33)$$

where k represents the numerical constant given above as 607. It is assumed that the course of the reaction (i.e., the value of n) is independent of temperature.

The temperature coefficient of k (which involves the density of mercury) is $+0.00012$ per degree. That of D can be estimated from the Nernst expression

$$D^0 = RT\lambda^0/zF^2 \ (= 2.67 \times 10^{-7}\lambda^0/z \text{ cm.}^2/\text{sec. at } 25°) \quad (3.34)$$

where R is the gas constant in volt-coulombs per degree, T is the absolute temperature, z is the charge on the diffusing ion and λ^0 is its equivalent conductance at infinite dilution, and F is the number of coulombs per faraday. Differentiating eq. (3.34) with respect to temperature gives

$$\frac{1}{D^0}\frac{dD^0}{dT} = \frac{1}{\lambda^0}\frac{d\lambda^0}{dT} + \frac{1}{T} \quad (3.35)$$

This is exactly true only at infinite dilution, but it does not appear to be seriously in error under polarographic conditions. For most ions the temperature coefficient of the equivalent conductance is very close to $+0.02$ per degree, and at 25° C. $1/T$ is 0.0034. The temperature coefficient of C for aqueous solutions is $-0.00025/\text{deg}$. Finally, as was mentioned in the preceding subsection, the temperature coefficient of $m^{2/3}t^{1/6}$ is about $+0.0015/\text{deg}$.

Combining all of these values gives the temperature coefficient of the diffusion current as $+0.013/\text{deg}$. In other words, the diffusion current increases about 1.3% for a one-degree rise in temperature. Nejedly (66) tested this prediction for half a dozen common ions, and obtained values ranging from 1.1 to 1.6%/deg. over the range of temperatures from 20 to 50°. It is because the temperature coefficient of the diffusion current is appreciable that temperature control is necessary in most practical polarographic analysis.

The temperature coefficient of the wave height may be much higher than this if the current depends on the rate of a chemical reaction occurring in the diffusion layer (Secs. VII and VIII): values as high as $+80\%/\text{deg}$. have been reported. This is the basis of another common test for ascertaining whether the height of a wave is diffusion-controlled. If the temperature coefficient is much larger than about 2%/deg., the current is probably at least partly kinetic or catalytic, for the rates of most chemical reactions increase much more rapidly with temperature than rates of diffusion do. This is not always true, however, and the criterion becomes too ambiguous to be useful when the chemical process is responsible for only a small fraction of the observed wave height. The test is best used to support conclusions drawn from examining the dependence of wave height on h_{corr}.

Temperature coefficients are so often calculated incorrectly from experimental data—as they were by Nejedly, for example—that a word about their computation may be in order. Suppose that a certain solution gives a diffusion current i_1 of 1.50 μamp. at 25° and that, without changing any other experimental condition, it is warmed to 65° and then gives a diffusion current i_2 of 2.70 μamp. Though the diffusion current has increased 80% over a 40° interval, the temperature coefficient is not $+2\%$/deg., but $(2.303/\Delta T) \log (i_2/i_1)$, or $+ 1.47\%$/deg. A little calculation will provide proof that the error incurred by using the incorrect formula increases as the temperature coefficient and the width of the temperature interval increase. One may certainly use the simple approximation over a range of a few degrees without committing any appreciable error. It is actually convenient to do this in laboratories where a water thermostat is not available and where the measurements have to be made at ambient temperature. Suppose, for example, that a standard curve has been obtained relating the concentration of a solution to its diffusion current at 25°, and that the diffusion current has been found to be 10% higher at 30° than at 25°. If an unknown solution gives a diffusion current of 1.02 μamp. at 26° it is perfectly reasonable to say that the temperature coefficient is very nearly $+2.0\%$/deg. and that the diffusion current of the unknown solution would have been 1.00 μamp. if it had been measured at 25°; the exact equations would give $+1.91\%$/deg. and 1.0007 μamp., respectively, and the difference is not worth the additional trouble required to make the calculation.

We have seen that the temperature coefficient of the diffusion current of an ion is practically equal to one-half of the temperature coefficient of its diffusion coefficient calculated from eq. (3.35); the other quantities in eq. (3.33) are much smaller than this and so have very little influence on the result. For an uncharged molecule eqs. (3.34) and (3.35) are meaningless. But the temperature coefficients of the diffusion currents of such substances as oxygen and most organic molecules are usually also of the order of $+1$ to 2%/deg.

D. THE SOLVENT AND SUPPORTING ELECTROLYTE

Since the diffusion current i_d depends on the diffusion coefficient of the electroactive species, which in turn depends on the viscosity of the solution, increasing the viscosity causes i_d to decrease. If the particles of the electroactive species are spherical and much larger than the molecules of the solvent, the diffusion coefficient may be described by the Stokes–Einstein relation

$$D = RT/6\pi\eta rK \tag{3.36}$$

where R is the gas constant in ergs per degree per mole, T is the absolute temperature, η is the viscosity of the solution in dyne-sec./cm.^{2}, r is the radius of the diffusing particles, and K is Avogadro's number. This predicts that D should be inversely proportional to η. According to the Ilkovič equation, therefore, i_d should be inversely proportional to $\eta^{1/2}$; the Koutecký equation predicts a more complex behavior because D also appears in the spherical correction term, but the difference is trivial for moderate variations of η. This is very often found to be the case with metal ions and relatively small organic molecules (67), and when it is it indicates that the change of viscosity is not accompanied by any change in the nature or size of the diffusing species.

But when such a change does occur the product $i_d\eta^{1/2}$ may be far from constant. For example, when ethanol is added to a solution containing a reducible metal ion, the product $i_d\eta^{1/2}$ increases with increasing ethanol concentration up to about 25%, then decreases again on further addition of ethanol. The initial increase is probably due to the decreasing activity of water, which leads to a decrease in the hydration number and therefore in the size of the solvated metal ion. At higher ethanol concentrations this is apparently overbalanced by increasing association of the metal ion with anions in the solution (ion-pair formation), which is favored by the decreasing dielectric constant and which leads to an increase in the size of the diffusing species (68). Since large changes of η are usually accompanied by changes in the solvation number or in the extent of association, $i_d\eta^{1/2}$ is rarely constant over a wide range of viscosities. In fact, evidence cited by Schwabe (69) shows that an equation of the form

$$i_d\eta^{1/2} = i_d^0(\eta^0)^{1/2}[1 + cN_s] \tag{3.37a}$$

is often obeyed; $i_d{}^0$ is the diffusion current obtained in an aqueous solution of viscosity η^0, while i_d is the diffusion current obtained in a similar solution having a viscosity η and containing a non-aqueous solvent such as methanol, dioxane, or acetone at a mole fraction N_s. For values of N_s up to about 0.2, the constant c appears to be typically of the order of 1, so that the product $i_d\eta^{1/2}$ is roughly 20% larger when $N_s = 0.2$ than in the aqueous solution. In other cases, however, an equation of the form

$$\log i_d\eta^{1/2} = \log i_d^0(\eta^0)^{1/2} + c'N_s^{1/2} \qquad (3.37b)$$

where the constant c' has a value of roughly 0.2, is said to be more satisfactory. It is not yet possible to explain the data or to make useful *a priori* predictions about any particular system. This is a severe hindrance to attempts to make quantitative correlations of diffusion-current data obtained in different non-aqueous solvents.

Changes in the composition of the supporting electrolyte can also affect the diffusion current because of complex formation between the electroactive substance and some constituent of the supporting electrolyte. Complexation of a metal ion (i.e., replacement of water in the coordination field by the ions or molecules of another ligand) has little effect if the new ligand is similar in size to the water molecules it replaces and if the change of ligand is not accompanied by an appreciable change of viscosity. For example, the diffusion current constant (3.15) of the aquozinc(II) ion in $1F$ sodium fluoride is exactly equal to that of the hydroxozinc complex in $1F$ sodium hydroxide. In other cases larger changes are found. The diffusion current constant (which, according to the Ilkovič equation, is proportional to $D^{1/2}$) of lead(II) in $1F$ nitric acid is 3.67; in $1F$ hydrochloric acid it is 3.86. In the first of these media the hydrated lead ion (or perhaps a nitrato complex) predominates, but when much chloride is present a chloro complex is formed, and this evidently diffuses more rapidly than the aquo complex. In $1F$ sodium hydroxide, however, the diffusion current constant is only 3.39, showing that the biplumbite ion, $HPbO_2^-$, which predominates in this medium has a diffusion coefficient appreciably smaller than that of the aquolead ion. In solutions containing tartrate, the diffusion current constant is even lower (about 2.4 at or above pH 9 in the presence of $0.5M$ tartrate ion) because the tartrato complex is much larger than the aquo or chloro complex.

Although the diffusion current constant of a substance may change considerably when the nature of the supporting electrolyte is changed, it is ordinarily not very sensitive to moderate changes in the concentration of any one supporting electrolyte. For example, the diffusion current constant of lead ion changes only from 3.86 to 3.80 between 1 and $0.1F$ hydrochloric acid. Hence the concentration of the supporting electrolyte need rarely be controlled to better than ± 10 to 20%. In extremely concentrated supporting electrolytes, of course, the diffusion current constant may have a value considerably different from that in an 0.1 or $1F$ solution. Usually it decreases as the concentration of the supporting electrolyte increases, for the decrease of diffusion coefficient produced by the increase of viscosity far overbalances any small increase due to a change of solvation number resulting from the decrease of the activity of the solvent. For example, the diffusion current constant of the first wave of osmium(VI) is 2.69 in $1F$ sodium hydroxide but only 1.06 in $9.4F$ sodium hydroxide. Other phenomena are occasionally encountered: the diffusion current constant of nickel(II) decreases from 3.3 in $0.1F$ sodium perchlorate to 1.5 in $1F$ sodium perchlorate and thence to 1.2 in $8F$ sodium perchlorate. The difference between the latter two figures is doubtless due to the higher viscosity of the more concentrated solution, but the difference between the first two has been attributed to a change in the mechanism of the reduction. In the polarography of organic compounds it is often found that the wave height is sensitively dependent on pH over part of the range at least, and when this is true the ratio of the concentrations of the components of a buffer mixture may have to be very carefully controlled. In any event, it is clear that the concentration of the supporting electrolyte can never be allowed to fluctuate randomly from one measurement to the next; how much variation can be tolerated is a question that must be settled by experiment in each individual case.

In inorganic polarography, which is usually carried out in purely aqueous media, it is not often very hard to separate the effects of the various factors that have been discussed. With organic compounds, however, changing the solvent and the nature and concentration of the supporting electrolyte may have much more complicated effects. Adsorption may occur at some pH values and not at others, a protonation essential to the further reduction of an intermediate may be fast in an acidic aqueous solution but may not occur at all in an aprotic solvent when a neutral salt is used as the supporting electrolyte (as in the reduction of nitro compounds), a reduction product may be stabilized by interaction with some constituent of the solution, double-layer effects may become very prominent (as when cycloöctatetraene is reduced in the presence of excess tetraalkylammonium ions), and so on. The possibilities are so numerous that each case must be judged on its own merits.

E. Polarographic Diffusion Coefficients

The diffusion coefficient of an ion at infinite dilution can be calculated from its equivalent conductance at infinite dilution by means of the Nernst expression

$$D^0 = \frac{RT}{zF^2} \lambda^0 \left(= 2.67 \times 10^{-7} \frac{\lambda^0}{z} \text{ cm.}^2/\text{sec. at } 25° \right) \quad (3.34)$$

in which the symbols were defined in subsection C above. Values of λ^0/z for some typical heavy metal ions are given in Table 3.5. Their average is roughly 25, which corresponds to a diffusion coefficient in the neighborhood of 6 to 7 $\times$ 10^{-6} cm.^{2}/sec. Replacing coordinated water by ammonia, chloride, cyanide, or any other small ligand has very little effect on the size of an ion and hence on its diffusion coefficient. A convenient generalization is that the value of D^0 for a typical metal ion is about 6 $\times$ 10^{-6} cm.^{2}/sec. at 25°.

TABLE 3.5.
Values of λ^0/z for Some Typical Metal Ions

Ion	λ^0/z	Ion	λ^0/z
Be^{++}	22.5	La^{+++}	23.2
Co^{++}	26.5	Mg^{++}	26.5
$Co(NH_3)_6^{+++}$	34.1	Pb^{++}	34.7
Cu^{++}	26.8	Sr^{++}	29.7
Eu^{+++}	22.6	UO_2^{++}	25.5
$Fe(CN)_6^{-3}$	33.7	Zn^{++}	26.4
$Fe(CN)_6^{-4}$	27.6		

Of course there are many exceptions to this generalization. For example, the values of λ^0/z for hydrogen, potassium, silver, and thallous ions are 349.8, 73.5, 61.9, and 74.7, respectively, and so the diffusion coefficients of these ions are larger than the average quoted above. Large ions have smaller diffusion coefficients than small ones, and complexes of metal ions with large ligands like citrate, tartrate, and ethylenediaminetetraacetate therefore have smaller diffusion coefficients than the corresponding aquo complexes. For the same reason, the diffusion coefficient of tetra-n-amylammonium ion (for which λ^0/z is only 17.5) is considerably smaller than the above value.

Equation (3.34) is of no use in dealing with uncharged species. A more useful approximation is obtained by combining the Stokes–Einstein relation, eq. (3.36), with an expression for the volume of a spherical molecule:

$$V = \frac{4}{3}\pi r^3 = \frac{M}{dK} \tag{3.38}$$

where r is the radius of the molecule (in centimeters) and M is its molecular weight, while d is the density of the pure substance (in grams per cubic centimeter) and K is Avogadro's number. Solving this for r, combining the result with eq. (3.36), and introducing the values of the numerical constants gives, at 25°,

$$D^0 = \frac{2.96 \times 10^{-7}}{\eta} \left(\frac{d}{M}\right)^{1/3} \text{cm.}^2/\text{sec.} \tag{3.39a}$$

Like eq. (3.34), this is valid only at infinite dilution, where η is the viscosity of the solvent. For water at 25° $\eta = 8.94 \times 10^{-3}$ poise, so that

$$D^0 = 3.31 \times 10^{-5} \left(\frac{d}{M}\right)^{1/3} \text{cm.}^2/\text{sec.} \tag{3.39b}$$

Typical values of D^0 calculated from eq. (3.39) are 6.1×10^{-6} cm.²/sec. for benzoin and 6.2×10^{-6} cm.²/sec. for azobenzene in water, or about 4.9×10^{-6} cm.²/sec. for each of these in ethanol (for which $\eta = 1.096 \times 10^{-2}$ poise at 25°). In water the approximation $D^0 = 6 \times 10^{-6}$ cm.²/sec. is evidently applicable to organic substances as well as to inorganic ones.

The diffusion coefficient is affected by the composition of the solution. For ionic species the limiting law is (70,71)

$$D_j = \frac{RT}{z_j F^2} \lambda_j^0 - 7.474 \times 10^{-8} \frac{\lambda_j^0 z_j F}{(\mathfrak{D}^3 RT)^{1/2}} \left[\mu^{1/2} \right.$$

$$\left. - \left(\sum \frac{\lambda_i^0 c_i z_i}{(\lambda_i^0/z_i) + (\lambda_j^0/z_j)} \right)^{1/2} \right] \qquad (3.40)$$

where j represents the diffusing ion while i represents the ions of the supporting electrolyte; $\mathfrak{D}$ is the dielectric constant and μ the ionic strength of the solution. In polarographic experiments μ is always practically identical with the ionic strength of the supporting electrolyte alone. The first term on the right-hand side of eq. (3.40) is identical with the right-hand side of eq. (3.34), and when the supporting electrolyte is a single salt present at a concentration of c moles per liter eq. (3.40) takes the form

$$D_j = D_j^0 - Ac^{1/2} \qquad (3.41)$$

Typical tracer diffusion coefficient data (72) are shown in Fig. 3.13, where the straight line represents the prediction of eq. (3.40). Little polarographic work is done at ionic strengths below about 0.05 to $0.1M$, which in this case corresponds to a value of about 0.2 to 0.3 for $c^{1/2}$. Even at this ionic strength the diffusion coefficient of an ion may differ considerably from its value at infinite dilution. It is, therefore, perilous to try to correlate polarographic diffusion currents, which are measured at substantial ionic strengths, with diffusion coefficients that pertain to infinitely dilute solutions.

Two approaches have been adopted in attempts to make valid correlations. One is to extrapolate diffusion-current data to infinite dilution for comparison with D^0; the other is to obtain values of D under polarographic conditions (that is, in the presence of a large excess of supporting electrolyte). To extrapolate the diffusion current constant to infinite dilution it is convenient to combine the Ilkovič equation and eq. (3.41) to yield

$$I^2 = (I^0)^2 - A'\mu^{1/2} \qquad (3.42)$$

where I^0 is the diffusion current constant at infinite dilution. The experimental values of I must, of course, be obtained in the presence of excess supporting electrolyte to ensure that I^0 will contain no contribution from the migration current, and this makes very low

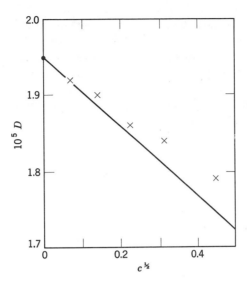

Figure 3.13. Tracer diffusion coefficients of thallous ion in potassium chloride solutions at 25° according to Wang and Polestra (72). The line represents the limiting law, eq. (3.40), which in this case is $10^5 D = 1.95 - 0.45\ c^{1/2}$, c being the concentration of potassium chloride in moles per liter. The solid circle is the value at infinite dilution obtained from eq. (3.34).

values of μ experimentally inaccessible. Nevertheless, plots of I^2 vs. $\mu^{1/2}$ are satisfactorily linear at ionic strengths up to roughly $0.1M$, and extrapolation yields $I^0 = 3.04$ for thallous ion and 12.72 for iodate ion; the values of n for these ions are 1 and 6, respectively. Substituting the equivalent conductances of these ions at infinite dilution into the Ilkovič equation (3.22) gives $I^0 = 2.71$ for thallous ion and 11.99 for iodate ion. On the average the experimental values are 9 per cent larger than the predicted ones. This corresponds to a real and substantial failure of eq. (3.22).

In supporting electrolytes having ionic strengths between about 0.1 and 1, a number of concordant measurements by different authors give the diffusion current constants of thallous and iodate ions as 2.70 ± 0.03 and 12.05 ± 0.05, respectively. These values are in nearly exact agreement with the values calculated from eq. (3.22) with the values of D^0, and similar agreement has been found in many other cases as well. This agreement has been the basis of a great many calculations of D^0 from diffusion-current data. Such calculations are very dangerous, however, for the agreement is quite fortuitous. It merely means that, in the cases which have been examined, the 9% error in the Ilkovič equation is almost exactly counterbalanced by a decrease of about 9% in $D^{1/2}$ on going from infinite dilution to this range of ionic strengths. The effect of this decrease is shown in Fig. 3.14 (73), which also illustrates the constancy of I in the range of ionic strengths from about 0.1 to 1.

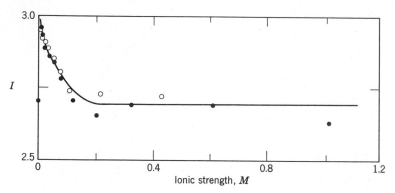

Figure 3.14.   Effect of ionic strength on the diffusion current constant of thallous ion. Open circles represent data obtained in perchloric acid media; solid circles represent data obtained in hydrochloric acid media. The solid circle at zero ionic strength is the value of I obtained from the diffusion coefficient at infinite dilution by means of the Ilkovič equation.

The Koutecký equation predicts $I^0 = 3.07$ for thallous ion and 13.17 for iodate ion under the conditions used in the above work; on the average the experimental values are about 3% smaller than these. As was mentioned in Sec. III above, however, this may simply mean that the experimental values, which were obtained with successive drops and were therefore affected by any depletion of the solution around the capillary tip produced by the preceding drops, are low to an extent that just compensates for an error of 10 to 20% in the Koutecký equation.

Attempts to measure diffusion coefficients under polarographic conditions have not been as successful as might be wished. For example, measurements of the diffusion coefficient of lead ion in $0.1F$ potassium chloride give 8.7×10^{-6} cm.^{2}/sec. by the classical Cottrell technique (16), but 7.5×10^{-6} cm.^{2}/sec. by a diaphragm-cell technique; for the diffusion coefficient of thallous ion in the same medium the diaphragm-cell technique gives 1.67×10^{-5} cm.^{2}/sec. while tracer diffusion (74) gives 1.84×10^{-5} cm.^{2}/sec. Strictly speaking, tracer diffusion coefficients are not exactly identical with the diffusion coefficients pertinent to polarography, for the concentration gradients involved are different, but the error introduced by the use of the tracer value is probably smaller than the errors in theoretical descriptions of the diffusion current (75). Using four different techniques, Adams et al. (76) found the diffusion coefficient of 3,3'-dimethoxybenzidine in $1F$ sulfuric acid to be 4.1, 4.1, 4.4, and 4.7×10^{-6} cm.^{2}/sec. An uncertainty of about ± 5 to 10% appears to be about the best that has been achieved. This is accurate enough for evaluating n as described in Sec. VI below unless n is fairly large, but it is hardly sufficient for a definitive test of the theory. Much worse discrepancies between diffusion coefficients calculated from polarographic and voltammetric results and the values obtained by other techniques may be caused by such phenomena as the formation of adsorbed films on electrode surfaces or the occurrence of unsuspected chemical complications in the electron-transfer process (76).

If, for want of any better estimate, one averages these values for thallous ion and combines the result with the Ilkovič equation, one obtains a predicted value of 2.54 for the diffusion current constant of thallous ion in $0.1F$ potassium chloride. As was stated above, the experimental value obtained in the ordinary way with successive drops is 2.70. Thus the predicted value is 6% lower than the experimental one, which is in reasonably good agreement with the discrepancy of 9% at infinite dilution. In Sec. III above a similar comparison of the predicted and experimental values for cadmium ion indicated that the Ilkovič equation predicted a diffusion current constant 9% lower than the experimental value. On the whole, therefore, it appears that the Ilkovič equation predicts currents that are very nearly 8% smaller than those obtained with successive drops. To put this another way, a diffusion coefficient calculated from the Ilkovič equation is likely to be about 15% higher than the truth.

For thallous ion in $0.1F$ potassium chloride, combining the mean of the above values of D with the appropriate values of m and t and with the Koutecký equation yields a predicted value of 2.88, which is 7% higher than the experimental one. At infinite dilution the predicted value was 3% too high, while for cadmium ion it was 1% too low, as was stated in Sec. III. These values are not very concordant; it appears that the differences among them may be attributable to the fact that the diffusion coefficient of thallous ion is larger than that of cadmium ion. That of hydrogen ion is much larger still: its value in 0.1F potassium chloride may be crudely approximated by combining the equivalent conductance of 0.1F hydrochloric acid, the transference number of hydrogen ion in 0.1F hydrochloric acid, and eq. (3.34). The result is 8.7 $\times$ 10^{-5} cm.^{2}/sec. The diffusion current constant of hydrogen ion in 0.1F potassium chloride is 5.60; with this value of the diffusion coefficient and the appropriate values of m and t, the Koutecký equation predicts a value 19% higher. This means that the Koutecký equation would yield a value of D that was something like 30% too low under these admittedly extreme conditions. Or, to put the matter in a different light, the Koutecký equation predicts a value of I for hydrogen ion that is roughly equal to, or perhaps even larger than, the value that would be obtained for the first drop growing into a previously undepleted solution. But as D decreases the predicted value of I becomes too small, as was argued in Sec. III above. On this basis it appears that even the form of the correction term in eq. (3.19) may be incorrect.

In the writer's opinion, diffusion coefficients should not be calculated from polarographic data.

V. Techniques for Measuring Wave Heights

This section is intended to acquaint the reader with the common techniques for measuring the height of a polarographic wave. It will be recalled that the wave height is defined as the difference between the limiting current and the residual current. As this definition implies, correction for the residual current is the essence of any technique of wave-height measurement. There are two ways of making the correction. One involves the direct measurement of the residual current, which may be done by recording the residual-current curve of the supporting electrolyte before the sample is added to it or, if a manual polarograph is being used, by measuring the residual current at the potential where the limiting current is to be measured. The other is to perform some sort of extrapolation on the recorded polarogram of the sample. The first of these is more accurate, both because it eliminates the uncertainty of an extrapolation and because it serves to prevent errors that sometimes result from the presence of reducible impurities in the solvent and supporting electrolyte when an extrapolation technique is used. However, extrapolation is quicker because it eliminates the separate recording or measurement of the residual current; blank determinations may be made to provide corrections for reducible impurities. In many practical analyses the supporting electrolyte is not prepared separately but is formed in the sample solution during the chemical operations that precede the analysis, while in others a major constituent of the sample serves as the supporting electrolyte in the determination of a minor one, and in still others the residual-current curve is altered by the substance being determined or some other constituent of the sample. In such cases extrapolation becomes the technique of choice.

In their simplest forms these techniques are illustrated by Fig. 3.15. Curves a and c, which are identical, are polarograms of $1F$ citric acid

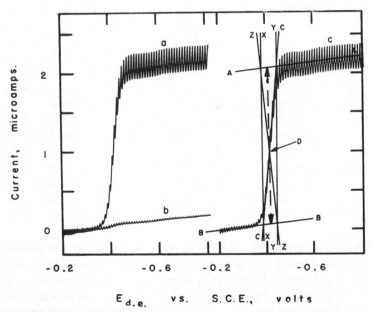

Figure 3.15.   Polarograms of $1.0F$ citric acid containing 0.002% Triton X-100 (b) alone (residual-current curve), (a) and (c) after adding approximately 0.25mM lead(II).

containing approximately 0.25mM added lead, and curve b is a polarogram of the citric acid solution alone.

To measure the height of the lead wave from curves a and b, one would select a potential in a region over which the plateau of the wave is fairly accurately parallel to the residual-current curve. In Fig. 3.15(a) this might be anywhere between -0.5 v. and the end of the curve at -0.8 v. Often, however, the choice will be more restricted than it is here; in Fig. 3.9(a), for example, it would be best to select a potential between about -0.8 and -1.1 v. so as to avoid the descending part of the curve after the maximum. The actual measurement of the wave height in Fig. 3.15 is performed by measuring the vertical distance (that is, along a line parallel to the current axis) from the midpoint of the oscillations on the residual-current curve to the midpoint of the oscillations on the plateau at the same potential. To avoid the possibility that the current at the particular potential selected for measurement may have been affected by a transient irregularity during the recording (which becomes increasingly probable as the potential becomes more negative), it is desirable to take an average value over a few oscillations to each side of the potential selected. One may draw a line through the midpoints of the oscillations on each curve and measure the vertical distance between the two lines at the potential selected. Or one may draw the envelope of the maximum currents and also the envelope of the minimum currents on each curve, draw a line halfway between each pair of envelopes, and measure the vertical distance between these two lines. Though these methods are equivalent in principle, some workers have strong preferences for one or the other of them. In either case the distance is easily measured with the aid of the coordinate scale on the chart paper, or with a ruler if the chart paper is unlined. If a ruler is used it should extend across the whole width of the chart so that it can be aligned with reference to the perforations at the top and bottom of the chart.

The lead wave in Fig. 3.15(a) is very well defined: its plateau is essentially parallel to the residual-current curve over quite a wide range of potentials. With waves occurring at, or extending to, more negative potentials there will be a small difference between the slope of the plateau and the slope of the residual-current curve because of the variation of $m^{2/3}t^{1/6}$ with potential, as illustrated by Fig. 3.12(a) at potentials between about -1.3 and -1.9 v. This is easily identified

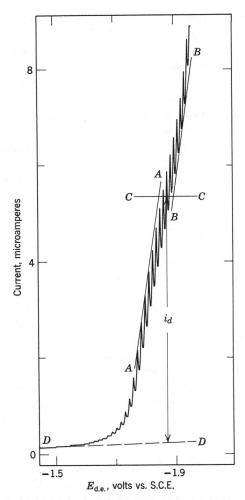

Figure 3.16. Polarogram of 0.9mM vanadium(V) in 0.1F sodium hydroxide, showing a technique for measuring the height of an extremely ill-defined wave. AA is drawn through the maxima of the oscillations for an arbitrarily chosen number of drops on the rising part of the wave, and BB is drawn parallel to AA through the minima of the oscillations for an equal number of drops after the region of minimum slope has been passed. CC is a horizontal line drawn through the point where the curve lies exactly halfway between AA and BB, and DD is the extrapolated residual-current portion of the curve. The wave height is taken to be the vertical distance between DD and CC at the point where the latter intersects a line (not shown here) joining the midpoints of the oscillations.

and discounted. The potential at which the wave height is measured in such a case is of little importance; much more important is that the same potential be used throughout the entire series of experiments. Fortunately, the effect looks larger than it is: the decrease of $m^{2/3}t^{1/6}$ as the potential becomes more negative is accompanied by a decrease in the widths of the oscillations, and this causes the envelope of the maxima of the oscillations to have a slope much larger than that of the line representing the average current. From Table 3.4 and the Ilkovič equation it is readily seen that the effect becomes larger as the potential becomes more negative, but that even in the vicinity of -1.7 v. a change of 0.1 v. in the potential produces a change of only a little more than 1 per cent in the wave height.

More troublesome is the situation illustrated by Fig. 3.16, where the wave occurs at so negative a potential that the plateau is hardly visible on the recorded curve. A similar situation arises when the wave of interest is closely followed by another, as in Fig. 3.9(b). In dealing with such ill-defined waves it is probably best to select the inflection point where the slope of the plateau is smallest. Less precise results will be obtained with such waves than with well-defined ones, and tinkering with the procedure of wave-height measurement will not improve them significantly; if the errors are large enough to be troublesome there is nothing to do but change the experimental conditions in the hope of obtaining a better defined wave. In some marginal cases the quality of the polarogram may be improved by changing the drop time or the rate of polarization (i.e., the span potential), as illustrated by Fig. 3.17; when these do not suffice the only recourse is to change the composition of the supporting electrolyte.

It is sometimes recommended that the averages of the oscillations be ignored, and that the peaks be used instead. To be sure, this simplifies the measurements somewhat because it eliminates the necessity of averaging the two sets of oscillations. But the time thus saved is only a negligible fraction of the total time required for an analysis, and it is saved at the expense of requiring that the damping be kept unchanged in successive analyses, which is not always convenient, and at the further disadvantage of preventing comparison of the results with literature data, which are nearly invariably based on average currents. It has been argued that measurements of the "maximum current" (which is actually a misnomer unless the recorder

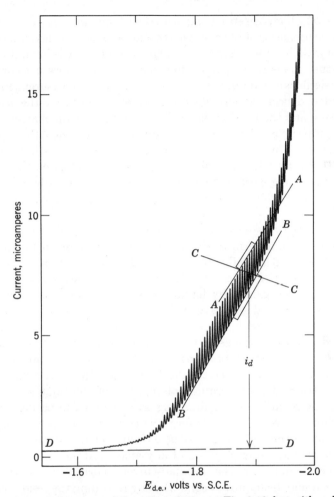

Figure 3.17.   Polarogram of the same solution as Fig. 3.16, but with a shorter drop time and a smaller span voltage, showing a different technique for measuring the height of an extremely ill-defined wave. AA is drawn to have the smallest possible slope while passing through the maxima of a number of oscillations, and BB is drawn similarly through the minima of a number of oscillations, which will not necessarily be the same as those whose maxima are used in constructing AA. The square brackets show the ranges employed in constructing these lines here. CC is drawn from the first maximum that lies on AA to the last minimum that lies on BB, and the wave height is taken to be the vertical distance between the extrapolated residual-current line DD and CC at the point halfway between AA and BB on the latter.

has a very high pen speed and is used without damping) are preferable to measurements of the average current because the maximum current is some 25% larger than the average current. This is invalid for three reasons: one is that such a difference of current does not correspond to a significant gain in precision, another is that measurements of the average deflection derive additional precision from the averaging process, and the third is that it is not at all a simple matter to apply the proper correction for the residual current when the maximum deflection is measured on the plateau. The last of these points is illustrated by Fig. 3.2, which shows that, depending on the purity of the supporting electrolyte, one will sometimes want the minima and sometimes the maxima of the oscillations on the residual-current curve.

While the existence of the oscillations will at first seem to be a nuisance, the experimenter soon becomes accustomed to using their regularity and reproducibility as a valuable criterion of the proper functioning of the capillary. In practical analysis, however, there is nothing to be gained by having oscillations more than a few milli- meters wide, and this is why recording polarographs are provided with damping circuits. In some early instruments these circuits pro- duced erroneous values of the average current under certain condi- tions even after calibrations with known steady currents. Each experimenter should ascertain for himself whether this is the case with his instrument by recording polarograms of the same solution with different settings of the damping switch and comparing the wave heights secured. If these differ, it is essential to select a single con- venient setting of the damping switch and use it throughout the development and application of any analytical method.

The accuracy of the residual-current correction by the above method may be improved somewhat by recording the residual-current curve at a higher sensitivity than is used to record the polarogram of the sample. The distances from the two curves to the respective zero-current lines are measured at the potential selected, and the correction for the residual current is calculated from the sensitivities used.

This method is especially well adapted to manual instruments because only two measurements are needed: one of the residual cur- rent and one of the limiting current at the same potential. It would be a waste of time to secure enough points with a manual instrument to apply an extrapolation procedure. However, one must of course have a complete polarogram in order to select the potential at which the wave height is to be measured.

One extrapolation method is shown in curve c of Fig. 3.15. A line AA is drawn through the midpoints of the oscillations on the plateau, exactly as described above, and another line BB is drawn through the midpoints of the oscillations on the portion of the curve just preceding the rising portion of the wave. The wave height is taken as the vertical distance between these two lines at some convenient potential: the half-wave potential is the usual choice. The measurement is most easily made by sliding a ruler across the polarogram, taking care to keep it perpendicular to the potential axis, until a point is found at which the average current on the rising part of the wave lies halfway between AA and BB, and the distance between these lines at this point is taken as the wave height. Some workers prefer to draw a line CC through the midpoints of the oscillations on the steepest part of the wave, find the point on CC that is equidistant from AA and BB, and measure the distance between AA and BB through this point. A still more elaborate graphical method is shown in the figure. A line XX is drawn perpendicular to the potential axis through the point of intersection of BB with CC, and another line YY is drawn parallel to XX through the point of intersection of AA with CC. The line ZZ is then drawn through the points of intersection of XX with AA and of YY with BB, and the vertical distance between AA and BB is measured through the point D at which ZZ and CC intersect. In the writer's opinion this formidable procedure adds more to the tedium of making the measurements than to their accuracy or reliability.

Close inspection of curve b of Fig. 3.15 reveals the presence of a small lead wave, which is due to an impurity in the citric acid. Measuring the vertical distance between curves a and b at, say, −0.6 v. serves to correct for the presence of this impurity, whereas measuring the wave height on curve c by any extrapolation procedure results in confounding the lead content of the supporting electrolyte with that of the sample. The severity of the problem may be gauged from a rough calculation of the percentage of lead in the citric acid: the height of the lead wave on curve a is 2.00 μamp., while that of the lead wave on curve b is 0.04 μamp., and since this difference of current corresponds to a difference of 0.25 mmole/l. in the concentrations of lead the solution of curve b must have contained approximately 0.005mM lead. This in turn corresponds to only about 0.0005% lead in the citric acid. The necessity of using relatively large concentrations of supporting electrolytes causes even trace impurities to have significant effects, and these naturally become more important as the concentration of the substance being determined decreases. The impurity need not be identical with the substance being determined; a trace of thallous ion (whose half-wave potential in this supporting electrolyte is practically identical with that of lead ion) would have exactly the same effect. So would a trace of cadmium ion (whose half-wave potential is about -0.6 v.) if its concentration were just too small to produce a distinct wave and if the line AA were based on potentials as negative as shown in Fig. 3.15, but in this case the analyst would probably draw AA with a larger slope, and this would lead to a decrease in the wave height measured at point D.

When one uses an extrapolation procedure, it is essential to carry out a blank determination with each new lot of reagents so that trace impurities can be corrected for. It is equally essential to obtain a set of polarograms with different concentrations of the substance being determined at the outset of any analytical program, because only by reference to such polarograms is it possible to tell whether some adventitious impurity in the sample is affecting the slopes of the extrapolated lines.

Figure 3.9 also illustrates some other problems that may be encountered. Curve a in this figure is the polarogram of a solution containing lead ion alone. To measure the height of this wave, it would be best to ignore the region of negative slope between about -0.55 and -0.8 v., and to draw line AA through the midpoints of the oscillations between about -0.8 and -1.1 v. This is not entirely satisfactory, both because the extrapolation is fairly long and because it crosses the potential of the electrocapillary maximum, where the slope of the condenser-current curve changes; unfortunately no better alternative is available. The analyst confronted by a curve like Fig. 3.9(b) is even more unfortunate. Extrapolating the lead "plateau" around -0.55 v. to more positive potentials will yield too large a value for the height of the lead wave, and extrapolating it to more negative potentials will also yield too large a value for the height of the cadmium wave. In this case the extrapolation indicates that the diffusion current of lead is 43.7 μamp. whereas the correct value is

39.5 μamp. Of course the shape of the "plateau" of the lead wave on curve *b* would indicate that something was amiss, and this particular problem can be cured by adding a maximum suppressor. However, not all distorted waves can be improved in this way. Careful attention to the slopes of the lines involved in an extrapolation is essential to the use of these procedures. It is always advisable to be skeptical of the result when the slopes are appreciably different.

If the wave occurs at a very negative potential, as does the one in Fig. 3.16, comparison with a separately recorded residual-current curve is much better than extrapolation whenever it is possible. In desperation one might adopt the procedure illustrated, which is described in the legend. This does not give an exact correction for the residual current, and consequently it does not yield wave heights that are proportional to concentration. Errors also arise when the polarogram contains an anodic wave and a cathodic one so closely spaced that only a very short portion of the residual-current curve appears between them, as in Fig. 3.18, where the extrapolation would have too narrow a foundation to inspire confidence. Exactly the same problem arises with any two closely spaced waves, as witness Fig. 7.1, and a trivially modified form of it arises with any substance reduced at such a positive potential that the residual-current curve has not become linear before the wave has begun, as in Fig. 2.11. With an oxidizing agent strong enough to oxidize mercury, the initial current rise actually overlaps the plateau of the wave, which then takes the form of the first wave on either of the curves in Fig. 2.10. Such waves are conventionally said to rise from zero applied e.m.f., and no portion of the residual-current curve appears on the polarogram. In all of these cases it is best to record the residual-current curve separately and measure the vertical distance from it to the plateau at some suitable potential. In a long series of similar analyses it may save time to measure the height of the midpoints of the oscillations above the zero-current line at some potential, then correct this for the similarly measured distance from the zero-current line to the midpoints of the oscillations on a residual-current curve obtained under the same conditions. These procedures are formally equivalent and differ only in the number of residual-current curves that have to be recorded.

The "compensation" technique of measuring wave heights, which is actually a special kind of extrapolation method, is sometimes useful

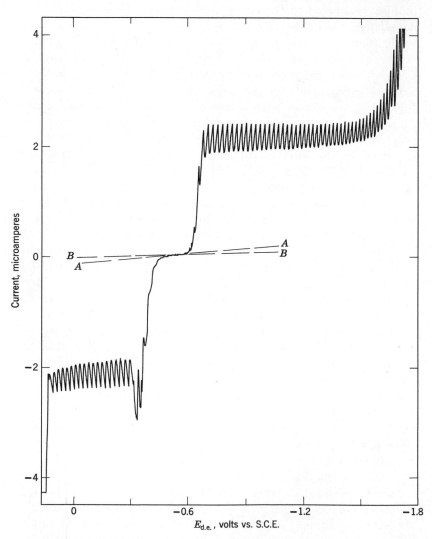

Figure 3.18.   Polarogram of 0.7mM tin(II) in 0.75F disodium citrate–0.25F trisodium citrate containing 0.001% Triton X-100. Lines AA and BB are possible extrapolations of the brief portion of the residual-current curve that appears between the anodic and cathodic waves.

in analyzing solutions containing two or more electroactive substances. Curve a of Fig. 3.19 is the polarogram of a solution containing
cadmium and zinc at such concentrations that the height of the
cadmium wave, which occurs first, is about 100 times that of the zinc
wave. It is a simple matter to measure the height of the cadmium
wave accurately, but it is less simple to measure that of the zinc wave
and there is even some danger of overlooking the zinc wave altogether
on casual inspection of the polarogram.

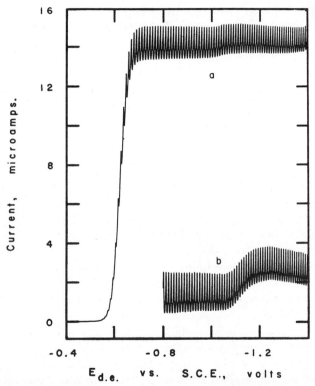

Figure 3.19. Polarograms of $0.1F$ potassium chloride containing $1.5mM$ cadmium ion, $0.02mM$ zinc ion, and 0.002% Triton X-100: (a) ordinary polarogram,
(b) after compensation of the cadmium diffusion current and magnification of the
zinc wave as described in the text. The ordinate scale is given for curve a; for
curve b each interval on the ordinate corresponds to 0.2 μamp., rather than to
2 μamp. as shown, and the zero-current line for curve b is about a meter below
the bottom of this page.

This is an extremely important and general problem in analyses by polarography and other voltammetric techniques, for it plays a crucial part in governing the sensitivity that can be obtained. The ultimate sensitivity of polarographic analysis is primarily dependent on the necessity of correcting for the residual current, but in the situation illustrated by Fig. 3.19 the ultimate sensitivity cannot be attained, and the sensitivity with which zinc can be detected and determined is instead governed by the necessity of distinguishing the small increase of current due to the reduction of zinc from the large current due to the reduction of cadmium. The concentration of zinc in the solution is large enough that it could easily be determined with good accuracy and precision if the cadmium were absent. On the other hand, if the concentration of cadmium were even ten times as large as it is here it would probably be impossible to see the zinc wave at all. The problem is not merely that two electroactive substances are present; Fig. 3.20 shows that as many as five can sometimes be determined from a single polarogram. Nor is it due to a simple disparity of concentrations; if the ratio were reversed it would be easy to increase the sensitivity to record the small cadmium wave, whose height could then be measured as easily and as accurately as if the cadmium were present alone. It is due to the specific combination of circumstances in which the major constituent is the more easily reducible one (or, if the waves are anodic, the more easily oxidizable one), and it is so important in practical analysis that it is discussed at length in Chap. 7 I-B*ii*.

The compensation technique of dealing with the problem involves the use of the circuit module shown in Fig. 2.8. After curve *a* of Fig. 3.19 had been recorded, the applied potential was returned to -0.8 v. and the downscale compensation control R_{82} was used to return the pen to nearly the bottom of the chart. The sensitivity was then increased until the pen was again nearly at the top of the chart, and thus the compensation control and the sensitivity setting were adjusted alternately until the sensitivity was ten times higher than that used for recording curve *a* while the pen was oscillating around a position near the bottom of the chart. The increase in sensitivity caused the oscillations to become inconveniently wide, and so the damping control was finally adjusted to reduce their width. Curve *b* shows the zinc wave recorded after these changes had been made.

While this procedure for magnifying a small wave is of much utility in practical work, it is not a panacea for all ills. Increasing the sensitivity magnifies not only the zinc wave, but also the normal small decrease of the diffusion current of cadmium with increasingly negative potential, and what is a small decrease on the scale of curve *a* becomes a large negative slope on the tenfold larger scale of curve *b*. Moreover, any small irregularities on the plateau of the cadmium wave would have been magnified as well. When the recorder is as heavily damped as it must be to obtain a curve like curve *b*, it becomes much too sluggish to follow the zinc wave faithfully, and so the half-wave potential of the zinc wave appears to shift from about -1.03 v. on curve *a* to about -1.15 v. on curve *b*. This is quite large enough to produce errors in identifying the substance responsible for the wave.

In the writer's opinion, the compensation technique should be used in careful work only when the preceding wave is very well defined and not more than about ten times as high as the wave of interest. In Fig. 3.19 the ratio of wave heights is larger than this, but the figure was recorded under very favorable conditions and is exceptionally free from irregularities. For anything more than an occasional analysis it is better to search for a supporting electrolyte in which the order of the waves will be reversed as long as there is any hope of finding one. Nor does the compensation technique often give as accurate results as could be gotten after a separation from the substance giving the large first wave. As a matter of fact, it does not necessarily even give better values than could be measured from the uncompensated polarogram. On the original curve from which Fig. 3.19 is reproduced, measurement of the height of the zinc wave on curve *a* gave 1.7 mm., while curve *b* (which should have given a value just ten times as large) gave 16 mm.; it is very doubtful whether the latter value is in any way preferable to the former. The compensation technique is principally valuable to the beginner, whom it often enables to detect a wave that he might otherwise overlook.

Figure 3.19 indicates that, in favorable cases, the compensation technique can be used to measure the height of a small wave following one a hundred times as large. But if the wave-height ratio is larger than this, attempts to deal with the situation by the compensation technique are hardly worth making. One rarely has a guarantee that this ratio will not be exceeded in any sample submitted for analysis, and so it is well to have other techniques available. The best course is to use a supporting electrolyte in which the minor constituent will give a wave preceding that of the major one. If one can be found, it is a simple matter to record the small wave and then decrease the sensitivity for recording the large one that follows. Otherwise a chemical or electrochemical separation may be employed. The controlled-potential electrolysis of a portion of the solution of Fig. 3.19 with a mercury cathode whose potential was kept constant at, say, -0.9 v. would constitute the easiest, fastest, and neatest procedure for removing the bulk of the cadmium prior to the determination of the zinc. Stripping analysis may be used to determine some

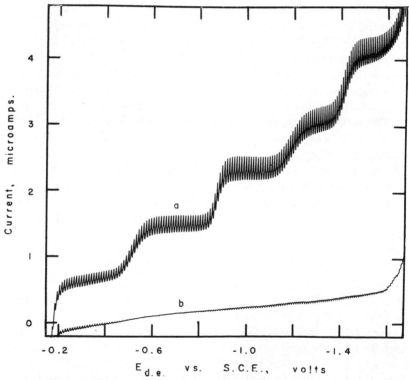

Figure 3.20. Polarograms of (*a*) approximately 0.1m*M* each of silver(I), thallium(I), cadmium(II), nickel(II), and zinc(II), listed in the order in which their waves appear, in 1*F* ammonia–1*F* ammonium chloride containing 0.002% Triton X-100, (*b*) the supporting electrolyte alone.

metals or halides, and techniques like square-wave polarography and derivative polarography have also been employed.

A simple and rapid method of measuring wave heights with a manual instrument (or by manual operation of the bridge of a recording instrument), the "increment" method, is illustrated by Fig. 3.20. In this figure the vertical distance between the two curves at about -0.3 v. is the diffusion current of silver ion; that at about -0.7 v. is the sum of the diffusion currents of silver and thallous ions; that at about -1.0 v. is the sum of the diffusion currents of silver, thallous, and cadmium ions, and so on. Once the residual current at a potential on the plateau of each of the five waves has been measured with a particular lot of reagents, the diffusion current of each of the five elements in an unknown solution can be obtained by simply measuring the limiting current at each of the five potentials selected. Each of these is corrected for the residual current at the same potential; then the "increment" in current between -0.3 and -0.7 v. is the wave height of thallous ion, while that between -0.7 and -1.0 v. is the wave height of cadmium ion, and so on. This is much more rapid that recording the entire polarogram, but of course it is essential to make sure that no other electroactive substance can be present, for it would be counted as one of the five being determined. If the potentials are so widely separated that the variation of $m^{2/3}t^{1/6}$ from one to the next is appreciable, corrections for this must be applied as described on p. 137.

VI. Estimation of n-Values from Diffusion-Current Data

In polarographic work one often has to decide which of a number of possible electrode reactions is responsible for a wave. Diffusion-current data are extremely valuable for this purpose, especially when supplemented by other polarographic and chemical information regarding the behaviors of the electroactive substance, the possible products, and other substances related to them. The ways in which the product of an electrode reaction can be deduced from polarographic and chemical evidence are described in this section. Other techniques include controlled-potential electrolysis and identification of the product, controlled-potential coulometry, and dropping-electrode coulometry, which are discussed in Chap. 10.

It is rarely possible to identify the product of an electrode reaction from purely polarographic data unless the wave height is diffusion-controlled; there have been a few exceptions, but these have all been fairly simple chemically. Before employing any of the methods outlined in this section, therefore, it is essential to make sure that this requirement is satisfied by studying the effects of the concentration of reducible substance, capillary characteristics (or h_{corr}), and temperature on the wave height. The phenomena observed with diffusion-controlled wave heights are described in the preceding sections of this chapter.

The estimation of n from data on the height of a single wave involves the use of the Ilkovič equation and some assumption about the diffusion coefficient of the electroactive substance. It will be recalled from Sec. IV-E that the diffusion current constant measured at ionic strengths between 0.1 and 1 is usually in fairly close agreement with the value calculated from the Ilkovič equation by using the diffusion coefficient at infinite dilution; the agreement is no less valuable for being accidental, and because it is usually necessary only to discriminate between integral values of n that are not too large it is not of much importance that the equation is inexact. Values of the diffusion coefficient at infinite dilution are available for many ionic substances through tabulated values of λ^0, the equivalent conductance at infinite dilution. For example, chromate ion in $1F$ sodium hydroxide gives a wave for which the diffusion current constant is 5.72. (The units of the diffusion current constant are always microamperes-millimole^{-1}-l.-mg.$^{-2/3}$-sec.$^{1/2}$.) The equivalent conductance of chromate ion is 80 (ohm^{-1}-cm.$^{-2}$-equivalent^{-1}). According to eq. (3.34), therefore,

$$D^0 = 2.67 \times 10^{-7} \frac{\lambda^0}{z} = 2.67 \times 10^{-7} \frac{80}{2} = 1.07 \times 10^{-5} \text{ cm.}^2/\text{sec.}$$

at 25°. This may be combined with eq. (3.22) to yield

$$I = 5.72 = 607 n D^{1/2} = 607 n (1.07 \times 10^{-5})^{1/2}$$

whence $n = 2.88$. Since n must be an integer, one would conclude that $n = 3$ and hence that the wave represents a 3-electron reduction to chromium(III).

When data on the equivalent conductance of the electroactive substance are unavailable, an estimate of the diffusion coefficient can be obtained in either of two ways. One is to use eq. (3.39) if the substance is molecular; the other is to assume the value of D^0 to be the same as that of another ion or molecule of similar size and structure for which the value is known. In $1F$ hydrochloric acid, osmium tetroxide gives a wave for which I is 9.59. Assuming that the diffusion coefficient of osmium tetroxide is the same as that of chromate ion, one has

$$n = I/607D^{1/2} = 9.59/(607)(1.07 \times 10^{-5})^{1/2} = 4.83$$

so that the wave represents a 5-electron reduction to osmium(III). Similarly, the n-value for the wave of cyclohexyl nitrate in dilute lithium chloride containing a little ethanol can be deduced by invoking the value of λ^0 for cyclohexanecarboxylate ion: with $\lambda^0 = 28.7$ and $z = 1$ this gives $D^0 = 7.66 \times 10^{-5}$ cm.^{2}/sec., and since the diffusion current constant of cyclohexyl nitrate is 3.06 eq. (3.22) gives $n = 1.82$. So the half-reaction must involve two electrons per molecule of cyclohexyl nitrate, and accordingly it can be presumed to be

$$RONO_2 + H_2O + 2e \rightarrow RONO + 2 \; OH^-$$

where R denotes the cyclohexyl group. If the reference substance is electroactive, calculations like these are equivalent to writing

$$I_u/I_{ref} = n_u/n_{ref} \tag{3.43}$$

where the subscript "u" denotes the substance for which n is to be evaluated while "ref" denotes the reference substance.

As a last resort, one may compare the value of I for the substance of interest with the values of I for several unrelated substances for which the values of n are known. For example, the diffusion current constant of the first wave of uranium(VI) in $0.1F$ hydrochloric acid is 1.54. For the two-electron reduction of cadmium ion in the same medium I is 3.5; substituting these values into eq. (3.43) gives $n = 0.86$ for the reduction of uranium(VI). Similar calculations using the data for iodate ion in a dilute phosphate buffer ($I = 12.0, n = 6$) and for zinc(II) in $1F$ sodium hydroxide ($I = 3.14, n = 2$) give $n = 0.75$ and 0.98, respectively. One would conclude that the reduction of uranium(VI) in $0.1F$ hydrochloric acid yields uranium(V). Values of I and n for appropriate reference substances are easily gleaned from the literature. In selecting these it is only necessary to avoid choosing reference substances whose behaviors will obviously be quite different from that of the substance of interest, and also to eschew data obtained in supporting electrolytes quite unlike the one in question. Hydrogen ion would have been a poor reference substance in this example, because its mobility is very atypical, and data obtained in saturated sodium hydroxide would have been useless because of its high viscosity. On the other hand, if one wanted to evaluate n for a wave obtained in saturated sodium hydroxide, data on the behaviors of other substances in the same medium would be preferable to any others. To avoid determining $m^{2/3}t^{1/6}$ in such cases one may simply measure the values of i_d/C for several reference substances with the same capillary and mercury pressure used in measuring i_d/C for the substance of interest. It is not worth worrying about variations of $m^{2/3}t^{1/6}$ with potential here, for they are unlikely to be appreciable in comparison with the possible differences among the diffusion coefficients of the different substances being compared.

Though this last technique of evaluating n is often found in the literature in one form or another, it is inherently rather dangerous and must be applied with great care. What is being assumed is that the diffusion coefficients of the unknown and reference substances are the same. If it is really true that nothing is known about the diffusion coefficient of the unknown substance, very little confidence should be placed in the result until other evidence has been obtained to support it. To be sure, the diffusion current constants of many ions and organic molecules are roughly equal to $1.5n$ (which is equivalent to saying that most diffusion coefficients are close to 6×10^{-6} cm.^{2}/sec. in water and other solvents of similar viscosity at 25°). But cases are known in which I/n is as high as 5.6 and as low as 0.4. From the diffusion current constants of lead in $1F$ potassium chloride (3.86) and $0.5F$ tartrate at pH 9 (2.30), each containing 0.01% gelatin, one might injudiciously calculate $n = 2(2.30/3.86) = 1.19$ in the tartrate medium, and conclude that the lead tartrate complex is reduced only to the $+1$ state. Of course the conclusion would be absurd: the smaller value of I in the tartrate medium merely reflects the larger size of the lead tartrate complex. It would be much better to choose cadmium(II) in the same tartrate medium as the reference substance, for the cadmium and lead tartrate complexes are probably at least approximately similar in size and therefore in diffusion coefficient: since $I = 2.34$ and $n = 2$ for cadmium in this supporting electrolyte, one obtains $n = 2(2.30/2.34) = 1.96$ for lead, and this is a much more satisfactory value.

A value of n obtained by any of these techniques should be regarded with much skepticism if it disagrees with other information or with reasonable expectation about the behavior of the substance being investigated. For example, the diffusion current constant of copper(II) in $1F$ sulfuric acid is 2.12; if copper(II) in $1F$ hydrochloric acid or potassium chloride (where $I = 3.39$, $n = 2$) is chosen as a reference substance, which is not an unreasonable choice, one calculates $n = 2(2.12/3.39) = 1.25$ for the reduction in $1F$ sulfuric acid. This suggests that n is actually 1, so that the reduction yields copper(I), but this is improbable because cuprous ion disproportionates rapidly in acidic solutions that do not contain a stabilizing ligand. Three- and five-electron reductions of organic compounds are equally suspect.

It is not often difficult to decide whether n is 1 or 2 or some other small value, but n-values above at most 6 should not be assigned by any of these methods because the values explicitly or implicitly assigned to D are too uncertain to permit fine discriminations. The diffusion current constant of picric acid in a dilute hydrochloric acid supporting electrolyte is 27.0. Using the value of λ^0 for picrate ion gives $D^0 = 8.12 \times 10^{-6}$ cm.^{2}/sec.; according to the Ilkovič equation this corresponds to $n = 15.6$, whereas the Koutecký equation gives $n = 14.2$ for $t^{1/6}/m^{1/3} = 1$, and the customary crude approximation $I = 1.5\ n$ gives $n = 18.0$. It would be grossly imprudent to accept any of these values; controlled-potential coulometry (Chap. 10 II) is far more reliable.

Even if n is small it does not always serve to identify the products unambiguously. This is illustrated in a very simple way by the behavior of cyclohexyl nitrate. It was inferred above that the reduction of this compound consumes two electrons per molecule and proceeds to the nitrite ester. This would probably be true in a neutral buffered solution. But in the lithium chloride medium cited, the solution becomes alkaline at the drop surface because hydroxyl ions are liberated in the half-reaction, and under these conditions the nitrite ester may hydrolyze so rapidly that the overall result is

$$RONO_2 + H_2O + 2e \rightarrow ROH + NO_2^- + OH^-$$

In fact, cyclohexanol and nitrite ion are obtained from controlled-potential electrolysis, in which there is plenty of time for the hydrolysis of the nitrite ester to proceed to completion.

Other kinds of ambiguities are also possible. A four-electron reduction of a *vic*-dioxime might *a priori* yield either an amine-oxime or a bishydroxylamine; a two-electron reduction of *p*-iodophenylpropiolic acid ($IC_6H_4C \equiv CCOOH$) might yield either *p*-iodocinnamic acid or iodide ion and phenylpropiolic acid. Various techniques are available for the resolution of such ambiguities. In the case of the iodophenyl-propiolic acid, it would be useful to obtain polarograms of phenyl-propiolic acid itself, its *p*-bromo- and *p*-chloro- derivatives, and *p*-iodocinnamic acid under the same conditions. If the reduction of *p*-iodophenylpropiolic acid yields *p*-iodocinnamic acid, the latter should not give a wave at any potential near the half-wave potential of the former, although it might give a wave at a considerably more negative potential on undergoing reduction to *p*-iodohydrocinnamic acid, in which event the same wave would also be expected to appear as a second wave on the polarogram of the iodophenylpropiolic acid. On the same supposition, the *p*-bromo- and *p*-chloro- compounds as well as phenylpropiolic acid itself should yield waves having more or less the same half-wave potential as that for the *p*-iodo- compound. Replacing iodine by bromine, chlorine, or hydrogen would of course have some effect on the ease of reduction of the carbon-carbon triple bond, but would be unlikely to change the half-wave potential more than one or two tenths of a volt. If, on the contrary, it is the halogen that is reduced (in accordance with the half-reaction $RI + H^+ + 2e \rightarrow RH + I^-$), one would expect *p*-iodocinnamic acid to give a wave with about the same half-wave potential as the wave of *p*-iodophenyl-propiolic acid, while the *p*-bromo- and *p*-chloro- compounds would give waves at successively and considerably more negative potentials. This is because the difficulty of reducing carbon–halogen bonds always increases in the order $RI < RBr < RCl$. On this second supposition, of course, the unsubstituted phenylpropiolic acid, if it gave a wave at all, could only give one with a half-wave potential considerably more negative than that of its *p*-iodo- derivative.

Controlled-potential electrolysis followed by identification of the products is probably both the easiest and the most generally applicable technique for dealing with such problems. In the above example a simple test for iodide in the solution resulting from the controlled-potential reduction of p-iodophenylpropiolic acid would settle the question at once. One could make assurance doubly sure by isolating the organic product and observing its spectrum in the $C=C$ and $C\equiv C$ stretch regions. Other polarographic grounds for discriminating between possible alternate reduction paths may sometimes be found in the kinetics of the rate-determining step of an irreversible process (Chap. 4 V).

As has been implied in the above discussion, it is often helpful to obtain a polarogram of the assumed reduction product in the same supporting electrolyte. In $1F$ sulfuric acid vanadium(IV) gives a single wave whose half-wave potential is -0.85 v., while vanadium(III) gives a wave whose half-wave potential is -0.51 v. Since -0.85 v. lies well on the plateau of a wave for which $E_{1/2} = -0.51$ v., it is clear that the vanadium(III) species having the latter half-wave potential would be reduced as rapidly as it could be formed at the surface of a dropping electrode at potentials near -0.85 v. Hence this species could not be the product of the reduction of vanadium (IV). However, the reduction of vanadium(IV) might perhaps yield a vanadium(III) species having a different composition or structure from, and only very slowly transformed into, the one reducible at -0.51 v. Several examples of such behavior have been identified, and it must therefore be emphasized that this argument would not prove that no form of vanadium(III) could be the product of reduction of vanadium(IV).

The interpretation of a polarogram is greatly facilitated if it contains two or more diffusion-controlled waves. Then the total diffusion currents of the successive waves are proportional to the total numbers of electrons consumed (the variation of $m^{2/3}t^{1/6}$ is again inappreciable for the purpose), and measuring the ratio or ratios of these often permits the n-values to be assigned without further ado. Consider the polarogram of copper(II) in an ammoniacal ammonium chloride supporting electrolyte, which is shown in Fig. 3.21. The total diffusion current of the double wave, measured at, say, -0.8 v., is just twice the diffusion current of the first wave, measured at about -0.4 v. If n_1 electrons are consumed in the half-reaction responsible for the first wave while n_2 electrons are consumed in the overall process, the data give $n_2/n_1 = 2$. In view of what is known about the redox chemistry of copper, the only tenable conclusion is that the first wave represents a one-electron reduction to copper(I) while the total double wave represents a two-electron reduction to the element. This interpretation is supported by the fact that the cathodic wave obtained with a similar solution of copper(I) has the same half-wave potential as the second wave of copper(II), and also by the further fact that the diffusion current constant of the total double wave (3.75) is not much different from that obtained in, say, $1F$ nitric acid, in which copper(II) can only be reduced to the metal.

It should be mentioned that the height of the second wave in Fig. 3.21 is governed by the diffusion coefficient of the cupric complex (predominantly $Cu(NH_3)_4^{++}$ under these conditions), whereas that of

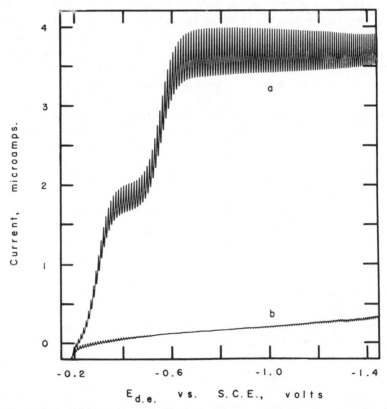

Figure 3.21.   Polarograms of (a) 0.45mM copper(II) in $1F$ ammonia–$1F$ ammonium chloride containing 0.002% Triton X-100, (b) the supporting electrolyte alone.

the cathodic wave obtained with copper(I) is governed by the diffusion coefficient of the cuprous complex (predominantly $Cu(NH_3)_2{}^+$). Hence there is no ground for expecting the diffusion current constants of these waves to be exactly the same despite the fact that they represent the same electron-transfer process.

In more complicated cases of this sort the ratio of wave heights may have to be supplemented by an estimate of the overall n-value. Osmium(VI) gives a double wave in moderately concentrated sodium hydroxide media; in $4F$ sodium hydroxide the ratio of wave heights corresponds very nearly to $n_2/n_1 = 1.5$. This could represent either $n_1 = 2$ and $n_2 = 3$, giving osmium(III) as the final product, or $n_1 = 4$ and $n_2 = 6$, giving the element. The total diffusion current constant is 3.4, which is reasonable if the overall n-value is 3 (one expects I/n to be somewhat smaller than the usual value of 1.5 because $4F$ sodium hydroxide has a higher viscosity than the ordinary dilute aqueous supporting electrolyte) but which can hardly correspond to an overall n-value of 6.

The polarography of nitroethane (77,78) affords a further illustration of the way in which the appearance of multiple waves may facilitate the interpretation of a polarogram. Acidic solutions of nitroethane give only a single wave, whose diffusion current constant cannot be measured accurately because the compound is so volatile that some of it escapes while the solution is being deaerated. This might cause some difficulty in attempting to decide among the possible half-reactions

$$C_2H_5NO_2 + 2H^+ + 2e \rightarrow H_2O + [C_2H_5NO] \rightarrow CH_3CH=NOH$$

$$C_2H_5NO_2 + 4H^+ + 4e \rightarrow H_2O + C_2H_5NHOH$$

$$C_2H_5NO_2 + 7H^+ + 6e \rightarrow 2H_2O + C_2H_5NH_3{}^+$$

But as the pH is increased to about 4.5 the final current rise, which is due to the reduction of hydrogen ion, moves to more negative potentials and reveals a second wave due to the nitroethane. The total double wave is 1.5 times as high as the first wave, which must mean that the first wave represents a four-electron reduction while the total double wave represents a six-electron reduction. Hence the first wave must correspond to reduction to β-ethylhydroxylamine and the second to further reduction to ethylammonium ion. This is supported by the fact that β-ethylhydroxylamine gives a wave having the same half-wave potential as the second wave of nitroethane. As the diffusion current of the first wave is not appreciably affected by varying the pH over this range, the four-electron reduction to the hydroxylamine must also be the process that occurs in solutions so strongly acidic that the first wave is the only one observed.

One often encounters double waves that represent, not successive stages of reduction or oxidation as in the preceding examples, but simply the presence of two substances related by an equilibrium of some sort. Two examples should suffice to illustrate the pitfalls inherent in such situations and the ways in which they may be avoided.

Ethylenediaminetetraacetate has been determined by adding an excess of copper(II) and recording a polarogram of the mixture (79). There are two waves: the first is for the reduction of the excess copper(II) and is the one whose height is measured in the analytical procedure, and the second is for the reduction of the chelonate. On the plateau of the first wave, cupric ions are reduced as rapidly as they reach the drop surface. Hence the equilibrium $Cu(EDTA)^= = Cu^{++} + (EDTA)^{-4}$ is displaced. This leads to the formation of a little more cupric ion at the drop surface, and so the height of the first wave is a little larger than the value corresponding to the actual equilibrium concentration of cupric ion in the bulk of the solution. The effect is immeasurably small, however: the concentration of cupric ion does not decrease quite to zero at the drop surface even at potentials on the plateau of its wave, and it is easily shown that only a very tiny fraction of the chelonate has to dissociate at any such potential to establish a new equilibrium. Hence the height of the first wave is virtually the diffusion current of the free cupric ion in the solution. One might by accident prepare a solution in which the diffusion currents of cupric ion and the chelonate happened to be the same. Incautious application of the ideas described in the preceding paragraphs might produce the incorrect conclusion that the reduction of copper(II) occurs in two one-electron steps in solutions containing ethylenediaminetetraacetate. The easy way to avoid the error is to vary the ratio of the concentrations of copper(II) and the chelon; this will produce a corresponding variation in the ratio of the wave heights, and will make the proper interpretation obvious.

Similar but more complex behavior is observed with solutions of pyruvic acid, $CH_3COCOOH$ (80). This gives two waves at pH values between 4 and 8, and their heights are equal at pH 5.8. From a polarogram obtained at pH 5.8 one might conclude that the reduction occurs in two two-electron steps, giving first lactic acid and then propionic acid. If it were recognized that lactic acid is not reducible and that the total height of the pyruvic acid wave corresponds only to $n = 2$, one might conclude instead that the reduction proceeds by two one-electron steps, giving first a free radical (which would probably be assumed to dimerize to give 2,3-dimethyltartaric acid) and then lactic acid. This is more sophisticated but is also incorrect. It would be found that the ratio of wave heights varied with pH and also that the height of the first wave was not diffusion-controlled (i.e., was not proportional to $h_{corr}^{1/2}$), and both of these facts should prohibit interpretation by the techniques described above. To anticipate what will be said in the following section, the first wave is a kinetic wave, which means that its height reflects the rate at which the substance responsible for it is formed by a chemical reaction occurring at the drop surface. It can be told, as described below, that the concentration of the substance responsible for the first wave is negligible in the bulk of the solution at pH values above about 5; since pyruvate ion predominates under these conditions (pK_a for pyruvic acid is 2.49 at 25°), the chemical reaction must be one in which pyruvate ion is transformed into a more easily reducible species. There are two possibilities: one is that pyruvate ion exists principally in the enol form and that this tautomerizes to the more easily reducible keto form at the drop surface, and the other is that the pyruvate ion reacts with hydrogen ion at the drop surface to give the more easily reducible molecular pyruvic acid. The first supposition is contrary to the experimental fact that pyruvate ion enolizes to only a very slight extent, and is further contradicted by the observation that phenylglyoxylic acid, $C_6H_5COCOOH$, behaves in the same way as pyruvic acid although it cannot enolize. It is, therefore, necessary to conclude that the first wave corresponds to the two-electron reduction of pyruvic acid and that its height reflects the rate at which pyruvate and hydrogen ions can combine at the drop surface, while the second wave corresponds to the two-electron reduction of pyruvate ions that do not undergo this protonation and reduction because of the limited rate of protonation at this pH.

Many other examples might be cited to emphasize the necessity of making sure that the wave heights are diffusion-controlled and that their ratio is independent of solution composition before assigning n-values to the waves. Here again controlled-potential electrolysis can be of much help: if electrolysis at a potential on the plateau of the first wave causes the heights of both waves to decrease, it is clear that the substances responsible for the two waves are in equilibrium with each other.

VII. Kinetic Currents

There are many cases in which the height of a wave is partly or wholly determined by the rate of a chemical reaction that produces an electroactive substance in a thin layer of solution around the mercury drop. The behavior of pyruvic acid in weakly acidic media, which was discussed in the preceding section, is a classical example. Formaldehyde behaves similarly (81–84): the diol, which predominates in aqueous solutions, is not reducible, but the aldehydo form is, and a wave is obtained whose height reflects the rate of transformation of the diol into the reducible aldehydo form. Aldoses give waves whose heights are governed by the rates at which the non-reducible ring forms that predominate are transformed into the reducible aldehydo forms at the drop surface (85,86).

Waves of this type are called kinetic waves. The general mechanism responsible for them may be written

$$Y \underset{k_b}{\overset{k_f}{\rightleftharpoons}} O \qquad (3.44)$$

$$O + ne \rightarrow R \qquad (3.45)$$

where k_f and k_b are the first- or pseudo-first-order rate constants (in sec.$^{-1}$) for the forward and backward reactions described by eq. (3.44). The species O is reducible, as shown by eq. (3.45), at potentials where Y is not, although in some systems it is possible to reduce Y directly at a more negative potential than is needed to reduce O. The behavior of the height of the kinetic wave depends on both the ratio of the equilibrium concentrations of Y and O in the bulk of the solution and the rate constants for their interconversion. It is convenient to begin by discussing the pure kinetic current that is obtained when the equilibrium concentration of O is negligibly small and when the transformation of Y into O is very slow.

Under these conditions it is easily seen that the current will be proportional to the rate of the transformation of Y into O. At the surface of the electrode, where the concentration of Y is C_Y^0, this rate is equal to $k_f C_Y^0$, but since the reaction is very slow very little Y will be consumed, and so C_Y^0 will be virtually identical with C_Y, the concentration of Y in the bulk of the solution. In addition, the current at any instant will be proportional to the area of the electrode at that instant—that is, by virtue of eq. (3.12), to $m^{2/3}\tau^{2/3}$—and to n, and it will also be affected by the rate of the backward reaction because this competes with the reduction of O. An explicit derivation gives (87)

$$i_k = 493n D^{1/2} C_Y m^{2/3} t^{2/3}(k_f/k_b^{1/2}) \qquad (3.46)$$

where i_k is the average kinetic current during the life of the drop and D is the diffusion coefficient of Y or O: it is reasonable to assume that these are equal because the molecules of these substances will probably have very nearly equal sizes. The value of i_k will be given in microamperes if C_Y is expressed in millimoles per liter.

With the aid of eq. (3.46) it is easy to recognize a kinetic current: since $m^{2/3}t^{2/3}$ does not vary with the height of the column of mercury above the capillary (cf. Table 3.3 and the accompanying discussion), the height of a kinetic wave is independent of h_{corr} if all other conditions are kept constant. This is quite different from the behavior of a diffusion current, which is described by eq. (3.31) or (3.32), and it constitutes the fundamental test for kinetic control of the wave height.

There are other differences between kinetic and diffusion-controlled waves. They are often useful as supporting evidence, but for one reason or another none of them permits a conclusive decision about the nature of an unknown wave, and it is therefore essential to apply the above test to any wave suspected of being kinetic. The height of a kinetic wave is larger than the diffusion current that would correspond to the equilibrium concentration of O in the solution, but is smaller than the diffusion current that would correspond to the reduction of the O and Y together. The latter can be approximated by applying the Ilkovič equation if n is known. However, it is not safe to conclude that a wave is kinetic because its height is unexpectedly small, for the same thing is true of adsorption waves. In a system being studied for the first time, one may not know the equilibrium concentration of the reducible species O and may not even know its identity *a priori*. The height of a kinetic wave is influenced by the experimental conditions that affect the reaction rates, including pH, temperature, and ionic strength. The pH dependence when hydrogen ion is involved in the rate-determining step, as is usually the case with kinetic waves of organic compounds, is discussed below, as is the related case that arises with certain metal complexes. The temperature coefficient of the height of a kinetic wave is usually much larger than that of a diffusion current, but its value in any particular case depends on the heats of activation of both the forward and backward reactions, and exceptions to the generalization are known. The effect of ionic strength depends, of course, on the charges borne by the species involved.

Once a wave has been found to be purely kinetic, much information about its rate-controlling chemical step can be obtained with the aid of eq. (3.46). The quantity $k_f/k_b^{1/2}$ can be evaluated with the aid of an estimate of $D^{1/2}$ obtained from eq. (3.22). This necessitates the measurement of a diffusion current, which can usually be made in one of two ways. By changing the composition of the supporting electrolyte so as to displace the equilibrium in favor of O one can often obtain a solution in which the concentration of Y is negligible and in which O gives a diffusion-controlled wave. When Y is reducible at a more negative potential than O, one can simply measure the total current on the plateau of the wave of Y. If neither of these is possible, the value of $D^{1/2}$ can be estimated as described in Sec. IV-E above. Once $k_f/k_b^{1/2}$ has been evaluated, the individual values of k_f and k_b can be obtained immediately if the ratio of the equilibrium concentrations of Y and O in the same solution is known. One has

$$C_O/C_Y = K' = k_f/k_b \tag{3.47}$$

where K' is the formal or conditional equilibrium constant of the reaction described by eq. (3.44) in the solution being considered. It follows from what has been said above that the ratio C_O/C_Y cannot be obtained from the height of the kinetic wave and the known total concentration of O and Y together; other information is necessary. For the kinetic wave of pyruvic acid in a buffered solution having a hydrogen-ion concentration equal to C_{H^+}, K' would be equal to

C_{H^+}/K_a, where K_a is the ordinary dissociation constant of the acid at the same ionic strength. Accordingly

$$\frac{1}{K'}\frac{k_f}{k_b^{1/2}} = k_b^{1/2} \tag{3.48}$$

and

$$\frac{1}{K'}\left(\frac{k_f}{k_b^{1/2}}\right)^2 = k_f \tag{3.49}$$

The foregoing treatment is restricted to conditions under which the equilibrium concentration of O is very small while the concentration of Y is constant throughout the solution, which means that the wave height must be much larger than the diffusion current of O but much smaller than the diffusion current of Y. If the equilibrium concentration of O is appreciable, the observed wave height i will be the sum of its diffusion current and a kinetic current arising from the transformation of Y into O at the drop surface, and can be approximated by combining eqs. (3.15) and (3.46) to give

$$i/m^{2/3}t^{1/6} = 607nD^{1/2}C_O + 493nD^{1/2}C_Y t^{1/2}(k_f/k_b^{1/2}) \tag{3.50}$$

Though this is not exact, it should permit useful approximations to the values of C_O and (since C_Y is easily obtained by difference) $k_f/k_b^{1/2}$ to be obtained from the intercept and slope of a plot of $i/m^{2/3}t^{1/6}$ vs. $t^{1/2}$. If, on the other hand, the transformation of Y into O is so rapid that the kinetic current is an appreciable fraction of the diffusion current of Y, one need only employ a more exact form of eq. (3.46):

$$i_k/(i_d - i_k) = 0.81(k_f/k_b^{1/2})\,t^{1/2} \tag{3.51}$$

where i_d is the diffusion current that would be obtained from the complete reduction of Y and i_k is the observed kinetic current, both averaged over the life of the drop. For further details and equations applicable to other mechanisms the original literature (88–97) should be consulted. A detailed review is available (98).

When eq. (3.46) is applicable, the variation of the kinetic current with the composition of the solution can be used to elucidate the stoichiometry of the rate-determining chemical step. If the mechanism were actually, say,

$$\text{Y} + p\text{H}^+ \underset{k'_b}{\overset{k'_f}{\rightleftarrows}} \text{O} \xrightarrow{+ne} \text{R} \qquad (3.52)$$

then the pseudo-first-order rate constant k_f of the preceding equations would be given by

$$k_f = k'_f C^p_{\text{H}^+} \qquad (3.53)$$

and so would vary with pH, while the rate constants k_b and k_b' would be identical and independent of pH. The kinetic current is measured for several different solutions satisfying the above requirements and having identical concentrations of Y, identical viscosities (so that the values of D are the same), and identical ionic strengths (to eliminate uncertainties arising from activity effects), but different pH values. Combining eq. (3.46) and (3.53) and differentiating gives (*99*)

$$d(\log i_k)/d(\text{pH}) = -p \qquad (3.54)$$

Other possible mechanisms can be treated in similar fashion.

A related case of special importance arises in work with complex metal ions. In solutions containing a metal ion M, an excess of a ligand X, and the successive complexes MX, MX_2, . . . , MX_j, it is often found that the metal ion or some lower complex is more easily reducible than the complex that predominates. In this event a kinetic wave may be obtained for the reduction of the metal ion or lower complex, and this is usually followed by a wave for the reduction of the predominating complex. If all of the equilibria are labile except one:

$$MX_p \rightleftharpoons MX_{p-1} + X \ (1 \leq p \leq j) \qquad (3.55)$$

if the substance responsible for the kinetic wave is either MX_{p-1} or some lower complex; if the product of each of the successive formation constants by the concentration of free X is large, so that $C_M \ll C_{MX} \ll C_{MX_2} \cdots \ll C_{MX_j}$; and if the concentration of free X is so large that the liberation of additional X by the reactions that occur at the drop surface does not affect its concentration appreciably, one obtains (*100–103*):

$$\frac{d[\log i_k/(i_d - i_k)]}{d(\log C_X)} = p - j - \tfrac{1}{2} \qquad (3.56)$$

where i_d is the diffusion current for the reduction of all of the complexes together and i_k is the height of the kinetic wave, both averaged over the life of the drop. For the simple case in which $i_k \ll i_d$, this is of the same form as eq. (3.54), though the derivation differs in that both the concentration of MX_p and the pseudo-first-order rate constant of the backward step depend on the concentration of X. Including the diffusion current on the left-hand side of eq. (3.56) provides for the case in which i_k is an appreciable fraction of i_d, as mentioned above in connection with eq. (3.51). For example, a kinetic wave is observed in the reduction of cadmium(II) from cyanide media; the predominating complex is $Cd(CN)_4^=$ (i.e., $j = 4$) and experimentally the left-hand side of eq. (3.56) is found (*101*) to be equal to $-3/2$, so that $p = 3$. Hence the rate-determining step is

$$Cd(CN)_3^- \rightleftharpoons Cd(CN)_2 + CN^-$$

On this evidence the species that actually accepts electrons from the electrode might be Cd^{++}, $Cd(CN)^+$, or $Cd(CN)_2$ itself. It can be identified with the aid of data obtained on the rising part of the kinetic wave, where the currents are influenced by the rate of the electron-transfer process as well as by that of the chemical step; on the plateau of the wave, electron transfer is so rapid that the chemical step is rate-determining. This is discussed in Chap. 4.

Various other kinds of behavior are possible and many have been observed. If the pseudo-first-order rate constant k_f is extremely small, so little Y will be transformed into O during the drop life that the kinetic current will be too small to detect; then the wave height of O will be diffusion-controlled and proportional to the concentration of O in the bulk of the solution. On the other hand, if k_f is extremely large the wave height will again be diffusion-controlled but will be proportional to the sum of the concentrations of O and Y because virtually all of the Y reaching the drop surface will be transformed into O and reduced. In intermediate cases, where the bulk of the solution contains appreciable concentrations of both O and Y and where the transformation of Y into O is neither practically instantaneous nor vanishingly slow, the wave height will be the sum of the diffusion current of the O already present and a kinetic current reflecting the formation of additional O at the expense of part of the Y at the drop surface as the equilibrium between them is displaced by the reduction. The diffusion current will be proportional to $m^{2/3}t^{1/6}$

or $h_{corr}^{1/2}$ within the ordinary limits of error of the Ilkovič equation; the kinetic current will be independent of h_{corr}. Depending on the position of the equilibrium between Y and O in any particular solution and on the rate at which it is attained, the wave height may show any behavior intermediate between that of a pure diffusion current at one extreme and that of a pure kinetic current at the other. So the wave height may be proportional to $h_{corr}^{1/2}$ or independent of h_{corr} or may increase as h_{corr} increases but less rapidly than the square-root relationship would predict. In the last of these cases the data are most easily dissected by employing the approximate eq. (3.50).

There are two reasons why it is inadvisable to use kinetic waves in practical analysis. One is that they afford poorer sensitivities than diffusion-controlled waves; the other, which is more important, is that an adventitious impurity may alter the height of a kinetic wave by catalyzing the rate-determining step. It is much better to seek conditions that yield a diffusion-controlled wave, and these can often be found by investigating the effects of such variables as pH and temperature. Only when no such conditions can be found should an analytical procedure be based on a kinetic wave.

VIII. Catalytic Currents

Catalytic waves arise from mechanisms like

$$O + ne \rightarrow R \tag{3.57}$$

$$\overset{k_f}{R + Z \rightarrow O} \tag{3.58}$$

in which a substance Z, which would not be reducible at a certain potential if it were present alone, causes the current obtained from the reduction of an electroactive substance O at that potential to increase by reacting with the product R to regenerate O or to form some other substance that is reducible.

For example, nitrate ion (= Z) does not give a wave in a supporting electrolyte containing $0.1F$ sulfuric acid and $0.2F$ sodium sulfate. Molybdenum(VI) gives a double wave: the first wave represents reduction to molybdenum(V), and the second represents reduction to molybdenum(III). Molybdenum(III) reacts fairly rapidly with nitrate in an acidic solution. At a potential on the plateau of the second wave of molybdenum(VI) in a solution containing nitrate, the molybdenum(III) formed by the electrode reaction is partially reoxidized by nitrate, and the oxidized molybdenum species is then reduced at the drop surface to give more molybdenum(III) which reacts with more nitrate, and so on. The increase of current resulting from the presence of the nitrate—that is, the difference between the total height of the wave and the diffusion current obtained in the absence of nitrate—is the catalytic current of nitrate.

Such catalytic waves are obtained (104–114) in many mixtures of transition-metal ions, such as tungstate, vanadate, molybdate, and titanium(IV), with oxidizing agents like nitrate, hydrogen peroxide, chlorate, perchlorate, and hydroxylamine, whose electrolytic reductions involve large overpotentials. The behavior of the limiting current in any particular case depends on the relative magnitudes of the diffusion and catalytic currents. It is convenient to describe the rate of the reaction represented by eq. (3.58) with the aid of the pseudo-first-order rate constant $k_f C_Z^0$, where k_f is the second- or pseudo-second-order rate constant and C_Z^0 is the concentration of Z at the surface of the electrode. If $k_f C_Z^0$ is small, very little R will be reoxidized, and the wave height will be practically equal to the diffusion current of O. But as $k_f C_Z^0$ increases, the catalytic current becomes more important, and if $k_f C_Z^0$ is very large the chemical reaction will produce much more reducible material at the drop surface than arrives there by diffusion from the bulk of the solution. For example, the wave height obtained with a typical dropping electrode in an $0.1F$ phosphate buffer of pH 4.9 containing $8 \times 10^{-7} M$ vanadium(V) and $0.007M$ hydrogen peroxide is 18.6 μamp., whereas the diffusion current of the vanadium(V) would be only a few thousandths of a microampere; nearly the entire current is due to the reduction of vanadium(V) regenerated by the reaction between vanadium(IV) and hydrogen peroxide at the electrode surface. An important analytical implication of such behavior is that it permits the detection and determination of exceedingly small concentrations of the original electroactive substance (115,116). Though the heights of catalytic waves are as sensitive to variations of pH, temperature, and other experimental conditions as those of kinetic ones, the use of a catalytic wave for analytical purposes may often be advantageous because of the high sensitivity that may be attained.

The average catalytic current over the life of a drop is given by
(98,117,118)

$$i_c = 493 n D_O^{1/2} C_O m^{2/3} t^{2/3} [(k_f + k_b) C_Z^0]^{1/2} \qquad (3.59a)$$

where C_O is expressed in the customary polarographic units of milli-moles/liter while the product in square brackets is expressed in sec.$^{-1}$. It is assumed that the quantity $(k_f + k_b) C_Z^0 t$ is larger than about 10, but that the concentration of Z is uniform throughout the solution, which implies that a large excess of Z is present and that the catalytic current is much smaller than the diffusion current of Z as estimated by the Ilkovič equation. In many cases k_b will be so much smaller than k_f that it can be neglected; in others the equilibrium constant k_f/k_b of the reaction may be known or measurable. In either event the value of k_f is easily obtained from eq. (3.59a), and data on its variation with solution composition can be used in obvious fashion to study the reaction described by eq. (3.58). If the diffusion current of O is appreciable it may be measured separately in the absence of Z and the catalytic current can then be obtained by difference. Like kinetic currents, catalytic currents can be identified by the fact that they do not vary with h_{corr}. In general these two kinds of currents behave very similarly, but they are easily distinguished because of the peculiar chemical circumstances in which catalytic waves appear.

Equation (3.59a) predicts that under otherwise constant conditions the catalytic current (and hence the wave height) should be proportional to the concentration of the electroactive substance O. This is not true of all catalytic waves, however, because other mechanisms are possible besides the simple one represented by eqs. (3.57) and (3.58). An example is given in Fig. 3.22, which shows that the ratio of the wave height (which is virtually equal to the catalytic current because the diffusion current of uranium(VI) under these conditions is only about 1% of the total wave height) to the concentration of uranium(VI) decreases considerably as the concentration increases. Hence the proportionality between wave height and the concentration of the electroactive species cannot be taken for granted in any unknown case.

Equation (3.59a) also predicts that the catalytic current will be proportional to the square root of the concentration of Z if C_O and the composition of the supporting electrolyte are kept constant and if $k_f C_Z$ is sufficiently large. For example, the catalytic currents ob-

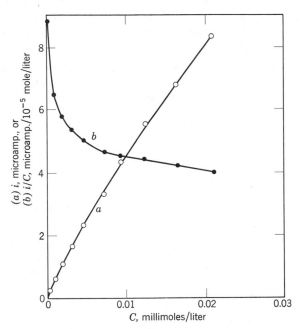

Figure 3.22. Effects of the concentration C of uranium(VI) on (*a*) the height of the catalytic wave obtained in 0.001F potassium nitrate–0.1F potassium chloride–0.01F hydrochloric acid, and (*b*) the ratio of the wave height to the concentration of uranium(VI).

tained with 0.015 to 0.18M solutions of hydrogen peroxide (= Z) containing 0.25mM ferric iron are proportional to $C_Z^{1/2}$ with a mean error of only $\pm 7\%$ (*117*) under conditions such that the value of $k_f C_Z t$ lies between about 3 and 30. In marginal cases where $(k_f + k_b) C_Z t$ is not very large, it is advantageous to use a more exact version of eq. (3.59a):

$$i_c/i_d = 0.812[(k_f + k_b)\ C_Z^0 t]^{1/2} + 1.92[(k_f + k_b)\ C_Z^0 t]^{-7/6} \quad (3.59b)$$

where i_d is the average diffusion current obtained during the drop life under certain conditions when Z is absent, while i_c is the average current obtained under identical conditions but in the presence of Z (*118*). This is accurate to better than 0.5% when $(k_f + k_b)\ C_Z^0 t$ is 9, but it predicts a value 10% too large if this quantity is as small as 4.

When it is equal to 9, the second term on the right-hand side of equation (3.59b) is barely over 5% as large as the first, and eq. (3.59a) may be obtained by neglecting the small second term and introducing the Ilkovič-equation description of i_d.

Another important type of catalytic current is observed in solutions containing a base B that is not reducible but that can catalyze the reduction of protons by the following mechanism:

$$B + HA \rightleftharpoons HB^+ + A^- \qquad (3.60a)$$

$$HB^+ + e \rightarrow HB \qquad (3.60b)$$

$$2HB \rightarrow H_2 + 2B \qquad (3.60c)$$

where HA may be hydronium ion or another proton donor. Such catalytic waves are obtained with many organic compounds, including amines, amino acids, proteins, thiols, disulfides, alkaloids, and phosphines, and display rather complex behavior. At very low concentrations of the catalyst B, the bimolecular reaction represented by eq. (3.60c) may be rate-determining on the plateau of the wave, where the electron-transfer reaction [eq. (3.60b)] is very fast, and then the wave height will increase more rapidly than C_B, the bulk concentration of B. But as C_B is increased the proton-transfer reaction [eq. (3.60a)] tends to become rate-determining, and then the observed behavior depends on whether this reaction occurs at the surface of the drop or in the bulk of the solution, and this in turn depends largely on the extent to which B can be adsorbed on the drop surface. Most often the ratio of wave height to the concentration of B decreases in the manner of an adsorption isotherm. The dependence on acidity is similarly complex: at moderate acidities the wave height may be proportional to the concentration of acid because the proton-transfer reaction is rate-determining, but at high acidities the regeneration of the catalyst [eq. (3.60c)] may become the rate-determining step and then the wave height increases less rapidly than the concentration of acid. An extensive review, which includes many literature references, should be consulted for further information (119).

Catalytic hydrogen waves are also observed with some inorganic substances. Occasionally (as with complexes of tungsten(VI) with certain carboxylic acids) they doubtless arise from a mechanism like the one just cited; in other cases (as with the ions of several of the platinum metals) they are probably due to effects of the deposited metals on the overpotential for hydrogen evolution.

IX. Adsorption Waves

If either the electroactive species or the product of the electrode reaction is adsorbed onto the surface of the drop, an adsorption wave (120,121) may be observed. Suppose that the product R of the electrode reaction $O + ne \rightarrow R$ is adsorbed. Its activity is lower in the adsorbed state than in solution, and this facilitates the reduction of O. At a very low concentration of O there will be a single wave, representing the reduction of O to adsorbed R. Its height will be diffusion-controlled, proportional to the concentration of O and also to $h_{corr}^{1/2}$. But as the concentration of O is increased, a point will be reached at which enough R is formed during the life of the drop to cover its entire surface. More than this amount of R can be formed only if the excess remains in the solution. Since it is more difficult to reduce O to dissolved R than to reduce it to adsorbed R, the reduction of the excess O will produce a second wave at a more negative potential. The original wave is the adsorption wave, whose height will be constant and independent of any further increase in the concentration of O; the second wave is the "normal" wave, which represents the reduction of O to dissolved R. The total height of the double wave corresponds to the reduction of all of the O diffusing to the surface of the drop, and is therefore diffusion-controlled and proportional to both the concentration of O and $h_{corr}^{1/2}$. None of these things, however, is true of either of the waves individually.

If, on the other hand, O is adsorbed and R is not, the single wave obtained at very low concentrations of O will represent the reduction of adsorbed O. On increasing the concentration of O, this wave will reach a limiting height when the amount of O diffusing up to the surface of each drop is just sufficient to cover the drop surface. At a still higher concentration, the excess of O remaining dissolved at the drop surface will produce a "normal" wave at a less positive potential.

In either of these cases the limiting height of the adsorption wave is proportional to the number of molecules adsorbed on the drop during its life. The total quantity of electricity corresponding to this number of molecules is given by

$$Q = i_a t = 10^{22} nF A_{max}/aN \qquad (3.61)$$

where Q is the number of microcoulombs flowing during the drop life, i_a is the average current (in microamperes) in the presence of a concentration of O sufficiently high to yield the limiting height of the adsorption wave, A_{max} is the maximum area of the drop (in cm.^{2}), a is the area (in Å.^{2}) covered by each adsorbed molecule, and N is Avogadro's number. The factor 10^{22} permits i_a to be expressed in microamperes (rather than amperes) and a to be expressed in Å.^{2} (rather than cm.^{2}). Combining this with equation (3.4) yields

$$i_a = 13.66 n m^{2/3} t^{-1/3}/a \tag{3.62}$$

The variations of m and t with h_{corr} (cf. Table 3.3) are such that $m^{2/3}t^{-1/3}$, and hence the limiting height of the adsorption wave, is proportional to h_{corr}, and this is the fundamental criterion for adsorption control of the wave height. Other valuable diagnostic criteria include the behavior of the wave height with increasing concentration of O and especially the appearance of a new wave at a certain value of this concentration, the frequently abnormally small temperature coefficient of the height i_a of the adsorption wave (which does not depend on the diffusion coefficient of O), and a highly characteristic effect of h_{corr} on the relative heights of the adsorption and "normal" waves.

The last of these may be illustrated by supposing that a certain substance O has a diffusion current constant of 3, that 2 electrons are consumed in reducing each molecule of it to an adsorbed product R that occupies 5 Å.^{2} per molecule, and that a polarogram of an 0.91mM solution of O is obtained with a capillary for which m is 2 mg./sec. and t is 4 sec. According to eq. (3.62), the limiting height of the adsorption wave is 5.46 μamp., while the Ilkovič equation gives exactly the same value for the diffusion current. The value of i_a represents the current that can be consumed in reducing O to adsorbed R; the value of i_d represents the current required to reduce all of the O that reaches the surface of the drop. Because these two values are equal, all of the O reaching the electrode surface will be reduced to adsorbed R, and the "normal" wave will not appear at all. The same thing will be true if h_{corr} is increased, because then the rate at which fresh surface is exposed will exceed the rate at which O can diffuse up to the electrode. (It may be noted that the adsorption current at any instant is proportional to $dA/d\tau$, as is evident from eq. (3.61), and this produces a characteristic decrease of current during the drop life which is similar to curve b of Fig. 3.2 and which is easily seen on a recorded polarogram.) But if h_{corr} is decreased to, say, half its previous value the limiting height of the adsorption wave will decrease to 2.73 ($= 5.46/2$) μamp., while the diffusion current decreases only to 3.86 ($= 5.46/\sqrt{2}$) μamp. More O now reaches the drop surface than can be reduced to adsorbed R, and consequently the "normal" wave must appear. Its height will be 1.13 ($= 3.86 - 2.73$) μamp., and the ratio of its height to that of the adsorption wave will increase still further if h_{corr} is made even smaller. In short, if the capillary characteristics are kept constant the "normal" wave cannot appear unless the concentration of O increases above a certain value; if the concentration of O is kept constant the "normal" wave cannot appear unless h_{corr} decreases below a certain value.

It should be clear from the foregoing discussion that the "normal" wave is actually abnormal in many respects. Its height increases linearly with the concentration of O above the value that yields the limiting height of the adsorption wave under the particular conditions employed, but is not proportional to the total concentration of O (though the sum of the heights of the adsorption and "normal" wave is). Nor is the height of the "normal" wave proportional to $m^{2/3}t^{1/6}$ or $h_{corr}^{1/2}$ (though again the sum of the two wave heights is). In a system that yields an adsorption wave the analyst is best advised to keep the concentration so low that the "normal" wave does not appear; otherwise he has no recourse but to measure the sum of the wave heights.

Adsorption waves have been observed in solutions of methylene blue (*120*), certain organic mercurials (*122*), thiols (*123*) and uracils (in which cases it is the mercury salt produced anodically that is adsorbed), arsenic(III) (*124*), and a few other substances. Data on their limiting heights have often been used to evaluate the areas of the adsorbed species by means of eq. (3.62).

X. Non-Additive Currents

The current that flows at any potential on a polarogram is almost always equal to the sum of the individual currents that it comprises. For example, the limiting current measured at -0.9 v. on curve a of Fig. 1.1 is equal to the sum of its two components (ignoring the negligibly small migration current): the residual current at this potential, which can be measured with the supporting electrolyte alone, and the diffusion current of cadmium ion at this potential. Similarly, the limiting current measured at -1.2 v. on curve a of Fig. 3.19 is equal to the sum of its three components: the residual current (which could be measured with a solution containing neither of the metal ions), the diffusion current of cadmium (which could be measured at this potential in a similar solution free from zinc), and the diffusion current of zinc (which could be measured in a cadmium-free solution). The additivity of wave heights is so nearly universal that it is generally taken for granted in interpreting polarograms, and yet it is not always true. This section describes the most important circumstances in which it is not.

One of these will be evident from Fig. 3.9 and the accompanying discussion. Others, including catalytic currents and also the possible catalysis of the process responsible for a kinetic current by the electroactive substance responsible for a different wave or by its reduction product, are too obvious to require discussion.

A less trivial problem arises from adsorption of the electroactive substance, the product of the electrode reaction, or an inert constituent of the sample onto the electrode surface. Whenever this alters the differential capacity $\varkappa$ of the double layer, it alters the charging component of the residual current in accordance with eq. (3.5). If it is the product of the reduction that is adsorbed and that is responsible for the change of $\varkappa$, the charging current will not be the same at potentials on the plateau of the wave when the sample is present as it is in the supporting electrolyte alone. Subtraction of the separately measured residual current then yields an erroneous result, and so does measurement of the wave height by extrapolation because the extrapolation is based on a region in which there is none of the reduction product available for adsorption. If it is the electroactive substance itself that is adsorbed, subtraction of the separately measured residual current should yield the correct result because $\varkappa$ cannot be affected by the presence of the adsorbable substance when this is reduced as rapidly as its molecules reach the electrode surface, but extrapolation yields an incorrect result because it tacitly assumes that the adsorption occurs on the plateau of the wave as well as at its foot. On the other hand, if it is an inert constituent of the sample that is adsorbed (as is the case when acrylamide monomer is determined in polyacrylamide), and if the extent of this adsorption is independent of

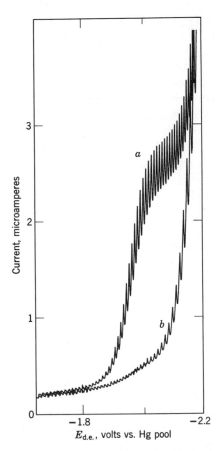

Figure 3.23. Polarograms of (a) 0.3mM acrylamide (present as an impurity in a sample of a low-molecular-weight polyacrylamide) in 0.1F lithium chloride in 90% (v/v) ethanol, (b) the supporting electrolyte alone, obtained in a cell of the type shown in Fig. 2.14(a).

potential, extrapolation is much more likely to yield the proper result. In any of these cases $\varkappa$ is unlikely to vary linearly with the concentration of the substance that is adsorbed, and deviations of i_d/C from constancy are to be expected. In the first two of these three cases it is appropriate to use a standard curve obtained with known solutions, as described in Chap. 7 V-Bi, to interpret the measured wave heights. But in the third case data obtained with pure standard solutions are useless and it is much better to use the standard-addition technique (Chap. 7 V-B*iii*) instead.

The problem is illustrated by Fig. 3.23, from which it can be seen on close inspection that the residual-current portion of curve *a*, obtained in the presence of polyacrylamide, does not quite coincide with the separately recorded residual-current curve. The effect is not large on this scale, but it is quite sufficient to produce prominent effects at lower concentrations. The figure illustrates another problem as well. The wave of acrylamide occurs at a potential where sodium and potassium ions can hardly be tolerated, as may be judged from the virtual coincidence of the wave due to sodium or potassium ion (present as an impurity in the lithium chloride) on curve *b* with the acrylamide wave on curve *a*. To prevent extensive contamination with sodium or potassium ion diffusing into the solution from a salt bridge, the analyst employed a cell with an internal mercury pool reference electrode. While the acrylamide wave on curve *a* was being recorded a certain amount of calomel was formed anodically at the surface of the pool. During the recording of curve *b*, on which the currents are much smaller, much less calomel would have been formed, and the result is that the potential of the pool is different during the final current rise on curve *a* than it is during the same portion of curve *b*. Hence the final current rise, which is due to the reduction of lithium ion, appears to begin much earlier on curve *b* than it does on curve *a*, and measurement of the height of the acrylamide wave from these two curves is impossible. The difficulty is minimized by using an extrapolation technique for measuring the wave height, but this makes it impossible to correct for the reducible impurities in the supporting electrolyte. It is much better to employ a properly poised reference electrode. With the cell of Fig. 2.14(*c*) one could poise the pool by applying a potential of, say, -2.1 v. to the dropping electrode for a few minutes before recording the residual-current curve, but with the cell of Fig. 2.14(*a*) this has no effect because the calomel formed anodically at the surface of the pool is re-reduced by the lithium amalgam that falls into it.

The simultaneous presence of two or more substances yielding adsorption waves is rare. But the analyst encountering this situation should be prepared to find that the concentrations at which these waves reach their limiting heights may be quite different in a mixture

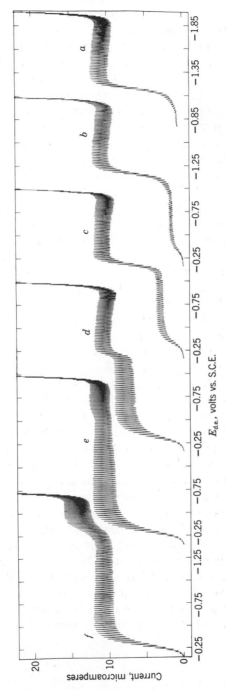

Figure 3.24. Polarograms of 0.50mM iodate in 1.0F potassium chloride containing (a) 0, (b) 0.08, (c) 0.24, (d) 0.72, (e) 1.08. and (f) 1.44mF added hydrochloric acid.

than with the respective pure solutions because of competition between the adsorbable species.

Another general problem, of which many special cases are known, arises when one reducible species can react rapidly in the diffusion layer with the product resulting from the reduction of another. An example is shown in Fig. 3.24. Curve a was obtained with a neutral unbuffered solution of iodate, in which the half-reaction can be described by the equation $IO_3^- + 3 H_2O + 6e = I^- + 6 OH^-$. As hydrogen ion is added to the solution two phenomena can be observed. One is that a part of the original iodate wave appears at a much less negative potential, for iodate is much more easily reduced according to the equation $IO_3^- + 6 H^+ + 6e = I^- + 3 H_2O$. This, however, can occur only to the extent that free hydrogen ions are available at the electrode surface: as long as the flux of hydrogen ion at the electrode surface, which according to linear-diffusion equations is equal to $C_{H^+}D_{H^+}^{1/2}$, is less than six times the flux of iodate ion, or $6C_{IO_3^-}D_{IO_3^-}^{1/2}$, fewer hydrogen ions are available at the drop surface than would be needed for the reduction of all of the iodate by the latter process. According to the Ilkovič equation, since n is 6 for the reduction of iodate while its diffusion current constant is 12.0, one has $(607)(6)$ $D_{IO_3^-}^{1/2} = 12.0$ while for hydrogen ion $(607)(1)D_{H^+}^{1/2} = 5.60$, so that an excess of hydrogen ion becomes available only when its concentration in the bulk of the solution exceeds $12.0/5.60 = 2.14$ times that of iodate, or $1.07mM$. On curve e, where the bulk concentration of hydrogen ion is barely larger than this, it can be seen that the original iodate wave around -1.15 volt has just completely been transformed into the one around -0.3 v. The half-wave potential of hydrogen ion in this medium is -1.6 v., and so it is plain that the currents on curves $b–e$ do not represent the simple addition of a current due to the reduction of hydrogen ion and the current depicted by curve a for the reduction of iodate.

Moreover, there is no trace of a wave for the reduction of hydrogen ion on curves $b–d$. Some of the hydrogen ions at the electrode surface are consumed in the process responsible for the first wave; others are neutralized by the hydroxyl ions produced by the one responsible for the second. Until the rate of diffusion of hydrogen ions toward the electrode surface exceeds the rate at which they are consumed as a result of the reduction of iodate, there can be no appreciable concentration of hydrogen ion at the electrode surface and no wave for its reduction can be observed. Only if the concentration of hydrogen ion in the bulk of the solution exceeds the value, 1.07mM, computed in the preceding paragraph can a hydrogen-ion wave be observed. A very small one can just be perceived on curve e. As long as $C_H + D_H^{1/2}$ does not exceed $6\,C_{IO_3^-}D_{IO_3^-}^{1/2}$, the total wave height at, say, -1.8 v. (which can be seen from curve f to lie on the plateau of the hydrogen-ion wave) remains equal to the diffusion current of iodate and completely unaffected by the addition of acid. But as soon as $C_H + D_H^{1/2}$ exceeds $6\,C_{IO_3^-}D_{IO_3^-}^{1/2}$, the total wave height at this potential becomes equal to the diffusion current of hydrogen ion and is completely unaffected by the fact that some of the hydrogen ions diffusing toward the electrode surface have been consumed chemically instead of having been reduced. That is, the current contributed by the reduction of each iodate ion is just counterbalanced by the disappearance of the current that would have otherwise resulted from the reduction of the six hydrogen ions consumed. To determine the concentration of hydrogen ion in the solution of curve f, one would have to measure, not the height of its wave alone by extrapolating the plateau of the preceding iodate wave, but the total distance from its plateau to the residual-current line. This behavior is observed whenever an unbuffered solution contains both hydrogen ion and a substance [such as oxygen (125) or an organic compound] in whose reduction hydrogen ions are consumed.

Similar behavior is observed with many heavy metal ions under a wide variety of circumstances. In a neutral unbuffered solution containing cupric ion and oxygen, the hydroxyl ions formed at the electrode surface as oxygen is reduced will diffuse away from the electrode surface and precipitate cupric ions diffusing toward the electrode. Any other substance whose reduction yielded hydroxyl ion as a product would have the same effect. This could of course be obviated by buffering the solution, but in other cases no such recourse is available. In a buffered solution containing cupric ion and iodate, cupric ions might be precipitated in the diffusion layer by iodide ions formed in the reduction of iodate. Cupric selenide is similarly precipitated by selenide ions resulting from the reduction of selenite ion (126). In a solution containing a heavy metal ion and a disulfide, the thiol resulting from the reduction of the latter will lead to precipitation of the heavy metal salt, and so on. Any of these interactions will produce effects like those described above provided that it is fast and essentially complete.

Still more subtle effects are possible. In a solution containing lead ion and the bismuth(III)–ethylenediaminetetraacetate complex, ethylenediaminetetraacetate will be liberated at the electrode surface as the bismuth chelonate is reduced. On diffusing toward the bulk of the solution this encounters and reacts with lead ions in the diffusion layer. The resulting lead complex diffuses more slowly than aquo-lead ions, and consequently the height of the lead wave is smaller than it would be if the lead ion were present alone under the same conditions. The same effect appears in a different guise in a solution containing free lead ion and the lead–ethylenediaminetetraacetate complex (*127*). In this case the first wave represents the reduction of the free ions and the second represents the reduction of the chelonate. At potentials on the plateau of the second wave, the free ions make a smaller contribution to the total current than they do at potentials on the plateau of the first wave, and the height of the wave for the chelonate is therefore smaller than its true diffusion current. Yet another similar situation arises in mixtures of dichromate and ferric ions (*128*). In acidic solutions both give waves rising from zero applied e.m.f., and all that can be observed is the total wave height. This is smaller than the sum of the separately measured wave heights, for in the mixture ferrous ions diffusing away from the electrode surface react with dichromate ions diffusing toward it. The ferric ions thus formed diffuse more slowly than dichromate ions do. In this last form the problem is often amenable to changes in the composition of the supporting electrolyte, which decrease the rate of the undesired reaction and render its effect negligible.

Amperometric titrations based on chemical reactions in the diffusion layer are discussed in Chap. 9 II-C.

XI. Capacity Waves and Related Phenomena

The general phenomenon of which one form is called a "capacity wave" arises from the effect of potential on the extent of adsorption of a substance that affects the capacity of the double layer when it is adsorbed onto the drop surface. The behavior of pyridine in strongly alkaline solutions will serve as an example. Over a considerable range of potentials around the potential of the electrocapillary maximum, pyridine is adsorbed onto a mercury surface. Its adsorption decreases the capacity of the double layer and, therefore, causes the residual currents in this range to be smaller than they would be if the pyridine were absent. As the potential of the dropping electrode is made more negative it is found that the pyridine is desorbed within a narrow range of potentials around -1.5 v. vs. S.C.E. The desorption is accompanied by an increase in the capacity of the double layer, and therefore the residual current increases toward the values observed when pyridine is absent. The increase of residual current gives the appearance of a wave. The effect is especially pronounced, and was indeed first observed, in oscillopolarography (*129*) and a.-c. polarography (*130*) (Chap. 10 IX), but it arises in d.-c. polarography as well.

Since the drop time tends to be decreased by the presence of the adsorbed substance, capacity waves are usually accompanied by anomalies on the electrocapillary curve, which may be used to aid in identifying them. In the absence of adsorption a plot of drop time versus potential has a parabolic shape, but adsorbed materials lower the interfacial tension and depress the curve. Many substances, such as Triton X-100 and gelatin, are adsorbed over very wide ranges of potential; they affect the residual current slightly, but because their desorption is very gradual they do not give rise to identifiable capacity waves. Others, like *n*-octanol and camphor, give curves that merge with the normal ones both at very positive and at very negative potentials, but that are nearly flat around the potential of the electrocapillary maximum. It is the comparatively sudden desorption of substances like these that gives rise to capacity waves at the potentials where the direction of the electrocapillary curve changes rapidly.

As capacity waves are due to changes of the residual current, their heights are unlikely to exceed a few tenths of a microampere, but this is quite large enough to be important even at the millimolar level. The phenomena observed, and the ways in which they can be handled, depend on whether the adsorbed substance is a constituent of the supporting electrolyte or of the sample. In the former case the capacity wave appears on the residual-current curve; though it may be taken to reflect the presence of an electroactive impurity, it is unaffected by attempts at purification. If the wave of interest overlaps the capacity wave, the use of extrapolation methods of wave-height measurement must be avoided. On the other hand, if the capacity wave is due to the desorption of another constituent of the sample, the measured wave height may vary linearly with the concentration of the substance sought but cannot be proportional to it. In this event analyses are probably best made by the "standard spike" method or a variant of it (Chap. 7 V-Biii) unless the concentration of the adsorbed substance is nearly the same in different samples, when the standard curve method (Chap. 7 V-Bi) might be considered. Finally, as was pointed out in connection with Fig. 3.23, if the substance being determined depresses the residual current until it begins to be removed from the drop surface at the foot of its wave, its wave height is unlikely to vary linearly with its concentration, and the standard curve method is then the one of choice.

Few examples of these phenomena have as yet been certainly identified, but they are probably much more common in organic polarography than the number of known cases would suggest.

References

(1) D. C. Grahame, *J. Electrochem. Soc.*, **98**, 343 (1951); *J. Am. Chem. Soc.*, **71**, 2975 (1949).
(2) A. Bresle, *Acta Chem. Scand.*, **10**, 947 (1956).
(3) G. C. Barker, *Anal. Chim. Acta*, **18**, 118 (1958).
(4) J. G. Nikelly and W. D. Cooke, *Anal. Chem.*, **29**, 933 (1957).
(5) A. Bresle, *Science Tools*, **3**, 9 (1956).
(6) J. Heyrovský, *Arhiv. Hem. i Farm.*, **8**, 11 (1934).
(7) D. Ilkovič, *Collection Czechoslov. Chem. Communs.*, **6**, 498 (1934).
(8) J. J. Lingane and I. M. Kolthoff, *J. Am. Chem. Soc.*, **61**, 1045 (1939).
(9) D. MacGillavry, *Rec. Trav. Chim.*, **56**, 1039 (1937); **57**, 33 (1938).
(10) S. Okada, S. Yoshizawa, F. Hine, and K. Asada, *J. Electrochem. Soc. Japan*, **27**, 140 (1959).
(11) Z. Zembura, A. Fulinski, and B. Bierowski, *Z. Elektrochem.*, **65**, 887 (1961).
(12) W. D. Cooke, M. T. Kelley, and D. J. Fisher, *Anal. Chem.*, **33**, 1209 (1961).
(13) D. MacGillavry and E. K. Rideal, *Rec. Trav. Chim.*, **56**, 1013 (1937).
(14) H. A. Laitinen and I. M. Kolthoff, *J. Am. Chem. Soc.*, **61**, 3344 (1939).
(15) F. G. Cottrell, *Z. Physik. Chem.*, **42**, 385 (1902).
(16) M. v. Stackelberg, M. Pilgram, and V. Toome, *Z. Elektrochem.*, **57**, 342 (1953).
(17) D. Ilkovič, *J. Chim. Phys.*, **35**, 129 (1938).
(18) O. H. Müller, National Bureau of Standards Circular 524 (August 14, 1953).
(19) J. J. Lingane and B. A. Loveridge, *J. Am. Chem. Soc.*, **72**, 438 (1950).
(20) H. Strehlow and M. v. Stackelberg, *Z. Elektrochem.*, **54**, 51 (1950).

(21) T. Kambara and I. Tachi, *Proc. 1st Intern. Polarogr. Congress*, Prague, 1951, Pt. I, p. 126; *Bull. Chem. Soc. Japan*, **25**, 284 (1952).
(22) H. Matsuda, *Bull. Chem. Soc. Japan*, **26**, 342 (1953).
(23) J. Koutecký, *Czechoslov. Cas. Fys.*, **2**, 50 (1953).
(24) J. Koutecký and M. v. Stackelberg, in *Progress in Polarography*, P. Zuman and I. M. Kolthoff, eds., Interscience, New York, 1962, Vol. I, p. 21.
(25) A. Walkley, *J. Am. Chem. Soc.*, **63**, 2278 (1941).
(26) J. J. Lingane, *Ind. Eng. Chem.*, *Anal. Ed.*, **15**, 583 (1943).
(27) L. Meites, P. Kabasakalian, and J. H. McGlotten, in *Handbook of Analytical Chemistry*, L. Meites, ed., McGraw-Hill, New York, 1963, pp. 5–53 to 5–111.
(28) J. J. Lingane and B. A. Loveridge, *J. Am. Chem. Soc.*, **68**, 395 (1946).
(29) B. A. Loveridge, Ph.D. Thesis, Harvard University, 1947.
(30) L. Meites, *J. Am. Chem. Soc.*, **73**, 1581, 3724 (1951).
(31) L. Meites and T. Meites, *J. Am. Chem. Soc.*, **73**, 395 (1951).
(32) D. J. Macero and C. L. Rulfs, *J. Am. Chem. Soc.*, **81**, 2944 (1959).
(33) H. Strehlow, O. Mädrich, and M. v. Stackelberg, *Z. Elektrochem.*, **55**, 244 (1951).
(34) W. Hans and W. Jensch, *Z. Elektrochem.*, **56**, 648 (1952).
(35) M. v. Stackelberg, *Z. Elektrochem.*, **57**, 338 (1953).
(36) J. K. Taylor, R. E. Smith, and I. L. Cooter, *J. Research Natl. Bur. Stds.*, **42**, 387 (1949).
(37) L. Meites and T. Meites, *J. Am. Chem. Soc.*, **72**, 4843 (1950).
(38) F. L. Steghart, *Chem. & Ind.* (*London*), 157 (1948).
(39) H. A. McKenzie, *J. Am. Chem. Soc.*, **70**, 3147 (1948).
(40) G. S. Smith, *Nature*, **163**, 290 (1949).
(41) L. Airey and A. A. Smales, *Analyst*, **75**, 287 (1950).
(42) F. E. W. Wetmore and J. G. MacDonald, *Trans. Faraday Soc.*, **47**, 553 (1951).
(43) J. J. Lingane, *J. Am. Chem. Soc.*, **75**, 788 (1953).
(44) J. W. Grenier, Ph.D. Thesis, Yale University, 1955.
(45) A. Bresle, *Acta Chem. Scand.*, **10**, 951 (1956).
(46) M. v. Stackelberg, *Z. Anal. Chem.*, **173**, 90 (1960).
(47) G. C. Barker and A. W. Gardner, in *Advances in Polarography*, I. S. Longmuir, ed., Pergamon, London, 1960, Vol. I, p. 330.
(48) W. Hans and W. Henne, *Naturwiss.*, **40**, 524 (1953).
(49) W. Hans, W. Henne, and E. Meurer, *Z. Elektrochem.*, **58**, 836 (1954).
(50) I. Smoleř, *Chem. Listy*, **47**, 1667 (1953); *Collection Czechoslov. Chem. Communs.*, **19**, 238 (1954).
(50a) J. M. Markowitz and P. J. Elving, *J. Am. Chem. Soc.*, **81**, 3518 (1959).
(51) I. Smoleř, *J. Electroanal. Chem.*, **6**, 465 (1964).
(52) J. Kůta and I. Smoleř, in *Progress in Polarography*, P. Zuman and I. M. Kolthoff, eds., Interscience, New York, 1962, Vol. I, p. 43
(53) C. N. Reilley, G. W. Everett, and R. H. Johns, *Anal. Chem.*, **27**, 483 (1955).
(54) L. Gierst, Thesis, University of Brussels, 1952, pp. 138–140.
(55) C. L. Rulfs, *J. Am. Chem. Soc.*, **76**, 2071 (1954).

(56) D. J. Macero and C. L. Rulfs, *J. Am. Chem. Soc.*,**81**, 2942 (1959); *J. Electroanal. Chem.*, **7**, 328 (1964).
(57) J. M. Los and D. W. Murray, in *Advances in Polarography*, I. S. Longmuir, ed., Pergamon, London, 1960, Vol. I, pp. 408, 425, 437.
(58) T. A. Kryukova and B. N. Kabanov, *Zhur. Fiz. Khim.*, **20**, 1179 (1946); **21**, 365 (1947).
(59) H. J. Antweiler, *Z. Elektrochem.*, **43**, 596 (1937); **44**, 719, 831, 888 (1938).
(60) L. Gierst and A. L. Juliard, *J. Phys. Chem.*, **57**, 701 (1953); *cf.* also P. Delahay, *J. Phys. Chem.*, **54**, 402 (1950); J. E. B. Randles, *Disc. Faraday Soc.*, **1**, 11 (1947).
(61) L. Meites and T. Meites, *J. Am. Chem. Soc.*, **72**, 3686 (1950).
(62) W. B. Schaap and P. S. McKinney, *Anal. Chem.*, **36**, 1251 (1964).
(63) F. Buckley and J. K. Taylor, *J. Research Natl. Bur. Stds.*, **34**, 87 (1945).
(64) L. Meites, *J. Am. Chem. Soc.*, **73**, 2035 (1953).
(65) D. C. Grahame, R. P. Larsen, and M. A. Poth, *J. Am. Chem. Soc.*, **71**, 2978 (1949).
(66) V. Nejedly, *Collection Czechoslov. Chem. Communs.*, **1**, 319 (1929).
(67) S. N. Mukherjee, A. M. Gosh, and A. Chakravarti, *J. Sci. Ind. Res.* (*India*), **20B**, 77 (1961).
(68) G. Matsuyama, Ph.D. Thesis, University of Minnesota, 1948.
(69) K. Schwabe, in *Progress in Polarography*, P. Zuman and I. M. Kolthoff, eds., Interscience, New York, 1962, Vol. I, p. 338.
(70) L. Onsager, *Ann. N.Y. Acad. Sci.*, **46**, 241 (1945).
(71) L. J. Gosting and H. S. Harned, *J. Am. Chem. Soc.*, **73**, 159 (1951).
(72) J. H. Wang and F. M. Polestra, *J. Am. Chem. Soc.*, **76**, 1584 (1954).
(73) L. Meites, *J. Am. Chem. Soc.*, **73**, 4257 (1951).
(74) J. H. Wang, *J. Am. Chem. Soc.*, **76**, 1528 (1954).
(75) R. J. Bearman, *J. Phys. Chem.*, **66**, 2072 (1962).
(76) T. A. Miller, B. Lamb, B. Prater, J. K. Lee, and R. N. Adams, *Anal. Chem.*, **36**, 418 (1964); T. A. Miller, B. Prater, J. K. Lee, and R. N. Adams, *J. Am. Chem. Soc.*, **87**, 121 (1965).
(77) F. Petru, *Collection Czechoslov. Chem. Communs.*, **12**, 620 (1947).
(78) P. E. Stewart and W. A. Bonner, *Anal. Chem.*, **22**, 793 (1950).
(79) W. C. Davies and W. Furness, *Proc. 1st Intern. Polarogr. Congress*, Prague, 1951, Pt. I, p. 28.
(80) R. Brdička, *Collection Czechoslov. Chem. Communs.*, **12**, 212 (1947).
(81) K. Vesely and R. Brdička, *Collection Czechoslov. Chem. Communs.*, **12**, 313 (1947).
(82) R. Bieber and G. Trümpler, *Helv. Chim. Acta*, **30**, 706 (1947).
(83) R. Brdička, *Z. Elektrochem.*, **59**, 787 (1955); *Collection Czechoslov. Chem. Communs.*, **20**, 387 (1955).
(84) N. Landqvist, *Acta Chem. Scand.*, **9**, 867 (1955).
(85) K. Wiesner, *Collection Czechoslov. Chem. Communs.*, **12**, 64 (1947).
(86) P. Delahay and J. E. Strassner, *J. Am. Chem. Soc.*, **74**, 893 (1952).
(87) P. Delahay, *J. Am. Chem. Soc.*, **74**, 3506 (1952).
(88) R. Brdička and K. Wiesner, *Collection Czechoslov. Chem. Communs.*, **12**, 138 (1947).

(89) J. Koutecký and R. Brdička, *Collection Czechoslov. Chem. Communs.*, **12**, 337 (1947).

(90) P. Rüetschi and G. Trümpler, *Helv. Chim. Acta*, **35**, 1957 (1952).

(91) J. Koutecký, *Collection Czechoslov. Chem. Communs.*, **18**, 11, 183, 311, 597 (1953); **19**, 857, 1045, 1093 (1954); **20**, 116 (1955); **21**, 652, 1056 (1956); **22**, 160 (1957).

(92) R. Brdička, *Collection Czechoslov. Chem. Communs. Suppl.*, **19**, 41 (1954).

(93) R. Brdička and J. Koutecký, *J. Am. Chem. Soc.*, **76**, 907 (1954).

(94) J. Koryta and J. Koutecký, *Collection Czechoslov. Chem. Communs.*, **20**, 423 (1955).

(95) W. Hans, *Z. Elektrochem.*, **59**, 807 (1955).

(96) P. Delahay, *Ann. Rev. Phys. Chem.*, **8**, 229 (1957).

(97) R. Brdička, *Z. Elektrochem.*, **64**, 16 (1960).

(98) R. Brdička, V. Hanuš, and J. Koutecký, in *Progress in Polarography*, P. Zuman and I. M. Kolthoff, eds., Interscience, New York, 1962, Vol. I, p. 145.

(99) R. I. Gelb and L. Meites, *J. Phys. Chem.*, **68**, 2599 (1964).

(100) J. Koryta, *Z. Elektrochem.*, **61**, 423 (1957).

(101) J. Koryta, *Z. Physik. Chem. (Leipzig)*, Sonderheft, 157 (1958).

(102) J. Koryta, *Collection Czechoslov. Chem. Communs.*, **23**, 1408 (1958); **24**, 3057 (1959).

(103) M. Pryszczewska, R. Ralea, and J. Koryta, *Collection Czechoslov. Chem. Communs.*, **24**, 3796 (1959).

(104) R. Holtje and R. Geyer, *Z. Anorg. Allgem. Chem.*, **246**, 258 (1941).

(105) I. M. Kolthoff, W. E. Harris, and G. Matsuyama, *J. Am. Chem. Soc.*, **66**, 1782 (1944).

(106) I. M. Kolthoff and E. P. Parry, *J. Am. Chem. Soc.*, **73**, 3728, 5315 (1951).

(107) G. P. Haight, Jr., *Anal. Chem.*, **23**, 1505 (1951).

(108) M. G. Johnson and R. J. Robinson, *Anal. Chem.*, **24**, 366 (1952).

(109) H. A. Laitinen and W. A. Ziegler, *J. Am. Chem. Soc.*, **75**, 3045 (1953).

(110) A. Blažek and J. Koryta, *Collection Czechoslov. Chem. Communs.*, **18**, 326 (1953).

(111) Z. Pospíšil, *Collection Czechoslov. Chem. Communs.*, **18**, 337 (1953).

(112) M. Březina, *Collection Czechoslov. Chem. Communs.*, **22**, 339 (1957).

(113) B. Matyska, *Collection Czechoslov. Chem. Communs.*, **22**, 1758 (1957).

(114) I. M. Kolthoff and W. Hodara, *J. Electroanal. Chem.*, **5**, 2 (1963).

(115) W. E. Harris and I. M. Kolthoff, *J. Am. Chem. Soc.*, **67**, 1484 (1945).

(116) A. T. Violanda and W. D. Cooke, *Anal. Chem.*, **36**, 2287 (1964).

(117) P. Delahay and G. L. Stiehl, *J. Am. Chem. Soc.*, **74**, 3500 (1952).

(118) J. Koutecký, *Chem. Listy*, **47**, 9 (1953); *Collection Czechoslov. Chem. Communs.*, **18**, 311 (1953).

(119) S. G. Mairanovskii, *J. Electroanal. Chem.*, **6**, 77 (1963).

(120) R. Brdička, *Z. Elektrochem.*, **48**, 278 (1942).

(121) O. H. Müller, *Trans. Electrochem. Soc.*, **87**, 441 (1945).

(122) R. E. Benesch and R. Benesch, *J. Phys. Chem.*, **56**, 648 (1952).

(*123*) M. Březina and P. Zuman, *Die Polarographie in der Medizin, Biochemie und Pharmazie*, Akademische Verlagsgesellschaft, Leipzig, 1956. English edition: Interscience, New York, 1958.
(*124*) L. Meites, *J. Am. Chem. Soc.*, **76**, 5927 (1954).
(*125*) I. M. Kolthoff and C. S. Miller, *J. Am. Chem. Soc.*, **63**, 1013 (1941).
(*126*) J. J. Lingane and L. W. Niedrach, *J. Am. Chem. Soc.*, **71**, 196 (1949).
(*127*) C. Auerbach, *Anal. Chem.*, **30**, 1723 (1958).
(*128*) S. L. Miller and E. F. Orlemann, *J. Am. Chem. Soc.*, **75**, 2001 (1953).
(*129*) J. Heyrovský, F. Sorm, and J. Forejt, *Collection Czechoslov. Chem. Communs.*, **12**, 11 (1947).
(*130*) K. S. G. Doss and A. Kalyanasundaram, *Curr. Sci. (India)*, **20**, 199 (1951); *Proc. Indian Acad. Sci.*, **35**, 173 (1952).

CHAPTER 4

THEORY OF THE CURRENT-POTENTIAL CURVE

The preceding chapter described the behavior of the current on the plateau of a wave, where it is nearly if not quite exactly independent of the potential of the dropping electrode. This chapter describes the manner in which the current is affected by electrode potential on the rising part of the wave.

On the plateau, electron transfer is so fast that the ions or molecules of the electroactive substance are reduced or oxidized as rapidly as they arrive or are formed at the electrode surface. As the potential moves from the plateau of the wave toward its foot, the rate of the electron-transfer process decreases and the reduction or oxidation becomes less and less complete. It is convenient to divide electrode reactions into two extreme classes. One is the class of "reversible" reactions, which are so rapid that thermodynamic equilibrium is very nearly attained at every instant during the life of a drop at any potential. For such reactions the variations of current with potential reflect the changing position of the equilibrium, which is described by the Nernst equation. At the other extreme is the class of "totally irreversible" reactions, which are so slow that they proceed only a fraction of the way toward equilibrium during the life of each drop. For these reactions it is the rate of the electron-transfer process and the manner in which this is influenced by the electrode potential that governs the relationship between current and potential. Between these two extremes there is an intermediate class of reactions that are fast enough to approach equilibrium during the drop life but not quite so fast that they appear to reach it within the experimental error of the measurements.

No electrode reaction is so fast that equilibrium is actually attained at every instant. The definition of reversibility is a practical one: a reaction is said to be reversible if, within the limits of experimental error, its behavior cannot be distinguished from that of an infinitely fast reaction. A reaction may appear to be reversible toward one technique but irreversible toward another in which the measurements arc made more rapidly, so that the lag in the attainment of equilibrium becomes apparent. Many processes appear to be reversible when studied potentiometrically because (ideally, at least) potentiometric measurements do not involve a displacement of the equilibrium, but are shown to be irreversible by polarographic measurements, in which the variation of potential forces them to occur at a finite rate in one direction or the other. Similarly, processes that appear reversible on the time scale of a polarographic measurement may become definitely irreversible when studied by still faster techniques like electrolysis with superimposed alternating voltage or hydrodynamic voltammetry.

Despite the empirical nature of this classification, much valuable thermodynamic information can be obtained from polarographic data on processes that are fast enough to appear reversible. At the other extreme, polarographic data serve to elucidate the kinetics of the rate-determining step in a totally irreversible process. In the remainder of this chapter we shall discuss the behaviors of several common types of reversible processes and the criteria used in establishing their reversibilities, then the behaviors and interpretations of totally irreversible processes of the simplest and most common type.

I. Reversible Processes Involving Simple or Complex Metal Ions and Metals Soluble in Mercury (1, 2)

The reduction of a simple (i.e., aquo-complex) metal ion to give metal atoms soluble in the mercury may be described by the equation

$$M^{n+} + ne + Hg = M(Hg) \tag{4.1}$$

If thermodynamic equilibrium is very rapidly attained, the concentrations of the metal ions and the metal atoms at the drop surface must conform to the Nernst equation:

$$E_{d.e.} = E_s^0 - \frac{RT}{nF} \ln \frac{f_a C_a^0}{a_{Hg}^0 f_s C_s^0} \tag{4.2}$$

where E_s^0 is the standard potential of the half-reaction, C_s^0 and C_a^0 are the molar concentrations of the dissolved ion and of the metal in the amalgam, both at the surface of the drop, f_s and f_a are the corresponding activity coefficients, and a_{Hg}^0 is the activity of the mercury in the amalgam at the drop surface. The standard potential E_s^0 differs from the standard potential of the half-reaction

$$M^{n+} + ne = M$$

because it includes the free energy of solution of the metal in mercury. Since the amalgams formed are quite dilute, a_{Hg}^0 is practically equal to the activity of pure mercury, and will be taken as unity.

It is assumed that the rate of diffusion of the metal ion M^{n+} to the drop surface, and hence the current i, is proportional to the difference between the concentrations of M^{n+} in the bulk of the solution and at the electrode surface:

$$i = k_s(C_s - C_s^0) \tag{4.3}$$

Throughout this chapter it is taken for granted that every current has been corrected for the residual current that flows at the same potential.

At any potential on the plateau of the wave, C_s^0 is virtually zero because the ions are reduced as rapidly as they reach the electrode surface, while the current is equal by definition to the diffusion current i_d. Hence

$$i_d = k_s C_s \tag{4.4}$$

so that, according to the Ilkovič equation, k_s is equal to $607 n_s D_s^{1/2} m^{2/3} t^{1/6}$. Since i, i_d, and k_s all fluctuate as the drops grow and fall, it is most convenient to speak of the average values of these quantities during the drop life.

Meanwhile the concentration of the metal atoms in the amalgam at the drop surface is also proportional to the current:

$$i = -k_a C_a^0 \tag{4.5}$$

where k_a has the same form as k_s but involves the diffusion coefficient of the metal atoms in the amalgam instead of that of the metal ions in the solution. The negative sign here and in the following equations reflects the fact that k_a is negative, as will be explained in connection with eq. (4.11). Combining eqs. (4.2) through (4.5) yields

$$E_{d.e.} = E_s^0 - \frac{RT}{nF} \ln\left(-\frac{f_a k_s}{f_s k_a}\right) - \frac{RT}{nF} \ln \frac{i}{i_d - i} \tag{4.6}$$

When the potential of the dropping electrode is equal to the half-wave potential $E_{1/2}$, $i = i_d/2$ by definition, and since the last term of eq. (4.6) then becomes zero one has

$$E_{\text{d.e.}} = E_{1/2} = E_s^0 - \frac{RT}{nF} \ln \left(-\frac{f_a k_s}{f_s k_a} \right) \qquad (4.7)$$

which may also be written

$$E_{1/2} = E_s^{0\prime} - \frac{RT}{nF} \ln \left(-\frac{k_s}{k_a} \right) \qquad (4.8)$$

where $E_s^{0\prime}$ is the formal potential of the half-reaction under the experimental conditions (ionic strength, temperature, etc.) employed. Equation (4.6) may now be written

$$E_{\text{d.e.}} = E_{1/2} - \frac{RT}{nF} \ln \frac{i}{i_d - i} \qquad (4.9)$$

or, at 25°,

$$E_{\text{d.e.}} = E_{1/2} - \frac{0.05915}{n} \log \frac{i}{i_d - i} \qquad (4.10)$$

In the above equations i is the cathodic current resulting from the reduction of M^{n+}. For a dropping metal-amalgam electrode in a solution of the supporting electrolyte alone, an anodic (negative) current will be obtained from the oxidation of the metal atoms. In this case

$$i_a = k_a(C_a - C_a^0) \qquad (4.11)$$

where i_a is the anodic current and C_a is the concentration of the metal atoms in the interior of the drop. It is evident that k_a must be negative, for a negative current is obtained if C_a exceeds C_a^0 (that is, if metal atoms are being oxidized at the drop surface), and this is why a negative sign appeared in eq. (4.5). The anodic diffusion current $(i_d)_a$ is given by

$$(i_d)_a = k_a C_a \qquad (4.12)$$

while

$$i_a = -k_s C_s^0 \qquad (4.13)$$

Here the negative sign arises because i_a is negative while both k_s and $C_s{}^0$ are positive. Combining eqs. (4.11) through (4.13) with eq. (4.2) yields

$$E_{\text{d.e.}} = E_s^0 - \frac{RT}{nF} \ln\left(-\frac{f_a k_s}{f_s k_a}\right) - \frac{RT}{nF} \ln \frac{(i_d)_a - i_a}{i_a} \qquad (4.14)$$

At the half-wave potential of the anodic wave $i_a = (i_d)_a/2$, and

$$E_{\text{d.e.}} = E_{1/2} = E_s^0 - \frac{RT}{nF} \ln\left(-\frac{f_a k_s}{f_s k_a}\right) \qquad (4.15)$$

which is identical with eq. (4.7). That is, the half-wave potential of the cathodic wave for the reduction of the metal ion must be precisely equal to that of the anodic wave for the oxidation of the metal amalgam if the half-reaction is reversible. This equality of the cathodic and anodic half-wave potentials of the oxidized and reduced forms of a couple is a necessary consequence of the assumption that the half-reaction is reversible, and is of course independent of the kind of couple considered. It is equivalent to asserting that the ratio of concentrations at the drop surface depends on the electrode potential but not on the bulk composition—or, in still other words, that the position of the equilibrium is important but that the direction from which it is approached is not. This is the fundamental criterion of polarographic reversibility.

Equations (4.14) and (4.15) may be combined to give an equation for the anodic wave at 25°:

$$E_{\text{d.e.}} = E_{1/2} - \frac{0.05915}{n} \log \frac{(i_d)_a - i_a}{i_a} \qquad (4.16)$$

and this in turn may be combined with eq. (4.10) to yield a description of the anodic–cathodic ("composite") wave that would be obtained with a dropping amalgam electrode in a solution containing the metal ion:

$$E_{\text{d.e.}} = E_{1/2} - \frac{0.05915}{n} \log \frac{i - (i_d)_a}{(i_d)_c - i} \qquad (4.17)$$

where i is the current at the potential $E_{\text{d.e.}}$, $(i_d)_a$ and $(i_d)_c$ are the anodic and cathodic diffusion currents, and $E_{1/2}$ is the half-wave potential given by eq. (4.7) or (4.15); the log term is so arranged that each difference of currents is positive at every point on the wave.

A typical family of reversible anodic, cathodic, and composite waves for a single redox couple will be shown in Fig. 4.3. Attempts to obtain such curves with couples like those considered here are infrequent, because dropping amalgam electrodes are rather intractable; they should be prepared and used in inert atmospheres because of the danger of air-oxidation of the dissolved metal to yield solid products that clog the capillary (3–7). Conclusive proof of the reversibility of a metal ion–metal amalgam couple is much more easily obtained by oscillographic polarography, cathodic and anodic hanging-drop voltammetry, or current-reversal chronopotentiometry, which obviate the mechanical difficulties likely to arise with dropping amalgam electrodes.

Slightly different descriptions of the half-wave potential are obtained by using the Ilkovič and Koutecký equations for the diffusion current to describe the values of the proportionality constants k_s and k_a. According to the Ilkovič equation the ratio $-k_s/k_a$ in eqs. (4.7) and (4.15) is equal to $607 n_s D_s^{1/2} m^{2/3} t^{1/6} / 607 n_a D_a^{1/2} m^{2/3} t^{1/6}$, or simply $D_s^{1/2}/D_a^{1/2}$; the negative sign disappears because n must be taken to be positive for the reduction of the metal ion (because this yields a cathodic diffusion current) but negative for the oxidation of the metal atoms, and the values of $m^{2/3} t^{1/6}$ disappear because they must be identical for any one capillary at the reversible half-wave potential. Thus the Ilkovič equation predicts

$$E_{1/2} = E_s^0 - \frac{0.05915}{n} \log \frac{f_a D_s^{1/2}}{f_s D_a^{1/2}} \tag{4.18a}$$

at 25°. From the Koutecký equation one obtains (8) in the present notation

$$E_{1/2} = E_s^0 - \frac{0.05915}{n} \log \frac{f_a D_s^{1/2}}{f_s D_a^{1/2}} - \frac{0.891}{n} (D_s^{1/2} - D_a^{1/2}) \frac{t^{1/6}}{m^{1/3}} \tag{4.18b}$$

which would be identical with eq. (4.18a) if the two diffusion coefficients were the same, but which predicts a small dependence on the capillary characteristics when they are not. However, it would be unusual for the diffusion coefficients to be so far different that the predictions of eqs. (4.18a) and (4.18b) differed by more than two or three millivolts.

If the solution contains a complexing agent, so that the metal ion is present as a complex rather than as the simple ion, the half-reaction can be described by the equation

$$MX_p^{(n-pb)+} + ne + Hg = M(Hg) + pX^{-b} \qquad (4.19)$$

It is convenient to imagine that the reduction proceeds in two steps:

$$MX_p^{(n-pb)+} = M^{n+} + pX^{-b} \qquad (4.20a)$$

$$M^{n+} + ne + Hg = M(Hg) \qquad (4.20b)$$

There is, of course, no suggestion that this is the actual mechanism; dividing the reaction into these two steps merely serves to facilitate the explanation of the thermodynamic relationships involved.

The concentrations of the different species present in the solution at the electrode surface are described by the equation

$$f_s C_s^0 = \frac{f_c C_c^0}{f_X^p (C_X^0)^p} K_c \qquad (4.21)$$

where the subscripts s, c, and X denote the species M^{n+}, $MX_p^{(n-pb)+}$, and X^{-b}, respectively. We shall assume that the solution contains X^{-b} at a concentration much higher than that of the complex $MX_p^{(n-pb)+}$. Then the liberation of X^{-b} at the electrode surface as the complex is reduced will have only a negligible effect on the concentration of X^{-b}, and C_X^0 can be equated to C_X, the concentration of X^{-b} in the bulk of the solution. The consequences of failure to satisfy this assumption are discussed for a related case in connection with eq. (4.39) in Sec. III below; here it need only be said that the algebra becomes much more complicated (9) and criteria of reversibility much more difficult to devise and use.

We shall further assume that K_c, the dissociation constant of the complex, is so small that the concentration of free M^{n+} in the bulk of the solution is negligible. Considerations similar to those outlined above lead to the equations

$$i = k_c(C_c - C_c^0) \qquad (4.22)$$

$$i_d = k_c C_c \qquad (4.23)$$

and

$$i = -k_a C_a^0 \tag{4.24}$$

which may be combined with the Nernst equation (4.2) to give

$$E_{\text{d.e.}} = E_s^0 - \frac{RT}{nF} \ln \left(-\frac{f_a k_c}{f_c k_a} \right) + \frac{RT}{nF} \ln K_c$$
$$- \frac{RT}{nF} p \ln f_{\text{X}} C_{\text{X}} - \frac{RT}{nF} \ln \frac{i}{i_d - i} \tag{4.25}$$

whence

$$E_{1/2} = E_s^0 - \frac{RT}{nF} \ln \left(-\frac{f_a k_c}{f_c k_a} \right) + \frac{RT}{nF} \ln K_c - \frac{RT}{nF} p \ln f_{\text{X}} C_{\text{X}} \tag{4.26}$$

and, at 25°

$$E_{\text{d.e.}} = E_{1/2} - \frac{0.05915}{n} \log \frac{i}{i_d - i} \tag{4.27}$$

which is identical with eq. (4.10) except that the two half-wave potentials are not the same. The interpretation of the difference between them is discussed in Chap. 5 I.

For the reversible oxidation of a metal dissolved in mercury to a complex ion, the anodic wave is described by eq. (4.16) and has the half-wave potential given by eq. (4.26). The composite wave obtained with a dropping amalgam electrode in a solution containing a complex ion of the metal and a large constant excess of the ligand is described by eq. (4.17), and the half-wave potential is again given by eq. (4.26). All of these statements are based on the Ilkovič equation; the Koutecký equation would yield an expression resembling eq. (4.18). If K_c is large or C_{X} small, so that the ratio K_c/C_{X}^p is comparable to 1, the term

$$- \frac{RT}{nF} \ln \left(1 - \frac{K_c f_c k_a}{(f_{\text{X}} C_{\text{X}})^p f_a k_c} \right)$$

should be added to the right-hand sides of eqs. (4.25) and (4.26) (10).

According to the foregoing equations, a plot of $-E_{\text{d.e.}}$ vs. log $i/(i_d - i)$ for the reversible cathodic wave resulting from the reduction of a simple or complex metal ion to a metal soluble in mercury

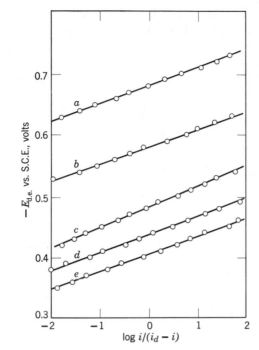

Figure 4.1.   Plots of $-E_{d.e.}$ vs. $\log i/(i_d - i)$ for the reduction of lead(II) from (a) $0.1F$ sodium hydroxide, (b) $1F$ potassium oxalate, pH 9.0, (c) $0.5F$ sodium tartrate, pH 5.5, (d) $1F$ potassium chloride, and (e) $1F$ potassium nitrate. The mean slope is 29.8 ± 1.7 mv.

should be linear and should have a slope of $0.05915/n$ v. at $25°$. Fig. 4.1 shows such plots for the reductions of lead(II) from several different supporting electrolytes. Each plot gives a good straight line over the entire range of values of the log term from -2 to $+2$ ($i = 0.01i_d$ to $0.99i_d$), and the slope of each line is very close to the theoretical value of 29.6 mv. for a reversible two-electron reduction. The differences in the positions of the lines along the potential axis reflect the influence of complex formation on the half-wave potential. This is discussed in Chap. 5.

II. Reversible Processes Involving a Solid Insoluble in Mercury

Half-reactions that yield a product soluble in mercury were considered in the preceding section; those whose products remain dissolved in the solution will be considered in the next one. If one of the products is completely insoluble in both phases, its activity would be expected to be independent of the current, rather than proportional to it as in these other cases. Thus, for the reduction of a simple metal ion to a metal insoluble in mercury the Nernst equation would become

$$E_{\text{d.e.}} = E_{\text{M}}^0 - \frac{RT}{nF} \ln \frac{1}{f_s C_s^0} \tag{4.28}$$

where E_{M}^0 is the standard potential for the reduction of the metal ion to the solid metal. Combining this with eqs. (4.3) and (4.4) gives

$$E_{\text{d.e.}} = E_{\text{M}}^0 - \frac{RT}{nF} \ln \frac{k_s}{f_s} + \frac{RT}{nF} \ln (i_d - i) \tag{4.29}$$

At the half-wave potential, where $E_{\text{d.e.}} = E_{1/2}$ and $i = i_d/2$,

$$E_{1/2} = E_{\text{M}}^0 - \frac{RT}{nF} \ln \frac{k_s}{f_s} + \frac{RT}{nF} \ln \frac{i_d}{2} \tag{4.30}$$

or, combining terms and employing eq. (4.4),

$$E_{1/2} = E_{\text{M}}^0 + \frac{RT}{nF} \ln \frac{f_s}{2} + \frac{RT}{nF} \ln C_s \tag{4.31}$$

so that the half-wave potential should vary with the concentration of the metal ion, in contrast to its constancy in the cases described in Sec. I above. If the process is reversible, a plot of $E_{\text{d.e.}}$ vs. log $(i_d - i)$ should be linear and have a slope of $0.05915/n$ v. at 25°. Combining eqs. (4.29) and (4.30) yields the equation of the wave, which at 25° is

$$E_{\text{d.e.}} = E_{1/2} - \frac{0.05915}{n} \log \frac{i_d}{2} + \frac{0.05915}{n} \log (i_d - i) \tag{4.32}$$

Figure 4.2 shows the calculated current-potential curve for a half-reaction obeying this equation. The sharp "break" at the foot of the wave and the asymmetry of the rising portion are noteworthy.

There are many metals insoluble in mercury (including molybdenum, tungsten, uranium, and vanadium) that cannot be obtained by reducing their ions at dropping mercury electrodes in aqueous solutions, and there are no known conditions under which the ions of

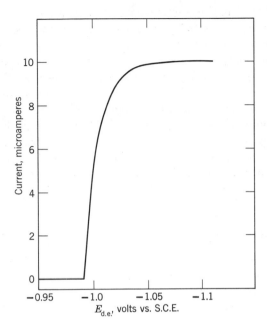

Figure 4.2. Calculated polarographic wave for the reversible two-electron reduction of a metal ion to a metal completely insoluble in mercury. The half-wave potential was assumed to be -1.000 v. and the diffusion current 10.00 μamp.

the metals that can be thus obtained (which include chromium, iron, and a few others) are reversibly reduced, although such conditions may perhaps be found in certain non-aqueous media. The above equations should apply to reversible reductions of metal ions to solid metals at solid microelectrodes, but with few exceptions the agreement between theory and experiment is poor because the activity of the deposited metal does not become constant until a layer of substantial thickness has been formed (11).

Equations like those above do, however, agree with current-potential curves obtained experimentally for the anodic oxidation of the electrode mercury to mercurous chloride. In a solution containing a small concentration of chloride ion, the half-reaction $2 \text{ Hg} + 2 \text{ Cl}^- = \text{Hg}_2\text{Cl}_2 + 2e$ gives rise to a well-defined anodic wave whose height is proportional to the chloride concentration and whose shape conforms closely to that predicted in the above fashion. Since here it is the oxidized form of the couple whose activity is constant, the sign of every term except E^0 must be changed in each of the above equations, and due regard must be paid to the fact that i, i_d, and k_{Cl^-} are all negative. The sharp rise in anodic current near the foot of an anodic chloride wave can be observed, for example, in Fig. A-6. Though other halides give similar waves, chloride is the only one known to give a reversible wave; the iodide wave is irreversible (*12*).

Waves having this shape are occasionally observed in circumstances in which it is difficult to envision a product of constant activity. Typical examples are the reduction of nitrate ion from a lanthanum chloride supporting electrolyte and the reduction of zinc(II) from a strongly alkaline solution containing pyridine. These have not yet been satisfactorily explained.

III. Reversible Processes Involving Only Dissolved Species

When all of the substances involved in a half-reaction are present in the solution phase, the dropping electrode functions as an inert metal indicator electrode. The simplest case is that in which an aquo-metal ion O is reduced to a lower oxidation state R according to the equation

$$O + ne = R \tag{4.33}$$

If the half-reaction is reversible, the Nernst equation

$$E_{\text{d.e.}} = E_s^0 - \frac{RT}{nF} \ln \frac{f_R C_R^0}{f_O C_O^0} \tag{4.34}$$

must be obeyed at every instant. The derivation is entirely analogous to that of eq. (4.6), and leads to the equations

$$E_{\text{d.e.}} = E_{1/2} - \frac{0.05915}{n} \log \frac{i}{i_d - i} \tag{4.35}$$

and

$$E_{1/2} = E_s^0 - \frac{0.05915}{n} \log \left(-\frac{f_R k_O}{f_O k_R} \right) \tag{4.36}$$

where E_s^0 is the standard potential of the couple involving the aquo-complex ions; unlike its counterpart in eqs. (4.2) through (4.27), this can often be found in any of several reference tables. Equations for the anodic wave obtained with R alone and for the composite wave obtained with a mixture of O and R may be obtained similarly; they are identical with eqs. (4.16) and (4.17), respectively, if the subscripts a and s are replaced by O and R. In each case the half-wave potential is the same and is independent of the concentrations of O and R. This is demonstrated by Fig. 4.3.

It is worth noting that the potential on the composite wave where the current is equal to the residual current (so that the value of i as defined above is zero) is the potential that would be obtained from an ordinary potentiometric measurement with an inert electrode of constant area.

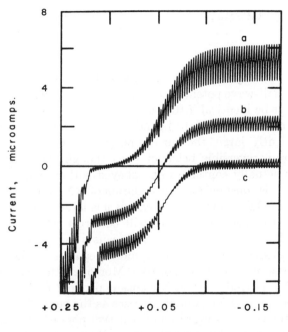

Figure 4.3. Polarograms of (a) 1.4mM ferric iron, (b) 0.7mM ferric iron and 0.7mM ferrous iron, and (c) 1.4mM ferrous iron, each in saturated oxalic acid containing 0.0002% methyl red. Each of the short vertical lines is drawn through the half-wave potential of the wave on which it appears.

For the reduction of a complex metal ion to a lower oxidation state according to the equation

$$OX_p^{(m-pb)+} + ne = RX_q^{(m-n-qb)+} + (p-q)\,X^{-b} \qquad (4.37)$$

if the concentration of X^{-b} in the bulk of the solution is so large [perhaps $20(p-q)$ times as large as the sum of the concentrations of the oxidized and reduced complexes] that it is practically unaffected by the occurrence of the electrode reaction at the drop surface, one again obtains, at 25°,

$$E_{\text{d.e.}} = E_{1/2} - \frac{0.05915}{n} \log \frac{i - (i_d)_a}{(i_d)_c - i} \qquad (4.38)$$

and

$$E_{1/2} = E_c^0 - \frac{0.05915}{n} \log\left(-\frac{f_{\text{RC}}k_{\text{OC}}}{f_{\text{OC}}k_{\text{RC}}}\right) - \frac{0.05915}{n}(p-q)\log f_{\text{X}}C_{\text{X}}$$

$$(4.39)$$

where the subscripts OC and RC denote the respective complex ions. Again the half-wave potentials of the cathodic, anodic, and composite waves must be identical if the half-reaction is reversible.

If the concentration of the ligand X^{-b} in the bulk of the solution is not sufficiently large, the current-potential curves may appear to deviate from reversible behavior even though the thermodynamic equations actually continue to be obeyed within experimental error (13). If X^{-b} is consumed in the oxidation of RX_q and liberated in the reduction of OX_p, as will be the case if p is larger than q, its concentration at the electrode surface will be larger when the current is cathodic than when it is anodic. This causes the half-wave potential of the cathodic wave to become more negative while that of the anodic wave becomes more positive. Moreover, the concentration of X^{-b} at the electrode surface becomes dependent on the current; on the cathodic wave, for example, it rises as the current increases, and so the displacement toward more negative potentials increases with increasing current. The wave becomes drawn out, a plot of $-E_{\text{d.e.}}$ vs. $\log i/(i_d - i)$ becomes curved instead of linear, and the slope of the plot approaches $0.05915/n$ v. only as a limit as the current approaches zero. Of course there is a trivial case in which $p = q$, so that C_{X}^0 is unaffected by the flow of current and these phenomena are not observed. Even when p and q differ, the thermodynamic relationships have been thoroughly worked out (14). But there is nothing to be gained by using so low a concentration of ligand that these complexities arise.

The equations that describe the reduction of a complex ion to a lower oxidation state are also applicable to the reversible reduction of an organic compound to a soluble reduced species; it is necessary only to change a few symbols. The reduction of an organic compound O may be described by the half-reaction

$$O + pH^+ + ne = RH_p \qquad (4.40)$$

The values of p and n are generally equal; the case in which they differ because O and RH_p are involved in different protonation equilibria is discussed in Chap. 5 II. The current-potential curve is again described by equation (4.39), while the half-wave potential is given by

$$E_{1/2} = E^0 - \frac{0.05915}{n} \log\left(-\frac{k_O}{k_{RH_p}}\right) - \frac{0.05915p}{n}\, pH \quad (4.41)$$

Just as it is desirable for C_X and C_X^0 to be equal in the reduction of a metal ion so as to obviate the complications mentioned in the last paragraph, it is desirable for the pH at the electrode surface to be the same as in the body of the solution. The electrode reaction consumes hydrogen ions and therefore tends to make the pH at the electrode surface higher than it is in the bulk of the solution. To render this change inappreciable the solution must be buffered, as discussed in the last paragraph of Chap. 3 II. It should be added that carbon dioxide–bicarbonate buffers, and perhaps a few others as well, are unsuitable for use in polarography because their equilibria are too slow to keep the pH at the electrode surface constant in the face of a reaction that is consuming or liberating hydrogen ions.

The number of organic systems giving reversible waves is rather small, and irreversible waves are far more numerous. The reversible systems include quinones and hydroquinones, azo- and hydrazo-benzenes, some dyes and their leuco forms, and a very few others.

IV. Criteria of Reversibility

The above equations form the bases of most of the practical criteria of polarographic reversibility. The fundamental criterion has been mentioned repeatedly, but it can do no harm to repeat it once more: if the half-reaction is reversible, the cathodic wave obtained with the oxidized form alone, the anodic wave obtained with the reduced form alone, and the composite wave obtained with a mixture of the two must all have the same half-wave potential, and all must obey an equation of the form of eq. (4.38). There are just two reservations. One is that, as was pointed out above, this will not be true, even though the couple is reversible, unless the concentrations of its oxidized and reduced forms are the only ones that can vary appreciably as the current changes; the concentration of every other substance involved in the half-reaction must be kept constant by employing a large excess of a ligand or a high concentration of a buffer system. The other is that one must be on his guard against the possibility that the anodic and cathodic waves may not represent a single redox couple (15). It is well worth while to make sure that the cathodic and anodic diffusion currents obtained with a solution containing equal concentrations of the oxidized and reduced species are approximately the same (that is, that the values of n for the two species are numerically equal).

There are various other criteria that help to establish the reversibility of an electrode reaction. For reasons that will be mentioned below, however, they should not be used alone; it is always better to employ the fundamental criterion wherever it is experimentally possible to do so.

The most widely applicable and most commonly used of these auxiliary criteria is based on the behavior of the so-called "log plot." For each of the systems discussed above (excepting those in which solid products are formed, which are not often encountered in practical work), the assumption of reversibility leads at 25° to equations of the form

$$E_{d.e.} = E_{1/2} - \frac{0.05915}{n} \log \frac{i}{(i_d)_c - i} \qquad \text{(cathodic wave)} \quad (4.42a)$$

$$= E_{1/2} - \frac{0.05915}{n} \log \frac{(i_d)_a - i}{i} \qquad \text{(anodic wave)} \qquad (4.42b)$$

$$= E_{1/2} - \frac{0.05915}{n} \log \frac{i - (i_d)_a}{(i_d)_c - i} \qquad \text{(composite wave)} \quad (4.42c)$$

Incidentally, these are valid, not only over the visibly rising portions of reversible waves, but over their whole extents, whether i is so small that no divergence from the residual-current curve can be detected or so nearly equal to i_d that the corresponding value of $E_{d.e.}$ lies on the plateau of the wave. In other words, there is a little of the reduced form present at the electrode surface no matter how positive the potential of the electrode may be, and by the same token there is a little of the oxidized form present at the electrode surface no matter how negative the potential may be.

It follows from eqs. (4.42) that a plot of $-E_{d.e.}$ vs. the log term appropriate to the kind of wave being considered should be linear and should have a slope of $59.15/n$ mv. at 25° (or, for example, $54.2/n$ mv. at 0°).

For best results it is advisable to construct the log plot from a polarogram specially obtained to permit accurate measurements on the rising part of the wave. It should be recorded with an initial potential that precedes the half-wave potential by at most 0.2 v. and a span potential that does not exceed 0.5 v. (or with the smallest span potential available if one as small as 0.5 v. cannot be secured with the instrument), and care should be taken to avoid excessive damping. This will yield a wave spread out over a large fraction of the length of the chart, minimizing errors in the measurement of the potential. On the resulting polarogram the means of the oscillations on the portion of the residual-current curve preceding the wave should be extrapolated toward the plateau. The extrapolation must not cross the potential of the electrocapillary maximum, where the slope of the residual-current curve changes, as explained in Chap. 3 I. To deal with waves near this potential or at potentials so near the initial or final current rise that the residual-current curve is distinctly nonlinear, it is better to record the residual-current curve separately on the same chart with the same instrument settings. This is best done by recording the polarogram first, then discarding the solution and recording the residual-current curve with another aliquot of the supporting electrolyte; it is embarrassing to record the residual-current curve first and then find that the polarogram runs off scale at the sensitivity employed.

At each of perhaps a dozen points, more or less equally spaced along the potential axis on the rising part of the wave, an oscillation is selected that shows no discernible irregularity (such as would result

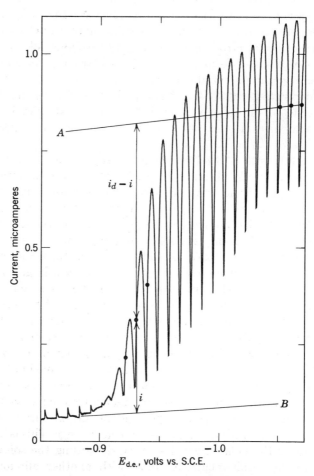

Figure 4.4.   Polarogram of 0.16 mM zinc(II) in 0.10F potassium chloride containing 0.07mF hydrochloric acid and 0.0015% Triton X-100, showing how i and $(i_d - i)$ should be measured in constructing a log plot. Line A is the extrapolation of the mean current on the plateau; line B is the extrapolation of the mean current at potentials preceding the wave. The curve was obtained with an excessively long drop time and a considerably underdamped recorder to draw out the oscillations and portray the measurements more clearly.

from a transient vibration, for example). On the rising part of each oscillation, the point halfway between its maximum and minimum is marked, as illustrated on Fig. 4.4. The rising part of the oscillation (where the pen is moving away from the residual-current line) is chosen because over most of the wave it is less steep than the falling part and is, therefore, more accurately traced by a recorder of finite speed. The vertical distance between each such point and the extrapolated residual-current line (or the interpolated mean current on the separately recorded residual-current curve) is proportional to the value of i at the corresponding potential. To obtain the value of $(i_d - i)$, the most accurate procedure is to extrapolate the means of the oscillations on the plateau backward toward the foot of the wave and to measure the vertical distance from this line to the previously located point on the rising part of the wave at each potential selected. Figure 4.4 was recorded under exaggerated conditions to portray the measurements more clearly. It may be noted that the extrapolated line B represents the mean residual current, which does not coincide with the means of the oscillations that precede the rising part of the wave (compare curve d of Fig. 3.2). When the slope of the plateau is not much different from that of the residual-current line, the measurements can be simplified by employing a constant value of i_d measured near the beginning of the plateau.

With a recording polarograph of the resistance-potentiometer type, the iR drop through the instrument may lead to erroneous values of the slope of a log plot if the full-scale sensitivity of the recorder is numerically larger than about 2 mv. Consider, for example, a cathodic wave obtained with a recorder having a sensitivity of 1 mv./in. If the value of i at some point on the wave corresponds to a pen deflection of 1.0 in. away from the zero-current line, there is an iR drop of 1.0 mv. through the instrument. Consequently the potential of the dropping electrode is 1.0 mv. less negative than the position of this point along the potential axis of the recorded curve indicates. Because the difference increases with increasing current, the slope of the log plot appears to be numerically larger than the true value, as illustrated by Fig. 4.5. Though the uncorrected plot (curve a) is not exactly linear, it is so nearly so that its curvature is almost certain to escape notice in practical work. Similar considerations apply to anodic waves, except that the sign of the iR drop is reversed; in the above illustration the actual potential would have been 1.0 mv. less positive than

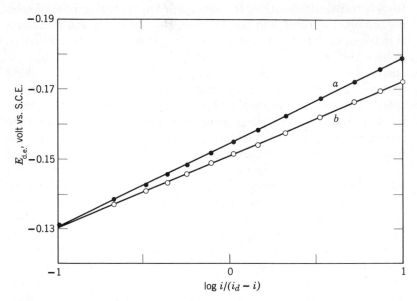

Figure 4.5.   Plots of $E_{d.e.}$ vs. log $i/(i_d - i)$ for bismuth(III) in $0.1F$ hydrochloric acid containing 0.0015% Triton X-100. Curve a is the uncorrected plot, which has a slope of -24.3 mv.; curve b, which has a slope of -21.0 mv., was obtained after correction for the iR drop through the polarograph. The original polarogram was obtained with a recorder having a 10-mv. span and with a sensitivity such that the iR drop was 7 mv. on the plateau of the wave.

the apparent value if the wave had been anodic. This effect will obviously also produce an apparent difference between the anodic and cathodic half-wave potentials of even a reversible couple, and corrections are therefore vital in attempts to assess the reversibility of a half-reaction. Exactly the same phenomena are produced by a substantial cell resistance, but here an accurate correction is virtually impossible to make unless the cell resistance is known.

On the final log plot there should be no systematic divergence of the points from a straight line over the range of values of the log term extending from at least -1.5 to $+1.5$. This corresponds to values of the current ranging from about 3 to 97% of the diffusion current. At smaller currents the correction for the residual current becomes increasingly uncertain, while at higher currents the relative error of the difference $(i_d - i)$ increases. Deviations from linearity beyond these extremes are, therefore, of little importance. So far as the slope is concerned, it is easily possible for the experimental errors to combine in such a way as to produce a deviation of perhaps 3 mv. from the truth. Curvature within the above range of values of the log term, or any larger difference between the experimental and theoretical slopes, must either reflect some defect in the apparatus or experimental technique or, if these are not at fault, mean that the wave is definitely irreversible. Systematic errors that give rise to such deviations include not only failure to correct for iR drops in the polarograph and the cell circuit, but also recorder lag due to either inherent sluggishness or overdamping, errors in the bridge and span-potential circuit, and the like. To avoid errors due to recorder lag, it is prudent to construct log plots from polarograms obtained with different settings of the damping switch but under otherwise identical conditions, at least until enough experience has been gained with the instrument to permit trustworthy evaluation of the results.

To minimize the time and trouble required to construct a log plot, many polarographers prefer to measure the current at the instant when the drop has attained its maximum size instead of the average current during the drop life. Though the two procedures are theoretically equivalent for the simple purpose of assessing reversibility, measurement at the end of the drop life is superior in theory as well as more convenient in practice for evaluating αn_a for a totally irreversible wave as described in Sec. V below. For this purpose the polarogram (and, if it is needed, the residual-current curve as well) is obtained as above but with an undamped recorder. Especially for the evaluation of αn_a the recorder period should not exceed 1 sec., but little if anything is gained if it is shorter. As was pointed out in Chap. 3 I, the condenser current is smallest at the end of the drop life, and therefore it is the minima of the oscillations on the residual-current curve that must be extrapolated provided that the oscillations have the shapes shown in curves a–c of Fig. 3.2. Exquisite care is necessary if they do not; inspection of curves d and e of Fig. 3.2 will reveal the nature of the problem. In that case it is advisable to purify the supporting electrolyte or the solvent so as to eliminate or at least greatly decrease the faradaic component of the residual current. The value of i_d is obtained from the maxima of the oscillations near the beginning of the plateau (or one may extrapolate these maxima in the fashion described above). On the rising part of the wave the desired values of i correspond to the maxima of the oscillations except near the foot, where Fig. 3.2 should again be consulted. Finding the end of the drop life is facilitated by using a fairly long drop time (or a fairly high chart speed if this is possible with the polarograph used) to separate the successive oscillations as widely as possible and permit the shape of each to be seen clearly. The point is emphasized because the technique is usually said in the literature to be based on the maximum current during the drop life; what is meant is the maximum current after correction for the residual current, and near the foot of the wave (or with an extremely dilute solution) this is not at all the same thing as the maximum of the recorded oscillation.

Though the difficulty decreases as the diffusion current increases because the residual current then becomes more and more nearly negligible, one should not try to circumvent it by employing a concentration of electroactive substance so high that correction for the residual current can be ignored. Not only would this increase the iR drop through the cell, but it would also involve additional dangers due to adsorption, maxima, and other phenomena that can be ignored at low concentrations but that produce distorted waves at higher concentrations.

Another criterion, which is equivalent to the slope of a log plot but is much more rapid and convenient to apply, requires the measurement of only $E_{1/4}$ and $E_{3/4}$ from the recorded polarogram. These are, respectively, the potentials at which the current (after correction for the residual current) is equal to one-fourth and three-fourths of the diffusion current. At $E_{1/4}$, for a reversible cathodic wave, eq. (4.42a) becomes

$$E_{1/4} = E_{1/2} - \frac{0.05915}{n} \log \frac{i_d/4}{i_d - i_d/4}$$

$$= E_{1/2} - \frac{0.05915}{n} \log \tfrac{1}{3} \qquad (4.43)$$

while

$$E_{3/4} = E_{1/2} - \frac{0.05915}{n} \log 3 \qquad (4.44)$$

so that

$$E_{3/4} - E_{1/4} = -\frac{0.05915}{n} \log 9 = -\frac{0.0564}{n} \qquad (4.45)$$

Consequently the value of $E_{3/4} - E_{1/4}$ for a reversible cathodic wave is equal to $-56.4/n$ mv.; for a reversible anodic wave it is equal to $+56.4/n$ mv.

The value of $E_{1/4}$ is most easily measured from a recorded polarogram in the following way. The linear portion of the residual-current curve preceding the wave is extrapolated toward the plateau, and the plateau is extrapolated backward toward the foot of the wave, in the same way described above. For assessing reversibility one may employ either the average currents or the currents at the ends of the drop lives, the latter being more convenient; for evaluating αn_a it is much better to use the currents at the ends of the drop lives as recorded on a polarogram obtained with minimum damping. A separate residual-current curve should be recorded if the extrapolations would cross the potential of the electrocapillary maximum or if the wave occurs at a potential either so positive or so negative that the residual current curve is sensibly nonlinear. A ruler is moved along the polarogram in such a way that the zero mark follows the extrapolated residual-current line while the straight edge remains perpendicular to the potential axis. It is not difficult to locate the potential at which the distance from the residual-current line to the curve is equal to one-fourth of the distance between the two extrapolated lines; this is $E_{1/4}$, and $E_{3/4}$ is found by an exactly similar procedure. Interpolation between successive oscillations is usually necessary, but the discomfort one feels on performing it decreases rapidly with practice and is greatly mitigated by recording the curve with a suitably small span potential.

The half-wave potential may also, of course, be measured in the same way. If a log plot has been constructed, further trouble may be saved, and a somewhat more precise value of the half-wave potential can be obtained, by locating the potential at which the log term is equal to zero. When the measurement is made directly from the polarogram, the necessary correction for the iR drop through the polarograph is easily evaluated by comparing the pen deflection at the half-wave potential with the sensitivity of the recorder; the error causes the half-wave potential to appear to be more negative than the truth if the current there is cathodic, but more positive than the truth if it is anodic. A value of $E_{1/2}$ obtained from a properly constructed log plot needs no correction for iR drop through the polarograph, for the correction will already have been applied in the construction of the plot if it is appreciable.

The value of $E_{3/4} - E_{1/4}$ read off the polarogram also needs correction for this iR drop unless the recorder span is smaller than about 2 mv.; the error increases the numerical value of $E_{3/4} - E_{1/4}$ regardless of whether the wave is cathodic or anodic. The correction is easily applied. It is only necessary to measure the difference between the pen deflections at the two potentials selected, convert this to millivolts by employing the known sensitivity of the recorder, and subtract the result from the numerical value of $E_{3/4} - E_{1/4}$. In careful work the corrected value should not differ by more than 2 mv. from the theoretical one for a wave known to be reversible.

Neither the slope of the log plot nor the value of $E_{3/4} - E_{1/4}$ can be used both to estimate n and to support a decision as to whether a wave is reversible or not. This would hardly deserve discussion were it not for the fact that papers are still occasionally published in which, for example, the fact that a log plot has a slope of about 59 mv. is interpreted to mean that the half-reaction involves one electron and that it is reversible. This is extremely perilous, for irreversible half-reactions involving two or more electrons very often give log plots having about this slope. The interpretation of the slope of a log plot for an irreversible wave will be discussed in Sec. V below; here it need merely be mentioned that the slope of a log plot for an irreversible wave is nearly always larger than for a reversible wave involving the same number of electrons. One should therefore not attempt to interpret the slope of a log plot until after the value of n has been obtained from diffusion-current data (Chap. 3 VI), controlled-potential coulometry (Chap. 10 II), coulometry with the dropping electrode (Chap. 10 III), or some other technique.

It is important to be quite clear about the nature of the information that can be deduced from the slope of a log plot or from the value of $E_{3/4} - E_{1/4}$. There are couples whose oxidized forms give cathodic waves for which these two parameters agree very well with the reversible values, but whose reduced forms either do not give anodic waves at all or give them at much more positive potentials. Conversely, there are couples whose reduced forms give anodic waves that seem to be reversible according to these criteria, but whose oxidized forms cannot be reduced at all or can be reduced only at much more negative potentials. This behavior arises from a mechanism like

$$A \pm ne = B \quad \text{(reversible)} \tag{4.46a}$$

$$B \rightarrow C \qquad \text{(slow)} \tag{4.46b}$$

in which a reversible electron-transfer step is followed by an irreversible rearrangement, precipitation, change in degree of hydration or association, or some other reaction. In such cases the difference between the cathodic and anodic half-wave potentials shows that the A–C couple is irreversible, and so one must not conclude that it is reversible from the fact that the slope of the log plot or the value of $E_{3/4} - E_{1/4}$ for the wave of A agrees with the reversible prediction. The agreement does indicate that the A–B couple is reversible, but there is a danger for the unwary. Ordinarily, the half-wave potential of a reversible wave is very close to the standard or formal potential of the couple, and consequently the temptation to extract thermodynamic parameters from data on reversible waves is very strong. Here, however, the half-wave potential for the quasireversible wave of A depends not only on the standard potential of the A–B couple and the usual small corrections for activity and diffusion coefficients, but also on the rate constant for the irreversible reaction that follows the electron-transfer step (16). Attempts to elucidate the thermodynamics of the A–B couple are therefore complicated by the difficulty of deciding whether a variation of the half-wave potential on changing some experimental condition is attributable to an effect on this couple or to a change in the rate of the subsequent chemical reaction. It may incidentally be pointed out that if the subsequent reaction is not first order with respect to B the log plot will be curved and the half-wave potential will vary with the concentration of A. Quasireversible waves are further discussed in Sec. VI below.

In this light it is probably advisable to take the position that the slope of a log plot and the value of $E_{3/4} - E_{1/4}$ can be used to prove that a couple is irreversible but not to prove that it is reversible. Thus, if the slope of a log plot appreciably exceeds $59.2/n$ mv. or if the numerical value of $E_{3/4} - E_{1/4}$ appreciably exceeds $56.4/n$ mv., the couple should be taken to be irreversible without further ado and thermodynamic interpretation of the half-wave potentials along the lines described in Chap. 5 should not be attempted. Such evidence is conclusive proof of irreversibility even though it is obtained with only one of the two substances involved in the couple; it may be of interest to study the behavior of the other, but its behavior cannot contradict this conclusion. On the other hand, even if the slope of the log plot or the value of $E_{3/4} - E_{1/4}$ for, say, the cathodic wave of the oxidized form of a couple agrees with the reversible value it is unsafe to conclude that the couple is reversible, for the behavior of the reduced form must still be investigated before this can be considered certain.

A maximum on a recorded polarogram (Chap. 6) has less serious effects on the application of these criteria than may at first appear. It decreases the numerical value of $E_{3/4} - E_{1/4}$ and renders a log plot convex toward the potential axis (thereby decreasing the slope of any line imposed on the experimental points). Either effect will cause an irreversible wave to appear more nearly reversible; if it still appears irreversible the question is settled, while if it appears reversible further proof is still needed, just as if the maximum were absent.

In addition to these common criteria of reversibility there are several others that are less often used, partly because they are less reliable and partly because special information must be obtained to permit their application. These are summarized briefly in the following paragraphs.

Except when the electrode reaction yields a solid product or involves a number of ions or molecules of the electroactive substance that is not the same as the number of ions or molecules of the product (as is the case for the anodic wave of cyanide ion, where the half-reaction is $Hg + 2CN^- = Hg(CN)_2 + 2e$, so that two cyanide ions are consumed but only one molecule of the product is formed), which require obvious modification of the thermodynamic equations given above, the half-wave potential of a reversible wave is independent of the concentration of the electroactive substance after correction has been made for any iR drop through the cell and polarograph. Since these exceptions are infrequent and easily recognized on chemical grounds, any appreciable variation of $E_{1/2}$ with concentration can usually be taken as conclusive proof of the irreversibility of the half-reaction. The converse does not hold true, however, for the half-wave potentials of most irreversible waves are also independent of concentration. The variation is due to some non-first-order step in the process.

The temperature coefficient of the half-wave potential of a reversible wave is usually small, typically between -2 and $+2$ mv./deg. Irreversible waves often have half-wave potentials with similarly small temperature coefficients (17), but there are some whose temperature coefficients are positive (the process is facilitated by an increase of temperature) and exceed several millivolts per degree. This of course reflects a substantial heat of activation. A large positive temperature coefficient of the half-wave potential, therefore, usually signifies that the half-reaction is irreversible.

The half-wave potential of a reversible wave is nearly independent of the drop time (18), while that of an irreversible cathodic wave becomes more positive as the drop time is increased (19,20). In Sec. V below it will be shown that, at 25°,

$$\Delta E_{1/2}/\Delta \log t = 0.02957/\alpha n_a \qquad (4.47)$$

for a totally irreversible wave. Values of αn_a ranging from about 0.1 to 2 for different processes have been reported in the literature, and correspondingly the values of $\Delta E_{1/2}/\Delta \log t$ may range from about 300 to 15 mv. Both extremes are unusual; in a typical case [the reduction of nickel(II) from $0.2F$ potassium nitrate] the half-wave potential varied from -1.016 v. vs. S.C.E. at $t = 2.09$ sec. to -0.959 v. at $t = 7.66$ sec., so that $\Delta E_{1/2}/\Delta \log t$ was 100 mv. A value of $\Delta E_{1/2}/\Delta \log t$ that exceeds a few millivolts is almost certain proof that the half-reaction is irreversible. In this connection it may be mentioned that, according to eq. (4.18b), the half-wave potential of a reversible wave should be completely independent of drop time if the oxidized and reduced forms of the couple have equal diffusion coefficients. The behavior that should be observed if they do not may be illustrated by assuming $D_s = 4 \times 10^{-6}$ (cm.²/sec.), $D_a = 9 \times 10^{-6}$, $n = 1$, and the relations among m, t, and h_{corr} described by Table 3.3; it is then easy to calculate that the half-wave potential should become 1.34 mv. more negative as h_{corr} is decreased from 100 to 10 cm., which corresponds to a 10-fold increase in the drop time. The amalgam diffusion coefficients of those few metals for which trustworthy data are available are more nearly equal to the diffusion coefficients of the corresponding aquo-complex ions in dilute aqueous solutions than has been assumed here; in most cases the variation of $E_{1/2}$ will be smaller than in this example. Hence the value of $\Delta E_{1/2}/\Delta \log t$ will usually be only a few tenths of a millivolt for a reversible wave, and it may be either positive or negative depending on which of the two diffusion coefficients is the larger. Unfortunately, experimental data on reversible waves (18) do not agree very well with these predictions; the observed variation of $E_{1/2}$ is considerably larger than that expected.

A final criterion has been left till last, although it is almost unimpeachable and serves to prove reversibility as well as irreversibility, because it is rarely possible to use. As has been shown in the preceding sections of this chapter, the half-wave potential of a reversible wave (except in the unusual case where the product has a constant activity) can be written in the form, at 25°,

$$E_{1/2} = E^{0\prime} - \frac{0.05915}{n} \log \frac{D_O^{1/2}}{D_R^{1/2}} \qquad (4.48)$$

[compare eq. (4.8) and the discussion following eq. (4.18b)]. The correction represented by the last term in eq. (4.18b) will usually be small enough to ignore. The ratio $D_O^{1/2}/D_R^{1/2}$ is equal to the ratio of the numerical values of the cathodic and anodic diffusion current constants, and can be evaluated experimentally; even in an extreme case where one of these was twice as large as the other the term involving this ratio would be only $18/n$ mv. If the formal potential of the couple is known under the conditions of the experiment, the half-wave potential can be calculated from this equation. If the experimental value for either the cathodic or the anodic wave agrees with the calculated one, the couple must be reversible, and the other wave must have the same half-wave potential; if the half-wave potential of either wave disagrees with the calculated value, the couple is irreversible and the anodic and cathodic half-wave potentials cannot be the same.

As an example we may cite the reduction of chromate in $1F$ sodium hydroxide. The formal potential of the half-reaction $CrO_4^= + 2H_2O + 3e = CrO_2^- + 4OH^-$ in this medium is -0.12 v. vs. N.H.E., or -0.36 v. vs. S.C.E. The half-wave potential of the cathodic wave of chromate is -0.85 v. vs. S.C.E. It would be a waste of time to bother with the second term on the right-hand side of eq. (4.48), for this could not possibly account for any significant fraction of the discrepancy of 0.49 v.: the couple is certainly irreversible. Only if the half-wave potential is within perhaps 30 mv. of the formal potential will a more refined estimate be worth the trouble required to make it.

The necessary formal potential will often be unavailable, and then one may base the criterion on the standard potential, though this is both less convenient and less satisfactory because of the necessity of taking activity coefficients and liquid-junction potentials into account. For the couple $V^{+++} + e = V^{++}$ the standard potential is -0.255 v.

vs. N.H.E., or -0.496 v. vs. S.C.E., while the half-wave potential of the cathodic wave of V^{+++} in $1F$ perchloric acid is -0.508 v. vs. S.C.E. The difference is small enough to warrant a more exact calculation. The diffusion current constants of V^{+++} and V^{++} in this medium are 1.41 and -1.74, respectively, the latter being negative because the wave is anodic. The conventional individual ionic activity coefficients of V^{+++} and V^{++} may be estimated as 0.91 and 0.96, respectively (*21*), and so one calculates

$$E_{1/2} = -0.496 - 0.05915 \log \left(- \frac{(0.91)(1.41)}{(0.96)(-1.74)} \right) = -0.489 \text{ v.}$$

The experimental half-wave potential is 19 mv. more negative than this. The liquid-junction potential across the boundary   saturated KCl$//1F$ HClO$_4$ is not known, but the probably very nearly equal one across the boundary $3.5F$ KCl$//1F$ HCl   is -16.6 mv. The sign signifies that an electrode in the acidic solution appears to have a more negative potential than it actually does, and inclusion of the liquid-junction potential therefore displaces the calculated half-wave potential about 17 mv. toward a more negative value. Hence the experimental half-wave potential differs from the expected one by only about 2 mv., which is much smaller than the combined errors of measuring and estimating the various quantities involved.

It may fairly be concluded from the above examples that there is no easier way to demonstrate the irreversibility of a wave in a clear-cut case if the formal or standard potential can be found in the literature, but that the approximations and calculations needed in a borderline case are less certain (and hardly less tedious) than measuring and comparing the anodic and cathodic half-wave potentials. In addition, so many polarographic measurements are performed with couples whose formal and standard potentials are as yet unknown that the criterion is of only rather occasional utility.

Other criteria of reversibility may be based on circuitry like that devised by Kalousek (*22–24*) or Ishibashi and Fujinaga (*25*), on oscillographic or a.-c. polarography (*25–34*), on current-reversal chronopotentiometry (*35*), on reverse-scan voltammetry with stationary electrodes such as the hanging drop and stationary pool (*36–42*), on voltammetry with annular rotating disc electrodes (*43,44*) and on a host of other techniques. Most of these are discussed in Chaps. 8 and 10.

V. Irreversible Processes

The practical significance of irreversibility in polarographic experiments is illustrated by Fig. 4.6. The lead wave in the figure is reversible: its half-wave potential is the same as that of the anodic wave obtained with a dropping lead-amalgam electrode and both of these are essentially identical with the formal potential of the lead(II)–lead amalgam couple in this medium, and the values of $E_{3/4} - E_{1/4}$ and of the slope of a plot of $E_{d.e.}$ vs. $\log i/(i_d - i)$ are equal within experimental error to the thermodynamic predictions of eqs. (4.45) and (4.10) for the reversible two-electron reduction of a metal ion to a

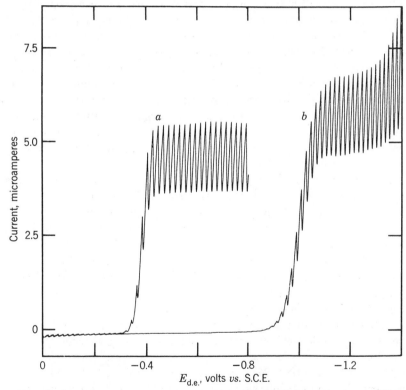

Figure 4.6. Polarograms of (a) 0.4mM lead(II) and (b) 0.5mM mickel(II) in 0.1F sodium chloride–0.001F hydrochloric acid containing 0.002% Triton X-100. Reproduced by permission from the *Treatise on Analytical Chemistry*, I. M. Kolthoff and P. J. Elving, eds., Part I, Vol. 4, Interscience, 1963.

metal soluble in mercury. The nickel wave, on the other hand, obeys none of these thermodynamic predictions. Its half-wave potential is nearly half a volt more negative than the formal potential of the nickel ion-nickel couple. The solubility of nickel in mercury is not definitely known. If, as is widely believed, it is very small, the half-wave potential should be described by eq. (4.31) and a plot of $E_{d.e.}$ vs. log $(i_d - i)$ should be linear. In fact, the half-wave potential is much more negative than the value predicted by eq. (4.31) and a plot of $E_{d.e.}$ vs. log $(i_d - i)$ is curved rather than straight, as would be expected from the fact that the wave does not have the shape shown in Fig. 4.2. If, on the other hand, nickel is fairly soluble in mercury, the half-wave potential should be more positive than the formal potential of the nickel ion-nickel couple because it should be easier to reduce nickel ion to the amalgam than to the solid metal, and this is not the case. Moreover, although the second of these assumptions does serve to account for the fact that a plot of $E_{d.e.}$ vs. log $i/(i_d - i)$ is straight, it does not account for the fact that the slope of this plot is numerically much larger than it should be for a reversible two-electron wave, as follows from the fact that the nickel wave in Fig. 4.6 extends over a wider range of potentials than the lead wave. There is no way to reconcile data on the nickel wave with any of the thermodynamic considerations presented above.

If, as an approximation, we neglect the difference between the diffusion coefficients of lead ion (or its chloro complex) and lead atoms, we can say that the current due to the reduction of lead ion at its formal potential is equal to half of the diffusion current because half of the lead ions reaching the electrode surface must be reduced in order to yield equal concentrations of lead ions and lead atoms at the electrode surface, as required by the Nernst equation. At the formal potential of the nickel ion–nickel couple, however, the rate of reduction of nickel ions is very small because the free energy of activation is very large. Hence the reduction of nickel ion occurs to only a negligible extent during the life of a drop, and only a very small current flows. This is much too small even to be detected with a dropping electrode in the face of the continuously changing residual current, though it is easily measured with a mercury pool electrode of constant area, which eliminates interference from the charging current. Because the reduction is so slow, thermodynamic equilibrium is not even approached, and the thermodynamic equations written in preceding sections are therefore irrelevant except that they do set an upper limit to the extent of reduction that might possibly be observed. Whereas the current flowing at any point on a reversible wave reflects the position of an equilibrium that is rapidly established and maintained throughout the drop life, the current flowing at any point on an irreversible wave reflects simply the rate of the half-reaction that occurs.

As the potential of the dropping electrode in the nickel solution of Fig. 4.6(b) becomes more negative, the rate constant for the reduction of nickel ion increases exponentially, and eventually becomes large enough (around -0.85 v.) to produce a detectable increase of current. At the same time the rate of oxidation of atomic nickel decreases exponentially; it is already small at the formal potential of the couple, which is close to -0.5 v. vs. S.C.E., and is therefore entirely negligible at any potential where nickel ion is reduced at an appreciable rate. Conversely, of course, the rate of reduction of nickel ion would be negligibly small at any potential where nickel could be oxidized at an appreciable rate. Couples of which this is true are called totally irreversible.

As the rate constant for the reduction of nickel ion increases exponentially on making the potential more negative, the current also increases exponentially until the rate of reduction has become large enough to result in a sensible depletion of the nickel ions at the drop surface. This may be considered to occur when the current is roughly a tenth of the diffusion current. At potentials more negative than this, the decrease of the concentration of nickel ion at the drop surface, which tends to decrease the current, opposes the continuing exponential increase of the rate constant, and hence the increase of current deviates more and more from an exponential dependence on potential. If the potential is made sufficiently negative, the rate constant for the reduction becomes so high that nickel ions are reduced practically instantaneously as they reach the drop surface. It is then the rate at which nickel ions arrive at the drop surface that governs the current, just as it would do if the reduction were reversible. The wave height has no relation to the reversibility or irreversibility of a wave; what was said about the limiting current in Chap. 3 applies to reversible and irreversible waves alike. These considerations explain why the shape of the irreversible nickel wave is generally similar to that of the reversible lead wave in Fig. 4.6.

In its simplest form, the mechanism responsible for a totally irreversible wave may be described by the equation

$$O + ne \rightarrow R \qquad (4.49)$$

The cathodic current i_c (in microamperes) that results from the reduction of O at any potential is described by the equation

$$i_c = nFAC_O^0 k' \exp\left[-\alpha nF(E - E')/RT\right] \qquad (4.50)$$

where F is the number of coulombs per faraday, A is the area of the electrode (in cm.^{2}), $C_O{}^0$ is the concentration of O at the surface of the electrode (in millimoles/1000 cm.^{3}), α is the transfer coefficient, R is the gas constant (in volt-coulombs per degree), and T is the absolute temperature; k' is the value of the rate constant for the electrode reaction when the electrode potential E is equal to the reference value E'. Because the reaction is heterogeneous (the electron transfer occurs across the phase boundary between mercury and solution), k' is expressed in cm./sec. rather than in sec.$^{-1}$ as the rate constant of a homogeneous first-order reaction would be.

Two choices of the reference potential E' are of interest. One is the formal potential $E^{0\prime}$ of the O–R couple in the solution under consideration. The value of k' at this potential is denoted by the symbol $k_{s,h}$, so that eq. (4.50) becomes

$$i_c = nFAC_O^0 k_{s,h} \exp\left[-\alpha nF(E - E^{0\prime})/RT\right] \qquad (4.51a)$$

For couples whose formal potentials are unknown or even (as is the case for many totally irreversible couples) unmeasurable, a more convenient though sometimes less readily interpretable choice is 0 v. vs. N.H.E. (-0.2412 v. vs. S.C.E.). Here the value of k' is denoted by the symbol $k^0{}_{f,h}$, so that eq. (4.50) becomes

$$i_c = nFAC_O^0 k_{f,h}^0 \exp\left[-\alpha nF(E + 0.2412)/RT\right] \qquad (4.51b)$$

where E is referred to the S.C.E.

Similar equations,

$$i_a = nFAC_R^0 k_{s,h} \exp\left[(1 - \alpha)\, nF(E - E^{0\prime})/RT\right] \qquad (4.52a)$$

and

$$i_a = nFAC_R^0 k_{b,h}^0 \exp\left[(1 - \alpha)\, nF(E + 0.2412)/RT\right] \qquad (4.52b)$$

in both of which it is the numerical or absolute value of n that appears in the exponent, may be written for the anodic current resulting from the oxidation of R. The value of $k_{s,h}$ appearing in eq. (4.52a) is identical with that in eq. (4.51a), as is easily shown on recognizing that if $C_R{}^0 = C_O{}^0$ the net current must be zero at the formal potential, which can be the case only if i_c and i_a are numerically equal though opposite in sign. Hence $k_{s,h}$ is a fundamental parameter characteristic of the couple. On the other hand, the value of $k^0{}_{b,h}$ (the rate constant for the backward or oxidation process at $E = 0$ v. vs. N.H.E.) may differ from that of $k^0{}_{f,h}$ by many orders of magnitude.

It is the value of $k_{s,h}$ that determines whether a half-reaction is reversible or irreversible. If it exceeds about 2×10^{-2} cm./sec., the rates of both oxidation and reduction at potentials near the formal potential will be so large that equilibrium will be very nearly attained in a time short compared to the drop life, and then the couple will appear to be polarographically reversible. But if $k_{s,h}$ is smaller than about 3×10^{-5} cm./sec., the rates of oxidation and reduction at the formal potential will be so small that only a very small current will flow in either direction, and consequently the couple will be totally irreversible. It is somewhat unfashionable to speak of the degree of reversibility, but the meaning of the notion is clear: the larger the value of $k_{s,h}$, the more nearly the couple approaches reversible behavior. Though $k_{s,h}$ is more useful for describing the behavior of a particular couple, it is $k^0{}_{f,h}$ (or, for anodic processes, $k^0{}_{b,h}$) that is more useful for comparing the behaviors of different totally irreversible couples. Another important consideration is that it is impossible to evaluate $k_{s,h}$ unless the formal potential is known or can be calculated from data obtained on both the cathodic and anodic waves for a couple. All too often, however, the formal potential is unknown, and unless both the cathodic and the anodic wave appear on polarograms there is no hope of calculating the formal potential or $k_{s,h}$. Hence we shall usually speak, below and in the following chapter, of $k^0{}_{f,h}$, which can always be evaluated from polarographic data. The discussions will be restricted to cathodic waves for the sake of brevity; anodic waves obey essentially identical equations, which may be obtained from those given below by replacing αn_a by $-(1 - \alpha)n_a$ and $k^0{}_{f,h}$ by $k^0{}_{b,h}$ wherever these appear.

Values of $k^0{}_{f,h}$ and the transfer coefficient α may be obtained in either of two ways by polarographic procedures. One involves

measurements of the currents at various potentials so near the foot
of the wave that $C_O{}^0$ can be regarded as virtually constant, then
applying eq. (4.51a) in an obvious fashion. The other involves measurements over the whole rising portion of the wave and necessitates
the use of relationships that take the variation of $C_O{}^0$ with current
into account. In either case the interpretation is facilitated by
measuring, not the average current during the drop life, but the
current at the end of the drop life, and this is what is meant by the
symbol i throughout the remainder of this chapter unless otherwise
specified. It is measured by recording the polarogram with an undamped recorder having a full-scale pen speed of 1 sec. or less.
Corrections for the residual current at each potential must be made
as described in the discussion of Fig. 3.2.

In employing the first of these techniques it is advisable to record
only the foot of the wave at a sensitivity so high that the pen runs off
scale when the current becomes equal to a tenth, or even a smaller
fraction, of the limiting current. Laitinen and Subcasky (45) recommended the use of a fairly concentrated (e.g., 25mM) solution of the
electroactive substance to decrease the uncertainty that would be
introduced by applying a substantial correction for the residual
current. But because of adsorption and other problems that often
arise at high concentrations it is probably better, especially in work
with organic substances, to employ a concentration of 1mM or less,
to use an appropriately high sensitivity in recording the desired
portion of the polarogram, to record the residual-current curve of
another aliquot of the supporting electrolyte on the same chart with
the same instrument settings and capillary characteristics, and to
make the correction for the residual current as best one can. It may
also be mentioned that both $k^0{}_{f,h}$ and αn_a are often drastically altered
by the presence of maximum suppressors and other surface-active
materials. This is partly because the adsorption of such a substance
onto the drop surface may change the structure of the electrical
double layer around the drop, and partly because it may hinder
certain orientations of an electroactive ion or molecule with respect
to the drop surface and thus alter the fundamental nature of the
process (46). It is essential to avoid the presence of any such substance
if meaningful data on irreversible waves are to be obtained. From the
resulting data one constructs a plot of log i vs. $E_{d.e.}$. A straight line
should be obtained; its slope at 25° is

$$\frac{d(\log i)}{dE_{\text{d.e.}}} = -\frac{0.434\alpha nF}{RT} = -\frac{\alpha n}{0.05915} \qquad (4.53)$$

according to eq. (4.51a) and its intercept at $E = E^{0\prime}$ is

$$\log i_{(E=E^{0\prime})} = \log nFAC^0_O k_{s,h} = 2.915 + \log n(mt)^{2/3} C^0_O k_{s,h} \quad (4.54a)$$

according to eqs. (4.51a) and (3.4). Similarly,

$$\log i_{(E=-0.241 \text{ v. vs. s.c.e.})} = \log nFAC^0_O k^0_{f,h} \qquad (4.54b)$$

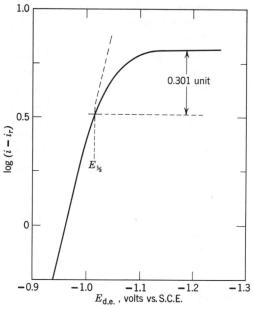

Figure 4.7. Plot of $\log(i - i_r)$ vs. $E_{\text{d.e.}}$ for the totally irreversible reduction of nickel(II) from $0.1F$ potassium chloride containing 0.001% Triton X-100. The slope of the initial linear portion, -10.3 v.$^{-1}$, corresponds to $\alpha n_a = 0.61$ according to eq. (4.53).

A typical plot of $\log i$ vs. potential for a totally irreversible wave is shown in Fig. 4.7. The current must be that at the end of the drop life (compare Figs. 3.2 and 4.4) and must be corrected for the residual current. The values of αn and $k^0_{f,h}$ are easily obtained from the slope and intercept of the initial linear portion. If the residual current is so much smaller than the diffusion current that it is negligible over nearly the whole rising portion of the wave, curves like the one in Fig. 4.7 can easily be recorded directly by using a logarithmic recorder instead of a linear one. Otherwise the usual correction for the extrapolated or separately measured residual current must be made, as was done in obtaining the curve shown here.

The other procedure is based on a plot of $E_{d.e.}$ vs. $\log i/(i_d - i)$. This is constructed exactly as for a reversible wave, as described in section 4 above, but it is the current at the end of the drop life that should be measured at each potential, and the theoretical foundation of the plot is quite different. Taking into account the variation of $C_0{}^0$ with current, Koutecký (47) calculated values of the function $F(\chi)$, where χ is described by the equation

$$\chi = \left(\frac{12}{7} \right)^{1/2} k_{f,h} \frac{t^{1/2}}{D_0^{1/2}} \tag{4.55}$$

in which t is the drop time, D_0 the diffusion coefficient of the electroactive substance [estimated, for example, from eq. (3.22)], and $k_{f,h}$ is the potential-dependent heterogeneous rate constant described by

$$k_{f,h} = k_{f,h}^0 \exp\left[-\alpha nF(E + 0.2412)/RT\right] \tag{4.56}$$

As above, the potential E is referred to the S.C.E. The function $F(\chi)$ is equal to the ratio i/i_∞, where i is the current (corrected for the residual current) that actually flows at the end of the life of a drop at the potential E, while i_∞ is the current that would flow if the electron-transfer step were extremely fast (that is, if the couple behaved reversibly). For a totally irreversible process i_∞ may be equated to the diffusion current, for the current i does not become large enough to be detected until the potential has become so much more negative than the formal potential that the plateau would be reached if the wave were reversible. For example, it is easily calculated from the considerations outlined in Secs. I and II above that the plateau of the nickel wave in Fig. 4.6(b) would begin at about -0.65 v. if the reduction were reversible.

From the values of χ and $F(\chi)$ given by Koutecký, it is found (48) that $\log \chi$ varies linearly with $\log\{F(\chi)/[1 - F(\chi)]\}$. Explicitly,

$$\log \chi = -0.0130 + 0.9163 \log \frac{F(\chi)}{1 - F(\chi)}$$

which becomes, on introducing the foregoing descriptions of χ and $F(\chi)$,

$$\log \left(\frac{12}{7} \right)^{1/2} k_{f,h} \frac{t^{1/2}}{D_O^{1/2}} = -0.0130 + 0.9163 \log \frac{i}{i_d - i} \qquad (4.57)$$

Combining this with eq. (4.56) yields

$$E_{\text{d.e.}} + 0.2412 = \frac{0.05915}{\alpha n} \log \frac{1.349 \, k_{f,h}^0 t^{1/2}}{D_O^{1/2}} - \frac{0.0542}{\alpha n} \log \frac{i}{i_d - i} \qquad (4.58)$$

which may be written

$$E_{\text{d.e.}} = E_{1/2} - \frac{0.0542}{\alpha n} \log \frac{i}{i_d - i} \qquad (4.59)$$

with

$$E_{1/2} = -0.2412 + \frac{0.05915}{\alpha n} \log \frac{1.349 \, k_{f,h}^0 t^{1/2}}{D_O^{1/2}} \qquad (4.60)$$

In these equations both $E_{\text{d.e.}}$ and $E_{1/2}$ are referred to the S.C.E. Equation (4.59) is very similar to the equations given earlier for the reversible cathodic waves obtained when the activities of both the oxidized and reduced forms of the couple vary with current. It differs from them only in the coefficient of the log term and in the fact that the currents are those at the ends of the drop lives. Kern (49) wrote equation (4.59) in the form

$$E_{\text{d.e.}} = E_{1/2} - \frac{0.05915}{\alpha n} \log \frac{i}{i_d - i} \qquad (4.61)$$

with average currents in the log term. Near the foot of an irreversible wave, where C_O^0 is essentially constant, it is clear from eqs. (4.51) that the current at any instant during the life of a drop should be simply proportional to the area of the drop at that instant, or, in view of eq. (3.12)

$$i_\tau \propto \tau^{2/3} \qquad (4.62)$$

As the potential is made more negative, however, depletion of the solution at the drop surface becomes more and more important, and on the plateau one has, as in eq. (3.13),

$$i_\tau \propto \tau^{1/6} \tag{4.63}$$

instead. Hence the ratio of the average current to the current at the end of the drop life increases as the potential approaches the plateau. Equations (4.62) and (4.63) indicate that the ratio should be 3/5 at the foot of the wave and 6/7 on the plateau. The latter figure is too large, as was mentioned in connection with eq. (3.28), but a variation from about 0.59 to 0.82 is observed (20), and is responsible for the difference between the numerical coefficients of the log terms in eqs. (4.59) and (4.61).

The most important consequence of this variation is that the values of all of the important potential-dependent parameters—including not only the slope of a log plot but also the half-wave potential and $E_{3/4} - E_{1/4}$—obtained by measuring average currents are slightly but definitely different from those obtained by measuring currents at the ends of the drop lives. No such effect is observed with reversible waves, for which the two kinds of measurements yield the same results. Hence it is essential in dealing with irreversible waves to select one kind of measurement and use it throughout. Measurements of currents at the ends of drop lives are recommended here for two reasons: one is that the results of Koutecký's calculations are more accurately reproduced by the empirical relationship described by eq. (4.57) than by the one that leads to eq. (4.61), and the other is that this is the technique preferred by almost all American workers.

Equations (4.58) through (4.60) should not be employed if the current is smaller than about a tenth of the limiting current, for the calculations on which they are based do not extend into this region, and eqs. (4.53) and (4.54) should be used there instead.

The variation of t with potential sometimes poses a problem in the use of these equations. For waves occurring between about 0 and -1.0 v. vs. S.C.E. the variation may generally be ignored, but outside this region it becomes much larger, as was shown by Table 3.4, and correction for it becomes increasingly important as the slope of the wave decreases. If t varies appreciably over the range of potentials covered by the rising part of the wave, the slope of an ordinary plot of $E_{d.e.}$ vs. log $i/(i_d - i)$ will vary as the height of the mercury column above the capillary is changed, and to avoid this it is best to rewrite eq. (4.58) as

$$E_{d.e.} + 0.2412 = \frac{0.05915}{\alpha n} \log \frac{1.349 k_{f,h}^0}{D_O^{1/2}}$$

$$- \frac{0.0542}{\alpha n} \left[\log \frac{i}{i_d - i} - 0.546 \log t \right] \qquad (4.64)$$

Values of t are measured at several different potentials on the rising portion of the wave such that i lies between about 10 and 95% of i_d, which are the approximate limits of validity of eqs. (4.57), (4.59), and (4.64). Interpolation yields values of $0.546 \log t$ that are sufficiently accurate for use in eq. (4.64); the most convenient technique of interpolation consists of plotting $\log t$ vs. $E_{d.e.}$. A plot of $E_{d.e.}$ vs. $[\log i/(i_d - i) - 0.546 \log t]$ has a slope of $-54.2/\alpha n$ mv. and an intercept, where the quantity being plotted along the abscissa is zero, which is equal to the parameter $E_{1/2}^0$ defined by the equation

$$E_{1/2}^0 = -0.2412 + \frac{0.05915}{\alpha n} \log \frac{1.349 k_{f,h}^0}{D_O^{1/2}} \qquad (4.65)$$

Typical plots of this kind are shown in Fig. 4.8.

It is shown by eq. (4.60) that the half-wave potential depends on drop time. Explicitly,

$$\frac{dE_{1/2}}{d(\log t)} = \frac{0.02957}{\alpha n} \qquad (4.66)$$

This may be used to evaluate αn, though the accuracy required in measuring $E_{1/2}$ is so stringent that it is better to employ eq. (4.53) or the slope of a plot of $E_{d.e.}$ vs. $[\log i/(i_d - i) - 0.546 \log t]$ for this purpose. On the other hand, the variation of $E_{1/2}$ with t may provide useful confirmation of a more reliable value secured by one of these other techniques. Some experimental results are shown in Fig. 4.9. The value of αn here is somewhat larger than usual, so that the variations of $E_{1/2}$ are smaller than usual. Even taking this into account, however, inspection of the dashed lines suggests that it would be rather perilous to deduce a value of αn from the slope of such a plot.

Though this variation of half-wave potential with drop time can be put to some use, it is more often a nuisance than not. It complicates the comparison of data obtained in different laboratories or in the

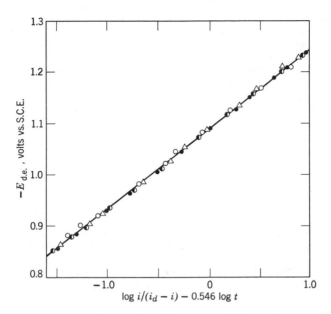

Figure 4.8.   Plots of $-E_{d.e.}$ vs. $[\log i/(i_d - i) - 0.546 \log t]$ for the reduction of 1.0mM chromate ion from 0.10F sodium hydroxide. The drop time at -0.80 v. was 7.5 sec. for the data represented by large open circles, 5.5 sec. for those represented by triangles, 4.1 sec. for those represented by half-solid circles, and 3.4 sec. for those represented by solid circles (48). Reproduced by permission of the *Journal of the American Chemical Society.*

same laboratory with different capillaries; it complicates the comparison of data obtained with different substances reducible at different potentials or with the same substance in different supporting electrolytes. For this reason it is suggested that those reporting the half-wave potentials of irreversible waves do so by reporting $E_{1/2}^{0}$ instead of (or in addition to) the less significant measured values. It is clear from eq. (4.65) that $E_{1/2}^{0}$ is a constant, independent of the drop time and therefore characteristic of the process responsible for the wave, and should be easily reproducible in different laboratories.

One may evaluate $E_{1/2}^{0}$ in either of two ways. One consists of obtaining values of $E_{1/2}$ with different heights of the column of mercury above the capillary, plotting $E_{1/2}$ against the logarithm of the drop time $t_{1/2}$ at the half-wave potential, and extrapolating to $\log t_{1/2} = 0$ (that is, to $t = 1$ sec.). It is unwise to try to decrease

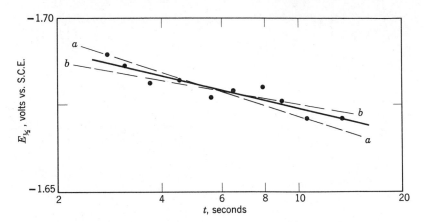

Figure 4.9. Plot of $E_{1/2}$ vs. log t for the wave of aluminum(III) in $1F$ potassium chloride. Plots like those in Fig. 4.8 gave $\alpha n = 1.28$ under the same conditions, which according to eq. (4.66) corresponds to $dE_{1/2}/d(\log t) = 23.1$ mv., and the solid line is drawn with this slope. The dashed lines aa and bb correspond to $\alpha n = 0.85$ and 1.92, respectively, 2/3 and 3/2 of the above value. The mean deviation of the points from the solid line is ±1.7 mv.; from either aa or bb it is ±2 mv.

the length of this extrapolation by employing drop times close to 1 sec., for the polarograms obtained at such short drop times are often deformed by maxima that render them useless for the purpose. The other consists of evaluating αn by means of eq. (4.53) or from the slope of a plot of $E_{d.e.}$ vs. [log $i/(i_d - i) - 0.546 \log t$], then calculating $E_{1/2}^{0}$ from the equation

$$E_{1/2}^{0} = E_{1/2} - \frac{0.02957}{\alpha n} \log t_{1/2} \qquad (4.67)$$

It was shown in connection with eq. (4.45) that the theoretical value of $E_{3/4} - E_{1/4}$ for a reversible cathodic wave is $-56.4/n$ mv. in the ordinary case where the activities of both the oxidized and reduced species vary with current. For a totally irreversible cathodic wave, a similar treatment of eq. (4.58) yields

$$E_{3/4} - E_{1/4} = - \frac{0.05172}{\alpha n} \qquad (4.68)$$

subject to the important condition that the drop time be essentially constant over this range of potentials. If the wave is very drawn out or occurs at potentials where the electrocapillary curve is steep, one should write

$$E_{3/4} - E_{1/4} = -\frac{0.05172}{\alpha n} + \frac{0.02957}{\alpha n} \log \frac{t_{3/4}}{t_{1/4}} \qquad (4.69)$$

instead. However, the correction will rarely be significant in comparison to the experimental error. Measurement of $E_{3/4} - E_{1/4}$ thus provides another technique for the evaluation of αn.

The above treatment is based on the assumptions that produce the Ilkovič equation for the diffusion current. Correction for spherical diffusion (50) in the fashion that produces the Koutecký equation (3.20) for the diffusion current has too small an effect on these equations to be worth taking into account in any but exceptionally precise work (48).

It has so far been assumed that the overall electrode reaction occurs in a single step as represented by eq. (4.49), but of course this is not necessarily true. One may have a rate-determining step involving n_a electrons, followed by one or more much faster steps in which additional electrons are consumed:

$$O + n_a e \to I \qquad \text{(rate-determining)} \qquad (4.70a)$$

$$I + (n - n_a)e \to R \quad \text{(fast)} \qquad (4.70b)$$

The overall reaction is still $O + ne \to R$, and its rate is still controlled by the rate at which O is reduced, but the total current obtained on reducing an ion or molecule of O depends on the number n of electrons involved in the overall reaction rather than on the number n_a involved in the rate-determining step. Hence, for example, eq. (4.51b) becomes

$$i_c = nFAC^0_O k^0_{f,h} \exp\left[-\alpha n_a F(E + 0.2412)/RT\right] \qquad (4.71)$$

where the product αn_a is needed in the exponent to describe the effect of potential on the rate-determining step, while n is needed in the coefficient to describe the total current obtained. The substitution of αn_a for αn is all that is needed to convert eqs. (4.50) through (4.69) into equations applicable to this mechanism.

The value of α may in principle vary from nearly 0 to nearly 1; in many cases it is not far from 0.5. Both adsorption and the neglect of double-layer structure (which is briefly discussed in Sec. VII below), however, may have appreciable effects, and a few values of α below 0.1 or above 0.9 have been reported. The value of n_a must obviously be integral, and in most cases it is probably 1. Though it is generally believed that only a single electron can be transferred at a time during the course of an electrode reaction, a value of n_a exceeding 1 would not necessarily mean that two or more electrons are actually added simultaneously, but merely that the successive steps are too nearly simultaneous to be distinguished on the time scale implicit in a polarographic measurement.

On the basis of these general principles it is often possible to make reasonable conjectures about the value of n_a, which is the parameter that is of most chemical interest. For example, the slope of a plot of $E_{\text{d.e.}}$ vs. $\log i/(i_d - i)$ for the cathodic wave of dichloroacetate ion in an ammoniacal ammonium chloride supporting electrolyte is -160 mv. According to eq. (4.58), this corresponds to $\alpha n_a = 0.34$, which strongly suggests that $n_a = 1$. Diffusion-current data, coulometry at controlled potential, and the formation of monochloroacetate on exhaustive controlled-potential electrolysis all show that $n = 2$, so that the overall reaction is $Cl_2HCCOO^- + H^+ + 2e \rightarrow ClH_2CCOO^- + Cl^-$. Accordingly the rate-determining step must involve the addition of a single electron and be followed by a much faster step in which the second electron is added.

A still more general class of reactions is that in which a fast equilibrium may precede the rate-determining electron-transfer step. Many organic compounds are reduced in accordance with the mechanism

$$O + pH^+ = O' \qquad \text{(fast)} \qquad\qquad (4.72a)$$

$$O' + n_a e \rightarrow I \qquad \text{(rate-determining)} \qquad (4.72b)$$

$$I + (n - n_a)e \rightarrow R \quad \text{(fast)} \qquad\qquad (4.72c)$$

To describe the cathodic current resulting from this mechanism one would write

$$i_c = nFAC_O^0{}'k_{f,h}^0 \exp{[-\alpha n_a F(E + 0.2412)/RT]} \qquad (4.73)$$

which is analogous to eq. (4.51b). If the solution is well buffered so that the concentration of hydrogen ion at the electrode surface is constant and independent of current, combining eq. (4.73) with the equation

$$K = C_O^{0\prime}/C_O^0 C_{H^+}^p \qquad (4.74)$$

for the equilibrium constant of the prior chemical step yields

$$i_c = nFA\,(C_O^0 k_{f,h}^0 KC_{H^+}^p)\exp\,[-\alpha n_a F\,(E + 0.2412)/RT] \qquad (4.75)$$

which has exactly the same form as eq. (4.51b) except that the product $k_{f,h}^0 KC_{H^+}^p$ must now be used instead of the $k_{f,h}^0$ alone that is appropriate for the single-step reaction.

A practically identical equation serves to describe the mechanism

$$O + pH^+ + n_a e \to I \quad \text{(rate-determining)} \qquad (4.76a)$$

$$I + (n - n_a)e \to R \quad \text{(fast)} \qquad (4.76b)$$

for which one obtains

$$i_c = nFA\,(C_O^0 k_{f,h}^0 C_{H^+}^p)\,\exp\,[-\alpha n_a F\,(E + 0.2412)/RT] \qquad (4.77)$$

Here $k_{f,h}^0$ is the heterogeneous rate constant, at 0 v. vs. N.H.E., for the $(p + 1)$th-order reaction described by eq. (4.76a), whereas the $k_{f,h}^0$ that appears in eq. (4.75) is for a first-order reaction. As elsewhere in chemical kinetics, the two mechanisms are experimentally equivalent; other information on the occurrence and equilibrium constant of a fast prior step like the one described by eq. (4.72a) is needed if they are to be distinguished. Equations (4.75) and (4.77) serve for the interpretation of data obtained at the foot of the wave; for data obtained over the whole rising part of the wave the essential equations [(4.58), (4.60), and (4.65)] become

$$E_{\text{d.e.}} = -0.2412 + \frac{0.05915}{\alpha n_a} \log \frac{1.349 k_{f,h}^0 t^{1/2}}{D_O^{1/2}} C_{H^+}^p - \frac{0.0542}{\alpha n_a} \log \frac{i}{i_d - i} \qquad (4.78)$$

$$E_{1/2} = -0.2412 + \frac{0.05915}{\alpha n_a} \log \frac{1.349 k_{f,h}^0 t^{1/2}}{D_O^{1/2}} - \frac{0.05915}{\alpha n_a} p\,(\text{pH}) \qquad (4.79)$$

$$E_{1/2}^0 = -0.2412 + \frac{0.05915}{\alpha n_a} \log \frac{1.349 k_{f,h}^0}{D_O^{1/2}} - \frac{0.05915}{\alpha n_a} p\,(\text{pH}) \qquad (4.80)$$

for the mechanism described by eqs. (4.76). For the mechanism described by eqs. (4.72), these need only be modified by replacing $k^0_{f,h}$ in each by the product $k^0_{f,h}K$. Evidently, in either case,

$$\frac{dE^0_{1/2}}{d(\text{pH})} = -\frac{0.05915}{\alpha n_a} p \qquad (4.81)$$

The same equation can be written for $dE_{1/2}/d(\text{pH})$ unless the change of half-wave potential with pH is accompanied by a significant change of drop time at the half-wave potential; unfortunately, such a change is by no means unlikely, and this is one reason why $E^0_{1/2}$ is a more useful parameter than the uncorrected half-wave potential $E_{1/2}$.

What was said above regarding the evaluation of $k^0_{f,h}$ and αn_a from data on waves corresponding to simpler mechanisms applies to these more complex mechanisms as well. A word of caution must be added, however, because of the changes in the composition of the supporting electrolyte that are contemplated here. Equation (4.81) is patently worthless unless αn_a is constant throughout the range of conditions investigated, and cases are known in which it is not. For example, in the reduction of iodate ion αn_a is 1.13 at pH 1; on increasing the pH, αn_a passes through a minimum value of 0.3 at about pH 7 and then increases again to 0.62 at pH values above about 9.5. Every attempt to elucidate the stoichiometry of the rate-determining step associated with a totally irreversible wave must therefore include a demonstration that αn_a is constant and independent of the experimental conditions that are varied. The problem is discussed further in Sec. VII.

Two examples should suffice to illustrate the application of these equations in studies of the mechanisms of irreversible processes. It was mentioned above that n_a is apparently 1 for the two-electron reduction of dichloroacetate ion. The half-wave potential of dichloroacetate is independent of pH; according to eq. (4.81) this must mean that $p = 0$, which in turn means that hydrogen ion is not involved either in the rate-determining electron-transfer step or in any prior chemical process. The mechanism of the reduction of dichloroacetate at the dropping electrode must, therefore, be

$$Cl_2HCCOO^- + e \rightarrow Cl H\dot{C}COO^- + Cl^- \quad \text{(rate-determining)}$$

$$Cl H\dot{C}COO^- + H^+ + e \rightarrow Cl H_2CCOO^- \quad \text{(fast)}$$

For the reduction of dimethylglyoxime at pH values between 1 and 3, the slope of a plot of $E_{d.e.}$ vs. $\log i/(i_d - i)$ is -0.103 v. The half-wave potential lies between -0.8 and -1.0 v. vs. S.C.E.; in this region the slope of the electrocapillary curve is small and consequently no appreciable error is made by neglecting the term in $\log t$ [cf. eq. (4.64)] in the construction of the log plot. According to eq. (4.64) this slope corresponds to $\alpha n_a = 0.53$. In employing eq. (4.64) it should be remembered that it was written for a single-step mechanism; in general the product αn_a should be written instead of αn in the denominator of the coefficient of each term on its right-hand side. From this value of αn_a it is most reasonable to conclude that $n_a = 1$. Meanwhile the value of $dE_{1/2}/d(pH)$ is -96 mv., and substituting this value along with $\alpha n_a = 0.53$ into eq. (4.81) yields $p = 0.86$ or, within the precision of the measurements, $p = 1$. Consequently the course of the reaction through the rate-determining step can be represented by the equation

$$
\begin{array}{cc}
\text{CH}_3\text{—C}=\text{NOH} & \text{CH}_3\text{—}\overset{\cdot}{\text{C}}\text{—NHOH} \\
| \qquad\qquad + \text{H}^+ + e \rightarrow & | \\
\text{CH}_3\text{—C}=\text{NOH} & \text{CH}_3\text{—C}=\text{NOH}
\end{array}
$$

As it is impossible, on the basis of polarographic data alone, to distinguish between a substance consumed in the rate-determining electron-transfer step and one consumed in a prior chemical equilibrium, the statement has occasionally been made that n_a is the total number of electrons consumed in the rate-determining electron-transfer step and in fast electron-transfer steps that precede it. However, this is a false analogy. If the mechanism were in fact

$$O + n_1 e \rightarrow I \quad \text{(fast)} \tag{4.82a}$$

$$I + n_2 e \rightarrow R \quad \text{(rate-determining)} \tag{4.82b}$$

the polarogram would have to consist of two waves: an n_1-electron wave for the reduction of O to I followed, at a more negative potential, by the possibly irreversible n_2-electron wave for the second step. This is because a potential where O is rapidly reduced to I must be a potential on the plateau of a wave: it is impossible for this reduction to occur rapidly without giving rise to an appreciable current at potentials where the second step is still very slow. The value of n_a must correspond to the first identifiable electron-transfer step.

Processes more complex than those considered here are possible and have been observed, but a detailed description of the phenomena to which they give rise would be outside the scope of this book. They fall into two principal categories. One is that of only moderately irreversible processes, for which $k_{s,h}$ is small enough to produce appreciable deviations from reversible behavior but not so small that the process can be considered to be totally irreversible. Such processes may be recognized by obtaining polarograms of the oxidized and reduced forms of the couple in the same supporting electrolyte under identical conditions: they produce cathodic and anodic waves that overlap but do not have identical half-wave potentials. Differences of the order of 50 mv. are not uncommon. It is then not possible to neglect the rate of, say, the anodic reaction (i.e., the reoxidation of material previously reduced) over most of the rising part of the cathodic wave. The properties of such waves have been described by Delahay (51). The other category is that of processes involving two or more comparably slow steps; if the individual values of α are sufficiently different, one of these steps may be faster than another near the foot of the wave but slower near the plateau. A plot of $E_{d.e.}$ vs. $\log i/(i_d - i)$ will then be curved, or may even consist of two line segments (52). This is the case in the reduction of iodate under certain conditions. A possibility distantly related to this is described by the mechanism

$$O + n_1 e \rightarrow I \quad \text{(rate-determining)}$$

$$I + n_2 e \rightarrow R \quad \text{(reversible)}$$

for which a plot according to eq. (4.53) may consist of a pair of parallel straight lines, $\log (n_2/n_1)$ unit apart on the log current axis, with a transitional region in the vicinity of the formal potential of the I–R couple (53).

In connection with eqs. (3.55) and (3.56) it was mentioned that the electroactive species responsible for a kinetic wave of a complex metal ion could be identified by measurements made on the rising part of the wave. It is assumed that the wave is totally irreversible, and that both the electron-transfer rate constant $k_{f,h}$ at any potential and the transfer coefficient α are independent of the concentration of the ligand X. The treatment is simplified by considering the current that flows at just a single potential. Assuming that $k_{f,h}$ is unaffected by ligand concentration amounts to assuming that there is no specific adsorption on the drop surface. Unless α is also constant, there can be only a single potential at which $k_{f,h}$ is constant, so that assuming α to be constant amounts to assuming that the following equations will be valid at any arbitrarily chosen potential. Before proceeding to the case of a kinetic wave, it is convenient to consider the consequences of eq. (4.57) for other simpler mechanisms. For the straightforward process described by eq. (4.49), one can differentiate eq. (4.57) and combine the result with eq. (4.56) to obtain

$$0.9163 \, d\left[\log \frac{i}{i_d - i} \right] = d(\log k_{f,h})$$
$$= d\{\log k_{f,h}^0 \exp \left[-\alpha nF(E + 0.2412)/RT \right]\} \qquad (4.83)$$

which signifies merely that $i/(i_d - i)$ will be constant at any fixed potential. For the mechanism described by eqs. (4.72), however, we saw that $k^0_{f,h}$ had to be replaced by the product $k^0_{f,h}KC^p_{H^+}$ in order to obtain eq. (4.75). Hence eq. (4.83) for this mechanism would become

$$0.9163 \, \frac{d[\log i/(i_d - i)]}{d(\log C_{H^+})}$$
$$= \frac{d\{\log (k_{f,h}^0 KC^p_{H^+}) \exp \left[-\alpha n_a F(E + 0.2412)/RT \right]\}}{d(\log C_{H^+})}$$
$$= p$$

or

$$\frac{d[\log i/(i_d - i)]}{d(\log C_{H^+})} = 1.091p \qquad (4.84a)$$

which could more usefully be written

$$\frac{d[\log i/(i_d - i)]}{d(\text{pH})} = -1.091p \qquad (4.84b)$$

Similarly, we may consider the reduction of a complex metal ion according to the scheme

$$MX_j = MX_p + (j - p)X \quad \text{(fast)} \qquad (4.85a)$$

$$MX_p + n_a e \rightarrow I \qquad \text{(totally irreversible)} \qquad (4.85b)$$

$$I + (n - n_a)e \rightarrow M + pX \quad \text{(fast)} \qquad (4.85c)$$

in which the predominating complex MX_j is not reducible, whereas a lower complex MX_p undergoes an irreversible reduction to yield an intermediate I and eventually the metal M itself. The processes represented here by eqs. (4.85b) and (4.85c) may, of course, take place in a single step. After making assumptions similar to those described in connection with eq. (3.55), considerations similar to those described in connection with eqs. (4.72) through (4.74) indicate that the $k^0_{f,h}$ appearing in eq. (4.51b) must be replaced by the product $k^0_{f,h}(K_j K_{j-1} \ldots K_{p+1}) C_X^{p-j}$ to obtain the equation for the wave. The quantities $K_j, K_{j-1}, \ldots, K_{p+1}$ represent the successive dissociation constants of the complexes; their product is the equilibrium constant of the reaction described by eq. (4.85a). Making the same substitution in eq. (4.83) yields

$$\frac{d[\log i/(i_d - i)]}{d(\log C_X)} = 1.091 (p - j) \qquad (4.86)$$

That is, if the complex MX_j itself undergoes a totally irreversible reduction at the drop surface, the quantity $i/(i_d - i)$ [or, more simply, the current] at any potential will not depend on the concentration of the ligand X, but if a fast dissociation precedes the reduction step a variation will be observed and will permit the constitution of the electroactive species MX_p to be deduced.

The behavior of a kinetic wave may now be described by envisioning the general mechanism

$$MX_j = MX_p + (j - p)X \qquad \text{(fast)} \qquad (4.87a)$$

$$MX_p \rightarrow MX_{p-1} + X \qquad \text{(slow)} \qquad (4.87b)$$

$$MX_{p-1} = MX_q + (p - q - 1)X \quad \text{(fast)} \qquad (4.87c)$$

$$MX_q + ne \rightarrow M + qX \qquad \text{(totally irreversible)} \qquad (4.87d)$$

in which the reduction is represented for simplicity as taking place in a single step. For convenience of comparison with equation (3.56), the result may be given in the form

$$\frac{d\{\log [i \, i_k/i_d(i_k - i)]\}}{d(\log C_X)} = 0.886 (q - j) \qquad (4.88)$$

where i is the average current at a potential on the rising part of the kinetic wave, i_k is the average kinetic current on the plateau, and i_d is the average diffusion current that would be obtained if the equilibria were very fast. The last of these may sometimes be measured experimentally at a more negative potential where MX_j or some other complex MX_m $(m \geq p)$ is reduced directly, or it may be estimated with the aid of data on other complexes of similar constitution and size. In this way it is found (54) that $(q - j)$ is equal to -2 for the kinetic wave obtained in solutions in which $Cd(CN)_4^=$ is the predominating complex, so that it is the $Cd(CN)_2$ formed in the rate-controlling chemical step that is reduced.

Finally, mention may be made of an extensive compilation (54a) of the electrochemical kinetic parameters for a great many half-reactions at mercury and other electrodes.

VI. Quasireversible Processes

Electrode reactions in which a reversible electron-transfer step is preceded or followed by a slow chemical transformation were briefly mentioned in connection with eqs. (4.46). Such processes are called quasireversible here, though the term has sometimes been used differently. Accurate descriptions of the current-potential curves and half-wave potentials that characterize such processes require rather complex equations (10,55–57), and the original literature must be consulted for details. Here it is possible to give only a single important result: for the generalized mechanism

$$O + ne = R \quad \text{(reversible)} \tag{4.89a}$$

$$R + pX = I \quad \text{(fast)} \tag{4.89b}$$

$$I + qX \rightarrow J \quad \text{(rate-determining)} \tag{4.89c}$$

$$J + rX = K \quad \text{(fast)} \tag{4.89d}$$

one obtains, using measurements of the average current throughout,

$$\frac{d(E_{d.e.})}{d[\log i/(i_d - i)]} = -\frac{0.05915}{n} \tag{4.90a}$$

$$\frac{d(E_{1/2})}{d(\log t_{1/2})} = -\frac{0.02957}{n} \tag{4.90b}$$

where $t_{1/2}$ is the drop time at the half-wave potential, and

$$\frac{d(E_{1/2})}{d(\log C_X)} = \frac{0.05915}{n}\left(p + \frac{q}{2}\right) \qquad (4.90c)$$

provided that the rate-determining chemical step represented by equation (4.89c) occurs with reasonable speed. It is assumed that C_X is high and that the equilibrium concentrations are in the order $C_K \gg C_J \gg C_I$. Equation (4.90a) indicates that the wave will satisfy the ordinary log-plot criterion of reversibility, but eq. (4.90b) provides a criterion for recognizing that a slow step is involved, and eq. (4.90c) can then be used to investigate the nature of that step. As the rate constant for the transformation of I into J decreases, however, more and more of the I escapes from the electrode surface into the bulk of the solution before undergoing this transformation. As this rate constant approaches zero (since it is assumed that the equilibrium concentration of J is much larger than that of I, the rate constant for the reverse transformation of J into I must be even smaller), the wave will more and more nearly represent the process $O + pX + ne = I$, and will more and more nearly obey the thermodynamic equations, such as eq. (4.41), describing that process. In the limit, of course, no anodic wave at all may be obtained with a solution of the stable species K of the reduced form of the couple. Many illustrations of this behavior may be found in both the inorganic and organic literature. Hale and Parsons (58) have discussed the evaluation of rate constants and formal potentials for couples of which one form yields a quasireversible wave, and their paper should be consulted for details.

VII. The Structure of the Double Layer and Its Effects on Kinetic Parameters

When a reaction is said to take place at the surface of an electrode, it is not implied that the electroactive species must come into actual physical contact with the electrode. There is a potential gradient around an electrode immersed in an electrolyte solution. The potential difference between the electrode and the bulk of the solution may be represented by $(E - E_{\max})$, where E is the potential of the electrode and $E_{\max}$ is the electrocapillary maximum potential or potential of zero charge. If this is negative, then any surface near the electrode will be at a more negative potential than the bulk of the solution, and the potential will become more and more negative as the electrode surface is more closely approached. An ion or molecule diffusing toward the electrode will reach a point (whose distance from the electrode surface is always negligible compared with the thickness of the diffusion layer under polarographic conditions) at which the potential is sufficiently negative to bring about its reduction. With a dropping electrode at any instant all these points will lie on a spherical surface. Just how far away from the electrode this lies is not at all certain. There is a simple case in which there is no specific adsorption at the electrode surface and in which the potential varies monotonically with distance from the electrode; there is a more complicated one in which specific adsorption does occur and in which the dependence of potential on distance from the electrode is not monotonic. These are depicted schematically in Fig. 4.10. Because of its complexity, very little can be said about the situation in which specific adsorption is appreciable. When it can be neglected, a number of important polarographic observations can be at least qualitatively described by assuming that the surface at which the reaction occurs

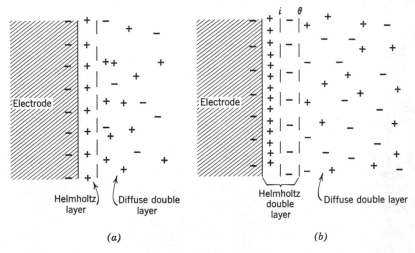

(a)   (b)

Figure 4.10.   Schematic diagrams of the electrical double layer at an electrode whose potential is more negative than the potential of the electrocapillary maximum: (a) in the absence of specific adsorption, and (b) when specifically adsorbed cations are present in the inner Helmholtz plane.

coincides with the boundary between the Helmholtz layer and the diffuse double layer. Only an abbreviated summary can be given here. A bibliography of the early work in this field was given by Breiter, Kleinerman, and Delahay (59). A more recent review (60) and a monograph (60a) by Delahay should also be consulted.

The electrode potential—that is, the potential difference $(E - E_{max})$—may be divided into two parts: the potential difference ϕ_{sb} between the reaction surface and the bulk of the solution, and the potential difference $[(E - E_{max}) - \phi_{sb}]$ between the electrode and the reaction surface. The former influences the concentration C_s of any charged species at the reaction surface:

$$C_s = C_b \exp\left[-zF\phi_{sb}/RT\right] \tag{4.91}$$

where z is the charge on the reacting species and C_b is its concentration in the bulk of the solution. The value of z may differ from the charge borne by a particle of the electroactive substance in the bulk of the solution, for dissociation, ion-pair formation, or some other chemical reaction must often precede the transfer of electrons. The potential difference between the electrode and the reaction surface influences the rate constant $k_{f,h}$ of the electron-transfer step:

$$k_{f,h} = k_{f,h}^* \exp\left[-\alpha n_a F[(E - E_{max}) - \phi_{sb}]/RT\right] \tag{4.92}$$

in which $k_{f,h}^*$ is the heterogeneous rate constant at the electrocapillary maximum potential E_{max}, where $\phi_{sb} = 0$. Combining these yields an equation similar to eq. (4.71):

$$i_c = nFAC_bk_{f,h}^*\exp\left\{-F[\alpha n_a(E - E_{max}) + (z - \alpha n_a)\,\phi_{sb}]/RT\right\} \tag{4.93}$$

Values of ϕ_{sb} can be obtained from measurements of the double-layer capacity by means of the Gouy–Chapman theory; in a cF solution of a z–z-valent electrolyte in the absence of specific adsorption

$$\phi_{sb} = \frac{2RT}{zF} \sinh^{-1}\left(\frac{\pi q^2}{2\epsilon kTc}\right)^{1/2} \tag{4.94}$$

where q is the surface charge density or integral capacity of the double layer in microcoulombs per square centimeter, ϵ is the static dielectric constant, and k is the Boltzmann constant. Figure 4.11 shows the values calculated by Russell (61) for several different concentrations of sodium fluoride, in which specific adsorption is less than in any other known medium. As the values of ϕ_{sb} increase with decreasing c, the correction becomes more important as the supporting electrolyte becomes more dilute. According to eq. (4.94) the same effect is produced by a decrease of dielectric constant, but although values of q are available for numerous aqueous media (62) and can be computed from data on the differential capacities (63) for many others of polarographic importance, detailed information on non-aqueous media is not available and would be of dubious significance because of the danger that specific adsorption will become more pronounced as the dielectric constant decreases.

There are several important consequences of these equations. One is that, in principle, attempts to evaluate αn_a by means of eqs. (4.53), (4.59), (4.61), or (4.66) should give plots that are curved instead of straight unless $(z - \alpha n_a) \phi_{sb}$ is constant over the range of potentials employed. Its variation is smallest when the species actually being

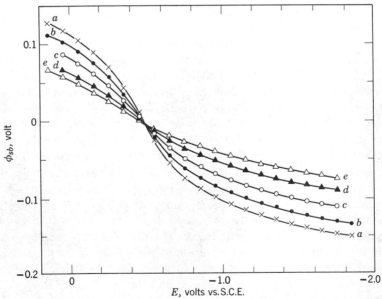

Figure 4.11. Variations of ϕ_{sb} with potential, according to Russell (61), for mercury electrodes in (a) 0.05F, (b) 0.10F, (c) 0.20F, (d) 0.50F, and (e) 1.00F sodium fluoride.

reduced has a charge of 0 or $+1$, when the supporting electrolyte is relatively concentrated, and when the range of potentials being investigated is not too close to the potential of the electrocapillary maximum. Otherwise the value of αn_a will vary from one range of potentials to another. Many examples of such a variation have been reported. Worse yet, the values of $k^0_{f,h}$ obtained from the equations in Sec. V will be in error if ϕ_{sb} is appreciable even though it is constant. The danger is that the variations of ϕ_{sb} with supporting electrolyte composition may correspond to variations of $k^0_{f,h}$ so large as to prevent interpretation of its behavior or lead to an incorrect mechanism. A similar difficulty may afflict attempts (cf. Chap. 5 III) to compare the values of $k^0_{f,h}$ for different compounds that are reduced at different potentials in the same medium.

Moreover, it follows from eq. (4.93) that any change in experimental conditions that alters ϕ_{sb} will produce a shift of the half-wave potential. This unfortunately includes the presence of most organic compounds (especially maximum suppressors), which are likely to be adsorbed onto the mercury surface except at potentials quite far removed (perhaps half a volt or more) from E_{max}. Consider, for example, the reduction of an anion or a neutral molecule [for which $(z - \alpha n_a)$ must be negative] at a potential more negative than E_{max} [where, as is shown by Fig. 4.11, ϕ_{sb} is also negative]. Increasing the concentration of the supporting electrolyte causes ϕ_{sb} to become less negative, so that the product $(z - \alpha n_a) \phi_{sb}$ in the exponential term of eq. (4.93) becomes less positive. To obtain the same current if C_b and A (the electrode area) are kept constant, the value of E must become more positive. Hence the wave must move toward more positive potentials on increasing the salt concentration. This is observed in the reduction of iodate in neutral or alkaline media and also in the reduction of 2-bromo-n-butyric acid at pH values sufficiently high to cause the wave to appear at potentials more negative than E_{max}. Data on the latter substance (64) are shown in Fig. 4.12, which also shows that the half-wave potential becomes more negative on increasing the salt concentration at pH values so low that $E_{1/2}$ is more positive than E_{max}. Here, of course, ϕ_{sb} is positive; increasing the ionic strength decreases its value and therefore causes the product $(z - \alpha n_a) \phi_{sb}$ to become less negative, necessitating a shift of E toward more negative values. Generally similar salt effects are observed (65) in the reduction of carbon tetrachloride.

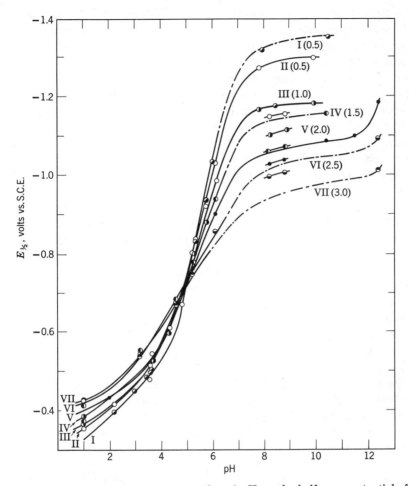

Figure 4.12. Effects of ionic strength and pH on the half-wave potential of 2-bromo-*n*-butyric acid, according to Elving et al. (*64*). Roman numerals identify the curves; the numbers in parentheses are ionic strengths. Line I represents a lower concentration of buffer than line II, and the short lines at pH values between 8 and 9 show data obtained in ammoniacal ammonium chloride buffers.

In the reduction of a cation, however, $(z - \alpha n_a)$ will usually be positive (because αn_a is usually less than 1), and then the effect of increasing the salt concentration will be precisely the reverse of that described above: if, for example, the half-wave potential is more negative than E_{max}, it should become still more negative on increasing the salt concentration. This is found to be the case (*66*) in the reduction of hydrogen ion; as the concentration of an alkali or alkaline earth metal chloride is increased from about 10^{-4} to $1F$, the half-wave potential becomes more negative and, at salt concentrations around $1F$, where ϕ_{sb} is small, it approaches a constant value. On increasing the salt concentration still further, however, complications set in: the identity of the species being reduced may change because of the decreasing activity of water, the structure of the bridge (if there is one) to the electrode surface may be altered, the reaction surface may no longer coincide with the boundary of the Helmholtz layer, and specific adsorption becomes increasingly important. For one or another of these reasons, the half-wave potential of hydrogen ion shifts from -1.55 to -1.13 v. vs. S.C.E. on increasing the concentration of a potassium thiocyanate supporting electrolyte from 1 to $10F$, and increasing the concentration of sodium perchlorate from 2 to $8F$ has a similar effect on the half-wave potential of nickel ion. These considerations suggest that electrochemical kinetic studies should be conducted in moderately concentrated (perhaps around $1F$) supporting electrolytes so as to minimize ϕ_{sb} and its variations, but that the use of too high concentrations will produce data that may fail to conform to even the elementary qualitative predictions of the theory.

It was stated above that the value of αn_a obtained by the procedures described in Sec. V depends on the range of potentials covered by the data, and this can now be examined in greater detail. What was done in Sec. V was equivalent to neglecting the term in ϕ_{sb} in the exponential of eq. (4.93), which would give

$$i_c = nFAC_b k_{f,h}^* \ \exp\ \{-F[\alpha n_a(E - E_{max})]/RT\} \qquad (4.95)$$

Comparing this with eq. (4.93), it can be seen that the value of αn_a secured by the techniques of Sec. V and described by eq. (4.95) is related to the true one described by eq. (4.93) by the equation

$$(\alpha n_a)_{app} = (\alpha n_a)_{true} + [z - (\alpha n_a)_{true}] \frac{\phi_{sb}}{E - E_{max}} \qquad (4.96)$$

As can be seen from Fig. 4.11, the ratio $\phi_{sb}/(E - E_{max})$ is always positive, regardless of whether E is more positive or more negative than E_{max}. If $(z - \alpha n_a)$ is negative, as it must be for the reduction of an anionic or uncharged species, this means that the apparent value of αn_a must be smaller than the true one. On the other hand, if $(z - \alpha n_a)$ is positive, as it is for the reductions of many cationic species, the apparent value of αn_a must be larger than the truth. The ratio $\phi_{sb}/(E - E_{max})$ varies with potential: it is largest at potentials near E_{max} and decreases as $(E - E_{max})$ increases. For example, in $0.05F$ sodium fluoride it is 0.210 at $E = +0.15$ v., 0.290 at $E = -0.15$ v., 0.255 at $E = -0.75$ v., and 0.181 at $E = -1.05$ v. If $(z - \alpha n_a)$ is negative, the result of this variation of $\phi_{sb}/(E - E_{max})$ will be that the apparent value of αn_a will pass through a minimum in the vicinity of the electrocapillary maximum potential; if $(z - \alpha n_a)$

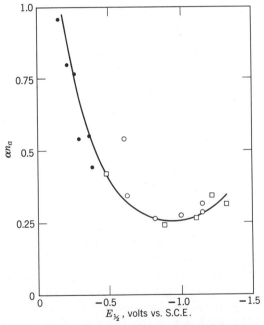

Figure 4.13. Values of αn_a and half-wave potentials for the reductions of a number of 2-bromo-n-alkanoic acids, according to Rosenthal, Albright, and Elving (67). Solid circles represent data for different acids in $0.5F$ potassium chloride containing enough hydrochloric acid to give pH 1.9; open circles represent data for different acids in $0.5F$ ammonium chloride containing enough ammonia to give pH 8.5 ± 0.3; squares represent data for 2-bromopropionic acid in various buffers having ionic strengths of 0.5.

is positive, the apparent value of αn_a will pass through a maximum in the same region.

Over the narrow range of potentials ordinarily covered by the rising part of a polarographic wave, these variations will often be inappreciable, and when they are a single value of αn_a will serve to describe the entire wave. In studies of the effect of pH and other experimental variables, however, the data may cover so wide a range of potentials that the effect becomes very pronounced. An example is shown in Fig. 4.13. The behavior here is complicated by the fact that most of the data on the left-hand branch of the curve correspond to reduction of a free uncharged acid whereas those on the right-hand branch correspond to reduction of an anion, so that $(z - \alpha n_a)$ is always negative but is much larger on the right-hand branch than on the left-hand one. This is responsible for the asymmetry of the curve and would also tend to displace the minimum toward a potential more negative than the electrocapillary maximum potential. Another factor responsible for this displacement may be specific adsorption of bromide ion liberated in the reduction or of chloride ion or some other constituent of the buffers employed. Exactly similar considerations serve to explain the variation of the apparent value of αn_a with pH (i.e., with potential) in the reduction of iodate, which was mentioned in connection with eq. (4.81).

The analog of eq. (4.96) for anodic waves is

$$[(1 - \alpha)n_a]_{\text{app}} = [(1 - \alpha)n_a]_{\text{true}} - \{z + [(1 - \alpha)n_a]_{\text{true}}\} \frac{\phi_{sb}}{E - E_{\max}}$$
$$(4.97)$$

where $(1 - \alpha)$ is the transfer coefficient for the anodic process. For the oxidation of a cationic or uncharged species, this predicts that $(1 - \alpha) n_a$ should pass through a minimum; for the oxidation of an anionic species for which z and α have values that $[z + (1 - \alpha) n_a]$ is negative, $(1 - \alpha) n_a$ should pass through a maximum. In the oxidation of hydrazine (68), where the value of $(1 - \alpha) n_a$ is 0.89 while the dependence of half-wave potential on hydroxyl-ion concentration is consistent with the mechanism

$$N_2H_4 + OH^- = N_2H_3^- + H_2O \qquad \text{(fast)}$$

$$N_2H_3^- \rightarrow N_2H_3^+ + 2e \qquad \text{(totally irreversible)}$$

(so that $z = -1$), the quantity $[z + (1 - \alpha) n_a]$ is nearly zero, and consequently $(1 - \alpha) n_a$ is constant within experimental error despite variations in hydroxyl-ion concentration that produce large variations of $E_{1/2}$.

Reinmuth, Rogers, and Hummelstedt (69) employed the electron-transfer theory of Marcus to arrive at equations and conclusions qualitatively very similar to those described above though slightly different in minor details. In addition, they concluded that, as an approximation,

$$\alpha n_a = \frac{n_a}{2} + \left(z - \frac{n_a}{2} \right) \frac{\mathrm{d}\phi_{sb}}{\mathrm{d}E} \qquad (4.97)$$

for cathodic processes. This implies that in moderately concentrated salt solutions at potentials fairly far removed from the electro-capillary maximum in the absence of specific adsorption, where $\mathrm{d}\phi_{sb}/\mathrm{d}E$ is small, α should approach $\frac{1}{2}$; if $(z - n_a/2)$ is negative, as in the reduction of an anion or a neutral molecule, α should exceed $\frac{1}{2}$, while if $(z - n_a/2)$ is positive, as in the reductions of most cationic species, α should be smaller than $\frac{1}{2}$. These predictions appear to be confirmed for many processes occurring in solutions of weakly adsorbed cations like sodium and potassium ions at potentials considerably more negative than $E_{\max}$, but on the positive side of the electro-capillary maximum most anions undergo specific adsorption and, as the left-hand branch of Fig. 4.13 suggests, α may then become quite anomalous. A similar increase of αn_a at the most positive potentials is observed in reductions of iodate ion. A detailed knowledge of the behavior of ϕ_{sb} is needed to interpret such observations, as is some assumption about the location of the reaction surface.

It may be pointed out that such anomalously high values of αn_a have important consequences for the log-plot criterion of reversibility. If a process for which n was 1 happened to occur at a potential where double-layer structure happened by coincidence to produce the value $\alpha n_a = 1$, the slope of a plot of $E_{d.e.}$ vs. log $i/(i_d - i)$ would be precisely equal to the reversible one-electron value even though the wave was in fact totally irreversible. It may be reiterated that agreement of the slope of a log plot with the theoretical value for a reversible process involving the same number of electrons does not prove the reversibility of the half-reaction. All that can properly be concluded is that the half-reaction is irreversible if there is a significant discrepancy between the experimental and theoretical slopes.

Although a description of specific adsorption would be outside the scope of this book, its most important effects deserve brief mention. On the positive side of the electrocapillary maximum, replacing an anion in the supporting electrolyte by another that is more strongly adsorbed (e.g., fluoride by chloride or chloride by iodide) makes ϕ_{sb} more negative. According to eq. (4.93), this would cause the half-wave potential for the reduction of an anion or neutral molecule to become more negative. On the negative side of the electrocapillary maximum, however, replacing a cation in the supporting electrolyte by one that is more strongly adsorbed (e.g., sodium or potassium by tetramethylammonium or tetramethylammonium by tetra-n-butylammonium) makes ϕ_{sb} more positive, and this would cause the half-wave potential for the reduction of a neutral or anionic species to shift toward less negative values, and at the same time the slope of the wave should increase because of the increase of αn_a demanded by eq. (4.96). Hence the wave should be steeper and better separated from the final current rise. As long as this is the only phenomenon involved, introducing specific adsorption in this way may be very advantageous in practical analysis (65,70); tetraethyl- and higher tetraalkylammonium salts are often used in organic polarography to permit very negative potentials to be attained, but this suggests a quite different reason for using them. However, the effect is not a universal one: adsorption of these bulky ions on the drop surface can also lead to other results (46) which would make their presence distinctly disadvantageous.

References

(1) J. Heyrovský and D. Ilkovič, *Collection Czechoslov. Chem. Communs.*, **7**, 198 (1935).
(2) J. J. Lingane, *J. Am. Chem. Soc.*, **61**, 2099 (1939).
(3) J. J. Lingane, *J. Am. Chem. Soc.*, **61**, 976 (1939).
(4) J. Heyrovský and M. Kalousek, *Collection Czechoslov. Chem. Communs.*, **11**, 464 (1939).
(5) M. v. Stackelberg and H. v. Freyhold, *Z. Elektrochem.*, **46**, 120 (1940).
(6) N. H. Furman and W. C. Cooper, *J. Am. Chem. Soc.*, **72**, 5667 (1950).
(7) M. Steinberg and N. H. Nachtrieb, *J. Am. Chem. Soc.*, **72**, 3358 (1950).
(8) J. Koutecký and M. v. Stackelberg, in *Progress in Polarography*, P. Zuman and I. M. Kolthoff, eds., Interscience, New York, 1962, pp. 21–42.
(9) J. Tomeš, *Collection Czechoslov. Chem. Communs.*, **9**, 81 (1937).

(10) R. P. Buck, *J. Electroanal. Chem.*, **5**, 295 (1963).

(11) L. B. Rogers, *Record Chem. Prog.*, **16**, 197 (1955).

(12) I. M. Kolthoff and Y. Okinaka, *J. Am. Chem. Soc.*, **83**, 47 (1961).

(13) I. M. Kolthoff and E. F. Orlemann, *J. Am. Chem. Soc.*, **63**, 644 (1941).

(14) J. Tomeš, *Collection Czechoslov. Chem. Communs.*, **9**, 150 (1937).

(15) J. J. Lingane and L. A. Small, *J. Am. Chem. Soc.*, **71**, 973 (1949).

(16) L. I. Smith, I. M. Kolthoff, S. Wawzonek, and P. M. Ruoff, *J. Am. Chem. Soc.*, **63**, 1018 (1941).

(17) J. Kamecki and L. Suski, *Roczniki Chem.*, **28**, 601 (1954).

(18) J. K. Taylor and S. W. Smith, *J. Res. Natl. Bur. Stds.*, **42**, 387 (1949).

(19) P. Delahay, *J. Am. Chem. Soc.*, **75**, 1430 (1953).

(20) P. Kivalo, K. B. Oldham, and H. A. Laitinen, *J. Am. Chem. Soc.*, **75**, 4148 (1953).

(21) R. P. Frankenthal and L. Meites, in *Handbook of Analytical Chemistry*, L. Meites, ed., McGraw-Hill, New York, 1963, pp. 1–6 to 1–8.

(22) M. Kalousek, *Collection Czechoslov. Chem. Communs.*, **13**, 105 (1948).

(23) M. Kalousek and M. Rálek, *Chem. Listy*, **48**, 808 (1954).

(24) M. Rálek and L. Novák, *Collection Czechoslov. Chem. Communs.*, **21**, 248 (1956).

(25) M. Ishibashi and T. Fujinaga, *Bull. Chem. Soc. Japan.* **23**, 261 (1950); **25**, 68 (1952).

(26) J. Heyrovský and J. Forejt, *Z. Physik. Chem.*, **193**, 77 (1943).

(27) J. Heyrovský, *Collection Czechoslov. Chem. Communs.*,**18**, Suppl. II, 54 (1954).

(28) J. Heyrovský, *Polarographie*, Springer, Vienna, 1941, pp. 234–240.

(29) R. Bieber and G. Trümpler, *Helv. Chim. Acta*, **30**, 971 (1947).

(30) A. Ševčík, *Collection Czechoslov. Chem. Communs.*, **13**, 349 (1948).

(31) J. E. B. Randles, *Trans. Faraday Soc.*, **44**, 322, 327 (1948).

(32) J. E. B. Randles and K. W. Somerton, *Trans. Faraday Soc.*, **48**, 937, 951 (1952).

(33) H. H. Bauer and P. J. Elving, *Anal. Chem.*, **30**, 334 (1958).

(34) B. Breyer and H. H. Bauer, *Alternating Current Polarography and Tensammetry*, Interscience, New York, 1963.

(35) P. Delahay and C. C. Mattax, *J. Am. Chem. Soc.*, **76**, 874 (1954).

(36) J. T. Porter, II, and W. D. Cooke, *J. Am. Chem. Soc.*, **77**, 1481 (1955).

(37) R. P. Frankenthal and I. Shain, *J. Am. Chem. Soc.*, **78**, 2969 (1956).

(38) W. H. Reinmuth, *J. Am. Chem. Soc.*, **79**, 6358 (1957); *Anal. Chem.*, **33**, 185 (1961).

(39) W. Kemula, in *Advances in Polarography*, I. S. Longmuir, ed., Pergamon, London, 1960, Vol. I, p. 135.

(40) O. Manoušek and P. Zuman, *Collection Czechoslov. Chem. Communs.*, **29**, 1432 (1964).

(41) W. Kemula and Z. Kublik, *Nature*, **182**, 793 (1958); *Roczniki Chem.*, **32**, 941 (1958).

(42) C. Olson, H. Y. Lee, and R. N. Adams, *J. Electroanal. Chem.*, **2**, 396 (1961).

(43) V. G. Levich, *Physicochemical Hydrodynamics*, Prentice-Hall, Englewood Cliffs, 1962.

(44) Z. Galus, C. Olson, H. Y. Lee, and R. N. Adams, *Anal. Chem.*, **34**, 164 (1962).

(45) H. A. Laitinen and W. J. Subcasky, *J. Am. Chem. Soc.*, **80**, 2623 (1958).
(46) S. R. Missan, E. I. Becker, and L. Meites, *J. Am. Chem. Soc.*, **83**, 58 (1961).
(47) J. Koutecký, *Collection Czechoslov. Chem. Communs.*, **18**, 597 (1953).
(48) L. Meites and Y. Israel, *J. Am. Chem. Soc.*, **83**, 4903 (1961).
(49) D. M. H. Kern, *J. Am. Chem. Soc.*, **76**, 4234 (1954).
(50) J. Koutecký and J. Čižek, *Collection Czechoslov. Chem. Communs.*, **21**, 836 (1956).
(51) P. Delahay, *J. Am. Chem. Soc.*, **73**, 4944 (1951); **75**, 1430 (1953).
(52) T. Berzins and P. Delahay, *J. Am. Chem. Soc.*, **75**, 5716 (1953).
(53) Y. Israel and L. Meites, *J. Electroanal. Chem.*, **8**, 99 (1964).
(54) J. Koryta, *Z. Physik. Chem. (Leipzig)*, Sonderheft, 157 (1958).
(54a) N. Tanaka and R. Tamamushi, *Electrochim. Acta*, **9**, 963 (1964).
(55) D. M. H. Kern, *J. Am. Chem. Soc.*, **76**, 1011 (1954).
(56) H. Matsuda and Y. Ayabe, *Bull. Chem. Soc. Japan*, **29**, 134 (1956).
(57) J. Koutecký, *Collection Czechoslov. Chem. Communs.*, **20**, 116 (1955).
(58) J. M. Hale and R. Parsons, *Collection Czechoslov. Chem. Communs.*, **27**, 2444 (1962).
(59) M. Breiter, M. Kleinerman, and P. Delahay, *J. Am. Chem. Soc.*, **80**, 5111 (1958).
(60) P. Delahay, in *Progress in Polarography*, P. Zuman and I. M. Kolthoff, eds., Interscience, New York, 1962, Vol. I, pp. 65–80.
(60a) P. Delahay, *Double Layer and Electrode Kinetics*, Interscience, New York, 1965.
(61) C. D. Russell, *J. Electroanal. Chem.*, **6**, 486 (1963).
(62) D. C. Grahame, *J. Am. Chem. Soc.*, **71**, 2975 (1949); **76**, 4821 (1954); *J. Electrochem. Soc.*, **98**, 343 (1951).
(63) G. C. Barker and R. L. Faircloth, in *Advances in Polarography*, I. S. Longmuir, ed., Pergamon, London, 1960, Vol. I, pp. 319–20.
(64) P. J. Elving, J. C. Komyathy, R. E. van Atta, C.-S. Tang, and I. Rosenthal, *Anal. Chem.*, **23**, 1218 (1951).
(65) J. J. Lothe and L. B. Rogers, *J. Electrochem. Soc.*, **101**, 258 (1954); L. E. I. Hummelstedt and L. B. Rogers, *ibid.*, **106**, 248 (1959).
(66) P. Herasymenko and J. Slendyk, *Z. Physik. Chem.*, **A149**, 123 (1930).
(67) I. Rosenthal, C. H. Albright, and P. J. Elving, *J. Electrochem. Soc.*, **99**, 227 (1952).
(68) S. Karp and L. Meites, *J. Am. Chem. Soc.*, **84**, 906 (1962).
(69) W. H. Reinmuth, L. B. Rogers, and L. E. I. Hummelstedt, *J. Am. Chem. Soc.*, **81**, 2947 (1959).
(70) R. M. Elofson, *Anal. Chem.*, **21**, 917 (1949).

CHAPTER 5

INTERPRETATION OF HALF-WAVE POTENTIALS

This chapter describes the chemical, thermodynamic, and structural information that may be obtained from measurements of the half-wave potentials of reversible and irreversible waves under varying experimental conditions.

I. Half-Wave Potentials for Reversible Reductions of Simple and Complex Metal Ions to Metals Soluble in Mercury

Equations for the half-wave potentials of the waves obtained when simple and complex metal ions are reversibly reduced to metal amalgams were given in Chap. 4 I. For the reversible reduction of a simple ion

$$M^{n+} + ne + Hg = M(Hg) \tag{5.1}$$

the half-wave potential $(E_{1/2})_s$ is given by

$$(E_{1/2})_s = E_s^0 - \frac{RT}{nF} \ln \left(-\frac{f_a k_s}{f_s k_a} \right) \tag{5.2}$$

where E_s^0 is the standard potential of the metal ion–metal amalgam couple, f_a and f_s are the activity coefficients of the metal atoms in the amalgam and the metal ions in the solution, k_a is the ratio of the anodic diffusion current to the concentration of metal in the amalgam, and k_s is the ratio of the cathodic diffusion current to the concentration of metal ion in the solution. According to the Ilkovič equation,

$$-k_s/k_a = D_s^{1/2}/D_a^{1/2} \tag{5.3}$$

For the reversible reduction of a complex ion

$$MX_p^{(n-pb)+} + ne + Hg = M(Hg) + pX^{-b} \tag{5.4}$$

the half-wave potential $(E_{1/2})_c$ is given by

$$(E_{1/2})_c = E_s^0 - \frac{RT}{nF} \ln \left(-\frac{f_a k_c}{f_c k_a} \right) + \frac{RT}{nF} \ln K_c - \frac{RT}{nF} p \ln C_{Xfx} \tag{5.5}$$

267

where the subscript c denotes the complex ion; K_c is the overall dissociation constant of the predominating complex $MX_p^{(n-pb)+}$, and C_X is the concentration of the ligand X, which is assumed to be so large (perhaps $20p$ times as large as the concentration of the complex ion) that it does not vary at the drop surface as the current changes.

Subtracting eq. (5.2) from eq. (5.5) yields a description of the difference between the half-wave potentials of the complex and simple metal ions; at 25°

$$(E_{1/2})_c - (E_{1/2})_s = \frac{0.05915}{n} \left[\log K_c - \log \frac{f_s k_c}{f_c k_s} - p \log C_X f_X \right]$$

(5.6)

It is tacitly assumed $(1,2)$ that K_c is much smaller than C^p_X, so that the concentrations of the simple ion and of any possible lower complex can be neglected in the presence of the excess of ligand. The same assumption is, of course, inherent in eq. (5.5). When it is satisfied, the half-wave potential of the complex ion will be at least $0.1/n$ v. more negative than that of the simple ion. The correction term that must be added to the right-hand side of eq. (5.6) when a smaller difference is encountered is given in the paragraph following eq. (4.27).

There are two important applications of eq. (5.6). It can be used to find the formula of the complex (that is, the value of p) from data on the variation of half-wave potential with ligand concentration, and it also serves for the evaluation of the dissociation constant K_c. Both of these applications are illustrated by the data shown in Fig. 5.1, which were obtained with solutions containing $0.6mM$ cadmium in $0.10F$ potassium nitrate and various concentrations of added ammonia.

Differentiation of eq. (5.6) gives

$$\frac{d(E_{1/2})_c}{d(\log C_X)} = - \frac{0.05915}{n} p$$

(5.7)

provided that the activity coefficients f_s, f_c, and f_X and the liquid-junction potential all remain constant as C_X is varied, and that the ratio k_c/k_s also remains constant.

As long as C_X does not exceed about $1M$, neither k_c nor k_s is likely to vary greatly, as was explained in Chap. 3 IV-D. At higher concentrations of X both k_c and k_s do change, but as they are similarly dependent on viscosity their ratio will change less than either of their

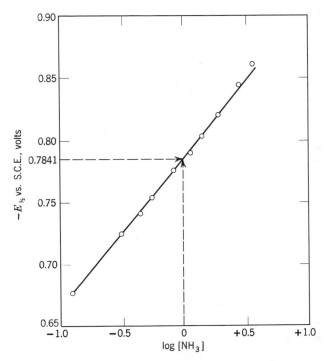

Figure 5.1. Effect of ammonia concentration on the half-wave potential of cadmium(II) in 0.10F potassium nitrate.

individual values. Usually k_c/k_s will be constant over a wide range of experimental conditions. The constancy of f_X, of the ratio f_s/f_c, and of the liquid-junction potential are more difficult to ensure. So far as the activity coefficients are concerned, the usual course is to maintain a constant ionic strength as C_X is varied. This is undoubtedly satisfactory within the ordinary margin of experimental error if X is non-ionic, as is the case with ammonia, ethylenediamine, o-phenanthroline, and many other ligands of interest. If X is ionic, however, the activity coefficients will almost surely not remain constant as an inert electrolyte like sodium perchlorate is replaced by an electrolyte containing X even though the ionic strength does not change. For example, the mean ionic activity coefficient of hydrochloric acid (and therefore doubtless also the single-ion activity coefficient of chloride ion) is not the same in $1F$ sodium perchlorate containing a trace of hydrochloric acid as it is in $1F$ hydrochloric acid. Moreover, in these circumstances there will also be a variation of the liquid-junction potential. One keeps the ionic strength constant and hopes for the best; the single-ion activity-coefficient problem being what it is, there is nothing better that can be done.

Subject to these assumptions and uncertainties, the value of p can be obtained directly from the slope of a plot like that in Fig. 5.1. Here, with ammonia concentrations between about 0.1 and $1.2M$, the experimental value of $dE_{1/2}/d(\log C_{\mathrm{NH_3}})$ is -0.118 v. Since $n = 2$ for the reduction of the cadmium(II) complex to cadmium amalgam, eq. (5.7) becomes

$$-0.118 = -\frac{0.05915}{2}\,p$$

whence $p = 4.0$. Consequently the predominating complex under these conditions must be $Cd(NH_3)_4{}^{++}$. At higher concentrations of ammonia the measured half-wave potentials become more negative than the extrapolated values, reflecting the formation of appreciable concentrations of $Cd(NH_3)_5{}^{++}$.

From the equation for the straight line through the experimental points in Fig. 5.1, it is found that $(E_{1/2})_c$ is -0.7841 v. vs. S.C.E. when the ammonia concentration is $1.00M$. The half-wave potential of the simple cadmium ion in $0.10F$ potassium nitrate free from added ammonia is -0.5777 v. vs. S.C.E. It is reasonable to suppose that the liquid-junction potential between the saturated potassium chloride in the S.C.E. and $0.1F$ potassium nitrate will be essentially identical with that between saturated potassium chloride and $0.1F$ potassium nitrate containing $1M$ ammonia. Equation (5.6) may now be written for $C_{\mathrm{X}} = 1M$

$$(E_{1/2})_{c,C_{\mathrm{X}}=1} - (E_{1/2})_s = \frac{0.05915}{n}\left[\log K_c - \log\frac{f_s}{f_c}\right.$$
$$\left. - \log\frac{k_c}{k_s} - p\log f_{\mathrm{X}}\right] \qquad (5.8)$$

To obtain K_c it is necessary to evaluate or make some assumption about each of the last three terms on the right-hand side of this equation.

The ratio k_c/k_s is given, according to the Ilkovič equation, by

$$\frac{k_c}{k_s} = \frac{D_c^{1/2}}{D_s^{1/2}} = \frac{I_c}{I_s} \tag{5.9}$$

so that it can be calculated from the corresponding diffusion current constants. An error of $\pm 10\%$ in this ratio corresponds to an error of only $\mp 2.4/n$ mv. in the difference between the two half-wave potentials. This is small enough to be ignored except in extremely precise measurements. Larger errors will arise, however, if the ligand is so large (as is true of the anions of many organic acids, like tartrate and citrate, as well as of most chelons, like ethylenediaminetetraacetate and $1,2$-diaminocyclohexane-N,N,N',N'-tetraacetate) that the diffusion coefficient of the complex ion is much smaller than that of the simple ion, or if the supporting electrolyte containing the complex ion has a much higher viscosity than the solution in which the half-wave potential of the simple ion was measured. Care should be taken in measuring the latter to choose a noncomplexing supporting electrolyte that has as nearly as possible the same viscosity as the solution in which the half-wave potential of the complex ion has been obtained.

The activity coefficients are more difficult to deal with. About the best approximation that can be made is to describe each of them by the extended Debye–Hückel equation

$$\log f_i = -\frac{0.51 z_i^2 \mu^{1/2}}{1 + 0.33 \overset{\circ}{a}_i \mu^{1/2}} + B_i \mu \tag{5.10}$$

Assuming, for want of anything better, that the distance of closest approach $\overset{\circ}{a}_i$ is equal to the typical value 4.5Å. for each of the ionic species and that the salting-out coefficients B_i are also equal, one obtains

$$\log (f_s/f_c) = (z_c^2 - z_s^2) L \tag{5.11a}$$

where

$$L = 0.51\mu^{1/2}/(1 + 1.5\mu^{1/2}) \tag{5.11b}$$

There are many cases in which z_c^2 and z_s^2 are equal, so that f_s and f_c will be at least approximately equal in solutions of identical ionic strength: this is true whenever the ligand is non-ionic and also often when it is ionic, as illustrated by the complexes $Cu(C_2O_4)_2^=$ and

$Cd(EDTA)^=$. In such cases it is reasonable to ignore the activity-coefficient ratio altogether, and in fact it has also often been ignored even when $z_c{}^2$ and $z_s{}^2$ differ, presumably on the ground that neglecting the activity coefficients is unlikely to produce an error much larger than the one that results from neglecting the liquid-junction potential.

On this subject it may be said that a comparison of the half-wave potentials obtained in two different supporting electrolytes is inherent in any use of eq. (5.6); each of the measured half-wave potentials necessarily includes a liquid-junction potential that is difficult or impossible to estimate and that may be appreciable or even large compared to the precision of measurement. For this reason there is rarely any substantial justification for assuming that the measured difference between the two half-wave potentials is meaningful to better than about five or ten millivolts. This is not at all the same thing as saying that a smaller difference between two half-wave potentials is never meaningful. If the half-wave potentials of two different substances are measured in the same supporting electrolyte, a difference of even a millivolt or two may be reproducible and significant (although better than average technique is needed to attain such precision) because a difference of liquid-junction potentials is not involved. It is often possible to alter the composition of a solution appreciably without producing much effect on the liquid-junction potential, for example by varying the concentration of a non-ionic ligand (provided that the range of variation is not too wide) or even of an ionic one if a swamping concentration of indifferent electrolyte is always present.

Taking all these considerations into account, we may now proceed to evaluate K_c for the tetramminocadmium(II) complex from eq. (5.8) and the data previously given. The difference between the half-wave potentials was given above as -0.2064 v. The ratio f_s/f_c may be taken as 1 because Cd^{++} and $Cd(NH_3)_4{}^{++}$ have the same charge. The diffusion current constant of cadmium in $0.1F$ potassium nitrate containing $1M$ ammonia is 3.85, while in $0.1F$ potassium nitrate alone it is 3.53. Hence $k_c/k_s = 3.85/3.53 = 1.09$. Taking the activity coefficient of ammonia as 1 because it is unlikely to differ appreciably from this for a non-ionic species at so low an ionic strength, eq. (5.8) becomes

$$-0.2064 = 0.02957(\log K_c - \log 1.09)$$

whence K_c, the thermodynamic dissociation constant of the complex, is

$$K_c = a_{Cd^{++}}a^4_{NH_3}/a_{Cd(NH_3)_4^{++}} = 1._1 \times 10^{-7}$$

in excellent agreement with values secured by other techniques.

There are several reasons why this is a favorable case. Uncertainties in the activity coefficients of the simple and complex ions and in the liquid-junction potential are small because these are hardly affected by the addition of ammonia. The uncertainty in the activity coefficient of the ammonia is small because it is non-ionic and because the ionic strength is not very high. The data are rather more precise than usual because they were obtained by measuring the currents at 1-mv. intervals on the rising part of the wave, using a manual polarograph, and consequently their probable error is only of the order of ±0.2 mv., which is considerably smaller than the best that can be obtained by interpolation on the curve secured with a recording instrument. Usually these errors and uncertainties are much larger than in this example, and so the experimental points may show much more scatter than those in Fig. 5.1 and the best straight line through them may have a slope that corresponds to a value of p differing appreciably from an integer. It may be pointed out that a linear plot of $(E_{1/2})_c$ vs. log C_X must mean that a single complex predominates over the entire range investigated. If the slope of such a plot gives $p = 1.5$, for instance, one may blame this on experimental error, on miscalculation, on the omission of some significant correction, or on fate, but not on the existence of a mixture of complexes for which p has values of 1 and 2, for such a mixture must give a curved plot. The mathematical treatment of data on such systems has been worked out by Hume, DeFord, and others (3–5), whose papers should be consulted for details.

Even when all of the factors in eq. (5.8) are taken into account, a value of K_c calculated from polarographic data should not be assigned an accuracy better than ±50% except under most extraordinary circumstances. When n is 2 this error corresponds to an error of only ±5 mv. in the difference between the half-wave potentials of the simple and complex ions; it is true that the values can be measured more precisely than this if a manual instrument is used as described above, but the activity coefficients and liquid-junction potentials will almost always contribute an uncertainty of several millivolts. Lest the reader be discouraged by the magnitude of this error, it may be pointed out that there are very few cases in which uncertainties much below ±50% have been achieved in measurements of thermodynamic dissociation constants even by the most refined techniques.

One of two things must be true if the treatment so far outlined is to be successful. Either the complex ion itself is reduced directly at the drop surface, in which case equilibrium in this electron-transfer step must be practically instantaneous; or the complex dissociates before reduction occurs, in which case both the dissociation and the reduction of the liberated metal ions must be practically instantaneous. There are, however, complexes of which neither of these things is true, and there are also circumstances in which the techniques described above are experimentally inconvenient. Other procedures for obtaining the formulas and dissociation constants of complex ions have therefore had to be devised; not all of these are based on measurements of the half-wave potential, but they are outlined here to provide a convenient summary of the field.

One closely related technique (6–8) is useful in dealing with complexes for which a reversible electron-transfer step cannot be obtained or for which the half-wave potential of a reversible wave would be so negative that a supporting electrolyte suitable for measuring it would be difficult to prepare and purify. Complexes of ions like cobalt(II), nickel(II), thorium(IV), and the like would fall into the first of these classes; complexes of the alkali and alkaline earth metal ions would fall into the second. If the dissociation equilibrium is rapid, one may obtain a reversible half-wave potential through the mediation of another metal ion that forms a reversibly reduced complex with the same ligand. Consider a solution in which both of the following equilibria are rapid:

$$MX_p + ne + Hg = M(Hg) + pX \qquad (5.12a)$$

$$NX_r = N + rX \qquad (5.12b)$$

Ionic charges are omitted for simplicity. Equation (5.12a) represents the ordinary reversible reduction of the complex of the mediating metal ion M; eq. (5.12b) represents the dissociation of the complex that is to be studied. Both this complex and the corresponding simple ion N are assumed to be present in large known excess: the solution may be prepared by adding a large excess of X to a solution of the simple ions M in an inert supporting electrolyte like sodium perchlorate, then adding a much larger excess of N to this mixture. If N and its complex are reduced at all, they must be reduced at potentials so much more negative than those over which the reversible wave of MX_p appears that the latter can be studied without interference. An equation for the half-wave potential of MX_p can be derived along lines identical with those followed in deriving eq. (4.26) except for the addition of a description of the equilibrium of the dissociation of NX_r:

$$f_X^p (C_X^0)^p = \left(K_{NX} \frac{f_{NX} C_{NX}^0}{f_N C_N^0} \right)^{p/r} \tag{5.13}$$

where K_{NX} is the dissociation constant of NX_r. In view of what was said in the paragraph following eq. (4.27), the value of $f_X^p (C_X^0)^p$ must be much larger than K_c, the dissociation constant of MX_p, and this implies (since C_N is much larger than C_{NX}) that K_c must be very much smaller than K_{NX}. The technique has, for example, been used to evaluate the dissociation constant of the sodium-ethylenediaminetetraacetate complex (i.e., $N = Na^+$, $X = EDTA^{-4}$) with thallous ion as the mediating ion M. The proper choice of the mediating ion is evidently essential to success. The derivation yields, at 25°,

$$E_{1/2} - (E_{1/2})_s = \frac{0.05915}{n} \left[\log K_c - \frac{r}{p} \log K_{NX} - \log \frac{f_s k_c}{f_c k_s} \right.$$
$$\left. - \frac{r}{p} \log \frac{f_{NX}}{f_N} - \frac{r}{p} \log \frac{C_{NX}}{C_N} \right] \tag{5.14}$$

where $E_{1/2}$ is the half-wave potential obtained in the presence of N and NX while $(E_{1/2})_s$ is the half-wave potential of the simple ion M; the subscripts s and c denote the ions M and MX_p, respectively. Since there is a large excess of N present, only very little of it will be bound as NX_r, and so C_N can be equated to the total added concentration of N without appreciable error; for the same reason, nearly all of the X will be bound as NX_r, and so the concentration of this complex can be equated to C_X/r, where C_X is the total concentration of X in the solution. Evidently, as long as all of the above conditions remain satisfied,

$$\frac{dE_{1/2}}{d \log (C_{NX}/C_N)} = - \frac{0.05915}{n} \frac{r}{p} \tag{5.15}$$

from which r is easily deduced if n and p arc known. In varying the ratio C_{NX}/C_N, which is most easily done by varying the total concentration of either X or N, care should be taken to keep the ionic strength and viscosity reasonably constant so that variations of the activity and diffusion coefficients appearing in eq. (5.14) can be ignored. Once r is known, K_{NX} can be evaluated from eq. (5.14) in the fashion described above.

Some complex ions cannot be reduced directly but must dissociate first: this is true of many metal chelonates (9,10) among others, probably because bridging from the metal ion to the electrode, which may occur with chloride and many other ligands, is then impossible. If the dissociation is slow, a kinetic wave is obtained, and if the resulting free metal ion is reversibly reduced it can be shown (11) that

$$(E_{1/2})_c = (E_{1/2})_k - \frac{0.05915}{n} \log \frac{i_d}{i_k} \tag{5.16}$$

where $(E_{1/2})_c$ is the half-wave potential and i_d the average diffusion current of the hypothetical reversible wave that would be obtained if the dissociation were instantaneous, while $(E_{1/2})_k$ and i_k are the half-wave potential and average wave height of the kinetic wave actually observed. The value of i_d may be estimated from data on similar complexes that do yield diffusion-controlled waves, and the value of $(E_{1/2})_c$ thus obtained may be interpreted as described above.

Two other techniques that do not depend on measurements of potentials, and that consequently do not require that the electron-transfer step be very rapid, may be mentioned more briefly. One (12–14) is based on a competition of two metal ions for the ligand. A solution containing stoichiometrically equivalent amounts of a metal ion M and the ligand X is prepared; the formula MX_p and the dissociation constant K_c of the resulting complex must be known, and the complex must be so stable that no wave for the free M ions is obtained. A known concentration C_N of the simple metal ion N is added. An equilibrium

$$qMX_p + pN = pNX_q + qM \tag{5.17}$$

is established and simple M ions are liberated. The wave now obtained for their reduction has a diffusion current equal to i_d. Both this equilibrium and the dissociation of MX_p must be very slow, so that the height of the M wave corresponds to the equilibrium concentration of free M ions in the solution. A solution containing M at the same total concentration C_M, but free from both X and N, gives a diffusion current equal to i_0. The equilibrium constant is

$$K = \frac{[NX_q]^p[M]^q}{[MX_p]^q[N]^p} = \frac{K_{MX_p}^q}{K_{NX_q}^p} \tag{5.18}$$

Writing conservation equations for the concentrations of the reacting substances and combining them with eq. (5.18) yields, after simplification,

$$K = \frac{(p/q)^p i_d^{(p+q)} C_M^q}{\left(i_0 - i_d\right)^p \left(i_0 C_N - \frac{p}{q} i_d C_M\right)^q} \tag{5.19}$$

Though the technique has as yet been applied only in cases in which both p and q are known, eq. (5.19) could obviously be used to evaluate q in an unknown complex. Once q is known, K is easily calculated, and from this K_{NX_q} is readily obtained with the aid of eq. (5.18).

Finally, the difference between the diffusion coefficients of a free and complexed metal ion may be used to evaluate the proportions in which these are present in a mixture. For a 1:1 complex MX, if the concentration C_X of free ligand is much larger than the total concentration C_M of metal ion, one obtains (8,15)

$$\overline{D} = \frac{D_M + D_{MX}K_cC_X}{1 + K_cC_X} \tag{5.20}$$

where $\overline{D}$ (the apparent diffusion coefficient corresponding to the total wave height for the simultaneous reduction of M and MX in the mixture), D_M (the diffusion coefficient of simple M ions), and D_{MX} (the diffusion coefficient of MX) are all estimated from the Ilkovič equation. The equilibrium must be very rapid and the mixture must contain roughly equal concentrations of M and MX. Because D_M and D_{MX} must be quite different, the method is most suitable for use with chelons and other bulky ligands; because a mixture containing excess X must also contain a fair proportion of uncomplexed M, it is restricted to complexes that have fairly large dissociation constants. An obvious way of circumventing the latter requirement would be to establish a competition for the ligand; if the solution also contained another metal ion N and its complex NX at high concentrations, and if both of the dissociation equilibria were rapid, eq. (5.20) would become

$$\overline{D} = \frac{D_M + D_{MX}K_cK_{NX}(C_{NX}/C_N)}{1 + K_cK_{NX}(C_{NX}/C_N)} \tag{5.21}$$

It would of course be necessary that neither N nor NX contribute to the current at the potential where the combined wave height of M and MX is measured. The competing ion N might advantageously be hydrogen ion in a well buffered solution. Apparently, however, this extension of the technique has not been put to use.

These techniques are so numerous, and the conditions required for their success are so varied, that polarography is one of the most versatile and widely used techniques for investigating the formulas and dissociation constants of metal complexes.

II. Half-Wave Potentials for Reversible Processes Involving Only Dissolved Species

Equations for the half-wave potentials of the waves obtained when simple and complex metal ions are reversibly reduced to lower oxidation states were given in Chap. 4 III. For the reversible reduction of an aquo-complex ion O to an aquo-complex ion R in a lower oxidation state

$$O + ne = R \tag{5.22}$$

the half-wave potential $(E_{1/2})_s$ is given by

$$(E_{1/2})_s = E_s^0 - \frac{RT}{nF} \ln\left(-\frac{f_R k_O}{f_O k_R}\right) \tag{5.23}$$

where E_s^0 is the standard potential of the half-reaction. The ratio k_O/k_R is easily evaluated from diffusion-current data: the Ilkovič equation gives

$$k_O/k_R = D_O^{1/2}/D_R^{1/2} = -I_O/I_R \tag{5.24}$$

It is plain that, with the aid of these equations and estimates of the activity coefficient ratio f_R/f_O and the liquid-junction potential, the standard potential can be estimated from the measured half-wave potential. The manner in which such estimates are made may be deduced from the discussion on page 231.

For the reduction of a complex ion

$$OX_p^{(m-pb)+} + ne = RX_q^{(m-n-qb)+} + (p - q) X^{-b} \qquad (5.25)$$

of which equation (5.22) represents merely the special case in which $p = q = 0$, the half-wave potential $(E_{1/2})_c$ is given by

$$(E_{1/2})_c = E_c^0 - \frac{RT}{nF} \ln \left(-\frac{f_{RC} k_{OC}}{f_{OC} k_{RC}} \right) - \frac{RT}{nF} (p - q) \ln f_X C_X \qquad (5.26)$$

where the subscripts OC and RC denote the oxidized and reduced complexes and E_c^0 is the standard potential of the half-reaction described by eq. (5.25). It can be shown that

$$E_c^0 - E_s^0 = \frac{RT}{nF} \ln \frac{K_{OC}}{K_{RC}} \qquad (5.27)$$

where K_{OC} and K_{RC} are the overall dissociation constants of the oxidized and reduced complexes, respectively. Equations (5.23), (5.26), and (5.27) may be combined to yield, at 25°,

$$(E_{1/2})_c - (E_{1/2})_s = \frac{0.05915}{n} \left[\log \frac{K_{OC}}{K_{RC}} - \log \frac{f_{RC} f_{OC} k_{OC} k_R}{f_{OC} f_{RC} k_R k_{RC} k_O} \right.$$
$$\left. - (p - q) \log f_X C_X \right] \qquad (5.28)$$

In these equations it is assumed that C_X is large and that $(E_{1/2})_c$ and $(E_{1/2})_s$ are obtained in solutions sufficiently similar to permit neglecting the difference between the liquid-junction potentials involved in measuring them.

These equations can be treated similarly to those in Sec. I, which describe the reductions of simple and complex metal ions to metals soluble in mercury. Provided that the activity and diffusion coefficients are not sensibly affected by varying the ligand concentration— that is, if a swamping concentration of an inert electrolyte is always present and if there is no gross anomaly in the ratios of the diffusion coefficients—one will have, at 25°,

$$\frac{d(E_{1/2})_c}{d(\log C_X)} = - \frac{0.05915}{n} (p - q) \qquad (5.29)$$

so that the value of $(p - q)$ is easily obtained from the slope of a plot of the half-wave potential vs. log C_X. For the reduction of a mixed complex

$$OX_pY_r^{(m-pb-rc)+} + ne =$$

$$RX_qY_s^{(m-n-qb-sc)+} + (p - q) X^{-b} + (r - s) Y^{-c} \quad (5.30)$$

eq. (5.29) is obeyed if the concentration of Y^{-c} is kept constant, while if the concentration of X^{-b} is kept constant while that of Y^{-c} varies one will have

$$\left(\frac{\partial(E_{1/2})_c}{\partial(\log C_Y)} \right)_{C_X} = - \frac{0.05915}{n} (r - s) \quad (5.31)$$

In principle, neither p nor q can be evaluated from eq. (5.29) unless the other is known, but information concerning one of them will often be available; if it is not, a reasonable guess can generally be made. In a desperate case one might try the following approach, which is based on the effect of ionic strength on the half-wave potential. Successively larger concentrations (beginning at perhaps $0.1F$) of an inert electrolyte like potassium nitrate or sodium perchlorate are added to a solution containing excess ligand and the half-wave potential is plotted against the quantity L defined by eq. (5.11b). The same considerations that led to eq. (5.11a) give (approximately, because the liquid-junction potential and the salting-out term for the ligand are neglected)

$$\frac{d(E_{1/2})_c}{dL} = (z_{RC}^2 - z_{OC}^2) + (p - q) z_X^2 \quad (5.32)$$

Given the value of $(p - q)$ obtained from eq. (5.29), various values of p and q can be assumed and the corresponding charges on the reduced and oxidized complexes can be used to compute values of $d(E_{1/2})_c/dL$ for comparison with the experimental value. The procedure fails if the ligand is uncharged, in which case the half-wave potential should be independent of L. Moreover, a danger arises from the fact that the concentration of a charged ligand at the reaction surface will vary with ionic strength even though its bulk concentration is unaltered; this effect is described by eq. (4.91). In the absence of specific adsorption, the values shown in Fig. 4.11 can probably be combined with eqs. (4.91) and (5.29), using the experimental value of $(p - q)$, to obtain sufficiently accurate corrections in cases that prove to be ambiguous when the effect is ignored. Though the value of $(p - q)$ obtained from eq. (5.29) is of course afflicted by the same phenomenon, the use of reasonably concentrated solutions should generally decrease the double-layer effect to manageable proportions. It may seem advantageous to measure half-wave potentials at fairly low ionic strengths so as to facilitate extrapolation to infinite dilution, but the advantage is illusory: because the magnitude of the double-layer correction increases with decreasing salt concentration, such measurements are actually of very uncertain significance.

Equation (5.26) can be used to evaluate $E_c{}^0$ if the half-wave potential is measured at (or extrapolated or interpolated to) $C_X = 1M$. The activity and diffusion coefficients must naturally be dealt with in the usual way if a very precise value of $E_c{}^0$ is wanted. For many purposes, however, a value may be very useful even though its precision is limited. In neutral solutions containing excess ethylenediaminetetraacetate, the cathodic half-wave potential of vanadium(III) and the anodic half-wave potential of vanadium(II) are both equal to -1.27 v. vs. S.C.E., and hence one might simply say that the standard potential of the couple is -1.27 v. vs. S.C.E. (or -1.03 v. vs. N.H.E.), for it would be hard to imagine any combination of effects that could alter this value by more than a very few hundredths of a volt. Exactly the same simple approach may be adopted in obtaining formal potentials from reversible half-wave potentials, and this has the further advantage of eliminating uncertainties due to the neglect of activity coefficients and liquid-junction potentials.

Just as eq. (5.29) suffices for the evaluation of the difference between p and q but does not reveal their individual values, so eq. (5.28) permits the calculation of the ratio K_{OC}/K_{RC} but cannot provide a value of either dissociation constant. The individual values of K_{OC} and K_{RC} can be found from polarographic data if, but only if, the reduced complex undergoes a further reversible reduction to the metal amalgam. In that case K_{RC} and q can be found from data on the half-wave potential of this cathodic wave of the reduced complex, as described in Sec. I; then K_{OC} and p can be found from eqs. (5.28) and (5.29).

It may be pointed out that the half-wave potential for the reversible reduction of a metal ion to a metal soluble in mercury must always be shifted toward more negative values by complex formation. When the reduced species remains in the solution phase, however, this is not necessarily true. Complexation will then cause the half-wave potential to become more negative if $K_{OC} < K_{RC}$ (so that the oxidized complex is more stable than the reduced one), will have no effect if $K_{OC} = K_{RC}$, and will cause the half-wave potential to become more positive if $K_{OC} > K_{RC}$. The first of these is the most common, but there are examples of the others. Thus, the half-wave potential of the reversible wave obtained in $1F$ potassium chloride for the reduction of copper(II) to copper(I) is more than a tenth of a volt more positive than the standard potential (-0.09 v. vs. S.C.E.) of the couple $Cu^{++} + e = Cu^{+}$. This is because K_{RC} [the dissociation constant of the dichlorocuprous complex] is much smaller than K_{OC} [the dissociation constant of the predominating monochloro complex of copper(II)].

Hydrogen ions are generally consumed when organic compounds are reduced and liberated when they are oxidized. If the substances involved in the half-reaction are not appreciably acidic or basic over the range of conditions being investigated, it is most convenient to describe the half-reaction by an equation of the form

$$O + pH^+ + ne = RH_p \tag{5.33}$$

and then, neglecting activity coefficients and the liquid-junction potential, one obtains [cf. eq. (4.41)]

$$\frac{dE_{1/2}}{d(pH)} = -\frac{0.05915}{n} p \tag{5.34}$$

whence p is easily evaluated once n is known. Subject to the uncertainties mentioned above, the standard potential may be equated to the half-wave potential measured at, or extrapolated or interpolated to, pH 0. This would suffice to explain the half-wave potentials obtained in, for example, the reversible reduction of a quinone to a hydroquinone in acidic media.

More generally, however, a fast chemical equilibrium—which in the majority of cases is a proton-transfer reaction—preceding or following the electron-transfer step has to be taken into account. The mechanism may then be described by the equations

$$O + pH^+ = H_pO^{p+} \tag{5.35a}$$

$$H_pO^{p+} + ne = RH_p \tag{5.35b}$$

Neglecting the activity and diffusion coefficients, the reversible half-wave potential at 25° will be given by

$$E_{1/2} = E^0 + \frac{0.05915}{n} \log \frac{[H^+]^pK}{[H^+]^pK + 1} \tag{5.36}$$

where E^0 is the standard potential (or, more accurately, the formal potential) of the electron-transfer process described by eq. (5.35b), while K is the equilibrium constant of the chemical process described by eq. (5.35a): that is, the formation constant of the protonated species. If $[H^+]^pK \gg 1$, then the protonated species H_pO^{p+} predominates in the solution, and the half-wave potential is practically independent of pH; if, however, $[H^+]^pK \ll 1$, it is the unprotonated species O that predominates, and in this region the half-wave potential varies with pH in accordance with eq. (5.34). Hence a plot of $E_{1/2}$ vs. pH consists of two straight-line segments, which may be extrapolated to intersect at the point where pH $= -pK/p$. If, on the other hand, it is the reduced species whose acidity or basicity must be taken into account, one may write

$$O + pH^+ + ne = RH_p \tag{5.37a}$$

$$RH_p = qH^+ + RH_{p-q} \tag{5.37b}$$

in which event, if K is the equilibrium constant of the reaction described by eq. (5.37b) [that is, the dissociation constant of the protonated form of R], the reversible half-wave potential will be given by

$$E_{1/2} = E^0 - \frac{0.05915}{n} \log \frac{[H^+]^{(q-p)}}{[H^+]^q + K} \tag{5.38}$$

In solutions so acidic that $[H^+]^q \gg K$, the reduced form will exist predominantly as RH_p and the variation of half-wave potential with pH will be described by eq. (5.34); at the other extreme, in solutions so alkaline that $[H^+]^q \ll K$, one will have

$$\frac{dE_{1/2}}{d(pH)} = -\frac{0.05915}{n}(p - q) \tag{5.39}$$

Plots of $E_{1/2}$ vs. pH occasionally consist of several linear segments, which correspond to regions in which different protonation equilibria predominate. As the above equations indicate, the slope in each region is proportional to the total number of protons consumed in reducing the predominating oxidized species to the predominating reduced species.

III. Half-Wave Potentials for Irreversible Processes. Correlations between Half-Wave Potential and Structure

Equations for the half-wave potentials of the totally irreversible waves produced by a number of typical mechanisms were given in Chap. 4 V, and the discussion there should be consulted for information on such matters as the dependence of half-wave potential on drop time and the elucidation of the stoichiometry of the reaction through the rate-determining step. In this section we shall consider the relationship between the half-wave potential and the structure of an organic compound yielding a totally irreversible wave.

In Chap. 4 V it was shown that for the simple mechanism

$$O + n_a e \rightarrow I \qquad \text{(rate-determining)} \qquad (5.40a)$$

$$I + (n - n_a)e \rightarrow R \quad \text{(fast)} \qquad (5.40b)$$

the half-wave potential obtained by measuring maximum currents is given by

$$E_{1/2} = -0.2412 + \frac{0.05915}{\alpha n_a} \log \frac{1.349 k_{f,h}^0 t^{1/2}}{D_O^{1/2}} \qquad (5.41)$$

Imagine that the half-wave potentials of two compounds having identical values of D_O and αn_a are measured under the same conditions and that the values of t at their half-wave potentials are also identical. The difference between their half-wave potentials will be given by

$$(E_{1/2})_1 - (E_{1/2})_2 = \frac{0.05915}{\alpha n_a} \log \frac{(k_{f,h}^0)_1}{(k_{f,h}^0)_2} \qquad (5.42)$$

The ratio of rate constants on the right-hand side can be described by the Hammett equation (16,17) if the compounds are m- and p-substituted benzene derivatives, by modifications of this for certain alicyclic, heterocyclic, and naphthalene derivatives (18–20), or by the Taft equation (21, 22) for certain aliphatic compounds and possibly certain o-substituted benzene derivatives. According to the Hammett equation

$$\log (k/k_0) = \rho\sigma \tag{5.43}$$

where k is the rate constant (that is, the value of $k^0_{f,h}$) for the compound under consideration; k_0 is the rate constant for the same reaction of the corresponding parent compound, containing hydrogen instead of the substituent in question; ρ is the reaction constant, characteristic of the parent compound, the reaction that occurs, and the medium in which it takes place; and σ is the substituent constant, a measure of the ability of the substituent to attract ($\sigma > 0$) or repel ($\sigma < 0$) electrons by a combination of inductive and resonance effects.

Combining eqs. (5.42) and (5.43) yields

$$\frac{dE_{1/2}}{d\sigma} = \frac{0.05915}{\alpha n_a} \rho \tag{5.44}$$

so that a plot of the half-wave potential against σ should be linear and should have a slope proportional to ρ. Linear variations of the half-wave potential with σ have indeed been observed for the great majority of the families of compounds studied, which have included substituted acetophenones, benzophenones, iodobenzenes, nitrobenzenes, quinoxalines, and others too numerous to list. Since the above argument in a trivially different form can be applied to reversible processes as well as to irreversible ones, similar correlations have been obtained in the reductions of quinones, azobenzenes, and others. It is not at all uncommon, however, for an occasional compound to have a half-wave potential widely divergent from the expected value; this is especially likely to be true of mercapto, primary and secondary amino, and other derivatives in which the substituent group would be expected to produce a marked increase in the extent of specific adsorption and thus a marked change in the double-layer effect. Moreover, there are a few families (e.g., 23) in which the dependence of half-wave potential on σ is reported to be too erratic to permit useful correlations to be made.

Little that is useful can as yet be said about the values of ρ for different families of compounds. Though ρ is surely affected by the composition of the solvent and supporting electrolyte as well as by the identity of the reducible group and the gross mechanism by which it is reduced, the same solvent and supporting electrolyte have too rarely been used for studying the behaviors of different families of compounds. There is no basis for a quantitative comparison of the data obtained for one family in $0.1F$ lithium chloride in 50% ethanol with those obtained for another in a McIlvaine buffer containing 10% dioxane. It would be much better to limit the variety of conditions employed in studies of this sort so that their results could be rationally and systematically compared. About equally deplorable is the fact that it has been customary to report, not ρ itself, but a distantly related parameter, which might be called ρ', and which is defined by the equation

$$\rho' = \frac{dE_{1/2}}{d\sigma} \left(= \frac{0.05915}{\alpha n_a} \rho \right) \qquad (5.45)$$

To a first approximation, αn_a is also characteristic of the reduction process for the members of any particular family (however, see Chap. 4 VII), but its value and that of ρ are so irretrievably scrambled in ρ' that the latter is of no more than purely empirical use. As a general guide it can be said that ρ' is most often of the order of $+0.3$ v.; if αn_a is 0.5, which is also a typical value, this corresponds to a value of about $+2.5$ for ρ, which is at least roughly comparable to the range of values ordinarily obtained in homogeneous reactions. Positive values of ρ' mean, of course, that electron transfer to the reducible group is facilitated by an electron-withdrawing substituent, as would be expected. Much smaller and occasionally even negative values of ρ' are sometimes encountered, however (e.g., 24); in some cases this appears to be associated with electron transfer to a positively charged site while in others it appears to be associated with a mechanism involving the addition of electrons across a double bond that is simply polarized by the substituent group, but the examples are too few to permit definitive generalizations.

Despite the frequency with which the above treatment has been applied (25–27), the dangers inherent in it have been persuasively argued (28–30). Variations of D_O and t among the different compounds examined are unlikely to be very large, and even if they were they could easily be dealt with by basing the treatment on a corrected half-wave potential, $(E_{1/2})_{corr}$, obtained from the experimental value for a totally irreversible wave by means of the equation

$$(E_{1/2})_{corr} = E_{1/2} - \frac{0.02957}{\alpha n_a} \log \frac{t}{D_0} \qquad (5.46)$$

in which D_0 may be estimated by employing eq. (3.22). Variations of αn_a among the different compounds are more drastic and more likely. The above treatment amounts to a comparison of rate constants at 0 v. vs. N.H.E. If the values of αn_a are the same for two compounds, the ratio of their rate constants will be the same at that potential as at any other, and so some significance can be attached to it. If they are different, the ratio will vary, perhaps over a great many orders of magnitude, with the potential chosen for the comparison, and in this case it cannot be relied on to mean anything at any potential. In Chap. 4 VII it was shown that, even for a single compound, αn_a will vary appreciably with potential unless it is equal to the charge z on the species actually reduced, which cannot be the case unless the latter is cationic; precisely similar variations can be expected to afflict the values of αn_a for different compounds that are reduced at different potentials. Only in the vicinity of the electro-capillary maximum, where αn_a is passing through a maximum or minimum value, would one expect these variations to be small, and this is precisely the region in which specific adsorption is most to be feared. It is always prescribed that the values of αn_a should be identical, within the experimental error involved in measuring them, for the waves of all of the compounds being subjected to this treatment, but it is an open question whether the prescription is a reasonable one: the cases in which it is satisfied may be very rare. Theoretically it would be much better to plot $\{E_{1/2} + [(z - \alpha n_a)/\alpha n_a] \phi_{sb}\}$ vs. σ, as suggested by eq. (4.93); prior correction of the half-wave potential in accordance with eq. (5.46) is necessary under the circumstances described in connection with that equation. This demands the evaluation of αn_a and the estimation of z outlined in Secs. V and VII of Chap. 4, as well as some knowledge of the parameter ϕ_{sb}. Unfortunately, values of the latter are not readily available in the non-aqueous solutions likely to be employed in studying organic compounds. This is a real difficulty, and systematic data on the magnitudes of the double-layer corrections in a variety of non-aqueous media would be of very great utility despite the residual uncertainty that would arise in their use because of the danger of specific adsorption and variations in its extent among different compounds of the same family. It is hardly possible to estimate the severity of the problem; if large differences among the extents of specific adsorption of related compounds were very common, one would expect random variations of $E_{1/2}$ with σ to arise more often than they do. At the same time it may be said that, by continuing to employ the bewildering variety of supporting electrolytes and solvents that have been used for these studies in the past, organic polarographers can only discourage their colleagues from obtaining these data and render them less useful when they are finally obtained.

Difficult though the proper treatment may be, however, the improper one, in which the double-layer effect is simply ignored, seems to the writer to be of very dubious value. Under any one fixed set of conditions, to be sure, it does usually produce a correlation between a series of half-wave potentials and a series of σ-values. However, a correlation that serves merely to reproduce the data used in deducing it is but a poor return for the labor involved in the deduction. It would be far more important to be able to make valid comparisons of the relationships obtained for different families of compounds and under different experimental conditions (31), and this is impossible unless the relationships are firmly based on theoretical considerations.

IV. Summary of Factors Affecting the Half-Wave Potential

The effects of a number of experimental variables on the half-wave potential, which have been discussed in preceding sections, are summarized here for convenient reference.

The temperature coefficient of the half-wave potential is most often between -2 and $+2$ mv./deg. For a reversible wave it may be either positive or negative; for an irreversible wave it is usually positive and may exceed several millivolts per degree.

The half-wave potential is almost always independent of the concentration of the electroactive species (i.e., of the diffusion current) after proper correction is applied for the iR drop. However, the half-wave potential of a reversible wave does vary with concentration if a solid product is formed or, more generally, whenever the number of the ions or molecules of the product of variable activity differs from the number of ions or molecules of reactant of variable activity in the equation for the half-reaction. Such variations can of course be described by thermodynamic equations. The half-wave potential of an irreversible wave may also vary with concentration of the reaction mechanism involves some rate-governing step that is not first- or pseudo-first order; when it does vary, it most often becomes more negative as the concentration increases.

The half-wave potential of a reversible wave is nearly independent of the capillary characteristics m and t. When the diffusion current obeys the Koutecký equation and when the diffusion coefficients of the oxidized and reduced species differ, a small dependence of the half-wave potential on $t^{1/6}/m^{1/3}$ can be predicted, and is described by eq. (4.18), but it can safely be neglected in all work except the very most precise. Changes in m, t, and the concentration of the electro-active species may, however, produce spurious apparent variations of the half-wave potential unless both the iR drop and the effect or recorder lag are eliminated or corrected for. The iR drop always produces an apparent shift of the half-wave potential toward more negative values for cathodic waves, toward more positive values for anodic ones, and the shift is proportional to the limiting current. Recorder lag due to excessive damping produces an apparent shift toward more negative values if the electrode potential is being made more negative during the recording of the wave, regardless of whether the wave is cathodic or anodic; if the dropping electrode is being polarized in the direction of increasingly positive potentials, the shift is always toward more positive values. The error can be identified by comparing the half-wave potentials obtained by polarization in opposite directions, and may be eliminated by using a sufficiently fast recorder. The accuracy and precision with which a half-wave potential may be determined with a recording polarograph can be increased by adjusting the initial voltage so that the recording begins at a potential just before the start of the wave and using a small span voltage to spread the wave over the maximum possible length of chart. In this way a precision of about ±1 mv. can be secured under optimum conditions; using a manual polarograph and interpolating between values obtained at a few closely spaced potentials on the rising part of the wave, a precision of about ±0.2 millivolt can be secured.

The half-wave potential of a totally irreversible wave, however, varies significantly with t, becoming more positive for a cathodic wave as t increases. The magnitude of the variation depends on αn_a and may be used for its evaluation. Typically, if $\alpha n_a = 0.5$, the half-wave potential becomes about 20 mv. more positive if t is doubled.

Changes in the nature and concentration of the supporting electrolyte may affect the half-wave potential in any of several ways. For reversible waves the most interesting effect is due to complex formation. Much information about the identities and dissociation constants of reversibly reduced metal complexes can be obtained from polarographic measurements. In the reversible reduction or oxidation of an organic compound it is the pH of the supporting electrolyte that is most important, and for such processes it is possible to obtain information concerning the occurrence and equilibrium constants of acid–base reactions involving the oxidized and reduced forms of the couple.

When a complex metal ion is reversibly reduced to a metal soluble in mercury, its half-wave potential is always more negative than that for the reversible reduction of the corresponding simple or aquo-complex ion, the difference being related to the free energy of dissociation of the complex. Complex formation also usually makes the half-wave potential more negative when a metal ion is reduced to a lower oxidation state and when the product remains dissolved in the solution phase. However, the opposite effect is occasionally observed, and when it is it signifies that the reduced complex is more stable than the oxidized one. Because hydrogen ion is nearly always consumed in the reversible reduction of an organic compound, the half-wave potential for such a process nearly always becomes more negative as the pH is increased, though it may remain constant over a certain range of pH values because of the influence of prior or subsequent proton-transfer reactions.

Complex formation may cause the half-wave potential for the irreversible reduction of a metal ion to become either more negative or more positive, depending on the nature of the ligand. For example, nickel ion has a half-wave potential of -1.01 v. vs. S.C.E. in $0.1F$ sodium perchlorate, but does not give a wave at all in ethylenediaminetetraacetate solutions; this is partly because the chelonate is much more stable than the simple metal ion, and partly because this ligand is a much poorer bridge for electron transfer than a water molecule is. In media containing thiocyanate, pyridine, or high concentrations of halide, however, the half-wave potentials of nickel(II) are considerably more positive than -1.0 v., for these ligands facilitate electron transfer and decrease the activation energy involved in the reduction. The half-wave potential for the irreversible reduction of an organic compound may also be affected by a chemical reaction with the supporting electrolyte: for example, the half-wave potentials of most carbonyl compounds are grossly altered by the addition of ammonia or hydroxylamine, which convert them into imines or oximes. However, this explanation of a change of half-wave potential resulting from a change of supporting electrolyte should not be advanced unless some reasonable reaction can be envisioned, for changes in one or more of the rate constants involved in the overall reaction, in the double-layer effects, and in the liquid-junction potential can also produce changes of the half-wave potential in the absence of any reaction with the supporting electrolyte.

Changes in the concentration of the supporting electrolyte may affect the half-wave potential of an irreversible wave by altering the rate of the electron-transfer step or the equilibrium position of some fast chemical reaction that precedes it. These effects can often be used to elucidate the stoichiometry of the reaction through the rate-determining electron-transfer step. They are complicated, however, by the fact that changes in salt concentration also affect, not only the concentration of a charged species at the surface where the reaction occurs by altering the work required to bring it to that surface from the bulk of the solution, but also the potential difference between the electrode and that surface and thus the rate of electron transfer. The directions and magnitudes of these double-layer effects depend on the potential at which the wave occurs, on the nature of the ionic medium, on the charge on the species actually reduced, and on the mechanism by which the reduction occurs. In some cases the half-wave potential becomes more negative on increasing the salt concentration, while in others it becomes more positive; shifts as large as 0.4 v. have been observed. For these reasons it is desirable to keep the nature and concentration of the supporting electrolyte as nearly constant as possible in studies of irreversible processes. It is often desirable to vary the pH over a considerable range in studying the behavior of an organic compound. When this is done by using a number of different buffer systems, variations of the double-layer effects may well obscure the effect of pH itself. Internally consistent results can generally be obtained by using buffers of identical ionic strengths (32).

The effects of salt concentration on the half-wave potentials of reversible waves are due to mass-action effects on complexation equilibria, changes of the activity coefficients of the species involved in the half-reaction, and variations of the liquid-junction potential (*33*). All of these are illustrated by data (*1*) on the half-wave potential of cadmium ion in nitrate solutions at ionic strengths up to $12M$. At zero ionic strength (by extrapolation), $E_{1/2}$ is -0.571 v. vs. S.C.E. At an ionic strength of 0.1 it is -0.578 v., and is independent of the identity of the salt present. This shift is primarily due to the formation of complex $CdNO_3^+$ ions. At higher ionic strengths specific effects become apparent: at an ionic strength of 1.0, $E_{1/2}$ is -0.586 v. in nitric acid or potassium nitrate but -0.578 v. in magnesium or aluminum nitrate. These variations are probably due primarily to differences in the activity coefficients of the various ions. At still higher ionic strengths the half-wave potential becomes more positive: at an ionic strength of 6.0, it is -0.569 v. in ammonium nitrate but -0.553 v. in aluminum nitrate. These values include fairly substantial liquid-junction potentials across the boundaries between the saturated potassium chloride in the S.C.E. and the different nitrate supporting electrolytes.

Though these variations are of little significance in practical analytical work, they must be taken into account whenever half-wave potentials in different supporting electrolytes are compared. For similar reasons it is extremely hazardous to attempt to draw any thermodynamic conclusions from the differences among half-wave potentials obtained in different solvents.

In non-aqueous media having low dielectric constants, electroactive ions will be largely converted into ion pairs or higher ionic aggregates. The resulting effect on the half-wave potential has been described by Schaap (*34*). In this connection it may be pointed out that one consequence of the Stern double-layer theory is that the dielectric constant decreases rapidly as the electrode surface is approached, becoming as small as 2 or 3 at the electrode-solution interface even in an aqueous solution. The transient formation of an ion-aggregate under these conditions has no effect on the half-wave potential of a reversible wave, but because it may alter the charge borne by the electroactive species it may affect that of an irreversible one.

V. Qualitative Polarographic Analysis

Qualitative polarographic analysis is carried out by matching four characteristics of the unknown electroactive substance with those of a known one, either measured separately or obtained from tables. The four characteristics are the half-wave potential, the shape of the wave, the wave pattern, and the manners in which these are affected by changing the supporting electrolyte and other experimental variables.

There are a few—but only a very few—cases in which a reasonably certain identification can be based on the measurement of a single half-wave potential. Suppose, for example, that an otherwise inert sample is suspected of containing antimony(III). Inspection of a table of inorganic half-wave potentials (e.g., *35*) reveals that in $8F$ hydrochloric acid antimony(III) gives a wave for which $E_{1/2}$ is -0.24 v. vs. S.C.E. and that no other metal ion of the fairly large number for which information is available gives a wave within a tenth of a volt of this potential. On inspecting a polarogram of a solution of the sample in $8F$ hydrochloric acid the presence or absence of antimony (III) could easily be judged. Similarly, a sample known to consist of either maleic or fumaric acid could easily be identified by obtaining a polarogram of it in an ammoniacal buffer of pH 8 to 9, in which the half-wave potentials of maleate and fumarate ions are about -1.4 and -1.6 v., respectively.

This simple approach is all too rarely feasible, however, for two reasons. One is that the half-wave potential is not often as uniquely characteristic of a single substance as in the first of these examples. Even if the list of possibilities is confined to the common metal ions, there are likely to be several whose half-wave potentials are so nearly equal to the observed value that only a tentative identification is possible, while in organic analysis the possibilities are still more numerous. The other is that, even when there is some medium especially favorable to the identification of a particular substance, the chance that it will be chosen is very small unless the presence of that substance is suspected.

With samples of unknown composition it is, therefore, usually necessary to obtain a polarogram in one supporting electrolyte and to compare the half-wave potential with tables to identify a fairly small number of possibilities, then to select another supporting electrolyte that will permit these to be distinguished from each other. For example, a sample believed to contain only a single electroactive substance may give a single wave, for which $E_{1/2} = -0.37$ v. vs. S.C.E., in saturated citric acid. In this medium there are three metal ions having half-wave potentials sufficiently near this value to require consideration: antimony(III), lead(II), and perhaps titanium(IV). "Sufficiently near" should usually be taken to mean within about 30 or even 50 mv.; the half-wave potential of an irreversible wave [like that of antimony(III) here] varies with drop time and may not be the same with the analyst's capillary as with the one used in obtaining the literature value. The inclusion of titanium(IV) in this list illustrates another fairly common problem: the half-wave potential of titanium(IV) is -0.37 v. in $0.2F$ citric acid but has not been reported in saturated citric acid, and it would be somewhat hazardous to attempt to predict its value in the latter medium. In such cases it is always better to include the doubtful ion in the list of possibilities: although this complicates the subsequent steps, the correct conclusion may otherwise be impossible to reach.

At this point it would be appropriate to measure the value of $E_{3/4} - E_{1/4}$ for the wave obtained. The value of this parameter is -56 mv. for titanium(IV) in $0.2F$ citric acid; this corresponds to a reversible one-electron reduction to titanium(III), and if the reduction is reversible in $0.2F$ citric acid it would surely be reversible in saturated citric acid as well. Hence the value of $E_{3/4} - E_{1/4}$ for titanium(IV) in saturated citric acid can safely be presumed to be -56 mv. From Chap. 4 VII it should be clear that a similar prediction could not be safely made for an irreversible wave. The values of $E_{3/4} - E_{1/4}$ for lead(II) and antimony(III) in saturated citric acid are -28 and -63 mv., respectively. One could not distinguish between antimony(III) and titanium(IV) with any degree of assurance on this basis, but lead could easily be identified. If $E_{3/4} - E_{1/4}$ is about -60 mv. for the unknown wave, either of two procedures is available. One may investigate the effect of drop time on the half-wave potential: since the titanium wave is reversible, changing the drop time should have practically no effect on its half-wave potential, but eqs. (4.66) and (4.68) show that $dE_{1/2}/d(\log t)$ should be close to $-0.572(E_{3/4} - E_{1/4})$, or $+36$ mv., for the irreversible wave of antimony(III). The other procedure is to obtain a second polarogram in another supporting electrolyte. This should be one in which both of the possible ions give waves (one in which only one of them gives a wave would be a very poor second choice, for obvious reasons) and in which these are fairly widely separated. For example, in $0.05F$ ethylenediaminetetra-acetate–$0.8F$ acetic acid the half-wave potential of titanium(IV) is -0.22 v. while that of antimony(III) is -0.62 v.

When a metal ion or an organic functional group undergoes step-wise oxidation or reduction and thereby gives rise to two or more waves, its polarogram is much more informative than one consisting of only a single wave, for the identification can then be based on the wave-height ratio as well as on the half-wave potentials. In many cases the half-wave potentials alone will suffice. For example, urani-um(VI) gives a double wave in saturated hydrazine dihydrochloride, and its half-wave potentials are -0.16 and -0.88 v. vs. S.C.E. Antimony(III), bismuth(III), and arsenic(III) also have half-wave potentials near -0.16 v. in this medium. But the first two of these give no other wave, and though arsenic(III) does give a second wave its half-wave potential is -0.57 v.; the two half-wave potentials taken together are uniquely characteristic of uranium(VI). In other cases the ratio of wave heights is needed as well. In $1F$ ammonia–$1F$ ammonium chloride the half-wave potentials of arsenic(III) are given in the literature as -1.41 and -1.63 v., while those of chromium(III) are given as -1.43 and -1.71 v. There would be no problem in distinguishing between these elements if their half-wave potentials had been measured with the same capillary and at the same drop time used in obtaining the polarogram of the unknown, for a difference of 80 mv. between the half-wave potentials of the two second waves is far outside any reasonable limit of experimental error. Both waves are irreversible, however, and so their half-wave potentials vary with drop time; the literature values may well have been obtained at drop times differing considerably from each other and from the drop time to be used by the analyst. Consequently it is very advantageous that the wave-height ratios are different for the two elements. For arsenic(III) the first wave height is only about a fifth of the total [each wave represents a three-electron reduction, but the six-electron reduction to arsine is apparently accompanied by a catalytic evolution of hydrogen which increases the total current], but for chromium(III) it is very nearly a third [the first wave represents the one-electron reduction to chromium(II), while the total represents the three-electron reduction to the metal]. Similar uses may be made of multiple waves for organic compounds: for example, in a weakly acidic solution a double wave in which the first wave height is two-thirds of the total is characteristic of nitro compounds.

The prudent analyst will, of course, take care to ensure that the multiple waves observed do really belong to a single substance instead of to a mixture whose constituents happen to be present in just such proportions as serve to counterfeit the behavior of a quite different substance. In the last example, a double wave for which the half-wave potentials are about -1.42 and -1.65 v. while the first wave is about a fifth as high as the total might represent a roughly equimolar mixture of chromium(III) and manganese(II) (whose half-wave potential is -1.66 v.); there might be no arsenic present at all. This possibility might be checked by obtaining another polarogram in $1F$ hydrochloric acid and comparing it with the behavior of arsenic(III) in that medium. In doing this, the total wave heights in the two media should be compared to guard against the possibility that both chromium and arsenic might be present; if this is so, the total wave height in the hydrochloric acid solution (which is due to arsenic alone) will be much less than in the ammoniacal solution.

Finally, many waves have individual peculiarities that greatly facilitate their recognition. Tellurium(IV) has a half-wave potential equal to -0.67 v. vs. S.C.E. in $1F$ ammonia–$1F$ ammonium chloride; at -1.2 v., in the middle of a long flat plateau, there is a large acute maximum that is uniquely characteristic of tellurium(IV) and that would serve to distinguish it from any other known element. In other cases a maximum near the start of the plateau or a distortion of the rising part of the wave may permit the assignment of the wave to a particular substance.

When applied to organic analysis these procedures can at most serve for the identification of the reducible group or of some portion of the structure of the molecule; there are too many possibilities to allow one compound to be unambiguously identified unless much *a priori* information is available. Thus, a substance giving a half-wave potential of -0.1 v. in a supporting electrolyte containing $0.1F$ hydrochloric acid might be a peroxide, a nitroso, nitroaromatic, or α-iodocarbonyl compound, or a naphthoquinone, among others, but it could not be an aliphatic nitro compound or an α-bromo- or -chlorocarbonyl compound or a p-benzoquinone or an anthraquinone. Some further distinction is possible: the wave of a peroxide is usually much more drawn out (that is, the numerical value of $E_{3/4} - E_{1/4}$ is much larger) than that of a nitroso or nitroaromatic compound, while that of a naphthoquinone is usually steeper still, having the slope expected for a reversible two-electron process. The half-wave potential of an iodo compound would be independent of pH, while that of a nitro or nitroso compound or a naphthoquinone becomes more negative as the pH increases. But after a reducible substance had been identified as a nitro compound, for example, there would be little hope of deciding, by purely polarographic means, which particular nitro compound it was.

It may fairly be said that polarography is of very limited use for the identification of an organic compound about which no prior information is available. It is far more useful for distinguishing among a limited number of compounds, and dozens of examples might be cited to support the contention that it is among the best of the techniques available for this purpose. A few groups of closely related compounds that could easily be distinguished by taking advantage of differences among their half-wave potentials are chalcone and flavanone and many of their hydroxy- and methoxy- derivatives; cis- and trans-3-(p-bromobenzoyl)-3-methacrylic acid and their methyl esters and amides; cis- and trans-1,2-dibenzoylethylene; the 6-hydroxychromans and 5-hydroxycoumarans; the C_1- through C_3-nitroparaffins; the isomeric nitro- and dinitrotoluenes, nitroanisoles, and related compounds; and the five isomeric aminoacridines. The analyst who wishes to distinguish among the members of any such group must always begin by obtaining polarograms of them under the same conditions, and in particular with the same drop time, that will be used in work with unknowns. This is because the half-wave potentials of irreversible waves are dependent on the drop time; the dependence is very important here because it may be large in comparison with the differences between the individual compounds. Half-wave potentials tabulated in the literature may serve to indicate that distinctions are possible but must not be relied on in making them. No matter how carefully a literature value may appear to have been obtained, it is useless for this purpose unless it is accompanied by enough information on t and αn_a to permit correcting it to the drop time used by the analyst. The correction would be easy to make by employing eq. (4.66), but unfortunately the required data have rarely been given. Those who report the half-wave potentials of irreversible waves

TABLE 5.1.

The Qualitative Analysis of a Four-Component Mixture

The first column gives the compositions of the supporting electrolytes in which successive polarograms might be obtained. The second gives the half-wave potentials that would be observed if the sample contained cobalt(II), manganese(II), nickel(II), and zinc(II) at roughly comparable concentrations. The third gives the half-wave potentials, taken from the literature, that would have to be considered in interpreting these observations. All half-wave potentials are in volts vs. S.C.E., and unusual elements like europium and gallium are ignored. "NR" means that no wave is obtained. The fourth summarizes the interpretation.

| Supporting electrolyte | Half-wave potentials | | Interpretation |
	Observed	Literature	
1F ammonia– 1F ammonium chloride	−1.10 −1.3 −1.66	As(III) −1.41, −1.63 Co(II) −1.29 Cr(III) −1.43, −1.71 Mn(II) −1.66 Mo(VI) −1.71 Ni(II) −1.10 Zn(II) −1.35	Ni(II) present; others possibly present
Saturated citric acid	−0.95	As(III) −0.58, −0.73, −1.02 Co(II) NR Cr(III) −0.78 Mn(II) NR Mo(VI) +0.04, −0.44 Ni(II) −0.98 Zn(II) −0.93	Co(II) and/or Zn(II) possibly present; As(III), Cr(III), and Mo(VI) definitely absent; Mn(II) must be present to account for wave at −1.66 v. in preceding medium
0.1F EDTA, 2F sodium hydroxide	−1.4	Co(II) NR Mn(II) NR Ni(II) NR Pb(II) −1.32 (pH 12) Sn(II) −1.36 (pH 12) Zn(II) −1.4	Pb(II) and Sn(II), if present, would have given cathodic waves around −0.4 v. in citric acid medium and are therefore absent; Zn(II) must be present to account for wave observed here

(continued)

TABLE 5.1 (*continued*)

| Supporting electrolyte | Half-wave potentials | | Interpretation |
	Observed	Literature	
0.05F sodium glutamate, 0.2 F sodium per- chlorate, 0.2F borate buffer, pH 9.5	−0.07(anodic) −1.26 −1.54	Co(II) −0.07(anodic) Mn(II) −1.53 Ni(II) −1.24, −1.55 V(IV) −0.11(anodic) Zn(II) −1.28	V(IV), if present, would have given anodic wave at −0.32 v. in am- monia-ammonium chloride and is therefore absent; Co(II) must be present to account for wave observed here

No evidence bearing on the presence of W(VI) has been obtained, because this gives no wave in any of these media; if it may be present, a fifth polarogram must be obtained in a medium (e.g., concentrated hydrochloric acid) in which its waves can be observed without interference from any of the four elements known to be present.

should either give both $E^0{}_{1/2}$ and αn_a or, if they prefer to quote the measured values of $E_{1/2}$, give the values of t and αn_a as well. In the latter case the value of t should of course be that at the half-wave potential and not, for example, that obtained when the capillary is disconnected from the polarizing circuit.

The qualitative analysis of a mixture is more difficult than the identification of a single substance; as is usual in qualitative analysis, it rapidly becomes still more difficult as the mixture becomes more complex and as the concentrations of its constituents become more widely disparate. A trace constituent is practically impossible to detect unless its wave can be made to precede the waves of all of the major constituents. In addition, special care must be taken to avoid overlooking substances that are polarographically inert in the sup- porting electrolytes used.

The analyst may be confronted by either of two questions. He may be asked whether a certain substance is present at a detectable concentration or not, or he may be asked what substances are present at detectable concentrations. The first question is often fairly easy to answer. Suppose, for example, that it is desired to know whether a sample contains cobalt. In a glutamate medium of pH 9.5, cobalt(II) gives an anodic wave which represents its oxidation to cobalt(III) and for which $E_{1/2}$ is -0.07 v. vs. S.C.E. Vanadium(IV) also gives an anodic wave, for which $E_{1/2}$ is -0.11 v., and this would interfere with the detection of cobalt. The interference of vanadium can be eliminated, however, by oxidizing it to vanadium(V), which gives a double cathodic wave at -0.4 and -1.3 v., sufficiently far away from the anodic cobalt wave to be innocuous. The preliminary oxidation would also eliminate possible interference from tin(II) and other strong reducing agents. In addition, if very much iron were known to be present, a separation of it would be advisable to obviate extensive loss of cobalt by coprecipitation in the alkaline glutamate.

The analysis of a completely unknown mixture is much more difficult. General precepts are so unlikely to be useful that Table 5.1 is offered as an example of what would have to be done in a not very complicated case. Four polarograms in different, carefully chosen supporting electrolytes are needed here to provide definite assurance that four elements are present and that most other common elements are absent; in fact a great deal more work might have to be done because one can hardly make the best choice of supporting electrolyte without knowing what is present. Hence polarography cannot be said to be suitable for this purpose. Organic mixtures are still harder to deal with, for several reasons: the possibilities are more numerous; variations of pH, drop time, ionic strength, and composition of the supporting electrolyte tend to have roughly similar effects on the behaviors of different and unrelated classes of compounds; and systematic data are much scarcer for organic substances.

References

(1) D. D. DeFord and D. L. Andersen, *J. Am. Chem. Soc.*, **72**, 3918 (1950).

(2) R. P. Buck, *J. Electroanal. Chem.*, **5**, 295 (1963).

(3) D. D. DeFord and D. N. Hume, *J. Am. Chem. Soc.*, **73**, 5321 (1951).

(4) D. N. Hume, D. D. DeFord, and G. C. B. Cave, *J. Am. Chem. Soc.*, **73**, 5323 (1951).

(5) P. K. Kamalkar, *Z. Physik. Chem.*, **218**, 189 (1961).

(6) A. Ringbom and L. Eriksson, *Acta Chem. Scand.*, **7**, 1105 (1953).

(7) N. C. Li, T. L. Chu, C. T. Fujii, and J. M. White, *J. Am. Chem. Soc.*, **77**, 859 (1955).

(8) Z. Zábranský, *Collection Czechoslov. Chem. Communs.*, **24**, 3075 (1959).

(9) J. Koryta, *Collection Czechoslov. Chem. Communs.*, **24**, 2903 (1959).
(10) M. Pryszczewska, R. Ralea, and J. Koryta, *Collection Czechoslov. Chem. Communs.*, **24**, 3796 (1959).
(11) J. Koryta, *Collection Czechoslov. Chem. Communs.*, **23**, 1408 (1958); **24**, 3057 (1959).
(12) G. Schwarzenbach, G. Anderegg, W. Schneider, and H. Senn, *Helv. Chim. Acta*, **32**, 1175 (1949).
(13) K. Bril and P. Krumholz, *J. Phys. Chem.*, **57**, 874 (1953).
(14) G. Schwarzenbach, R. Gut, and G. Anderegg, *Helv. Chim. Acta*, **37**, 937 (1954).
(15) V. Kačena and L. Matoušek, *Collection Czechoslov. Chem. Communs.*, **18**, 294 (1953).
(16) L. P. Hammett, *Physical Organic Chemistry*, McGraw-Hill, New York, 1940, pp. 184–199.
(17) H. H. Jaffé, *Chem. Revs.*, **53**, 191 (1953); R. R. Wells, *ibid.*, **63**, 171 (1963).
(18) J. D. Roberts and W. T. Moreland, Jr., *J. Am. Chem. Soc.*, **75**, 2167 (1953).
(19) R. C. Elderfield and M. Siegel, *J. Am. Chem. Soc.*, **73**, 5622 (1951).
(20) C. C. Price and R. H. Michel, *J. Am. Chem. Soc.*, **74**, 3652 (1952).
(21) R. W. Taft, Jr., *J. Am. Chem. Soc.*, **74**, *2729*, 3120 (1952); **75**, 4231 (1953); *J. Phys. Chem.*, **64**, **1805** (1960).
(22) R. W. Taft, Jr., and I. C. Lewis, *J. Am. Chem. Soc.*, **80**, 2436 (1958).
(23) G. S. Krishnamurthy and S. I. Miller, *J. Am. Chem. Soc.*, **83**, 3961 (1961).
(24) M. P. Strier and J. C. Cavagnol, *J. Am. Chem. Soc.*, **80**, 1565 (1958).
(25) E. Imoto, *Rev. Polarogr. (Kyoto)*, **9**, 185 (1961).
(26) P. Zuman, in *Advances in Polarography*, I. S. Longmuir, ed., Pergamon, London, 1960, Vol. III, p. 812.
(27) P. Zuman, *J. Polarogr. Soc.*, **7**, 66 (1961); *Rev. Polarogr. (Kyoto)*, **11**, 102 (1963).
(28) T. Berzins and P. Delahay, *J. Am. Chem. Soc.*, **75**, 5716 (1953).
(29) P. Delahay and C. C. Mattax, *J. Am. Chem. Soc.*, **76**, 5314 (1954).
(30) W. H. Reinmuth, L. B. Rogers, and L. E. I. Hummelstedt, *J. Am. Chem. Soc.*, **81**, 2947 (1959).
(31) P. Zuman, *Collection Czechoslov. Chem. Communs.*, **25**, 3225 (1960).
(32) P. J. Elving, J. M. Markowitz, and I. Rosenthal, *Anal. Chem.*, **28**, 1179 (1956); P. J. Elving, in *Handbook of Analytical Chemistry*, L. Meites, ed., McGraw-Hill, New York, 1963, p. 5–112.
(33) D. E. Sellers and N. E. Vanderborgh, *J. Am. Chem. Soc.*, **86**, 1934 (1964); **87**, 1206 (1965); N. E. Vanderborgh and D. E. Sellers, *ibid.*, **86**, 2790 (1964).
(34) W. B. Schaap, *J. Am. Chem. Soc.*, **82**, 1837 (1960).
(35) L. Meites, in *Handbook of Analytical Chemistry*, L. Meites, ed., McGraw-Hill, New York, 1963, pp. 5–53 to 5–103.

CHAPTER 6

MAXIMA AND MAXIMUM SUPPRESSORS

The idealized polarographic wave described by the equations in Chap. 4 is a smooth S-shaped curve. In the great majority of cases it is symmetrical around the half-wave potential. If the half-reaction occurring at the dropping electrode is cathodic, the current increases monotonically as the potential becomes more negative, and it finally approaches a practically constant value. This value, known as the wave height, is not quite completely independent of potential, but it is nearly so. Its variation with potential results from changes in the capillary characteristics m and t. The effects of these changes differ for diffusion-controlled, kinetic or catalytic, and adsorption waves,

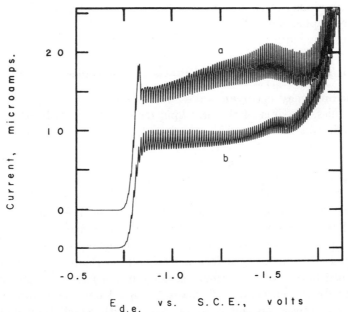

Figure 6.1.   Polarograms of 3mM lead(II) and 0.25mM zinc(II) in 2F sodium hydroxide: (a) in the absence of a maximum suppressor, and (b) after the addition of 0.002% Triton X-100.

but are predictable if the reaction mechanism is known. Once the plateau has been attained, any further increase of current that cannot be accounted for by a change of capillary characteristics must reflect either another stage of reduction or the reduction of another electroactive substance.

Many waves, however, do not conform to this description. Two kinds of deviations from it may be distinguished, and both are illustrated by Fig. 6.1(a). On the rising part of the wave the current may increase to a value larger than that on the plateau, then decrease more or less sharply and approach the plateau from above. This is called a "maximum of the first kind," and may be observed at about -0.8 v. on this curve. The other deviation is called a "maximum of the second kind," and here it takes the form of a "false" or "anomalous" wave, with an increase of current beginning at about -0.9 v., rising slowly to a maximum value at about -1.3 v., and then decreasing more rapidly than can be accounted for by the decrease of $m^{2/3}t^{1/6}$ at these potentials.

Both kinds of maxima are disadvantageous in nearly all practical polarographic work. This chapter deals with their behaviors, effects, causes, and suppression.

I. The Characteristics and Practical Significance of Maxima

Maxima may occur on waves due to anions, cations, or neutral molecules. Maxima of the first kind may occur on both anodic and cathodic waves. They seem to occur less frequently with complex than with simple ions, with anodic than with cathodic waves, and with strongly alkaline than with neutral or strongly acidic supporting electrolytes. So many exceptions to these precepts are known, however, that they can hardly be relied on in making predictions. To the extent that they are valid, they may possibly be due in large part to the different extents to which different kinds of reagents are contaminated by traces of surface-active materials, which serve to suppress maxima. The role of surface activity in maximum suppression is outlined in Sec. III. Strongly alkaline media may perhaps contain miniscule concentrations of soaps derived from the hydrolysis of traces of grease on the walls of vessels with which they come in contact, and soaps are very efficient maximum suppressors. The fact that maxima of the first kind are somewhat less often observed on anodic than on cathodic waves may simply reflect the fact that most anodic waves are obtained in alkaline solutions, where maximum formation is less likely than in neutral or acidic media. Similarly, traces of surface-active impurities in an organic complexing agent, or even a small degree of surface activity on the part of the complexing agent itself, would suffice to prevent maxima on polarograms of the complexes formed when metal ions are added. Many electroactive organic compounds are themselves surface-active to some extent, as are their reduction products, and maxima are, therefore, somewhat less common in organic than in inorganic polarography. Another important consideration is that maxima of the first kind tend to be more prominent when they occur on waves whose half-wave potentials are more positive than the electrocapillary maximum potential than when they occur on waves at more negative potentials. Both increasing alkalinity and the presence of complexing agents tend to shift waves from the positive to the negative side of the electrocapillary maximum, and this is another possible explanation of the fact that maxima of the first kind appear less frequently under these conditions.

Both kinds of maxima are affected by the concentration of the supporting electrolyte, but they are affected in different ways. Maxima of the first kind tend to be most prominent in dilute supporting electrolytes and are usually suppressed by increasing the conductivity—which is to say the concentration—of the supporting electrolyte. This is illustrated by Fig. 6.2. As if to emphasize the difficulty of making rigorous general statements about maxima, however, they do occasionally appear even in media having extremely high conductivities, such as concentrated hydrochloric acid. Usually an increase in the concentration of a supporting electrolyte is accompanied by an increase in its viscosity, and because maxima are due to streaming of the solution past the drop surface they tend to be suppressed by an increase of viscosity. Maxima of the first kind do not appear in solutions that are both highly conductive and fairly viscous, such as concentrated solutions of sodium hydroxide, hydrazine dihydrochloride, or phosphoric, tartaric, or citric acids.

Maxima of the second kind, on the other hand, are rarely observed in supporting electrolytes less concentrated than roughly $0.2F$. They tend to increase in height as the concentration of the supporting electrolyte increases, and so they are very prominent in media that

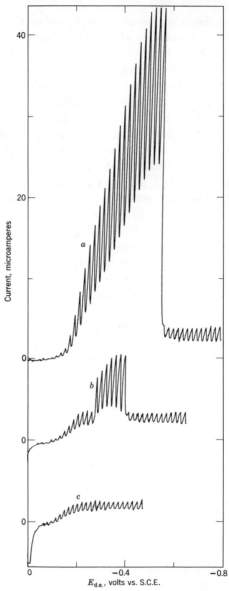

Figure 6.2. Polarograms of oxygen in air-saturated solutions containing (a) 0.01, (b) 0.10, and (c) 1.0F potassium chloride, showing the effect of the concentration of the supporting electrolyte on the height of a maximum of the first kind.

are highly concentrated but not very viscous, such as concentrated hydrochloric acid. However, an increase of viscosity tends to suppress maxima of the second kind as well as those of the first. Usually, therefore, increasing the concentration of the supporting electrolyte increases the height of a maximum of the second kind (or of the false or anomalous wave that reflects its existence) up to a certain point and then begins to decrease it again. As with maxima of the first kind, the suppression may sometimes be due in part to traces of surface-active materials in the reagents employed or to a slight surface activity of the supporting electrolyte itself. Whatever the reason, maxima of the second kind and the false or anomalous waves associated with them are much more common at supporting electrolyte concentrations between about 0.5 and $3F$ than at either higher or lower concentrations.

The occurrence and shape of a maximum are influenced by the potential at which the wave occurs. As was mentioned above, a maximum of the first kind is likely to be larger if the half-wave potential of the wave is more positive than the electrocapillary maximum potential than if it is more negative. An extreme case is

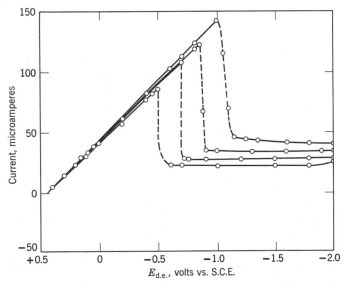

Figure 6.3. Polarograms of 4.5mM silver(I) in 0.10F potassium nitrate. The drop time at -1.0 v. vs. S.C.E. was (a) 0.9, (b) 1.5, (c) 2.3, and (d) 3.7 sec.

illustrated by Fig. 6.3. It is noteworthy, however, that maxima of the first kind do not appear on waves whose half-wave potentials are very nearly equal to the electrocapillary maximum potential. This is why, in Fig. 3.9, the lead wave has a maximum of the first kind while the cadmium wave does not.

Anomalous waves due to maxima of the second kind usually appear at very nearly the same potential in any particular supporting electrolyte regardless of the identities of the substances responsible for the waves they afflict. Their positions can be described by quoting their apparent half-wave potentials, though of course this is only a convenience and is devoid of thermodynamic or chemical significance. For example, nearly every metal ion that is reducible in concentrated hydrochloric acid gives an anomalous wave for which the apparent half-wave potential is -0.60 ± 0.05 v., while in $1F$ disodium malonate–$1F$ sodium hydroxide the corresponding value is -1.22 ± 0.07 v. An important practical consequence of this fact is that maxima of the second kind take on different aspects for substances that are reduced at different potentials. With lead(II) in $2F$ sodium hydroxide the maximum of the second kind appears in the guise of an anomalous wave, as shown in curve a of Fig. 6.1. On a polarogram of zinc(II) in the same medium it appears in a purer form and is shown in curve c of Fig. 6.4. Here the plateau of the zinc wave begins at very nearly the same potential as the peak of the anomalous wave in Fig. 6.1(a). Hence the only apparent abnormality is that the wave height decreases more rapidly than usual as the potential becomes more negative, as may be seen by comparison with Figs. 3.12 and 3.21. However, the wave height is actually the sum of the diffusion current of zinc and the current due to the maximum, and it would be decreased considerably if a maximum suppressor were added. If the reducible substance had a half-wave potential intermediate between those of lead(II) and zinc(II), the plateau would have a positive slope until the potential became equal to about -1.3 v., and a negative slope thereafter. If the half-wave potential were much more positive than that of lead(II), the plateau would be very nearly parallel to the residual current curve until a potential of about -0.9 v. was reached; then the anomalous wave would begin and would have very nearly the same shape as when it is superimposed on the lead wave. Substances having half-wave potentials more negative than that of zinc(II) would give polarograms resembling curve a of Fig. 6.4.

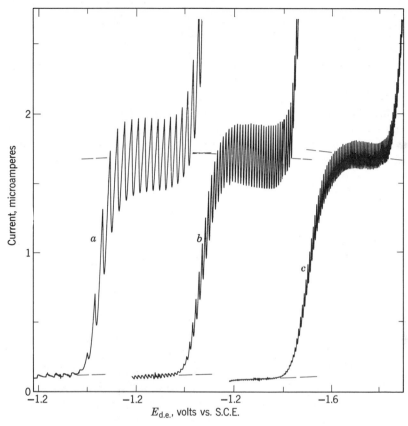

Figure 6.4.   Polarograms of 0.5mM zinc(II) in 2F sodium hydroxide. The drop time at -1.6 v. vs. S.C.E. was (a) 12, (b) 4, and (c) 1.4 sec. The dashed lines are extrapolations of the midpoints of the oscillations on the plateaus. The current scale is shown only for curve a; in recording the other curves the sensitivity was adjusted to keep the wave height nearly constant, and therefore each division along the vertical axis corresponds to 0.88 microampere for curve b and to 1.59 microampere for curve c.

The height of a maximum of either the first or the second kind increases as the drop time decreases for any one capillary. So, of course, does the height of an anomalous wave reflecting a maximum of the second kind. This is illustrated by Figs. 6.3 and 6.4. It is not actually the drop time that is the significant variable, at least so far as a maximum of the second kind is concerned, but the velocity of the stream of mercury emerging from the capillary tip into the drop. Consequently the maxima obtained with different capillaries may have very different heights even though the drop times are the same. All other factors being equal, however, the value of t for any one capillary is inversely proportional to the linear velocity of flow of mercury.

Finally, the height of a maximum depends on the concentration of the substance responsible for the wave. Maxima of the first kind rarely appear at concentrations below about 0.1mM, though this is only a very rough approximation. Decreasing the drop time or the concentration of the supporting electrolyte, for example, will decrease the concentration of electroactive substance at which a maximum is first observed. Once the maximum has appeared, its height increases rapidly as the concentration of electroactive substance is further increased. A maximum of the second kind, however, may appear even in very dilute solutions, and its height is very nearly proportional to the concentration of the substance responsible for the wave (1,2).

Another phenomenon that is related to maxima of the first kind, although it presents a rather different aspect on a recorded polarogram, often arises at very low concentrations (3). It consists of a considerable difference between the slope of the plateau of the wave and that of the corresponding portion of the residual-current curve. Usually, but not always, the wave height appears to decrease as the potential becomes more negative. If the wave occurs at a very negative potential a maximum of the second kind may also be involved, but this behavior is also observed at potentials much too positive for this to be the only explanation. The phenomenon is of much analytical importance. If the extrapolation method (Chap. 3 V) is used to measure the height of such a wave, the value secured must differ from the truth, and it is generally found that the ratio of the apparent wave height to the concentration of the electroactive substance decreases as the concentration increases. It then becomes necessary to construct an empirical plot of concentration versus apparent wave height from data on solutions of known concentrations. The same capillary, the same pressure of mercury above the capillary, the same supporting electrolyte, and the same carefully standardized technique of measuring the apparent wave height must be used in constructing this plot as in analyzing unknown solutions with its aid. When only a single electroactive substance is present in the solution, it is usually possible to measure the true height of such an abnormally shaped wave at a more negative potential: this must be so negative that the current has decreased to a constant value, but of course not so negative that an anomalous wave has begun. Unfortunately, this is not always possible in practical work, either because the wave of some other constituent may intervene or because an anomalous wave may begin almost as soon as the plateau of the desired wave is reached, as in curve a of Fig. 6.1. In either event there is no alternative to adding a maximum suppressor and/or increasing the drop time. As these expedients do not always eliminate the difficulty altogether, the analyst may have to content himself with mitigating it as much as possible and then resorting to the empirical procedure just described.

Both kinds of maxima are almost always disadvantageous in practical polarography. Maxima of the first kind always hinder, and often completely prevent, the measurement and interpretation of the half-wave potential and of the relation between current and potential on the rising part of the wave. The height of the maximum is all important. One as small as that in Fig. 6.1(a) would produce only a small error in the half-wave potential and would not seriously affect a decision as to whether the wave was reversible; one as large as any of those in Fig. 6.3 would make the measured half-wave potential meaningless and any decision about reversibility impossible. Maxima of the first kind may also extend over so wide a range of applied voltages that they prevent the resolution of different waves, as in Fig. 6.3. Even under less unfavorable conditions they can have very severe effects on the accuracy and precision of an analysis, as would be the case with Fig. 3.9(b). Maxima of the second kind complicate the measurement and interpretation of the wave height, and by distorting the wave they also have adverse effects on the current-potential data obtained on its rising part. The anomalous waves due to these maxima may in some cases be mistaken for waves, and in other cases they may serve to conceal the existence of a wave, as in Fig. 6.1.

For all of these reasons it is almost essential to use a maximum suppressor in practical analytical work unless the wave whose height must be measured happens not to have a maximum under the conditions employed. Maximum suppressors and their effects are discussed in Secs. III and IV below. Here it need only be said that it is as bad to use maximum suppressors indiscriminately as to fail to use them when they are needed. Even when they are needed, care must be taken to use no more than the smallest concentration that just suffices to eliminate the maximum, for too high a concentration of a maximum suppressor often suppresses the wave along with the maximum.

II. The Interpretation of Maxima

Although much work has been devoted to attempts to develop satisfactory explanations of the existence and properties of maxima, it must be admitted that our understanding of them is still very defective. A comprehensive description of the results that have been obtained and of the explanations that have been advanced would be far beyond the scope of this book; only the principal tenets of the most successful and widely accepted theory can be given here.

Maxima of both the first and second kinds reflect streaming of the solution past the drop surface. This was proven for maxima of the first kind by Antweiler (4) by photomicrography, and for maxima of the second kind by Kryukova (5) by observing the motion of particles of carbon dispersed in the solution. The streaming is, however, attributed to different causes. That accompanying maxima of the first kind is believed to be due to electrocapillary motion—that is, to motion of the double layer caused by the asymmetry of the electrical field around the drop. Assuming that the behavior of the lower and middle portions of the drop is the same as if it were falling freely through the solution, Frumkin and Levich (6) concluded that the tangential surface velocity of the solution accompanying the flow of current should vary with potential as shown by curve a in Fig. 6.5. On this basis a maximum of the first kind is supposed to arise in the following way. The foot of curve c in Fig. 6.5 represents the onset of reduction of some electroactive species. As the potential becomes more negative, the current increases by virtue of the thermodynamic or kinetic arguments given in Chap. 4, and curve b would result if the solution remained perfectly stationary. The motion of solution increases the rate at which the electroactive substance reaches the drop surface, and the current is therefore larger than on curve b. Near the beginning of the plateau the excess of current is large because the surface velocity is high, but it decreases as the potential becomes more negative because this decreases the surface velocity. At sufficiently negative potentials the surface velocity becomes small, and the current approaches the value that would result from diffusion alone: curve c eventually merges with curve b.

Curve c in Fig. 6.5 thus depicts the variation of current with electrode potential, but what is drawn by the polarograph is a plot of current against the voltage applied to the cell. Superimposed on the difference of potential across the cell, there is an iR drop, which is included in the voltage coordinate of every point on a recorded polarogram. The result is portrayed by Fig. 6.6. Curve a is identical with curve c of Fig. 6.5. Curve b was obtained from curve a by adding the potential at each point on the latter curve to an iR drop proportional to the current at the same point. The shape of curve b is very nearly identical with that of the experimental polarogram shown in curve a of Fig. 6.3.

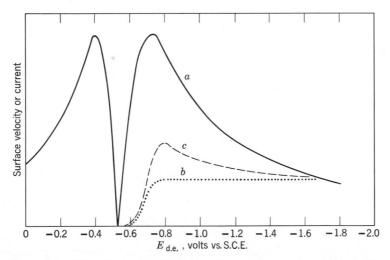

Figure 6.5. The effects of potential on the surface or tangential velocity of solution past a mercury drop and of this velocity on the current-potential curve. Curve a shows the effect of potential on the tangential velocity at constant current. Curve b shows the effect of potential on the current in the absence of tangential motion. Curve c shows how the occurrence and rate of tangential motion increase the currents over those shown on curve b.

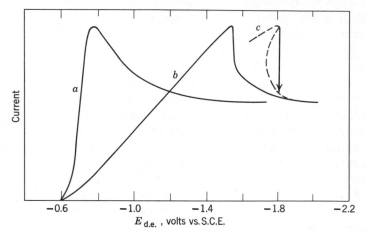

Figure 6.6.   Explanation of maxima of the first kind. Curve a is the current–potential curve obtained in the presence of tangential motion, and is identical with curve b of Fig. 6.5. Curve b includes the iR drop through the cell and shows how the current will vary with applied voltage. The dashed curve c shows the effect of a larger cell resistance: since the actual recorded trace must follow the arrow rather than the dashed line, the initial portion of the plateau is much more nearly flat than in curve b.

It is because of the role of the iR drop in this picture that maxima of the first kind do not appear if the electroactive substance is very dilute or if the conductivity of the supporting electrolyte is very high. It is because there is no net charge in the layer of the solution adjacent to the electrode surface at the electrocapillary maximum potential, so that the tangential velocity is zero at, and very small near, this potential, that maxima of the first kind do not arise there. Finally, it is because these maxima are due to motion of the solution past the drop surface that they are suppressed by adding surface-active agents or by increasing the viscosity of the solution.

If the cell resistance is appreciable and the currents sufficiently large, the variation of applied voltage on the rising side of a maximum will be almost entirely due to the increase of the iR drop as the current increases. That is, the difference between the potentials at the foot and peak of curve c in Fig. 6.5 will be only a small fraction of the difference between the corresponding iR drops. Under these conditions the rising part of the maximum will be almost (but not exactly) linear. It has often been implied, and sometimes even definitely asserted, that the potential of the dropping electrode does not vary at all on the rising part of a maximum, that the variation of average or maximum current with applied voltage on the rising part of a maximum is perfectly linear, and that the slope of the line is equal to the reciprocal of the cell resistance. These statements are only approximate, however; none of them can be exactly true.

The streaming that accompanies maxima of the second kind, on the other hand, is attributed to turbulence arising inside the drop because of the flow of mercury into it. This increases as the rate of flow of mercury increases, as was mentioned in Sec. I, and in addition it is most efficiently transmitted to the surrounding layer of solution at the potential of the electrocapillary maximum, where the interfacial tension between the drop and the solution is greatest. Moreover, the effect depends on the concentration of the supporting electrolyte: increasing the concentration increases not only the velocity of the solution at any one potential, but also the range of potentials over which the velocity is appreciable. All of these statements are illustrated by Fig. 6.7. On this basis the behavior shown in Fig. 6.4 is easily explained in the following way. Consider curve c, for example: the value of m is relatively high, and the plateau is reached at a potential where the motion of the mercury is efficiently transferred to the solution, with the result that the current near the start of the plateau considerably exceeds the diffusion current. As the potential becomes more negative the motion of the solution with respect to the electrode surface becomes less and less rapid, less of the electroactive substance reaches the electrode surface, and the current decreases toward the diffusion current as a limit. On curves b and a the effect is smaller, not because the drop time is longer, but because the flow of mercury into the drop is less rapid.

This is a very abbreviated sketch of the theory that is currently most popular. A fuller description of it, as well as of the experimental observations that support it, is given by Levich (7). Only a few of its consequences and corollaries will be given here.

The theory predicts that the applied voltage at any point on the rising part of a maximum of the first kind must always be more negative than the potential of the dropping electrode if the wave is cathodic, or more positive if it is anodic, the difference in either case being equal to the iR drop. This implies that the addition of a

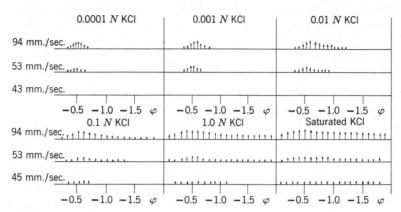

Figure 6.7. Effects of potential and concentration of the supporting electrolyte on the tangential velocity responsible for maxima of the second kind (γ). The height of each vertical arrow is proportional to the tangential velocity at the corresponding potential. The linear velocities of flow of mercury through the capillary are given on the left-hand side. Reproduced from V. G. Levich, *Physicochemical Hydrodynamics*, by permission of Prentice-Hall, Inc., Englewood Cliffs, New Jersey.

maximum suppressor should always cause the rising part of a cathodic wave to shift toward more positive values as the height of the maximum decreases. Often, however, the shift is in the opposite direction, as in Fig. 6.8. This is the usual behavior when the maximum is not very large and when the conductance of the solution is fairly high. It means that the iR drop is small and that the suppression of the maximum merely causes the dashed curve in Fig. 6.5 to be replaced by the dotted one as the tangential motion is eliminated. In this case, the suddenness of the descent from the peak reflects the cessation of tangential motion around the electrocapillary maximum potential; in most others it is due to the iR drop. The shape of the curve following this descent is governed by the cell resistance. In Fig. 6.6(b) the resistance was arbitrarily chosen to have such a value that the increase of potential on the falling side of curve a is almost exactly counterbalanced by the decrease of iR drop, and so the falling side of the maximum on curve b is almost perfectly vertical. With a larger resistance the iR drop decreases more rapidly than the potential increases, and this would have the effect shown by curve c but for the fact that the chart cannot run backwards: what is actually

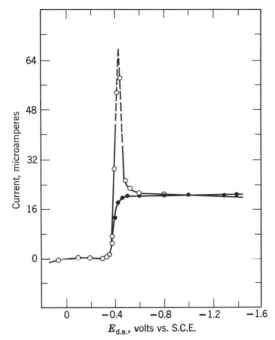

Figure 6.8. Polarograms of 2.3 mM lead(II) in 0.1F potassium chloride: (a) in the absence of a maximum suppressor and (b) after the addition of 0.0002% sodium methyl red. By permission from *Polarography*, by I. M. Kolthoff and J. J. Lingane, Interscience, 2nd edition, 1952.

observed is a decline as precipitous as, but more prolonged than, that on curve b. The recorded curve follows the arrow rather than the dashed line. The effect is illustrated by comparing curves b–d in Fig. 6.3 with curve a. Finally, eliminating the motion of the solution by adding a maximum suppressor should not only eliminate the maximum but also decrease the current at every potential on the plateau, but in fact, as is shown by Fig. 6.8, the current at the most negative potentials is often increased by the presence of a maximum suppressor. At these potentials the motion is slight even in the absence of the maximum suppressor, and the decrease of current resulting from the elimination of the last trace of motion is overbalanced by an increase of current resulting from the elimination of the transfer of concentration polarization from one drop to the next as discussed in Chap. 3 III.

Though the theory of maxima of the second kind accounts very well for the behavior shown in Fig. 6.4, it is not so successful with that shown in Fig. 6.1. It predicts that the motion should be greatest at the potential of the electrocapillary maximum, where the interfacial tension is greatest. This is not far from -0.5 v. vs. S.C.E. in $2F$ sodium hydroxide, while the highest current is found to flow at a considerably more negative potential. Sometimes this may be due to adsorption of some constituent of the solution onto the electrode surface over a certain portion of the range of potentials in which the motion would ordinarily be appreciable. When it is absorbed, this material prevents or decreases streaming past the electrode, but at more negative potentials it begins to be desorbed. Then the rising part of the anomalous wave is more or less equivalent to a desorption isotherm, and the peak current occurs at the potential where desorption is approaching completion. Kryukova and Frumkin (8) have shown that this serves very well to account for the effects of substances like n-butanol on maxima of the second kind. Even relatively small ions can suppress maxima when they can be adsorbed onto the drop surface. For example, the maximum of the first kind on a polarogram of nickel(II), which occurs at a potential more negative than the electrocapillary maximum potential, is suppressed by the ions of the alkaline earth metals, aluminum, and lanthanum, which are adsorbed to varying extents at such potentials (9). Similarly, iodide ions are adsorbed at potentials more positive than the electrocapillary maximum potential and can suppress maxima of the first kind that occur there (10). Desorption is nearly always gradual and not sudden: even at a potential somewhat more negative than the electrocapillary maximum potential there will be a little iodide adsorbed onto the drop surface from an iodide solution, and so the potential will have to be made quite negative to obtain complete desorption. Much less than a monomolecular layer of adsorbed material may suffice to suppress a maximum, and therefore the suppressive effect of an adsorbed substance may persist over quite a wide range of potentials, beginning to diminish only as the desorption becomes nearly complete. Thus the false or anomalous wave in Fig. 6.1 may simply reflect the progressive desorption of some surface-active contaminant of the supporting electrolyte. This would serve to explain why different substances generally give anomalous waves having very nearly the same apparent half-wave potentials in any particular supporting electrolyte.

As yet it is impossible to give a convincing explanation of why phenomena related to maxima of the second kind do not seem to afflict anodic waves. Anomalous waves would rarely be observed, to be sure, because they usually occur at fairly negative potentials, and only a very few anodic waves have half-wave potentials even as negative as -1.0 v. Near the electrocapillary maximum potential, the appearance of the expected rounded peak in the anodic current may often be prevented by traces of surface-active contaminants or by adsorption of one or another of the ions of the supporting electrolyte onto the mercury surface. However, it is very curious that in concentrated hydrochloric acid, in which every cathodic wave occurring at a more positive potential is followed by an anomalous wave at about -0.6 v.—whose occurrence presumably reflects desorption of chloride ion at a potential just more negative than the electrocapillary maximum potential—there is no trace of any abnormality at that potential on the plateau of the anodic wave of uranium(III), for which $E_{1/2}$ is about -0.9 v. The difficulty might be evaded by assuming that the uranium(IV) complex produced at the drop surface by oxidation in this range of potentials is sufficiently surface-active to prevent the stirring, but no evidence in support of this *ad hoc* explanation is available.

III. Maximum Suppressors

A maximum suppressor is a substance, usually of moderately high formula weight, that is adsorbed onto the surface of a dropping electrode and then retards or prevents motion of the solution past the drop surface.

The substances that have been used to suppress maxima at one time or another are both numerous and varied. They include such materials as proteins and related substances (gelatin, glue, gum arabic, agar, peptone, and gum ghatti), dyes (methyl red, fuchsin, methylene blue, bromophenol blue), cationic and anionic soaps (dodecyltrimethylammonium and hexadecyltrimethylammonium bromides and the sodium salts of lauric, myristic, and dodecylsulfonic acids), non-ionic detergents (Triton X-100), and such miscellaneous materials as thymol, camphor, tylose, methylcellulose, and even the substances introduced into a solution by passing it through filter paper or bringing it in contact with a cork stopper.

Non-ionic or amphoteric materials are preferable to ionic ones for two reasons. One is that they are adsorbed, and therefore effective, over wider ranges of potential. For example, the "cationic" or zwitterion form of methyl red in acidic solutions can be adsorbed at potentials more negative than the electrocapillary maximum potential, and so it can suppress the maximum of the first kind that occurs on a polarogram of nickel ion in this region of potentials. Lead and thallous ions, however, give waves on which the maxima of the first kind occur at potentials more positive than the electrocapillary maximum, and because the zwitterion is desorbed at these potentials it does not suppress these maxima. The anionic form of the indicator present in neutral solutions has precisely the opposite effects. This is, of course, the same phenomenon mentioned at the end of Sec. II. Uncharged or amphoteric substances, however, can suppress all of these maxima in both acidic and neutral solutions. Because different maximum suppressors are desorbed at different potentials, they differ in efficiency to some extent. For example, a maximum occurring at a very positive potential in an acidic solution may be much more efficiently suppressed with peptone than with gelatin, probably because the former remains adsorbed under these conditions while the latter does not. Similarly, a cationic maximum suppressor might be especially valuable in dealing with a maximum occurring at a very negative potential. This is why a fairly large number of maximum suppressors was listed in the preceding paragraph; in each group the listing is roughly in the order of descending frequency of use. The other general drawback of ionic maximum suppressors is that they may react with many inorganic species to give precipitates, such as heavy metal soaps and long chain quaternary ammonium salts of complex anions.

The maximum suppressor most widely used in this country now appears to be Triton X-100, which is a polyethyleneglycol ether of monoisooctylphenol and is manufactured by the Rohm and Haas Co., Philadelphia. Gelatin was almost universally used before Triton X-100 was proposed in 1951, and is still widely used in Europe, but the Triton is much the better of the two. There is little difference between their abilities to suppress maxima. But a solution of gelatin is much more difficult to prepare than one of the Triton, and in addition it decomposes so rapidly that it must be freshly prepared every day or two, whereas a stock solution of Triton X-100 is easily prepared in a few minutes and can be used for years.

It is convenient to prepare a stock 0.2% solution of Triton X-100 by shaking 0.2 g. of the commercial product very thoroughly with 100 ml. of water. In the writer's laboratory one such solution had the same polarographic effects when it was nine years old that it had had when fresh. It is impossible to prescribe exactly how much of this stock solution should be used in any particular case, for this depends on the chemical system involved and also on the drop time. As a rough guide it may be said that the desired final concentration will rarely be far from 0.002%, which corresponds to the presence of 0.1 ml. of the stock solution in each 10 ml. of the solution being analyzed or studied. In general, however, less of the Triton should be used if the drop time exceeds about 4 sec., both because less is needed and because the distortions that are produced by too high concentrations become more pronounced as the drop time increases. These distortions are described in Sec. IV. As little as 0.001% of the Triton may often suffice. On the other hand, concentrations as high as 0.004% are occasionally needed to eliminate anomalous waves, especially at fairly short drop times and in moderately concentrated supporting electrolytes, in which maxima of the second kind are most pronounced. At the outset of any program of research or analysis a little effort should be devoted to finding the minimum concentration of the Triton that will just suffice to produce the desired result, and this concentration should be used throughout the work that follows. Identical considerations apply with equal force to all other maximum suppressors as well.

Gelatin that is to be used as a maximum suppressor should be granular or powdered so that it will dissolve readily, it should be practically colorless, and its solutions should be nearly neutral and perfectly odorless. Only the purest gelatin, such as that sold for bacteriological work, is worth purchasing for polarographic purposes.

It is most convenient to prepare a stock 0.5% solution of gelatin. This is best done by allowing 0.5 g. of gelatin to stand in 100 ml. of water in a small flask at room temperature for about 30 min. with occasional swirling. The flask is then placed on a steam bath or in a large beaker of hot water, and is warmed to about 70° for about 15 min., or until no more undissolved particles can be seen. The solution must not be boiled or heated over a free flame.

Stale gelatin solutions may produce distorted waves, erratic drop times, irregular galvanometer or recorder oscillations, inaccurate diffusion currents, and other undesirable phenomena. It is, therefore, advisable to discard the stock solution after at most 48 hr., or perhaps 72 hr. if it is kept in a refrigerator continuously. Attempting to save trouble by using it for a longer period is very unwise.

With gelatin as with Triton X-100, only a very rough guide can be given to the final concentration desired. Formerly 0.01% was often employed, but this is almost always too large, and 0.005% is a much better estimate. This corresponds to 0.1 ml. of the stock 0.5% solution in each 10 ml. of the solution being analyzed. A higher concentration should not be used unless the maximum persists with 0.005% gelatin, while if suppression is complete with 0.005% a smaller concentration should be tried. Should the maximum appear even with 0.01% gelatin, it is better to try another suppressor than to increase the gelatin concentration still further.

Like Triton X-100, methyl red has the advantage over gelatin of being stable for long periods of time in aqueous solutions; in addition, it gives rise to fewer of the undesirable phenomena described in Sec. IV. An 0.04% stock solution of methyl red may be prepared by dissolving 0.1 g. of the indicator in a barely sufficient volume of $0.01F$ sodium hydroxide, adding very dilute ($0.001F$) perchloric or sulfuric acid dropwise until the yellow color just begins to change to orange, and diluting to 250 ml. The desired concentration of methyl red in the final solution is usually between 0.0002 and 0.0004%, which corresponds to 0.05 to 0.1 ml. of the stock 0.04% solution in each 10 ml. of the solution being analyzed.

Since methyl red itself gives both anodic and cathodic waves at a dropping electrode, it will interfere seriously in trace analysis if too much of it is added. If a maximum is not suppressed by 0.0004% (0.01mM) methyl red, another maximum suppressor should be tried. An important disadvantage of methyl red is that it has practically no effect on maxima of the second kind and anomalous waves in neutral or alkaline media. This is because its anionic form is repelled from the dropping electrode at the negative potentials where these phenomena occur.

Methylene blue has been much less widely used than methyl red, but as it suppresses several maxima that methyl red does not it may deserve more consideration than it has received. A concentration of the order of 0.001% will usually suffice; as with methyl red, higher concentrations must not be used because methylene blue is reducible.

IV. The Effects of Maximum Suppressors

In addition to suppressing maxima, maximum suppressors affect polarograms and polarographic data in a number of other ways. Their ability to suppress maxima is due to their ability to undergo adsorption onto the electrode surface. Polar molecules present at very low concentrations are adsorbed to form what can be regarded as a two-dimensional gas; the molecules lie flat on the electrode surface and are so far apart that the interactions among them are small. As the concentration increases, the adsorbed molecules come closer together, their mutual interactions increase, and a more or less definite orientation appears. This orientation depends on the molecular structure: strongly polar molecules tend to have their least polar groups directed toward the electrode surface, while the orientation of a zwitterion is influenced by the sign of the electrode potential with respect to the electrocapillary maximum potential. The structures of most maximum suppressors are such that hydrocarbon or other side chains extend, almost like tentacles, for some little distance into the solution, and these serve to inhibit tangential motion of the solution with respect to the mercury drop. Maxima are suppressed as a result, but the presence of the adsorbed film and the fact that the extent of adsorption usually increases with increasing drop age affect electron-transfer and mass-transfer processes as well.

The effects of maximum suppressors on electron-transfer processes —that is, on the reversibility of an electrode reaction and on the parameters αn_a and $k^0_{f,h}$ for irreversible reactions—result from changes in the structure of the double layer. The adsorbed molecules displace ions from the Helmholtz layer, thereby altering the charge distribution in the double layer, and they may also displace the reaction surface away from the electrode. Both of these effects alter the potential at the reaction surface. In addition, a bridge that may serve to effect electron transfer from the electrode to an ion or molecule at the reaction surface when the maximum suppressor is absent may become impossible to construct when it is present; the entire mechanism of the electron-transfer process may change. The effect of an ionic maximum suppressor depends to a large extent on its charge and on that of the species actually being reduced: a cationic maximum suppressor usually inhibits the reduction of a cation but favors that of an anion, whereas an anionic one has the opposite effects (*11–13*). For example, the reduction of copper(II) in a perchloric acid solution is normally irreversible, but becomes reversible in the presence of an anionic surface-active material. The effects of non-ionic maximum suppressors are less predictable, but by far their most common effect is to decrease the rate constants $k_{s,h}$ and $k^0{}_{f,h}$, and the value of αn_a for an irreversible process is usually decreased as well: that is, reversible processes tend to become irreversible while irreversible ones tend to become more so when such a material is added. Thus, the reduction of vanadium(III) in acidic media appears to be reversible in the absence of a maximum suppressor, but is made noticeably irreversible and is shifted toward more negative potentials by the addition of 0.005% gelatin. Similarly, the wave of lead(II) in an alkaline tartrate solution, which is extremely well defined in the absence of a maximum suppressor, becomes so badly distorted when

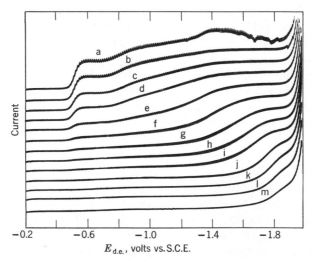

Figure 6.9. Polarograms of 4mM copper(II) in 0.5F potassium sodium tartrate–1.0F sodium hydroxide containing (*a*) 0, (*b*) 1.02, (*c*) 2.00, (*d*) 2.94, (*e*) 4.72, (*f*) 6.40, (*g*) 7.97, (*h*) 9.42, (*i*) 10.8, (*j*) 18.8, (*k*) 34.0, (*l*) 55.4, and (*m*) 87.1 × 10^{-3}% gelatin (*14*).

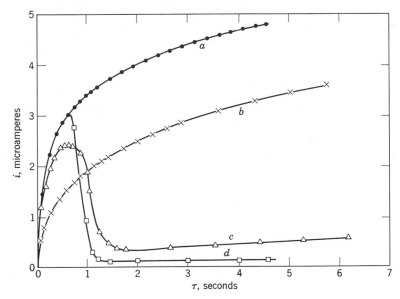

Figure 6.10. Effects of surface-active substances on current-time curves for individual drops: (a) 1mM copper(II) and 0.01F ethylenediaminetetraacetate in 0.1F acetate buffer, pH 4.6; (b) same with 0.001% thymol; (c) same as (a) with 0.00025M camphor; (d) in 0.1F tartrate buffer, pH 3.5, with 0.003% Triton X-100. Each curve was obtained at −0.6 v. vs. S.C.E. (15).

more than 0.02% gelatin or 0.007% Triton X-100 is added that its height becomes impossible to measure. Not all waves are thus affected, however: in neutral media the anodic wave of benzohydroquinone is unaltered by even a considerably higher concentration of either gelatin or Triton X-100 than would ever be used in practical work. Moreover, the effects of different maximum suppressors are often quite different. The reduction of cadmium ion becomes irreversible in the presence of camphor, but not in that of gelatin even though this is more strongly adsorbed than camphor; adding gelatin to a solution of cadmium ion containing camphor results in the replacement of camphor by gelatin on the surface of the drop, and the value of $k_{s,h}$ increases as a result.

The decrease of the rate of electron transfer is often so great that the wave disappears altogether in the presence of a sufficiently high concentration of maximum suppressor. An example is shown in Fig.

6.9. Even as little as 0.001% gelatin decreases the height of the wave at -0.5 v. to 89% of its original value, and 0.02% gelatin eliminates it completely. As the electrode potential becomes more negative, however, the rate of electron transfer increases again, and so the wave reappears at a more negative potential. At concentrations too small to eradicate the wave completely, different maximum suppressors have different effects on the current-time curves obtained for individual drops, as shown in Fig. 6.10. These depend on whether it is the diffusion of the maximum suppressor to the drop surface or the position of its adsorption equilibrium that governs the extent of surface coverage and thus the current; curves b and d represent these two extremes, while curve c represents an intermediate case in which both are important. The reacceleration of electron transfer at more negative potentials is depicted by Fig. 6.11. No matter what the

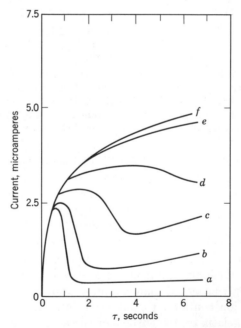

Figure 6.11.   Effect of potential on current–time curves for individual drops in the presence of a surface-active agent. The solution contained 1mM copper(II) and 0.01F ethylenediaminetetraacetate in 0.1F acetate buffer, pH 4.6, with 0.0003M camphor, and the potential was (a) -0.6, (b) -0.8, (c) -0.9, (d) -0.95, (e) -1.0, and (f) -1.1 v. vs. S.C.E. (15).

mechanism, however, the average current during the drop life would decrease at potentials near the beginning of the plateau of the original wave, then increase again as the potential is made more and more negative, producing the effect shown in Fig. 6.9. This behavior is used to advantage in the technique of "electrochemical masking" described in Sec. V.

In addition to all these effects, the presence of the adsorbed material may have other important consequences if some chemical step must occur in the double layer before the electron transfer can take place. Part of the electrode surface is blocked by the adsorbed film, and the current density at the free sites therefore tends to increase; unless the prior chemical step is extremely fast it will eventually become rate-determining and the current will become partly or wholly kinetic. The effect is aggravated when the rate of the chemical step is decreased by the presence of the adsorbed film (17).

Changes of wave height may also occur even when the electron-transfer process is so little affected that the half-wave potential and wave shape are unaltered by the presence of the maximum suppressor. For example, the addition of 0.01% gelatin decreases the wave height of lead(II) in an alkaline pyrophosphate solution more than 10%, and decreases that of iron(III) in a slightly acidic citrate medium about 30%. This is attributed to inhibition of mass transfer through the adsorbed film (13,18). The rate at which the electroactive species can penetrate through the film—or at which bridge formation across the film can occur—depends on its charge, size, and structure, and also on the characteristics of the film. It may be pointed out that, although decreases of wave height are observed more often than increases, the latter are not unknown. In an ammoniacal ammonium malonate solution, for example, molybdenum(VI) gives a wave whose height is nearly tripled by the addition of 0.005% gelatin; the wave is probably due, at least in part, to catalytic hydrogen evolution, and presumably the gelatin serves to accelerate the catalytic step.

So many factors are involved in all of these effects that general rules for predicting their occurrence are impossible to give. Each case must be investigated and judged on its own merits.

It is because of the existence of these effects that scrupulous care must always be taken in practical work to use no more maximum suppressor than is absolutely needed to suppress a maximum or eliminate an anomalous wave. If the data wanted can be secured in the absence of a maximum suppressor, which may be the case even when the polarogram shows a maximum, none should be added. If a troublesome maximum is not suppressed by 0.004% Triton X-100, 0.01% gelatin, or 0.0004% methyl red, a different maximum suppressor should be tried. Undesirable effects may, however, arise at much smaller concentrations. It should not be concluded that these concentrations can always be used with impunity, but merely that they cannot be exceeded without grave danger. Schmid and Reilley (15) found that even 0.0015% Triton X-100 had marked effects on current-time curves for individual drops in the reduction of the copper(II)–ethylenediaminetetraacetate complex from acidic tartrate media; the even more substantial effect of 0.001% gelatin on the wave of copper(II) in alkaline tartrate was mentioned in connection with Fig. 6.9. It is always prudent to compare polarograms obtained in the presence of a maximum suppressor with others obtained in its absence to ensure that the quantity of interest has not been drastically altered at the same time that the unwanted maximum has been suppressed.

Sometimes the conditions recommended for carrying out an analysis are such that the wave height will be appreciably affected by even a small change in the concentration of the maximum suppressor. When this is the case, special care must be taken to use the same concentration of the suppressor for every polarogram, and the drop time should be very carefully controlled as well. Since the optimum concentration of the suppressor depends on the drop time, the question should always be investigated by obtaining polarograms of known solutions containing concentrations of the maximum suppressor that are both higher and lower than the recommended value.

Because maximum suppressors affect the interfacial tension between the mercury and the solution, they change both the drop time and the limiting current. As was pointed out in Chap. 3, this must be taken into account when comparing data obtained in the presence and in the absence of a maximum suppressor. The addition of a maximum suppressor at the concentration most often used (0.002% Triton X-100 or 0.005% gelatin) decreases the drop time roughly 10% over a wide range of potentials.

A minor disadvantage of the use of a maximum suppressor is that it increases the tendency of the solution to foam, and thereby decreases the rate at which deaeration can be effected by bubbling nitrogen or another gas through it. Naturally the same problem is encountered when the substance being determined or some other constituent of the sample is surface-active. This is of little moment with cells like those of Figs. 2.13–2.15, in which deaeration is slow and inefficient at best, because the bubbles of gas that enter the solution are so large that severe foaming is virtually impossible; with a cell like that of Fig. 2.16, however, it necessitates the use of a gas stream much slower than could otherwise be employed. The problem can be mitigated without apparent adverse effects by adding a small concentration of a commercial silicone antifoam fluid to the stock solution of maximum suppressor (19,20), or by adding a droplet of n-octanol to the sample before deaeration is begun.

V. Analytical Applications of Maxima and Maximum Suppressors

The fact that maxima are suppressed by surface-active agents makes it possible to employ them for evaluating the activities of surfactant preparations and for other similar purposes. Known concentrations of the surface-active material to be determined are added to a standard solution in which a maximum of the first kind is obtained. Air-saturated 0.01F potassium chloride is often used. Too large a concentration of electrolyte decreases the height of the maximum obtained in the original solution, while too small a concentration increases the effects of non-surface-active electrolytes in the sample. The analysis is performed by comparing the height of the maximum obtained with an unknown sample with the calibration curve obtained with the standards. The concentration and pH of the supporting electrolyte, the capillary characteristics, and the concentration of the electroactive substance must all be rigorously controlled. The technique was first proposed by Heyrovský (21), who called it "adsorption analysis." It has been used for the determination of surface-active constituents in such materials as refined sugars (22) and natural waters (23). A related technique, in which the applied voltage at the peak of the maximum is measured instead of its height (24), has been used for the determination of detergents in commercial products. Adsorption analysis is inherently unspecific because all surface-active agents have qualitatively similar effects on maxima. Hence it cannot be used to determine a single constituent of a sample unless it is known·that the desired constituent is the only surface-active one or unless the proportions of the different surface-active constituents are the same in all of the samples. If neither of these conditions is satisfied it gives merely an empirical measure of the surface activity of the sample.

Electrochemical masking (14,25) consists of adding a maximum suppressor at a concentration sufficiently large to eliminate the wave of one constituent of a mixture while that of another is unaffected (26–29). Its application in the determination of thallium will serve as a typical example. In an acetate buffer of pH 4–5 containing diethylenetriaminepentaacetate, thallium(I) remains virtually uncomplexed while most other heavy metals form chelonates. When 0.01% Triton X-100 is added, the wave of thallium(I), for which $E_{1/2}$ is -0.46 v., is unaffected while the half-wave potentials of most of the chelonates are shifted from their original values to about -1.3 v. It is thus a simple matter to measure the height of the thallium wave in the presence of other metal ions that would normally interfere (30). Similarly, lead ion can be determined in the presence of the bismuth(III)–ethylenediaminetetraacetate complex by suppressing the wave of the latter with Triton X-100 (15); in the absence of the Triton the height of the lead wave would not be proportional to the lead concentration, as was mentioned in Chap. 3 X.

Electrochemical masking can thus be used to suppress waves of chelonates while leaving those of simple metal ions unaffected. In some cases it serves to discriminate between different chelonates. In the diethylenetriaminepentaacetate medium mentioned above, the half-wave potential of the iron(III) chelonate is shifted only to -0.65 v. by the addition of 0.01% Triton X-100, and this might permit iron to be determined in the presence of another heavy metal ion that would normally give a prior or overlapping wave. It can also be used to consolidate two or more waves into one that is more easily measurable and that extends over a narrower range of potential, thereby permitting the heights of other waves to be measured as well (31).

Electrochemical masking has so far been employed only in supporting electrolytes containing large ligands like chelons and triphosphate, because of the importance of the size of the electroactive species. Maximum suppressors also have substantial effects on the waves of many complexes involving small ligands: for example, the half-wave potential of the first wave of iron(III) in neutral $1F$ potassium fluoride is shifted from -0.7 to -1.1 v. by the addition of

0.03% gelatin, and so the technique may be one of fairly wide potential utility. Its applicability in organic analysis has not yet been investigated, but it may very probably serve to permit the determinations of many substances in the presence of others whose molecules are much larger.

Though no example of its use for this purpose is known to the writer, ion flotation may prove to be another valuable technique of masking in polarographic analysis. It is introduced here because, like electrochemical masking, it depends on the surface-active properties of maximum suppressors. An ion (the "colligend") giving an unwanted wave may be removed from a solution by adding an excess of a surface-active ion (the "collector") of the opposite charge and then deaerating the mixture in the usual way. The collector accumulates at the interface between the solution and the gas bubbles, and there forms a precipitate with the colligend. That this process resembles coprecipitation is too obvious to need discussion. The bubbles carry the precipitate to the surface, where it forms a froth that then collapses to give a scum or sublate. Very complete separations from very dilute solutions have been achieved in this fashion. Its originator's descriptions of the technique and its applications (32) should be consulted for further details.

References

(1) E. F. Orlemann and I. M. Kolthoff, *J. Am. Chem. Soc.*, **64**, 833 (1942); I. M. Kolthoff and E. F. Orlemann, *Ind. Eng. Chem., Anal. Ed.*, **14**, 321 (1942).

(2) T. A. Kryukova, *Zavodskaya Lab.*, **14**, 767 (1948); **17**, 134 (1950); *Z. Physik. Chem. (Leipzig)*, **212**, 247 (1959).

(3) F. Buckley and J. K. Taylor, *J. Res. Natl. Bur. Stds.*, **34**, 87 (1945).

(4) H. J. Antweiler, *Z. Elektrochem.*, **43**, 596 (1937); **44**, 719, 831, 888 (1938).

(5) T. A. Kryukova, *Zh. Fiz. Khim.*, **20**, 1179 (1946); **21**, 365 (1947).

(6) A. N. Frumkin and V. G. Levich, *Zh. Fiz. Khim.*, **21**, 1335 (1947).

(7) V. G. Levich, *Physicochemical Hydrodynamics*, Prentice-Hall, Englewood Cliffs, 1962, pp. 561–589.

(8) T. A. Kryukova, *Acta Physicochim. U.S.S.R.*, **22**, 381, (1947) *Zavodskaya Lab.*, **14**, 639 (1948); T. A. Kryukova and A. N. Frumkin, *Zh. Fiz. Khim.*, **23**, 819 (1949).

(9) N. V. Emilianova and J. Heyrovský, *Trans. Faraday Soc.*, **24**, 257 (1928).

(10) I. M. Kolthoff and Y. Okinaka, *J. Am. Chem. Soc.*, **83**, 47 (1961).

(11) A. N. Frumkin, *Trans. Faraday Soc.*, **55**, 156 (1959).

(*12*) A. N. Frumkin, N. Nikolaeva-Fedorovich, and R. Ivanova, *Can. J. Chem.*, **37**, 253 (1959).

(*13*) I. M. Kolthoff and Y. Okinaka, *J. Am. Chem. Soc.*, **81**, 2296 (1959).

(*14*) L. Meites and T. Meites, *J. Am. Chem. Soc.*, **73**, 177 (1951).

(*15*) R. W. Schmid and C. N. Reilley, *J. Am. Chem. Soc.*, **80**, 2087 (1958).

(*16*) J. Heyrovský and M. Matyáš, *Collection Czechoslov. Chem. Communs.*, **16**, 455 (1951).

(*17*) M. Matyáš, *Collection Czechoslov. Chem. Communs.*, **16**, 496 (1951).

(*18*) V. V. Losev, *Dokl. Akad. Nauk S.S.S.R.*, **107**, 432 (1956).

(*19*) S. A. Moros and L. Meites, unpublished experiments, 1957.

(*20*) H. Flaschka, personal communication.

(*21*) J. Heyrovský, *Polarographie*, Springer, Berlin, 1941, p. 408.

(*22*) I. Vavruch, *Anal. Chem.*, **22**, 930 (1950).

(*23*) K. E. Schwarz, H. J. Schröder, and M. v. Stackelberg, *Z. Elektrochem.*, **48**, 6 (1942).

(*24*) M. v. Stackelberg and H. Schütz, *Kolloid-Z.*, **105**, 20 (1943).

(*25*) C. N. Reilley, in *Trace Analysis*, J. H. Yoe and H. J. Koch, eds., Wiley, New York, 1957, pp. 342–3.

(*26*) C. N. Reilley, W. G. Scribner, and C. Temple, *Anal. Chem.*, **28**, 450 (1956).

(*27*) T. Fujinaga and K. Izutzu, *Bunseki Kagaku*, **10**, 63 (1961).

(*28*) P. R. Subbaraman and P. S. Shetty, *Anal. Chim. Acta.*, **26**, 179 (1962); P. S. Shetty, P. R. Subbaraman, and J. Gupta, *Anal. Chim. Acta*, **27**, 429 (1962).

(*29*) T. Fujinaga, T. Nagai, and T. Inque, *J. Chem. Soc. Japan, Pure Chem. Sect.*, **85**, 110 (1964).

(*30*) E. Jacobsen and G. Kalland, *Anal. Chim. Acta*, **29**, 215 (1963).

(*31*) G. Conradi and M. Kopanica, *Chemist-Analyst*, **53**, 4 (1964).

(*32*) F. Sebba, *Nature*, **184**, 1062 (1959); **188**, 736 (1960); *Ion Flotation*, Elsevier, Amsterdam, 1962.

CHAPTER 7

QUANTITATIVE POLAROGRAPHIC ANALYSIS

This chapter deals with the design and execution of methods of quantitative analysis using the polarograph. Any such procedure involves three steps: the preparation of the solution, the recording of its polarogram, and the interpretation of the wave height. To the chemist designing an analytical method it is the first of these that is the most important, for the success and elegance of an analytical method are chiefly governed by his ability to choose the simplest conditions that will yield useful polarograms. The user of a method is primarily concerned with the second and third, and numerous special techniques have been devised to aid him in their execution.

Polarographic methods of analysis can be divided into two classes: direct and indirect. A direct method is one in which the substance being determined is itself electroactive and is responsible for the wave whose height is measured. There are several kinds of indirect methods. In one, the substance being determined is converted into an equivalent amount of some other substance, and it is the latter that is actually determined. In another, it is allowed to react with an excess of some electroactive substance, and the analysis is based on the amount of the latter that is consumed. Methods of these two kinds include preliminary chemical steps that are not needed in direct methods, but the actual analyses of the solutions resulting from these steps involve principles and techniques so similar to those employed in direct methods that the latter are given the most emphasis below. Throughout this chapter, references to the substance being determined should be understood to include the product of, or the other reactant in, the prior chemical step in an indirect method. A third kind of indirect method is based on the effect of the substance being determined on the wave of some electroactive substance, as in adsorption analysis (Chap. 6 V). A fourth is based on the principles of kinetic analysis. On chemical grounds many amperometric titrations might be classified as indirect methods, but as they involve somewhat different principles and techniques they are discussed separately in Chap. 9.

In both direct and indirect methods the best results are obtained when the wave whose height is measured is reasonably well defined in a pure solution. A well-defined wave is one whose plateau is nearly parallel to the residual-current curve over a range of potentials wide enough to permit precise measurement of its height. The first task of the designer of an analytical method is to identify conditions under which this is the case. From these he must then select conditions under which the wave will be well separated from any wave due to another constituent of the sample. Waves that overlap the desired wave are especially to be avoided. Whether or not a non-overlapping wave will interfere depends on its position and height. Interferences can often be eliminated by careful choice of the supporting electrolyte and the experimental conditions. When they cannot, some sort of prior separation becomes virtually essential.

I. Selection of Conditions for Measuring the Wave Height

In designing an analytical method, the first step is to find a set of conditions under which the substance being determined will give a well-defined wave when it is present alone. Such conditions can often be identified from tables of polarographic data, but often they cannot, and the considerations that guide a search for them are, therefore, discussed here at some length. Of course there are many such sets of conditions for each substance. If only one is known, it may be simpler to use it than to attempt to discover others. But it is very advantageous to know several, for then it is often possible to select one that will eliminate or minimize interferences from other constituents of the sample.

A. SELECTION OF THE SOLVENT

Most inorganic polarographic analyses are carried out in aqueous solutions, for several reasons. One is that data on the behaviors of different inorganic species in different supporting electrolytes are so very much more extensive for aqueous than for non-aqueous media that methods are far easier to design in aqueous media. Another is that samples are so universally dissolved in aqueous solutions that the steps required to prepare a non-aqueous solution may complicate the analysis instead of simplifying it. A third is that non-aqueous media offer few if any advantages in determinations of the common metal ions.

There is, however, a real use for non-aqueous solvents in inorganic polarographic analysis. Aquo-complex ions may often be much more easily reduced if their water is replaced by another ligand, and this replacement is facilitated by decreasing the activity of water in the solution. Ions that are extensively hydrolyzed and polymerized in neutral aqueous solutions do not give waves because their reductions are so slow that appreciable currents are not obtained at any potential up to the start of the final current rise. This is the case with niobium, beryllium, zirconium, and many others. Waves may indeed be obtained for some of these ions in strongly acidic media, but these are somewhat disadvantageous on other grounds: the useful range of potentials is quite short, so that much overlapping of waves is encountered, and catalytic hydrogen evolution is very likely and may be very sensitive to small variations of experimental conditions. The situation can be much improved by adding a moderate concentration (at least 10 or 20% by volume) of a solvent like ethylene glycol, or by using n-butanol saturated with hydrogen chloride gas. In much the same fashion, beryllium may be determined (1), after an extraction that serves to remove water as well as interfering metal ions, in a mixture of dimethylsulfoxide and acetylacetone, using tetraethylammonium perchlorate as the supporting electrolyte; in aqueous media the hydrolysis of beryllium is so extensive at acidities low enough to prevent interference from the reduction of hydrogen ion that its wave is unfit for analytical use. As more information is obtained on the behaviors of the less common elements in non-aqueous media, these will surely come to be very useful in practical analysis.

In organic analysis the situation is rather different. Largely because most organic compounds are soluble to only a limited extent in water, the advantages of non-aqueous media have long been clearly visible to organic analysts.

Solubility considerations are of great importance in choosing a solvent for the determination of an organic compound or the analysis of an organic sample. The solubility of the substance being determined is, of course, crucial. To ensure its complete solution, a solvent must be selected in which its solubility is several times as large as the highest concentration that might be obtained from any sample. If, for example, one wished to determine o-nitrobenzaldehyde in the presence of the p- isomer, one would first adopt a sample weight and solution volume that would yield a wave high enough to be easily measurable even with the smallest expected percentage of the o-compound. Then one would have to seek a solvent or solvent mixture of which this volume would dissolve at least as much o-nitrobenzalde-hyde as might be present in this weight of the sample containing the largest expected percentage of it. It is very desirable to choose a solvent in which the entire sample will be readily soluble, for other-wise a lengthy extraction may be necessary to ensure that the substance being determined is completely dissolved. For example, in determining the peroxide content of an oil or fat it is much better to employ a mixture of benzene and methanol to dissolve the entire sample than to select a solvent in which the peroxide would be soluble while the oil or fat would not.

A hardly less important consideration is the ability of the solvent to dissolve electrolytes, for enough salt must be present to provide adequate electrical conductivity and buffer capacity. Solvents such as benzene, toluene, chloroform, aniline, and the like are unsuitable for polarographic work because their dielectric constants are too low to permit sufficiently high concentrations of dissolved salts to be secured. Mixtures of one of these with a more polar liquid like methanol do, however, find occasional use, as was mentioned in the preceding paragraph.

The meaning of adequate buffer capacity was discussed in Chap. 3 II; it depends on the reaction mechanism. If hydrogen ions are not involved in the rate-determining step or in any fast chemical step preceding it—if, experimentally, the half-wave potential is indepen-dent of acidity—the analysis may be performed in a neutral un-buffered supporting electrolyte like lithium chloride. Lithium and tetraalkylammonium salts tend to be more readily soluble in non-aqueous media than the corresponding sodium or potassium salts. When buffering is necessary, it can usually be most easily provided by mixing an organic acid, such as acetic, diethylbarbituric, or citric acid with an appropriate amount of lithium or tetraalkylammonium hydroxide, or by mixing an amine with an appropriate amount of hydrochloric, benzenesulfonic, or some other acid. When a tetra-alkylammonium salt is added for either of these reasons it should be recognized that the adsorption of a tetraalkylammonium ion increases with increasing chain length and may have pronounced effects on the half-wave potentials, shapes, and even the number of the waves obtained. It is advisable to try both tetramethylammonium and tetra-n-butylammonium salts in order to obtain truer and more complete pictures of the behaviors of the different substances involved and to facilitate the selection of the optimum conditions.

The electrical conductivity required depends primarily on the apparatus employed. In a cell with an internal reference electrode one can tolerate a much smaller specific conductance than in an H-cell or a Kalousek cell, in which the current path is much longer. Electrical compensation for the iR drop through the cell also permits the use of smaller concentrations of supporting electrolyte. In general, a salt concentration of the order of 0.05 to $0.1M$ usually yields a satisfactory value of the cell resistance.

Numerous solvents have been employed. They may be divided into two groups: those usually used in mixtures with water, and those whose utility depends on the absence of water. Of those in the first group, alcohols such as methanol, ethanol, isopropanol, and ethylene glycol have been the most frequently used. Ethers, among which 1,4-dioxane has been by far the most popular while tetrahydrofuran has been much less so, have also often been used. Difficulties arise, however, because of peroxide formation when they are exposed to air and light. The peroxides are reducible at the dropping electrode, and cause the residual current not only to be larger than it would be with pure solvent, which adversely affects the sensitivity attainable, but also to change with time, which adversely affects the precision as well. The problems become worse as the concentration of the substance being determined decreases. It is, therefore, advisable to remove peroxides by distillation from freshly precipitated ferrous hydroxide or by some other standard procedure, and then to store the ether under an inert gas in the dark until it is used. Especially in work with very dilute solutions, the residual-current curve should be checked at intervals of two or three days to ensure that no appreciable concentration of peroxide has been formed. The Cellosolves (monoalkyl ethers of ethylene glycol) seem to be considerably superior to dioxane in this regard, but have been used much less frequently. N,N-Dimethylformamide, formamide itself, and such other solvents as acetic acid and pyridine have also been relatively little used but may be advantageous in special cases.

Most organic polarographers favor the use of as small a percentage of the non-aqueous solvent in a mixture with water as will suffice to secure the desired solubility of the sample and the substance being determined. There are two reasons for this. One is that the solubilities of electrolytes usually decrease as the concentration of non-aqueous solvent rises, while at the same time the extent of ion association usually increases because of the decrease of dielectric constant, and these changes aggravate the problems of conductivity and buffer capacity. The other is that the apparent pH of a buffer solution almost always increases substantially as non-aqueous solvent is added; part of the increase is due to changes in the activity of hydrogen ion, but appreciable liquid-junction potentials are also involved. Since these increase as the proportion of the non-aqueous solvent increases, the meaning, such as it is, of the pH scale becomes more and more obscure, and this makes the data more and more difficult to interpret and correlate with those obtained in purely aqueous solutions. For analytical purposes, however, the second of these reasons is of little moment, and there is some question as to whether the solubility considerations are important enough to warrant sacrificing a variable to them. Surprisingly little attention has been paid to the effects of the concentration of a non-aqueous solvent on the half-wave potentials and shapes of polarographic waves. In general, the half-wave potentials of most organic compounds become more negative on increasing the ratio of non-aqueous solvent to water. The variations may be quite large: for example, the half-wave potential of γ-hexachlorocyclohexane shifts from about -1.07 v. to about -1.43 v. when the mole fraction of n-propanol is increased from 0.1 to 0.5. Different solvents have effects that are qualitatively similar but that may be quite different in magnitude: the half-wave potential of γ-hexachlorocyclohexane is a quarter of a volt more negative in a solution containing 40 mole per cent n-propanol than in one containing 40 mole per cent methanol, while ethanol, acetone, and isopropanol give intermediate values. What is potentially most important in analytical work is that different waves are affected differently, which means that only a part of the effect is due to changes of the liquid-junction potential. Changes of activities, double-layer effects, and sometimes even gross changes of mechanism may be involved. In solutions containing 25 vol.-% ethanol, benzophenone produces two waves at pH values between 3.4 and 5.1. As more ethanol is added, the half-wave potential of the first wave becomes more negative while that of the second is unaffected; with 50 vol.-% ethanol only a single wave is obtained over this range of pH values (*2*). It is not unreasonable to suppose that different substances may be differently affected, and this would permit two waves to be distinguished at one concentration of non-aqueous solvent even though they overlapped at another one. In any case where this was possible the analyst would be amply repaid for struggling with the solubility problems that would arise at higher concentrations of non-aqueous solvent.

Anhydrous alcohols have properties too much like those of water to be advantageous except perhaps in an occasional case where the absence of water might facilitate the dissolution of some organic constituent. Far more useful anhydrous solvents are the protophilic and inert ones like pyridine, dimethylsulfoxide, acetonitrile, and *N*,*N*-dimethylformamide. The last two of these have been the most widely investigated; both have dielectric constants near 38 and are therefore fairly good solvents for inorganic salts, while at the same time they are excellent solvents for many organic compounds, both polar and nonpolar. *N*-Methylformamide has a dielectric constant that is much higher still (184), but it hydrolyzes so rapidly that great care must be taken to protect it from moisture during purification, storage, and use. The utility of aprotic solvents arises from the fact that they considerably alter the reduction patterns obtained when protons are available. Compounds like nitrobenzene and other nitro-aromatics, tetracyanoethylene, and many others undergo one-electron reductions to free radical anions in aprotic solvents. Because of the simplicity of such processes, they are often reversible although the more complicated reactions, typically involving two or even four electrons and an equal number of protons, that occur in aqueous media are not. Because the solutions of the free radical anions are fairly stable (*3*), they may perhaps provide a useful approach to the problem of wave order discussed in the following subsection. These solvents must be purified by procedures that remove not only reducible impurities but also proton donors like water and acetic acid (*4*).

Completely anhydrous media cannot, of course, be used in H-cells, for they would rapidly become contaminated with water extracted from an agar bridge. One may use a cell with an internal reference electrode, a Kalousek cell, or an external reference electrode like that shown in Fig. 2.18. In either of the last two cases the reference electrode itself must be prepared with the solvent being used. The same thing is true of solvent mixtures containing large proportions of non-aqueous solvents, for an agar bridge deteriorates rapidly in contact with such solutions, shrinking as it loses water, and hence the sample becomes contaminated with the metal ion present in the reference-electrode solution. Moreover, salts such as potassium chloride tend to precipitate at the interface between the bridge and the solution being examined, considerably increasing the cell resistance. This also is best solved by employing a Kalousek cell or a reference electrode of the form shown in Fig. 2.18, with appropriate modification of the solution in the reference electrode to prevent precipitation.

Half-wave potentials secured in different solvents are difficult to compare. Whenever an external reference electrode is used, it is a simple matter to measure the voltage that has to be applied across the polarographic cell to yield a current equal to half of the wave height after correction for the residual current. But this voltage includes not only the desired half-wave potential, but also the iR drop through the cell and the liquid-junction potential between the reference electrode and the solution. Correction for the iR drop becomes more and more difficult as the resistance of the cell increases, as explained in Chap. 2 III, and a further uncertainty is introduced by the liquid-junction potential. It has been suggested that the liquid-junction potential between a non-aqueous solution and an aqueous reference electrode can be evaluated from measurements of the reversible half-wave potentials of either the ferricinium ion–ferrocene couple (5), the tris(4,7-dimethyl-1,10-phenanthroline)-iron(III)–(II) couple (6), or the rubidium ion–rubidium amalgam couple (6a) in water and in the solution in question. The difference varies from one couple to another because the difference between the free energies of the oxidized and reduced forms depends on their charges as well as on the dielectric constant of the medium. Hence the half-wave potentials of different reversible couples are affected differently by changes of dielectric constant. Allowance for this can be made if the charges on the species are certainly known, and estimates made in the above way are probably satisfactory as long as the dielectric constant is not too low. Whether they remain useful in solvents having such small dielectric constants that extensive ion-aggregation can be expected is dubious: in such media changes of supporting electrolyte often produce large variations of half-wave potentials that cannot reasonably be ascribed to complexation (6a).

Oxygen is much more soluble in most organic solvents than it is in water, and such solutions must, therefore, be deaerated with special care before their polarograms are recorded. Whenever the constituents of the solvent have widely different vapor pressures—which is no less true of an aqueous solution of ammonia than of a mixture of water and, say, acetone—it is wise to pass the gas used for deaeration through an efficient gas-washing bottle filled with the mixed solvent and immersed in the thermostat. A bottle through which the gas passes in giant bubbles is useless; the only satisfactory type is that in which a sintered-glass gas-dispersion disc or cylinder is used to disperse the gas stream into many tiny bubbles.

Finally, it may be mentioned that maxima of both the first and second kinds seem to be suppressed by the presence of a substantial proportion of a non-aqueous solvent, because this both lowers the interfacial tension and increases the adsorption of ionic species onto the mercury surface.

B. Selection of the Supporting Electrolyte

In selecting a supporting electrolyte the analyst has three problems to consider. One is the definition of the wave obtained when the substance being determined is present alone. This is too simple a matter to deserve discussion. The second is the separation of the desired wave from the wave of any other electroactive constituent of the sample. The third is the important problem of wave order. In the following subsections we shall first outline the problems of wave separation and wave order and summarize the techniques by which they can be handled with the aid of data available in the literature. Unfortunately, the available data on the behaviors of organic compounds are far less extensive and systematic than those on the behaviors of inorganic ones, and therefore the organic analyst frequently finds it necessary to begin by examining the polarographic characteristics of the substances that he expects to be present. We shall, therefore, conclude by outlining the principles that should govern such examinations.

i. The Problem of Wave Separation

For the purposes of this subsection we shall assume that the sample contains two electroactive constituents A and B, A being the one that is to be determined, that each gives only a single wave, and that the wave of A precedes that of B on the polarogram. The last of these

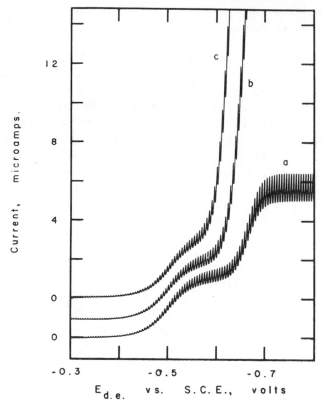

Figure 7.1. Polarograms of 0.5mM thallous ion and (*a*) 0.5, (*b*) 5, and (*c*) 50mM cadmium ion in 1F potassium chloride containing 0.002% Triton X-100.

assumptions means that the half-wave potential of A is less negative than that of B if both waves are cathodic, but is more negative than that of B if both waves are anodic.

The nature of the problem and its practical consequences are illustrated by Fig. 7.1, in which A is thallous ion and B is cadmium ion. On curve *a* the waves are well separated: the plateau of the thallium wave is reasonably long and reasonably parallel to the extrapolated or separately recorded residual-current curve, and the wave height can therefore be measured without difficulty. As the concentration of cadmium ion increases, the separation becomes poorer. The onset of the reduction of cadmium ion leads to a rise in current that begins at less and less negative potentials, and this causes the plateau of the thallium wave to become not only shorter but also less nearly parallel to the residual-current curve. These phenomena have two effects. One is that the difficulty of measuring the height of the thallium wave increases as its plateau becomes shorter. It is plain that the effect illustrated by Fig. 7.1 could not be carried much further without causing the plateau to vanish altogether. No less important is the fact that an extrapolation technique of measuring the height of the thallium wave will necessarily yield a value that corresponds to a more positive potential when it is applied to curve c than when it is applied to curve a. This is because the plateau on curve c does not extend to as negative potentials as the one on curve a. As a result, the apparent wave height decreases in going from curve a to curve c.

For example, extrapolating the residual-current portion of the polarogram to more negative potentials and the plateau of the thallium wave to more positive ones, and measuring the vertical distance between the extrapolated lines at the point where the curve lies halfway between them gives the height of the thallium wave as 2.52 μamp. for curve a, 2.01 μamp. for curve b, and only 0.82 μamp. for curve c. Measuring the wave height at the inflection point on the plateau (which is equivalent to drawing a line through this point parallel to the residual-current line) yields 2.91, 2.73, and 2.56 μamp., respectively. These values are much better, because they are much less affected by the changing slope of the plateau, but a result that varies even this much with the concentration of cadmium ion would hardly be tolerable except in very crude work. The optimum procedure is to measure the vertical distance between the curve and the residual-current line at an arbitrarily selected potential so positive that no contribution to the current there is obtained from the reduction of B even at the highest concentration encountered. Measurements at -0.54 v. in Fig. 7.1 give 2.52, 2.52, and 2.54 μamp., respectively, and the precision of these values leaves very little to be desired. However, inspection of curve a or a polarogram of thallous ion alone would be unlikely to lead to such a choice of potential, for the plateau is not reached before about -0.57 or -0.58 v. The fact that the first and third of these techniques yield identical values for the wave height on curve a is purely coincidental: the third yields a value smaller than the diffusion current because it is measured at a point where the plateau has not yet begun, and the first also yields a smaller value because the plateau has a small positive slope. It is vitally necessary to employ exactly the same technique in dealing with standard solutions as with unknowns to ensure that the relation between the concentration and the measured wave height will be the same for both.

The separation of two waves depends on three factors: the difference between their half-wave potentials, the slopes of their rising portions, and the ratio of their heights. In Fig. 7.1(a) the half-wave potentials of thallous and cadmium ions differ by 0.16 v., and the separation is adequate because both waves are steep and because their heights are nearly equal. As the half-wave potentials become more nearly equal the separation naturally becomes poorer: the difference in Fig. 7.1(a) is nearly if not quite the smallest at which adequate separation is ever obtained.

The value of $E_{3/4} - E_{1/4}$ is a convenient practical measure of the steepness of a wave. Waves less steep than those in Fig. 7.1 have numerically larger values of this parameter, and a greater difference between their half-wave potentials is necessary to permit the plateau of the first to be distinguished. For example, the half-wave potentials of the two waves in Fig. 3.12 differ by about a volt, and the plateau of the first extends over about 0.4 v.; if the two half-wave potentials differed by only 0.5 v. the plateau of the first would not be attained before the second began to produce a further increase of current. This is because the numerical value of $E_{3/4} - E_{1/4}$ for the second wave is very large.

The magnitude of $E_{3/4} - E_{1/4}$ for a reversible wave is determined by its n-value. In Fig. 7.1(a) the cadmium wave, for which n is 2, is considerably steeper than the thallium wave, for which n is 1. As the values of n increase, the required difference of half-wave potentials decreases. If either wave is irreversible, its rising portion generally occupies a wider range of potentials, and a correspondingly greater difference of half-wave potentials is needed.

The effect of the ratio of wave heights is illustrated by Fig. 7.1. It results from the fact that the current due to the reduction of B is proportional to the concentration of B at any potential on the rising portion of its wave provided that the half-wave potential is independent of concentration. Near the foot of a reversible wave, the potential at which any given increase of current is observed becomes $0.059/n_B$ v. more positive for each tenfold increase of concentration; for an irreversible wave the corresponding figure is $0.059/(\alpha n_a)_B$ volt, which is larger than it would be if the wave were reversible. Hence the difference of half-wave potentials required to yield an adequately well defined plateau for A at any fixed concentration increases with increasing concentration of B. If a trace of thallous ion had to be determined in the presence of a very large excess of cadmium, it would be desirable to find a supporting electrolyte in which their half-wave potentials differed by considerably more than 0.16 v. On the other hand, if the solution contained very much more A than B, very little error would be made in the determination of A even if the entire wave height of B were included in the measured wave height of A. The required difference of half-wave potentials decreases continuously in this case as the ratio i_B/i_A of the two wave heights decreases.

Similar but exactly converse reasoning applies when it is B that is to be determined. Here the required difference of half-wave potentials increases as i_B/i_A decreases: the smaller the wave of B, the more essential it becomes for the plateau of the A wave to reach its full development before the reduction of B begins.

Ordinarily we may consider two waves to be well enough separated for practical analytical work if their half-wave potentials differ by 0.3 v. or more, but it should be clear from what has been said that this is only an arbitrary rule of thumb. The requirement might be stated more generally in some such form as

$$|\Delta E_{1/2}| \geq 0.05 + 1.5(|E_{3/4} - E_{1/4}|_A + |E_{3/4} - E_{1/4}|_B) \pm |E_{3/4} - E_{1/4}|_B \log i_B/i_A \qquad (7.1)$$

although it can be expressed in any of a number of more or less equivalent ways. If A alone is to be determined, the positive sign should be taken before the last term; if B alone is to be determined, the negative sign should be taken; if both A and B are to be determined, the absolute value of the last term should be added to the sum of the first two terms. For two reversible two-electron waves of equal heights this demands a difference of 0.13 v. between the two half-wave potentials, and this is about the minimum that can be tolerated by conventional techniques unless some accuracy and precision can be sacrificed.

However, there are ways of dealing with waves that are not as well separated as eq. (7.1) demands. Measurement at an arbitrarily selected and accurately reproduced potential on the rising part of the A wave, as was recommended in connection with Fig. 7.1, makes it possible to obtain satisfactory results even if the separation is only two-thirds or even half of that required by eq. (7.1). Since the measured current is then dependent on potential, uncertainties are minimized by avoiding the steepest part of the wave, recording the polarogram with the polarograph set to provide the smallest feasible span potential, and checking the potential of the reference electrode at frequent intervals. In non-aqueous or strongly acidic or alkaline solutions, where the liquid-junction potential in the cell is large, its variation from one analysis to another must be minimized by taking great care to avoid variations in the composition of the solvent and supporting electrolyte. A variant of this technique was devised by Frisque, Meloche, and Shain (7), who employed measurements of the current at two potentials, one on the plateau and the other on the rising part of the combined wave, to determine two electroactive substances whose half-wave potentials differed so little that the plateau of the wave of A could not be discerned at all on a polarogram of the mixture. Israel (8) similarly employed measurements at three or more potentials on a polarogram of a mixture of the three isomeric nitrobenzoic acids, all of whose half-wave potentials are comprised within a range of 0.08 v. at pH 4, to determine all three of the acids at once; using determinants or least-squares equations as described by Bauman (9) gave results that were accurate to a few per cent when the concentrations of the three acids were roughly equal. Derivative polarography aids to some extent in the resolution of overlapping waves, although the results obtained by using it are not very accurate when the overlapping is really serious. It is discussed briefly in Chap. 10 VIII.

All of these techniques require that there be some difference between the half-wave potentials, but others can be devised that do not. A measurement of the total height of a combined wave can be used, together with some other independent datum, to deduce the concentrations of two substances even though their half-wave potentials are exactly the same. One (10) employs controlled-potential coulometry to provide the second datum and depends on a difference between the two diffusion coefficients. Another (11) employs a measurement of the total wave height in a second supporting electrolyte and depends on a difference between the ratios I_A/I_B of the diffusion current constants in the two media. Such simultaneous analyses require rather special conditions, and their errors always increase rapidly as the concentrations become more disparate. Consequently their practical utility is very limited.

The inorganic analyst can usually deal with the problem of wave separation by differential complexation. In $1F$ potassium chloride the half-wave potentials of thallous and lead ions are -0.48 and -0.44 v., respectively. Replacing the potassium chloride by $1F$ sodium hydroxide has no effect on the half-wave potential of thallous ion because thallous hydroxide is a strong base, but the half-wave potential of lead shifts to -0.76 v. because of the stability of its hydroxo complex. Similarly, the half-wave potentials of nickel(II) and cobalt(II) in $0.1F$ potassium chloride are -1.1 and -1.2 v., respectively, too nearly equal to permit resolution of these irreversible waves. In $5F$ calcium chloride, however, they are -0.56 and -0.82 v., and similar separations can be achieved in media containing ammonia, pyridine, thiocyanate, or any of several other ligands. Other techniques are also available and are discussed in the following subsection.

The weapons at the disposal of the organic analyst are less powerful, and his use of them is often hampered by a paucity of systematic data on their effects. In most cases the pH is the most convenient variable because it has been more thoroughly investigated than any other. All too often, however, its utility is limited because really large differences among its effects on the half-wave potentials of different compounds are rare, especially when, as is usually the case in practical work, the compounds have similar reducible groups. Nevertheless, differences in basicity and changes in reduction mechanism do often cause two waves that are practically superimposed at some pH values to become reasonably well separated at others. Thus, the waves of maleic and fumaric acids overlap at pH 5–6, where their half-wave potentials are -1.12 and -1.21 v., respectively, but in a potassium phosphate or ammoniacal ammonium chloride buffer of pH 8–9 the half-wave potential of fumaric acid is 0.28 v. more negative than that of maleic acid. Hence a polarogram obtained at the latter pH would serve quite well for the determination of maleic acid in the presence of not too large an excess of fumaric acid or of fumaric acid in the presence of not too large an excess of maleic acid. Similarly, the half-wave potentials of *o*- and *p*-hydroxybenzaldehyde, which differ by less than 0.15 v. at pH 1.8 and by only 0.04 v. at pH 6.8, are nearly 0.3 v. apart at pH 11.5. Variations of ionic strength may also occasionally serve to resolve overlapping waves, and so, though probably even more rarely, may electrochemical masking. The latter is most likely to be useful when the interfering molecules are considerably larger than those being determined, and especially when the former are reduced by a mechanism in which a hindered reducible group must approach the electrode surface, for these are the circumstances in which a film of adsorbed material on the electrode surface can be expected to have the most pronounced effects. Changes of the double-layer effect, produced by replacing a weakly adsorbed cation by a more strongly adsorbed one, often steepen and sometimes shift waves observed at potentials more negative than the electrocapillary maximum potential. At potentials more positive than this, however, it is the anion of the supporting electrolyte that should be changed in attempting to take advantage of these effects.

There are also a few specific effects. The waves of carbonyl compounds are shifted toward more positive potentials in supporting electrolytes containing ammonia, other amino compounds like glycine, or hydroxylamine, for the imines and oximes produced are more easily reduced than the free carbonyl compounds. Aldehydes can often be masked by bisulfite. Carbonyl and *vic*-dihydroxy compounds react with borate, and their polarograms in borate buffers are therefore often markedly different from those in other buffers at the same pH.

When none of these expedients serves to separate the waves, two recourses are available. One is to employ an indirect method; the other is to resort to a separation of some kind. These are discussed in Secs. II and III below.

ii. The Problem of Wave Order

This problem arises when the wave of A, the substance being determined, is preceded by that of another electroactive constituent B, and is illustrated by Fig. 3.19. According to the criteria given in the preceding subsection, the wave of zinc (= A) is very well separated from that of cadmium (= B), and yet not only is the height of the zinc wave difficult to measure accurately, but in addition the wave might be overlooked completely by the beginner. The same phenomenon appears in curve b of Fig. 6.1, but in a much less severe form, because here the height of the second wave is about a tenth of that of the first wave, whereas in Fig. 3.19 the ratio is more nearly 1/100. The severity of the problem depends on the ratio of wave heights. Because polarographic analysis is most often used for the determination of minor and trace constituents, situations even far more unfavorable than that shown in Fig. 3.19 are not at all uncommon.

There are a number of general solutions. The compensation technique and its limitations were discussed in connection with Fig. 3.19. An easier and better technique, whenever it is feasible, is to select a supporting electrolyte in which the wave of A precedes that of B. For example, the determination of antimony(III) in the presence of excess lead might be carried out in $1F$ hydrochloric acid, where the antimony wave ($E_{1/2} = -0.15$ v.) precedes the lead wave ($E_{1/2} = -0.44$ v.). But the determination of lead in the presence of excess antimony would be better performed in an alkaline tartrate medium, in which the lead wave ($E_{1/2} = -0.75$ v.) precedes the antimony wave ($E_{1/2} = -1.32$ v.).

Generally analogous procedures can sometimes be employed in organic analysis. In neutral solutions containing a lithium or tetramethylammonium salt as the supporting electrolyte, both acrylonitrile and acetaldehyde have half-wave potentials near -1.9 v. To determine acetaldehyde, a high concentration of either ammonia or hydroxylamine might be incorporated in the supporting electrolyte to form a more easily reducible imine or oxime. Conversely, acrylonitrile might be determined by adding excess bisulfite to convert the acetaldehyde into its nonreducible bisulfite-addition product; as bisulfite itself would produce a wave, care would have to be taken not to add too large an excess of it. However, the measurement of the height of the acrylonitrile wave would not be seriously affected by a preceding wave of moderate height, and so enough excess bisulfite could be used to ensure that the acetaldehyde was essentially completely converted to the non-reducible form. Similar results can occasionally be produced by variations of pH. The half-wave potentials of maleic and fumaric acids are -1.43 and -1.71 v., respectively, at pH 8–9, but in $0.1F$ lithium hydroxide and half-wave potential of fumarate is nearly 0.3 v. more positive than that of maleate. However, because the half-wave potentials of similar compounds tend to vary similarly with pH, a change of pH is much less often able to reverse the order of two waves than to produce a separation between them. The considerations outlined in Chap. 4 VII lead one to expect that reversals of wave order might sometimes be produced by variations of salt concentration, but no example is available, and here again the half-wave potentials are rather unlikely to be differently affected unless the compounds are dissimilar or are reduced by different mechanisms.

A supporting electrolyte in which the substance of interest gives an anodic wave is uniquely well suited to its determination: far fewer substances interfere, and the problem of wave order is often very different with anodic than with cathodic waves. For example, there is no known supporting electrolyte in which manganese(II) is more easily reducible than cobalt(II), and if their cathodic waves were the only ones available it would, therefore, be necessary to separate the two elements before manganese could be determined in the presence of a large excess of cobalt. It may be admitted that a separation by controlled-potential electrodeposition of the cobalt into a mercury-pool electrode would be trivial to design and simple to execute. Nevertheless, it would be still more elegant to take advantage of the fact that manganese(II) gives an anodic wave, whose half-wave potential is -0.40 v., in a strongly alkaline tartrate solution, whereas cobalt(II) does not. Even if the half-wave potential of the anodic manganese wave happened to coincide with that of the cathodic wave of some other constituent of the sample, it would still be possible to measure the height of the anodic wave by selecting a potential so positive that the cathodic wave has not yet begun. It would be impossible to measure the wave height by an extrapolation technique in such circumstances; one would instead have to measure the residual current separately and subtract it from the limiting current measured at the selected potential on the anodic plateau. The special precautions that should be taken in working with solutions that give anodic waves are described in Sec. IV below.

An especially important characteristic of anodic waves is that, for reversible reactions, they occur in the opposite order from the corresponding cathodic waves. In saturated tartaric acid iron(III) gives a wave rising from zero applied e.m.f. (cf. the discussion of Fig. 3.18), while the half-wave potential of titanium(IV) is -0.44 v. This medium would be suitable for the determination of iron(III) in the presence of excess titanium(IV), but not for the determination of titanium(IV) in the presence of excess iron(III). Since both reductions are reversible, the fact that iron(III) is more easily reducible than titanium(IV) means that titanium(III) is more easily oxidizable than iron(II). If both elements are reduced with zinc or some other powerful reducing agent, titanium(III) will give an anodic wave having a half-wave potential of -0.44 v., while iron(II) would be so much more difficultly oxidizable that its anodic wave would be masked by the initial current rise. This fact is used to advantage in stripping analysis (Chap. 10 V). The reversible waves obtained for many organic compounds in aprotic solvents might be put to analytical use in this fashion: if the compound being determined is more difficultly reducible than another present in large excess, both could be reduced to their free radical anions by controlled-potential electrolysis, and then the desired compound could be determined by taking advantage of the fact that its free radical anion would give an anodic wave preceding the one obtained from the interfering substance.

A similar generalization cannot be made for irreversible waves, for the half-wave potential of the anodic wave for an irreversible couple depends not only on the cathodic half-wave potential but also on the formal potential (or on the value of $k_{s,h}$, because of the relationships among these). If the irreversible cathodic wave of B precedes that of A, the reduced form of B may give an anodic wave preceding, following, or even coinciding with the anodic wave of the reduced form of A.

Another general technique for dealing with the wave-order problem without resorting to a prior separation involves the use of differential reduction or oxidation. The former is usually easier when it is possible, for an excess of reducing agent is rarely deleterious. Hence it is very often feasible to incorporate a reducing agent in the supporting electrolyte. Ferric iron interferes with the measurement of the wave height of copper in most media because its wave precedes the copper wave. If one had to determine a trace of copper in the presence of much iron, it would be convenient to employ a supporting electrolyte like saturated hydrazine dihydrochloride or dilute perchloric acid containing excess hydroxylamine. Each of these is capable of reducing ferric iron to the ferrous state, which does not give rise to a wave before the final current rise begins, but neither reduces copper(II).

The reduction of ferric iron in the first of these media can be catalyzed by a trace of molybdate.

Differential oxidation can be used in either of two ways. A metal ion that gives an interfering wave when present in a lower oxidation state can sometimes be made inert by oxidizing it. Lead could hardly be determined in the presence of excess arsenic(III) in a dilute hydrochloric acid medium, for the arsenic wave precedes the lead wave. Arsenic(V), however, is not reduced in this medium, and therefore the determination might be accomplished by adding excess permanganate to oxidize the arsenic, then excess oxalate, hydroxylamine, or some other reducing agent to destroy the excess permanganate. It is usually necessary to destroy or remove the excess oxidant in such procedures because it would be reduced at a still more positive potential if it were left in the solution, so that one interfering substance would merely have been replaced by another, and for the same reason the reducing agent added for this purpose must be one whose oxidation product is polarographically inert in the range of potentials where the desired wave appears.

Differential oxidation can also be employed to convert the substance being determined into a more easily reducible form. In most media the wave of nickel(II) precedes that of cobalt(II). However, cobalt may be oxidized to the $+3$ state by shaking a weakly acidic oxalate solution with excess lead dioxide; the resulting oxalato complex of cobalt(III) is reduced at a much more positive potential than nickel(II), which is not affected by this treatment. The excess solid lead dioxide, of course, does not interfere. A very similar approach to the same problem involves treatment with excess permanganate in an ammoniacal ammonium chloride solution, which oxidizes cobalt(II) to a mixture of ammino complexes; the excess permanganate may be destroyed by adding excess hydroxylamine. Oxidations of this type may be carried out with sodium perborate, ammonium persulfate, hydrogen peroxide, or any other suitable reagent, provided that the excess oxidant is removed by boiling or some other method, and that the reduced form of the oxidizing agent is more difficultly reducible than the substance being determined if it is reducible at all.

A number of procedures generally similar to those described here are available for use in organic analysis as well. So many of them involve prior chemical steps carried out under conditions different from those employed in recording the polarogram, however, that it is convenient to discuss them separately in Sec. II below.

Data on the behaviors of the elements in different supporting electrolytes were reported rather unsystematically in the early days of polarography. More recently, however, quite systematic and detailed information has become available for a wide variety of supporting electrolytes. At least as far as the commoner elements are concerned, it is often fairly easy to design procedures for the analysis of even fairly complex mixtures. As an illustration we may consider the analysis of a sample containing nickel, cobalt, and manganese, which Milner (*12*) described not long ago as "a combination of elements which gives difficulties in direct polarography." A search through a table of polarographic data shows that the half-wave potentials of the divalent ions of these elements are -0.96, -1.22, and -1.53 v., *seriatim*, in a supporting electrolyte containing $0.1F$ ammonia and $0.1F$ ammonium tartrate; all three waves are well defined in pure solutions, and the respective values of $E_{3/4} - E_{1/4}$ are -52, -43, and -35 mv. Comparing these data with the requirements of eq. (7.1) shows that the medium could be used directly for analyzing a mixture in which the three were present at comparable concentrations. A mixture containing very little nickel but much larger concentrations of cobalt and manganese would pose no problem: after recording the small nickel wave, the sensitivity of the polarograph could be decreased for recording the larger waves that follow. Trouble would arise only if the concentration of cobalt were less than perhaps a twentieth of that of nickel, or if the concentration of manganese were less than about a twentieth of the sum of the concentrations of nickel and cobalt. In general, if their waves are sufficiently well separated, two or more substances can be determined with the aid of a single polarogram unless their concentrations differ much more than an order of magnitude and the order of increasing concentration differs from the order in which the waves appear. The first of these situations could be handled by measuring the height of the anodic wave of cobalt(II) in a weakly alkaline glutamate solution, where neither nickel nor manganese will interfere; or by oxidizing the cobalt to the $+3$ state in the presence of excess ammonia or ethylene-diamine or in an acidic oxalate solution, any of which will give a wave for cobalt(III) that precedes and is well separated from the waves of the others. Similarly, a trace of manganese could be determined in a strongly alkaline tartrate solution, where it gives an anodic wave, or by oxidizing it to the $+3$ state in an acidic pyrophosphate medium.

Even more complex mixtures can be handled. Figure 3.20 was originally obtained in developing a procedure for the simultaneous determination of silver, cadmium, nickel, and zinc in cyanide plating wastes. The polarographic characteristics of iron, copper, nickel, cobalt, and manganese in ammoniacal ammonium tartrate and in sodium hydroxide–sodium tartrate solutions indicate that all five of these could probably be determined at once in an appropriate mixture of tartrate, ammonia, and a strong base. Polarograms can actually be made showing well separated waves for as many as eight or nine different metal ions, though it is very improbable that this could be achieved with any real sample.

iii. The Examination of a New Compound

In proportion to the number of substances with which he may have to deal, the data available to the organic analyst are far less extensive and also far less systematic than those available to his inorganic colleague. Most organic analyses must, therefore, begin with an examination of the behaviors of the different compounds present in the sample. Some indication of the behaviors to be expected can often be gleaned from results obtained with similar compounds and reported in the literature. The following procedure, which assumes for the sake of completeness that nothing is known or can reasonably be predicted about the behaviors of the different compounds, permits the rational selection of conditions for carrying out an analysis.

Prepare an approximately $1mM$ solution of the compound in water or 10, 25, 50, or 75% ethanol, dioxane, or one of the other solvents listed in subsection i above. For fear of decomposition on warming, it is best to prepare a more dilute solution or to employ a higher proportion of non-aqueous solvent if the compound is difficultly soluble. By mixing this stock solution with each of a number of buffers prepared in the same solvent, obtain polarograms of approximately $0.1mM$ solutions of the compound at a number of different pH values. Suitable buffers include 0.1 to $1F$ perchloric or sulfuric acid, acetate or citrate buffers having pH values near 4 or 5, phosphate buffers having pH values near 7, bicarbonate–carbonate or ammonia–ammonium chloride buffers having pH values near 10 or 11, and 0.1 to $1F$ sodium, lithium, or tetramethylammonium hydroxide. Whenever a wave is obtained, let the solution stand for 30 to 60 min. in the absence of air and record a second polarogram under identical conditions; it is convenient to have several cells available so that one can be set aside and other polarograms recorded in the interim. If no wave is obtained under any of these conditions, or if literature data on compounds similar to the one being determined indicate that a wave cannot reasonably be expected (as would be the case with an unsaturated hydrocarbon, for example), an 0.1F solution of tetra-n-butylammonium chloride or hydroxide should be tried. Tetraalkylammonium salts used for polarographic purposes should be free from alkali metal ions as well as from the more easily reducible trialkylammonium ions. If no waves are obtained in the last of these media for the substance being determined, or if no waves sufficiently well defined for analytical purposes have been obtained, an indirect method may still be contemplated. In the latter case it may be worth while to investigate a different solvent, preferably a non-aqueous one.

Assuming that waves are obtained in at least some of these media for the substance being determined and for one or more of the other possible constituents of the sample, polarograms of several different concentrations (e.g., 0.05, 0.2, and 1mM) should then be obtained for each compound yielding a wave. In each case, polarograms should be obtained with several different heights of the mercury column above the capillary at both the highest and the lowest concentration used. The polarograms should then be examined for:

(1) Possible instabilities of the solutions

(2) Control of the wave heights by diffusion or some other process

(3) Proportionality, or a deviation from it, between wave height and concentration

(4) The effects of pH on the ratios of wave height to concentration

(5) The effects, if any, of concentration on the half-wave potentials

(6) The reversibilities of the waves, including estimates of αn_a for irreversible waves

(7) The presence of maxima

(8) The effect of pH on the separation between the desired wave and the waves of the other electroactive constituents of the sample.

From this information one can choose a range of pH values for more detailed investigation: it is still too early, however, to concentrate attention on a particular supporting electrolyte. If, for example, the characters and separation of the waves appear from the above examination to be best at pH 7, one should still retain an open mind about at least the range of pH values from 5 to 9. If they appear to be best in dilute mineral acid, a more concentrated acid might be used as well in the work to follow. Some weakly basic compounds give excellent waves in $10F$ perchloric or hydrochloric acid. The former, however, should not be used for this purpose by anyone who is not fully aware of the hazards that may arise from mixing organic substances with concentrated perchloric acid.

Over this narrower range of pH values one should first check any deviations from ideal behavior revealed by the previous broader study. If, for example, a pH value near 7 had seemed to be best while a much smaller wave height had been obtained at pH 10, the wave height and the ways in which it depends on the mercury pressure and the concentration should be checked at pH 8 and 9. At the same time, the half-wave potentials of the different compounds should be measured at intervals no wider than 1 pH unit. This would be unnecessary if the waves were so far apart that a little more or less separation would not matter. But increasing the difference between two half-wave potentials by even as little as 30% may greatly improve the ease with which an analysis can be carried out and the accuracy and precision that can be obtained.

Polarograms should now be obtained for each of the compounds over as wide a range of ionic strengths as can be covered in each of the buffers now being employed. If maxima of the second kind or anomalous waves appear at high ionic strengths, they should be eliminated by adding the smallest concentration of a maximum suppressor that will suffice. It is also advisable to investigate the effect of a large excess of maximum suppressor—say, 0.05% Triton X-100 or 0.1% gelatin. The effect of 0.05 to $0.1F$ tetra-n-butylammonium iodide on the polarogram should be investigated; if it produces an appreciable change, the considerations outlined in Chap. 4 VII will usually permit this to be attributed to either the tetra-n-butylammonium or the iodide ion, and the effect can then be investigated over a wider range of concentrations of the ion responsible for it.

It is true that this program may consume more time than can be afforded if only a very small number of samples must be analyzed, and it is also true that many good practical methods of analysis have been devised with the aid of less information than it will provide. If a wholly satisfactory set of conditions can be identified before all of this work has been done, there is little to be gained by persisting in order to discover other sets that would also serve. But there will certainly be many analytical problems that can be more easily and elegantly solved with all of this information than with only part of it.

II. Indirect Methods of Analysis

Indirect methods of polarographic analysis are those in which the substance being determined is converted into, or made to react with, an equivalent amount of some other substance having more favorable polarographic characteristics. They are used for the determination of substances that are polarographically inert, that give waves so ill defined that their heights are impossible to measure with satisfactory precision, or that behave unfavorably in other ways. Usually the half-wave potential of the substance whose wave height is actually measured in an indirect method is considerably more positive than the half-wave potential of the substance being determined, and therefore indirect methods usually mitigate or eliminate the wave-order problem in the analysis of mixtures. Several procedures conforming to this definition and involving differential oxidation or reduction prior to polarographic analysis were mentioned in Sec. I-B*ii* above, and will not be discussed further here.

One indirect method consists of precipitating the substance sought by treating it with an excess of a reagent having more desirable polarographic characteristics, then determining the amount of reagent contained in the precipitate. Thus, sulfate ion can be determined polarographically by precipitating it as lead sulfate, removing excess lead ion by filtering or centrifuging and washing thoroughly, dissolving the precipitate in ammonium acetate solution, diluting to known volume, and recording the polarogram. From the height of the lead wave it is easy to calculate the amount of lead present in the precipitate and hence the amount of sulfate present in the sample. Similarly, sodium can be determined in the presence of potassium, which is impossible by direct methods because their half-wave potentials are almost identical, by precipitating sodium zinc uranyl acetate, dissolving this in acid, and measuring the height of the wave of uranium(VI) in the resulting solution.

A second method consists of measuring the decrease in the wave height of an electroactive reagent caused by the addition of the substance being determined. Most procedures of this type involve the formation of a precipitate, although other possibilities can of course be envisioned. For example, the wave of magnesium ion is very badly defined in aqueous media and, to make matters worse, the ions of the alkalies and other alkaline earths give waves that precede or merge with it. An indirect method is, therefore, preferable to a direct one. One may precipitate the 8-hydroxyquinolate from an ammoniacal solution, allow this to settle out, and obtain a polarogram of the supernatant solution. The height of the resulting wave of 8-hydroxy-quinoline is proportional to the excess employed. Another solution is prepared in exactly the same way but without any magnesium; comparing the height of the oxine wave on this polarogram with its height in the presence of magnesium permits the calculation of the fraction of the total amount of oxine that was precipitated by the magnesium, and from this it is easy to calculate the amount of magnesium in the sample. Calcium can be determined by adding excess picrolonic acid and measuring the wave height of the excess reagent remaining after precipitation is complete. Filtration and washing are unnecessary in such procedures. Generally the entire suspension is made up to known volume and the small volume of the precipitate is simply neglected. If the wave height i_l of the reagent is proportional to its concentration C (in millimoles per liter), so that $i_l = kC$, the number N of micromoles of the substance being determined is given by

$$N = (\nu V/k)(i_l^0 - i_l) \qquad (7.2)$$

where ν is the number of moles of the substance being determined that react with each mole of reagent, V is the volume (in milliliters) of the final solution, i_l^0 is the wave height obtained in the absence of the substance being determined, and i_l is the wave height obtained in the analysis employing the same amount of reagent under identical conditions.

Two requirements are essential to success in either of these methods. One is that there be no appreciable coprecipitation of either the reagent or any other constituent of the sample. Sometimes, to be sure, data secured by analyzing known solutions do permit the calculation of an empirical correction for coprecipitation of the reagent, but analyses based on such corrections are rarely very satisfactory. The other requirement is, of course, that the sample contain no other substance that reacts with the reagent. In addition, the second method virtually demands that only a relatively small excess of reagent be employed. Otherwise the difference $(i_l^0 - i_l)$ will be small, and the relative error incurred in its measurement will be correspondingly large. Even if only a twofold excess of reagent is employed, the relative error of the analysis may be twice as large as the relative error in measuring i_l and i_l^0. Hence it is very desirable to have some prior knowledge of the amount of the substance being determined, and so the method is best suited to the analysis of a large number of samples of very similar compositions. Lacking such knowledge, it is generally better to employ the first method even though it is more time-consuming.

A third indirect method is based on a reaction between the metal ion being determined and an excess of an electroactive ligand to give a soluble complex whose wave height is measured. The stoichiometry of the reaction must be known, and the wave of the complex must be well separated from that of the excess free ligand and also from the wave of any other electroactive constituent of the sample. The coordinated metal ion behaves like an electron-withdrawing substituent, so that the half-wave potential for the reduction of the ligand from the complex is more negative than that for the reduction of the free ligand, and this gives rise to the additional requirement that the concentration of the free ligand must not greatly exceed that of the complex, for if it does the wave height of the latter will be difficult and perhaps even impossible to measure. The method has been applied to the determination of aluminum (13): a solution of the sample is treated with an excess of the dye Pontachrome Violet SW in an acetate buffer at pH 4–5. The resulting solution gives two waves; the height of the first is proportional to the concentration of the excess dye, while the height of the second is proportional to the concentration of the complexed dye and thus to the concentration of aluminum. Other substances (such as cobalt, copper, iron, titanium, and vanadium) that react with the dye interfere, and so do substances (such as citrate, fluoride, and phosphate) that bind aluminum ion more strongly than the dye does. Thorium can be determined similarly by the use of Solochrome Violet RS (14). In either of these examples, one might of course measure the decrease of the wave height of the free dye (thus employing the second method above) rather than the wave height of the metal-dye complex.

A fourth indirect method depends on a reaction between the metal ion being determined and a complex of another metal ion; the second metal ion is liberated and its wave height is measured. The complex of the second metal ion must of course be less stable than that of the ion being determined, but it must be sufficiently stable that no wave is obtained for its free metal ion when it is present alone, for otherwise difficulties will arise when the unknown concentration is small. For example, thorium may be determined by measuring the wave height of the lead ion liberated by the reaction between thorium ion and the lead-ethylenediaminetetraacetate complex (15).

A fifth method finds occasional use when no wave can be obtained for one of two constituents in a solution except in a medium in which the other gives an overlapping wave. This is more closely allied to the simultaneous methods cited in Sec. I-Bi above than to the other indirect methods discussed here. For example, the wave of lead ion (for which $I = 3.52$) practically coincides with the second wave of tin(IV) (for which $I = 3.49$) in $4F$ ammonium chloride–$1F$ hydrochloric acid–0.005% gelatin, and also in all of the few other media in which tin(IV) is reducible. In $1F$ sodium hydroxide, however, lead gives a wave for which $I = 3.40$, while tin(IV) is polarographically inert. Lingane (16) determined tin and lead in the same sample by measuring the height of the combined wave and the value of $m^{2/3}t^{1/6}$ in the acidic medium, together with the height of the lead wave and the value of $m^{2/3}t^{1/6}$ in the sodium hydroxide solution. In each case the same volume, v ml., of the solution being analyzed was made up to the same volume, V ml., with the supporting electrolyte. The height of the combined wave in the acidic medium is given by

$$i_1 = (3.49C_{Sn} + 3.52C_{Pb})\, v(m^{2/3}t^{1/6})_1/V \qquad (7.3a)$$

while that of the lead wave in the sodium hydroxide medium is given by

$$i_2 = 3.40C_{Pb}\, v(m^{2/3}t^{1/6})_2/V \qquad (7.3b)$$

which can easily be solved for the concentration, C_{Sn}, of tin in the solution being analyzed. Naturally the relative error of a determination of tin by this method is always greater than it would be if the wave height of tin could be measured alone, and the uncertainty increases as the lead:tin ratio in the sample increases. If the ratio were even as large as 5:1, satisfactory results would be very difficult to obtain.

Other methods applicable to inorganic problems were summarized in Sec. I-B above.

The need for indirect methods has been even more pressing in organic than in inorganic analysis, and a great many procedures have, therefore, been devised to permit or simplify the determinations of various kinds of organic compounds. The great majority of them involve either the introduction of an electroactive functional group or the replacement of such a group already present in the molecule being determined by another that is more easily reducible.

Nitration, which is the most common procedure of the first type, is used to permit the polarographic determination of benzene and many of its derivatives, including anilines, phenols, and toluenes. Concentrated nitric acid, alone or mixed with ammonium nitrate or concentrated sulfuric acid, or another suitable nitrating agent may be used; the choice is governed by the reactivities of the compound being determined and of the other constituents of the sample. The usual aim is to secure an essentially quantitative yield of a single nitrated product, for both the ease with which the wave height can be measured and the accuracy with which it can be interpreted may suffer if a mixture is obtained. However, in some cases it does not matter very much whether this aim is achieved or not, as may be illustrated by considering the determination of benzene. The expected product, m-dinitrobenzene, gives two four-electron waves, whose half-wave potentials are -0.46 and -0.64 v. in a buffer of pH 9. If a little 1,3,5-trinitrobenzene were formed by too vigorous nitration, it would give three four-electron waves, having half-wave potentials of -0.34, -0.48, and -0.65 v. in the same supporting electrolyte. The second and third of these waves would merge with the two waves of the dinitrobenzene. If the diffusion coefficients of the di- and trinitro compounds were the same, the diffusion current constants of their individual waves would also be the same because each involves four electrons, and so the height of either of the two combined waves would be exactly the same as if only the dinitro compound had been formed. As the diffusion coefficients are not quite identical, an error does result, but the difference is too small for the error to be of much importance. In other cases the effects may be much more serious: the half-wave potentials of the different products may be too far apart to yield a combined wave whose height can be measured with reasonable precision, but not far enough apart to permit any one wave to be distinguished. Generally, therefore, the nitration must be performed under such conditions that the other constituents of the sample are unaffected. Otherwise a separation either before or after nitration is usually necessary.

Changes of various kinds can be rung on this theme. Benzene can be determined in the presence of toluene or the xylenes by oxidizing the mixture of nitration products with chromium(VI) in an acidic solution, separating the m-dinitrobenzene from the nitrocarboxylic acids by solvent extraction from an alkaline solution, and obtaining the polarogram of the dinitrobenzene (17,18). Naphthalene yields a wave in its own right, but at such a negative potential (-2.50 v. in 75% dioxane) that a tetra-n-butylammonium salt must be used as the supporting electrolyte; the charging current is large at such potentials and capillary noise is pronounced, so that both the sensitivity and the precision are adversely affected, and so many substances are more easily reducible that numerous interferences can be anticipated. The 1-nitro derivative obtained by nitration under mild conditions yields a wave much easier to work with. Conversely, the procedure can be used to determine nitrate after its reaction with 2-xylenol (19).

Other similar methods include the conversion of secondary amines to N-nitrosoamines by treatment with nitrite in acidic solutions (20,21), the bromination of unsaturated compounds to yield the much more easily reducible vic-dibromo compounds, and the determination of carbon disulfide after reaction with diethylamine to convert it into diethyldithiocarbamate. Many vic-dihydroxy, α-hydroxycarbonyl, and probably also α-hydroxyamino compounds can be determined by oxidation to formaldehyde or acetaldehyde with periodate, permanganate, or other oxidizing agents. Lactic acid (22), glycerol (23), ethylene and 1,2-propylene glycols and (after hydrolysis) chlorohydrins (24), and many others have been determined by the last of these methods. An indirect method based on the decrease of the wave height of the reagent may be used if the organic product is ill-suited to direct polarographic determination (24a).

The conversion of carbonyl compounds into more easily reducible imines and oximes was mentioned in an earlier section. Imines are the more widely used, but their formation is often far from complete, and this severely affects the sensitivity that can be attained. Methylamine

(*25*) and *n*-butylamine (*26*) are preferable to ammonia because they react more completely, and *o*-phenylenediamine, glycine, hexamethylenediamine, semicarbazide, and others have also been recommended. Primary amines have been determined by a converse procedure, and carbonyl compounds can also be determined after converting them to their Girard derivatives by condensation with an appropriate hydrazide. Electrophoretic or chromatographic separations of their 2,4-dinitrophenylhydrazones, followed by polarographic determinations, have been employed in analyzing mixtures of keto acids and of aliphatic aldehydes.

Certain compounds can be determined by taking advantage of their abilities to complex electroactive metal ions (*27*,*28*). In a solution containing 1,2-propylenediamine and excess copper(II), two waves are obtained: the first for the reduction of the excess uncomplexed cupric ion, the second for the reduction of cupric ion bound by the diamine. Chelons like ethylenediaminetetraacetate can be similarly determined. Amino acids can be determined by shaking with a carefully prepared precipitate of copper(II) phosphate, and determining either the concentration of copper present in the saturated solution as a result of complex formation or, after filtration and dissolution in excess ethylenediaminetetraacetate, the amount of copper remaining in the precipitate (*29*).

It may often be possible to analyze mixtures of closely related substances by taking advantage of differences among the rates at which they react with a chemical reagent, measuring a limiting current as a function of time and employing the familiar considerations of kinetic analysis (cf. Sec. V-B*v*).

III. Separations Preceding Polarographic Analyses

The ideal polarographic analysis is one in which, by proper choice of the solvent and supporting electrolyte, the substance being determined or some derivative of it yields a wave well separated from every other wave on the polarogram and preceding every larger wave. When this ideal can be attained, as it often can be, prior separations are unnecessary. Among other reasons why this is desirable is the important fact that a separation is always the most time-consuming step in a polarographic analysis. When only a single constituent is being determined in each of a large number of similar samples, it takes no more than two or three minutes to obtain its wave with a recording polarograph, and this would mean that 15 to 20 analyses can easily be performed in an hour if lengthy and time-consuming separations can be avoided.

This is a convenient place to discuss the claims made by the manufacturers and distributors of fast-sweep polarographs to the effect that their instruments save much time in analytical work because they provide complete polarograms in a few seconds instead of about ten minutes. There are two reasons why such claims are overstated. One is that a complete polarogram is rarely needed or even useful, and no one would spend ten minutes to record the entire polarogram when two minutes suffice to obtain what is wanted. The other is that there are but few practical analyses in which the actual recording of the polarogram is the rate-determining step, even with a conventional polarograph. To the writer the only real advantage of the fast-sweep instruments seems to be in studying the intermediates formed in moderately fast chemical reactions.

Separations are, unfortunately, often essential in polarographic analyses. They may be used to remove the substance being determined from the other constituents of the sample, to remove the interfering constituents, or to divide the sample into a number of fractions that are analyzed separately.

There are five cases in which the polarographic determination of a substance A in a sample that contains another electroactive constituent B must be preceded by a separation of A and B:

(1) When the wave of B precedes that of A and the concentration of B is much larger than that of A or the wave of B is ill defined (cf. Fig. 3.19);

(2) When the wave of B closely follows that of A and the concentration of B is much larger than that of A (cf. Fig. 7.1(c));

(3) When the waves of A and B are so nearly coincident that the height of the wave of A cannot be accurately measured no matter what the ratio of concentrations may be;

(4) When A and B can react chemically in the supporting electrolyte selected; and

(5) When B forms a precipitate with some constituent of the supporting electrolyte and A is coprecipitated (as would be the case in an ammoniacal supporting electrolyte when A = copper(II) and

B = lead), or when B catalyzes or induces some other process that affects the concentration of A.

It is only in the third and fourth of these cases that a quantitative separation is required; indeed, the third can sometimes be handled without any separation at all, as was mentioned in Sec. I-B*i* above. In the other cases it usually suffices to remove enough of the B to bring its concentration down to about the same as that of A.

With the single exception of gas chromatography, there is probably not a single technique of separation that has not, at one time or another, been used to prepare solutions for polarographic analysis. Those that have found the most frequent use and that seem to the writer to be the most meritorious are listed and briefly discussed in the following subsections.

A. Precipitation

Precipitation can be employed either to separate the substance being determined or, if coprecipitation is known to be negligible, to remove other constituents of the sample. Thus, chromate might be determined in the presence of ferric iron in either of two ways: by precipitating lead or barium chromate and determining chromate in a solution of the precipitate, or by precipitating hydrous ferric oxide with ammonia or another suitable reagent and determining the chromate in the supernatant solution.

The first procedure would probably yield better results, for two reasons. One is that a separation from other possible contaminants is more likely to be achieved in the same operation. The other is that the errors resulting from coprecipitation would probably be much less severe. Not only is it much more probable that a large precipitate of hydrous ferric oxide would carry down appreciable amounts of chromate than that the small precipitate of lead or barium chromate would carry down much ferric iron, but the results would be quite different in the two cases. The loss of chromate by coprecipitation would obviously be irreparable, whereas it might well be possible to find conditions under which the wave height of chromate could be measured without interference from a small amount of coprecipitated iron.

It is sometimes advantageous to carry out a precipitation in a solution containing 10 to 25% ethanol to decrease the solubility of the precipitate and hasten the attainment of solubility equilibrium.

Whether this significantly increases the contamination of the precipitate in any particular case is a question that must be settled by experiment.

Coprecipitation can often be turned to good advantage, as in the Lingane-Kerlinger procedure for the removal of chromium(III) from nickel and cobalt (*30*): an excess of iron(III) is added, and hydrous ferric oxide is precipitated from a pyridine–pyridinium chloride buffer having a pH near 5. Chromium(III) is quantitatively coprecipitated, though it would not precipitate at all in the absence of iron, while all of the nickel and cobalt remain dissolved.

When precipitation is used to remove an interfering substance prior to analysis of the supernatant solution, it is rarely necessary to separate the precipitate. One can simply carry out the precipitation in a volumetric flask of suitable size, dilute the entire suspension to the mark, and take an aliquot of the clear supernatant solution after settling. The error caused by neglecting the volume of the precipitate is almost never significant.

Precipitation can rarely be employed in organic analysis. One of its very few applications is in the removal of proteins from biological samples by treatment with 5-sulfosalicylic acid or perchloric acid.

B. Extraction

Three kinds of extraction procedures have been employed in polarographic analysis. The extraction of a solid sample with a solvent hardly needs discussion here. Some use has been made of the familiar procedure in which the distribution coefficient of one substance between two solvents is so much larger than that of another that a quantitative separation is attained in a small number of extractions. An advantage of this technique is that a solution of the extracted substance much more concentrated than the original one can often be prepared by evaporating the combined non-aqueous phases and dissolving the residue in a small volume of supporting electrolyte, or by re-extraction into a small volume of an appropriate aqueous solution. Iron(III) and uranium(VI) have been determined polarographically after extraction from aqueous hydrochloric acid solutions by isopropyl ether and by tri-*n*-octylphosphine oxide in cyclohexane, respectively. Similarly, peroxides and aldehydes in ethers can be determined after extraction into dilute aqueous lithium hydroxide. Many metals have been determined polarographically after re-extracting their dithizonates into acidic aqueous solutions. This offers no advantage over a photometric analysis of the organic phase if the original extraction was specific, but if several metals were extracted together they are much more likely to be resolved on a polarogram than on a spectrum.

The third technique involves the repeated partition of several compounds, whose distribution coefficients are too nearly equal to permit them to be separated quantitatively by simple techniques, between different solvents. The total combined wave height of the substances being determined is measured either in each of the successive extracts or in the original phase after each extraction. If n components are present, n extractions must be performed in the first case, or $(n - 1)$ in the second; in either event, n simultaneous equations can be written, employing proportionality constants obtained in identical extractions of known solutions of the individual compounds, and these equations are solved for the concentrations in the mixture. Binary mixtures of acetaldehyde with n-propionaldehyde or n-butyraldehyde have been successfully analyzed in this way, employing partition between water and benzene (31). The analysis of ternary mixtures is less satisfactory, however, for the relative errors are then much larger, which means that larger differences among the distribution coefficients are required for success.

C. CHROMATOGRAPHIC AND RELATED TECHNIQUES

The chromatographic or electrophoretic fractionation of a sample has often been followed by polarographic analysis of the different fractions obtained. Polarography is easily able to deal with the small amounts of material that can conveniently be isolated by such techniques, and provides much better accuracy and precision than can be obtained by procedures such as scanning densitometry or reflectimetry.

For example, keto acids have been determined in biological materials by converting them to their 2,4-dinitrophenylhydrazones, which are separated by paper electrophoresis. Each of the resulting spots is cut out, the dinitrophenylhydrazone is leached out of the paper with water and extracted into a small volume of ether, the combined ether extracts are evaporated, the residue is dissolved in a small volume of acid, and the concentration of the dinitrophenylhydrazone is obtained from its wave height on a polarogram of the resulting solution (32). A one- or two-dimensional paper chromatogram can be treated similarly, and the same principle can be employed in analyzing the successive fractions obtained in adsorption and ion-exchange column chromatography.

More interesting, however, is the use of polarography for the continuous analysis of the effluent from a chromatographic column; Kemula, who developed the technique, has called the combination "chromato-polarography" (33). The effluent is passed directly from the column into a cell suitable for the analysis of flowing solutions (cf. references 32a–41 of Chap. 2). The dropping electrode is maintained at a constant potential on the plateau of the last wave on a polarogram of the mixture being resolved. Since every electroactive component of the mixture yields its limiting current at this potential, the current at any instant is a measure of the total concentration of electroactive material in the solution emerging from the column. Cases can be envisioned in which a different choice of potential, or even the use of the circuit shown in Fig. 2.13, would permit one constituent to be determined in the presence of another that emerged from the column at the same time if their waves were sufficiently well separated.

The column effluent must have a composition suitable for polarographic analysis: that is, a supporting electrolyte should preferably be included in the solution entering the column. Since this also seems to aid in obtaining symmetrical and sharply separated elution peaks, injection of a supporting electrolyte between the column and the cell has apparently not been attempted, although it would not be difficult to do with a precise metering pump and might be advantageous when the medium giving the best chromatographic separation is ill suited to polarographic analysis. If the solutions are reasonably concentrated, dissolved oxygen can be ignored; if they are very dilute, compensation of the limiting current of oxygen is necessary (34) and has served for determining amounts of material of the order of a few micrograms with errors of ±10% or less. Removal of oxygen from the solution entering the column would be desirable in work with very dilute solutions despite the slightly greater complexity of the apparatus that would be needed.

Either the elution or the frontal method may be used; Fig. 7.2 shows the plots they yield for a mixture of the three isomeric nitroanilines. The abscissa scale of such a plot can be established by measuring the total effluent, collected in a graduated cylinder, at

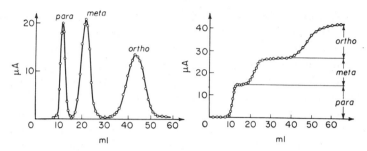

Figure 7.2. Chromato-polarographic analyses of a mixture of o-, m-, and p-nitroaniline by elution (left-hand curve) and frontal (right-hand curve) techniques. The column was packed with particles of rubber swollen in benzene, and the mobile phase was 0.2F potassium iodide in methanol–water (30:70) (33).

various times, and correlating the measured volumes with the time scale of the recorder chart; by employing a known constant flow rate; or in any of several other obvious ways. As in other chromatographic techniques, one may measure either the peak height or the peak area when using the elution method; in the frontal method, of course, one measures the heights of the successive steps. Kemula considered the frontal method to be the more precise, but it is not clear that this would be so if the elution method were employed with a column operating at a constant flow rate and a recorder equipped for precise integration.

Although the quality of the results is greatly affected by the natures of the support and the stationary and mobile phases, the technique is still too new for extensive and systematic information to have been obtained as yet. Attempts to use solid adsorbents like alumina or ion-exchange resins have not as yet been very successful, although some good results have been obtained with the latter at elevated temperatures. Powdered rubber swollen with an organic solvent like n-heptane or 2,2,4-trimethylpentane has been the most widely used, but other materials are being actively investigated.

Chromato-polarography has been used to analyze mixtures of the mono-, di-, and trinitrobenzenes, of a number of 1- and 2-nitroalkanes, and of the 2,4-dinitrophenylhydrazones of several n-alkanals, among others. It is one of the most promising techniques for the polarographic analysis of complex mixtures of closely related substances.

D. Other Physical Techniques

Simple volatilization has found few applications in polarographic analysis. It can, however, be used in determining certain trace impurities in samples of tin: the sample is dissolved in hydrochloric acid, excess nitric acid is added, and stannic chloride is volatilized by repeatedly adding hydrochloric acid and evaporating to near dryness. Another example is cited in subsection F below.

Distillation has been more often used. The formaldehyde and acetaldehyde resulting from oxidations of certain hydroxy compounds with periodate are customarily separated from the reaction mixture by distillation to avoid interference from excess periodate, iodate formed during the oxidation, and other organic constituents of the sample. Tetranitromethane has been separated from nitrobenzene by distillation and determined polarographically in the distillate. A more complex application is akin to the last one mentioned in subsection B above: a mixture of aliphatic aldehydes can be analyzed by passing a stream of gas through their solution and measuring the total wave height of the remaining aldehydes at various times (35). The rate of flow of gas, the extent to which it is dispersed (which, if a sintered-glass disc or cylinder is used, will depend on the age of the cell and on the conditions to which it has been subjected), the volume of the solution, and the geometry of the cell must all be controlled with great care, however. In general, chemical processes provide sounder foundations for methods of kinetic analysis than do physical ones.

Despite the inordinate length of time that it consumes, dialysis has been used to separate electroactive substances of low molecular weight from such materials as polymers and serum proteins.

E. Chemical Reduction

Treatment with a suitable chemical reducing agent can often remove an interfering substance or at least render it innocuous. This can sometimes be accomplished by including a reducing agent in the supporting electrolyte; hydrazine, hydroxylamine, hypophosphite, and several others have been used. Sometimes, however, it is more convenient to effect the reduction separately. Thus, the interference of copper with the determination of iron can be eliminated by treating the solution with a reducing agent, such as amalgamated zinc, that is powerful enough to reduce copper to the metal while reducing iron only to the ferrous state. The concentration of iron could then be determined by measuring the height of the anodic ferrous wave in an acidic oxalate medium, or by reoxidizing it to the ferric state and measuring the height of the cathodic wave in some suitable supporting electrolyte. What is most important is that actual separation is not required; masking by conversion to a non-electroactive lower oxidation state serves equally well. The analyst who had to determine benzaldehyde in the presence of much nitrobenzene would find it much easier to reduce the latter to aniline, which is inert, than to make a separation.

F. Electrolytic Techniques

Electrolytic procedures for preparing solutions for polarographic analysis have important advantages over chemical ones. They are more versatile: there are many wave-order problems that are difficult, and some that are even impossible, to solve by other techniques of separation or masking, but there are very few that cannot be handled electrolytically. They are more selective: not only do they serve for the resolution of any mixture yielding waves that are well separated, but because the wave-separation problem takes a rather different form they can also be used to resolve mixtures that give waves insufficiently well separated for polarographic analysis, and in fact they can sometimes be used even with mixtures that give waves having identical half-wave potentials. They involve less contamination: usually they can be carried out in the same supporting electrolyte used for the polarographic analysis, and this avoids the necessity of adding other reagents that might have to be destroyed before the solution could be analyzed or that might be contaminated with interfering impurities. They are easier to design: the polarographic data used in choosing the conditions of analysis are directly applicable to the choice of conditions for the electrolysis. They are easier to perform: they involve fewer steps and few if any transfers of material, and in general they proceed with little or no supervision from the analyst.

Two classical techniques are useful in inorganic analysis. One is the electrolysis of an acidic solution of the sample between a large stirred mercury cathode and a platinum anode, using voltages of 3 to 6 v. and currents of 2 to 5 amp. This serves very well for the removal of many elements, such as iron, copper, chromium, nickel, and manganese, which are reduced to the metallic state and deposited in the mercury, from others, such as aluminum, titanium, vanadium, uranium, and the alkalies and alkaline earths, which are not deposited. The deposited metals can be recovered by distilling off the mercury and dissolving the residue in acid (*36*), but this is so unpleasant and hazardous that the technique is rarely if ever considered unless the element to be determined is one that remains in the solution. Such electrolyses have been used in procedures for the determination of vanadium in steels and other ferroalloys and of aluminum in steels and copper-base alloys.

The solution that results from the electrogravimetric determination of a major constituent of a sample by deposition onto a platinum cathode is often well adapted to a polarographic determination of one or more of the minor or trace constituents. In analyzing zinc-base alloys containing much more copper than lead or cadmium, the copper can be deposited onto a platinum cathode from a solution containing nitric acid; after the deposition is complete, a little urea or sulfamic acid may be added to destroy oxides of nitrogen and the lead and cadmium may be determined polarographically without further ado.

By far the most elegant and generally useful technique, however, is that in which the solution is electrolyzed with a mercury pool electrode whose potential is kept constant by means of a potentiostat. In principle this is not very different from the classical technique, in which the cathode potential is ultimately limited by the discharge of hydrogen ion, but the practical difference is enormous, for a very much wider variety of separations is made possible by controlling the potential.

To determine the nickel and zinc present in a reagent-grade copper salt, for example, one may dissolve a sample of the salt in an ammoniacal ammonium chloride solution and electrolyze this at a cathode potential of about -0.85 v. vs. S.C.E. At this potential copper(II) is reduced to copper amalgam, while nickel and zinc are unaffected, as can easily be deduced from the polarographic half-wave potentials, which in $1F$ ammonia–$1F$ ammonium chloride are -0.24 and -0.51 v. for the double wave of copper, -1.10 v. for nickel, and -1.35 v. for zinc. It is only necessary to prolong the electrolysis sufficiently to decrease the concentration of copper to a value comparable with the concentrations of nickel and zinc. The time required depends on the cell design; typically, an hour or less would suffice to decrease the copper concentration by a factor of 10^6. The attention of the operator would be required, however, for only the few minutes needed to place the solution in the cell and adjust the controls of the potentiostat; the electrolysis itself is completely automatic. In this way it is possible (37) to determine as little as $10^{-5}\%$ of nickel or zinc in a sample of copper or a copper salt with an accuracy difficult to equal by any other method. The sensitivity could often be still further extended by employing stripping analysis, which could hardly be applied to the original solution because of the danger of intermetallic compound formation in amalgams containing high concentrations of one or more deposited metals. Stripping analysis is discussed in Chap. 10 V.

Other wave-order problems are equally easily solved. A trace of bromoacetic acid can be determined in the presence of a large excess of the more easily reducible iodoacetic acid, a trace of acetophenone can be determined in the presence of a large excess of benzophenone, and so on. Garn and Halline (38) employed the technique to eliminate interferences from nitrocellulose and maleic and fumaric acids in determining phthalic anhydride in alkyd resins.

The efficiency that can be attained in such a separation is easily assessed. Consider, for example, the separation of cadmium from zinc. In $0.1F$ potassium chloride their waves are well separated, as is shown in Fig. 3.19. The cadmium wave is reversible and the zinc wave nearly so; each can be described by eq. (4.2), which for present purposes can be written

$$E = E_s^0 - 0.02957 \log \frac{f_a C_a}{a_{Hg} f_s C_s} \tag{7.4}$$

The bulk concentrations C_a and C_s in the amalgam and solution phases are written here instead of the interfacial concentrations $C_a{}^0$ and $C_s{}^0$ because each phase will be homogeneous when equilibrium is reached. Unless a very large amount of cadmium is deposited, a_{Hg} will remain virtually equal to unity. Since the values of k_a and k_s appearing in eq. (4.7) are unlikely to be grossly different for either cadmium and cadmium ion or zinc and zinc ion, one can write

$$E = E_{1/2} - 0.02957 \log [M]_a/[M^{++}]_s \tag{7.5}$$

for each of the two metals. Since

$$C_i = N_i/V_i \tag{7.6}$$

for each species, where N_i is the number of moles of it present at equilibrium while V_i is the volume of the phase containing it, eq. (7.5) becomes

$$E = (E_{1/2})_{Cd} - 0.02957 \log (V_s/V_a) - 0.02957 \log (N_{Cd}/N_{Cd}^{++}) \tag{7.7}$$

$$= (E_{1/2})_{Zn} - 0.02957 \log (V_s/V_a) - 0.02957 \log (N_{Zn}/N_{Zn}^{++})$$

Inspection of Fig. 3.19(a) suggests that $E = -0.90$ v. might be a suitable choice; the reduction of cadmium ion should be very nearly complete here, while the zinc wave has not yet begun. The half-wave potentials of cadmium and zinc ions in $0.1F$ potassium chloride are -0.599 and -0.995 v., respectively, and, therefore, eq. (7.7) gives $N_{Cd}/N_{Cd}^{++} = 4 \times 10^9$ and $N_{Zn}/N_{Zn}^{++} = 1.6 \times 10^{-4}$ for the electrolysis of 100 ml. of solution with 25 ml. of mercury. Less than a billionth of the cadmium ion will remain unreduced, while less than 0.02% of the zinc ion will be reduced. These figures imply that zinc could be successfully isolated from something like a 10^{11}-fold excess of cadmium. One could hardly analyze the resulting solution by polarography; even stripping analysis with a hanging drop electrode, which is much more sensitive, would be severely strained. With a sample of less extreme composition, of course, the electrolysis could be terminated at a very much earlier stage.

At the other extreme, we may consider a determination of cadmium in a sample of trichloroacetic acid. In an ammoniacal supporting electrolyte their half-wave potentials are -0.83 and -0.73 v., respectively, too nearly equal to permit the waves to be resolved on a polarogram. However, the wave of trichloroacetate is totally irreversible, and so it will be quantitatively reduced even if the electrolysis is performed at, say, -0.75 v., where the considerations outlined in the preceding paragraph show that less than 0.1% of the cadmium would be deposited. The reduction of trichloroacetate is slower at this potential than on the plateau of its wave, but this merely necessitates some prolongation of the electrolysis.

Another procedure that takes advantage of a difference in reversibility can be illustrated by the determination of zinc in the presence of nickel. In $0.1F$ potassium chloride their respective half-wave potentials are -1.00 and -1.1 v., and the plateau of the zinc wave cannot be discerned. Electrolysis at -1.1 v. until the reduction of zinc is complete will yield an amalgam containing essentially all of the zinc together with part of the nickel; only a part of the nickel will be deposited because the reduction of nickel ion on the rising part of its wave is slower than the reduction of zinc ion on its plateau. The solution may now be discarded and replaced with a fresh portion of $0.1F$ potassium chloride, which is electrolyzed with the mixed amalgam electrode at a potential of perhaps -0.8 v. Because the zinc ion–zinc amalgam couple is nearly reversible, the zinc will be quantitatively reoxidized at this potential, but because the nickel ion–nickel amalgam couple is irreversible the nickel will remain in the amalgam phase. After the reoxidation of zinc is complete the concentration of zinc ion can be determined polarographically in the ordinary way. To avoid complications resulting from intermetallic compound formation in the amalgam, the concentrations of both elements would have to be fairly small (39).

Very complex solutions can readily be analyzed in this way. A polarogram of the solution is recorded at a sensitivity so chosen as to give an easily measurable height for the first wave. The solution is electrolyzed with a mercury cathode whose potential is maintained constant at a value on the plateau of this wave if it is reversible or on its rising part if it is irreversible and poorly separated from the wave that follows. When the electrolysis is essentially complete a second polarogram is recorded and the height of the second wave is measured, and so on. It is convenient to insert a dropping electrode directly into the working-electrode compartment of the electrolysis cell ($40,41$), for the electrolyses can then be performed and the polarograms recorded without any transfer of solution. In this technique the wave-order problem practically vanishes. It would be a most unusual sample in which the wave heights were so widely disparate that one would need a more nearly perfect separation than can be thus achieved. As the last two examples have shown, the wave-separation problem is often very much mitigated as well.

For these reasons it is safe to say that controlled-potential electrolysis is easily one of the most valuable techniques at the analyst's disposal. This should be particularly true in organic analysis. As yet it has been applied to few practical organic analyses, but this merely reflects the fact that the attention of those active in the field has been chiefly concentrated on inorganic problems and on studies of kinetics and mechanisms. The experimental techniques and some other applications of controlled-potential electrolysis are described in Secs. I and II of Chap. 10.

IV. Techniques of Practical Analysis

The preceding sections of this chapter have dealt with the choice of conditions for the performance of a polarographic analysis and with the preparation of the solution whose polarogram is to be obtained. This section deals with the problems that may arise during the recording of the polarogram and with the techniques that are available for handling them.

A. PROBLEMS OF POLAROGRAPHIC TRACE ANALYSIS

By the use of electrodes such as the hanging drop or the stirred mercury pool and techniques such as square-wave polarography and stripping analysis, it has been possible to devise procedures for the analysis of solutions in the range of concentrations down to about 10^{-10} or even $10^{-11}M$. The more promising of these electrodes and techniques are described in Chaps. 8 and 10. Chiefly because of the continuous variation of drop area and consequently of residual current, conventional polarography is less sensitive by several orders of magnitude. Compensation of the residual current, electrical filtering to decrease the amplitudes of the recorded oscillations, and modifications of capillary design to decrease the capillary noise enable polarography to be used for analyzing solutions as dilute as 10^{-7} or even, though more rarely, $10^{-8}M$. However, these expedients become less effective at both very negative and very positive potentials, where both the average charging current and its variation during the drop life are much larger than in the vicinity of the electrocapillary maximum potential. In the routine laboratory the lower limit of utility of conventional polarography with ordinary apparatus is best taken as about $10^{-6}M$ ($0.001\text{m}M$).

At this level of concentration the height of a typical diffusion-controlled wave is of the order of 0.01 μamp. Larger currents are of course secured, so that correspondingly more dilute solutions can be analyzed, with catalytic waves; on the other hand, kinetic waves have

smaller heights and provide poorer sensitivities. A wave height of
0.01 μamp. corresponds to a deflection of roughly 3 mm. at the most
sensitive setting of the ordinary commercially available polarograph.
The limit is not, however, due to problems of instrumental sensitivity,
for much smaller currents could be recorded without much difficulty
if they could be used. Higher sensitivities are in fact available on
several commercial instruments, as is shown in Table 2.1, and can be
added to others by the "range extender" (catalog no. S-29315)
available from E. H. Sargent & Co. But effective use can be made of
these higher sensitivities only if two major problems are solved. One
is the problem of reagent purity, which is inherent in trace analysis
by any technique but is particularly severe in polarography because
of the relatively large amounts of salts that must be used as supporting electrolytes. The other is the purely polarographic problem of
arranging matters so that the very small waves obtained with dilute
solutions are reasonably well defined and so that the residual-current
correction can be made with satisfactory accuracy.

Suppose that the zinc content of an unknown is to be determined
and that 100 ml. of $2F$ sodium hydroxide is to be used as the supporting electrolyte. If there is even as little as 0.001% of zinc in the
solid sodium hydroxide from which this solution is prepared—and
reagent-grade sodium hydroxide often contains several thousandths
of a per cent of zinc—the solution would contain 0.012mM zinc even
if there were none whatever in the sample being analyzed. Under such
conditions it would be pointless to try to analyze samples containing
so little zinc that they contribute less than about 0.01mM zinc to the
final solution. Curve a in Fig. 7.3 is a polarogram of just such a
solution of sodium hydroxide, recorded at a sensitivity approximately
equal to the highest sensitivity available on a typical commercial
instrument. Curve b of Fig. 3.15 similarly demonstrates the presence
of a trace of lead in a sample of reagent-grade citric acid.

The effect of an impurity naturally varies from one analysis to
another. Most important are the relationships between the half-wave
potential and wave height of the impurity and those of the substance
being determined. Barium ion ($E_{1/2} = -1.92$ v.) present as an impurity in a lithium chloride supporting electrolyte would have far
more serious effects in a determination of acrylonitrile ($E_{1/2} = -1.96$
v.) than in that of a compound reducible at a much more positive
potential. This is, of course, merely another aspect of the wave-order

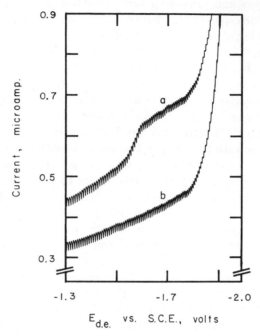

Figure 7.3.   Polarograms of $2F$ sodium hydroxide, (a) before purification and (b) after removal of reducible impurities by controlled-potential electrolysis with a mercury pool cathode at -1.80 v. vs. S.C.E. (*42*).

problem (Sec. I-B*ii* above). As was illustrated by Fig. 3.15, a trace of barium ion would cause little difficulty if the concentration of acrylonitrile were large; the recording of a separate residual-current curve would permit the necessary correction to be made with little uncertainty or trouble. Obviously the curve would have to be obtained afresh whenever a new batch of supporting electrolyte was prepared. Segregation of impurities in solid salts is so common that it is advisable to prepare a large volume of a stock solution of the supporting electrolyte to ensure that the concentration of impurity will be the same from one analysis to the next. Far more difficulty would be encountered if the height of the barium wave were comparable to or larger than that of the acrylonitrile wave. Less common, and far more insidious because its presence is not revealed by a separately obtained residual-current curve, is an impurity that can be catalytically reduced in the presence of the sample, that affects the rate of the reaction responsible for the kinetic or catalytic wave of interest, that alters the wave height by undergoing adsorption onto the drop surface, or that exerts some other effect on the wave height of the substance being determined.

All of these problems are best investigated in two independent ways. The residual-current curve should always be recorded separately because of the direct information it provides about electroactive impurities in the supporting electrolyte. But in addition one should prepare standard solutions of the substance being determined over the whole range of concentrations likely to be of interest, and obtain the value of i_l/C for each. If this varies appreciably with concentration, or if a plot of i_l versus C is linear but has a substantial intercept (which may be either positive or negative), an impurity may be responsible. Other causes are also possible, however, as mentioned in Chap. 3 IV-A.

There are three different ways of dealing with impurities in the reagents. Two of them involve the automatic subtraction of the residual current from the polarogram of the sample. In one (43), a curve follower is used to translate the pen deflections on a previously recorded residual-current curve into an electrical input to the balancing circuit of the recorder during the recording of the polarogram. The circuitry is rather complex but is available commercially; even if the supporting electrolyte is perfectly pure, it provides more accurate compensation of the condenser current than the simple module of Figure 13, while the latter is of course powerless to compensate for the presence of impurities. In another (44,45), one dropping electrode is placed in a cell containing the supporting electrolyte (or a blank) alone, while another is placed in a second cell containing the solution to be analyzed. The two electrodes are kept at the same potential, which is varied with time in the usual fashion, and the difference between the currents flowing through them is plotted against their potential. This is called "differential" or, more specifically, "subtractive" polarography, and is discussed at greater length in Chap. 10 VIII. In principle these techniques provide solutions to the problem of wave order as well as to that of reagent purity, and they also permit work with waves that merge with the final current rise and are, therefore, ill-defined on ordinary polarograms. However, they have not been used as widely as these advantages would seem to justify. The third technique involves the purification of the reagents; it is the most widely used of the three and is also the only one capable of dealing with impurities that are not electroactive.

Procedures for the purification of reagents by recrystallization, distillation, solvent extraction, and the like hardly need to be discussed here. Unfortunately, they are generally so tedious, wasteful, and inefficient that chemists are reluctant to resort to them except in case of dire necessity. A difficulty is that the identities of the impurities are very often unknown, so that procedures for their removal are hard to design.

A peculiarly advantageous technique of reagent and solvent purification consists of controlled-potential electrolysis with a mercury cathode. The supporting electrolyte or, for greater economy of time, a concentrated stock solution of it, is simply electrolyzed for 30 to 60 min. at a potential barely preceding the final current rise. The technique was used to purify the sodium hydroxide solution whose polarogram was shown in Fig. 7.3(a). The electrolysis was performed at -1.8 v., which is sufficiently negative to deposit the zinc quantitatively. Figure 7.3(b) shows the polarogram of the solution after electrolysis for 45 min. During most of this time the electrolysis proceeded without attention as the potential of the mercury cathode was automatically kept constant by a potentiostat; the operator's attention was needed only for a few minutes at the beginning and a few more at the end. Practically none of the sodium hydroxide was lost, and the purity of the resulting solution is shown by the fact that no trace of a zinc wave can be detected on curve b. The electrolysis served to remove not only zinc but also such other impurities as lead, whose reduction is responsible for the fact that the current between -1.3 and -1.5 v. is higher on curve a than on curve b. This technique can be applied whenever the interfering impurity can be reduced or oxidized to a polarographically inert substance by electrolysis at a mercury, platinum, or other electrode; an actual separation is not necessary. Thus it can be employed to remove peroxides, carbonyl compounds, and other reducible impurities from organic solvents as well as for the removal of metal ions like copper, lead, and zinc from inorganic salts. It can also be used to remove some impurities that are not electroactive. To remove a trace of sulfate from a supporting electrolyte that is to be used for the determination of lead, for example, one might treat it with excess lead salt, filter off the precipitated lead sulfate, and then remove the excess lead ion by controlled-potential deposition into a mercury cathode.

The peculiarly polarographic problems that arise in trace analysis are of two kinds: mechanical and electrical. The mechanical problem is that of capillary noise. This manifests itself as a series of random fluctuations of the residual current, and has evident effects on the sensitivity and precision that can be obtained. It can be mitigated by the use of a modified capillary like that shown in Fig. 2.19, and sometimes also by the use of more dilute supporting electrolytes. It may be mentioned that capillary noise is very much more severe with dirty capillaries than with clean ones; the accumulation of a film of grease inside the lumen is especially deleterious. Recording a residual-current curve at a very high sensitivity provides a simple and stringent way of evaluating the performance of a capillary and its suitability for trace analysis.

The electrical problems seem to be due primarily to the presence of stray alternating current in the circuit. Much improvement can often be effected by suitable grounding. The water bath can be grounded by adding a few grams of sodium chromate to provide adequate electrical conductivity, then connecting the metal heating and stirring units to a water pipe or other good ground. The dropping electrode can be grounded by shorting the appropriate input terminal of the polarograph to the grounded chassis. In severe cases it is appropriate to use a twisted pair of wires to make the connections from the polarograph to the cell.

In the analysis of extremely dilute solutions it is advisable to take extra precautions to ensure that deaeration is complete, that anomalous waves like that shown in Fig. 6.1(a) are completely suppressed, and that any other possible sources of distortion of the polarogram are guarded against. However, polarograms of such solutions are rarely as amenable to accurate measurement as those of more concentrated solutions. In part this is attributable to the relatively large slope of the residual-current curve when it is recorded at as high a sensitivity as must be used, although this can be mitigated by the compensation module of Fig. 2.12. But in addition it is a little unusual for the polarogram of a very dilute solution to be as free from flaws as is Fig. 7.3. One often finds that the slope of the plateau of the wave is markedly different from that of the residual-current curve at the same potential. Consequently wave heights in trace analysis are almost always measured by extrapolation to some arbitrarily chosen potential, usually the half-wave potential, and often deviate from proportionality to the concentration of the substance being determined. The treatment of this phenomenon is discussed in subsection V below.

B. SPECIAL TECHNIQUES FOR HANDLING UNSTABLE SOLUTIONS

Ideally, the solution whose polarogram is recorded should be perfectly stable toward oxidation by dissolved air, reduction by metallic mercury or by the metal of an internal reference electrode if one is used, and reaction with any other substance (such as agar and potassium chloride) with which it comes in contact while in the cell. But sometimes the use of a supporting electrolyte in which one or another of these desiderata is not fulfilled will serve to avoid a separation that may be much more lengthy and troublesome than the steps needed to counteract the instability of the solution.

i. Solutions of Strong Reducing Agents

The standard potential for the reduction of oxygen to water (+0.99 v. vs. S.C.E.) is so positive that every reducing agent powerful enough to yield an anodic wave in the region of potentials accessible to the dropping electrode is also powerful enough to react quantitatively with dissolved oxygen. Many oxidations by dissolved oxygen are very slow in homogeneous solutions, but the majority of those of polarographic interest are either fairly fast or are accelerated by the presence of metallic mercury. The half-wave potential for the reduction of oxygen to hydrogen peroxide at a mercury electrode varies slightly from one medium to another, but is typically about -0.05 v. vs. S.C.E. This means that the reduction begins to proceed at an appreciable rate on a mercury surface if the potential is even as negative as about $+0.05$ v. If the solution contains a reducing agent that can be oxidized at this potential, its oxidation and the reduction of dissolved oxygen can occur simultaneously at any mercury surface: the surface of the dropping electrode, of a mercury pool reference electrode, or of the mercury that has flowed through the capillary and accumulated at the bottom of the cell.

In this way a reducing agent whose anodic half-wave potential is more negative than about $+0.1$ v. may be fairly rapidly air-oxidized in a polarographic cell even though it might be quite stable in a homogeneous solution. Reducing agents that have half-wave potentials more positive than this, as does p-benzohydroquinone in a very weakly acidic medium, can usually be determined polarographically even in the presence of dissolved air, for oxygen rarely reacts with them at an appreciable rate and does not yield appreciable currents at the relatively positive potentials where their waves occur. But the great majority of solutions yielding anodic waves must be prepared in the absence of oxygen and air must be rigorously excluded while their polarograms are being recorded.

Such solutions are usually best prepared by deaerating a known volume of the supporting electrolyte in the cell, then adding a known volume of a concentrated solution of the sample in a medium in which air-oxidation does not occur. Dilute mineral acids are usually suitable. A very rapid stream of nitrogen should be bubbled through the supporting electrolyte while the addition is being made, and then it should be diverted over the surface of the mixture while the polarogram is recorded as quickly as possible.

Even an aqueous solution of the sample will contain about 0.25mM dissolved oxygen if it is saturated with air; a non-aqueous one may contain much more. Unless this is very much smaller than the concentration, in the same solution, of the substance being determined, the sample solution should also be deaerated before being added to the supporting electrolyte. This is conveniently done in a microburet provided with a three-way stopcock connected to the nitrogen line. Nitrogen can then be bubbled through the sample solution while the supporting electrolyte is being deaerated. A known volume of the air-free sample solution is added to the air-free supporting electrolyte in the fashion described above. The addition should be made through a small hole in the stopper of the cell, which should then be closed with a cork or neoprene stopper to prevent ingress of air. The entrance of air through the annular opening around the dropping electrode is not worth worrying about if a rapid stream of nitrogen is passed into the cell continuously. It is wise to provide a fairly large bulb at the top of the microburet to avoid blowing the solution out of it by a too rapid stream of gas.

As was mentioned in Chap. 2 V, even prepurified nitrogen should be scrubbed with chromous or vanadous chloride or passed through an efficient copper heater to remove traces of oxygen in work with easily oxidized solutions. The addition of a few grams of heavily amalgamated zinc to the microburet (*46,47*) is a convenient way of ensuring the complete reduction of a powerful reducing agent like chromous, vanadous, or titanous ion.

Oxygen can be quantitatively removed from many neutral or alkaline solutions by reaction with sulfite, and the addition of 0.05 to 0.1F sodium sulfite to such supporting electrolytes therefore often serves to increase the stabilities of many powerful reducing agents. Hydrazine has the same effect in ammoniacal and alkaline media, but because hydrazine yields an anodic wave it cannot be used unless the wave of interest occurs at a fairly negative potential. The sulfite-oxygen reaction has been shown to be strongly catalyzed by the traces of copper present in most polarographic supporting electrolytes, and the rate of the hydrazine-oxygen reaction is also presumably much increased by copper or some other common impurity because conditions are known under which it is much slower than polarographic experience has indicated. In using either of these substances one should be on his guard against other phenomena, such as the precipitation of lead sulfate or the formation of metal–hydrazine complexes, that may result from their presence.

Whether or not sulfite or hydrazine is used, it is wise to locate the tip of the dropping electrode as far below the surface of the solution as possible. Then the upper layers of the solution will usually absorb any oxygen that enters the cell and prevent it from reaching the vicinity of the capillary tip.

These procedures serve very well for work with reducing agents of which stable solutions can be prepared in media different from that used to obtain the polarogram. Many other strong reducing agents, however, like uranium(III), are too powerful to be stable toward air-oxidation under any conditions, while others, like manganese(I), can be obtained only in the supporting electrolyte in which the polarogram is to be recorded. The polarogram of such a substance is best obtained by preparing a solution of the corresponding oxidized form in the desired supporting electrolyte, reducing this electrolytically in a controlled-potential electrolysis cell, and inserting a dropping electrode into the working-electrode compartment of this cell so that the polarogram can be recorded without transferring the reduced solution or exposing it to air.

Anodic waves whose half-wave potentials are more negative than about −0.6 v. correspond to the oxidation of reducing agents so powerful that they are capable of reducing water or hydrogen ion. Such waves should be very useful in practical analysis, especially if controlled-potential electrolysis is used as described above to prepare the solutions: any prior or nearby cathodic waves will be eliminated automatically by the electrolysis, while there are so few substances that yield anodic waves in any one medium that a wave occurring at a very negative potential is virtually certain to be very well separated from all the others. It would seem at first glance that such solutions would be much too unstable to be analytically useful, and consequently their potentialities have not yet been seriously investigated. Nevertheless, the decompositions are often quite slow, and simple, accurate, and highly specific methods can easily be devised along these lines for the determination of numerous elements, including uranium, manganese, and vanadium, in even very complex samples.

Much less stringent precautions are needed to obtain satisfactory results in work with anodic waves that involve the oxidation of mercury, as do those of halides, thiosulfate, cyanide, sulfide, thiols, acetylenes, enolizable ketones, and many other substances. In most such cases air-oxidation does not occur in the absence of mercury, and therefore all that is necessary is to remove mercury completely from the solution compartment of the cell before adding a sample and to delay the introduction of the dropping electrode until deaeration is complete. Should it be desirable to record the residual-current curve of the supporting electrolyte alone before adding a concentrated stock solution of the sample, either the latter should be deaerated separately or the mercury should be protected by one of the expedients described in the following subsection.

ii. Solutions of Strong Oxidizing Agents

For the purposes of this subsection it is convenient to define a "strong" oxidizing agent as one that is powerful enough to oxidize metallic mercury in the supporting electrolyte being employed. A consequence of this ability is that the rising part of the cathodic wave must occur at potentials where the rate of oxidation of mercury is appreciable, and so the wave "rises from zero applied e.m.f." and has the appearance shown in Fig. 2.10. Analytical methods based on such waves suffer from the disadvantage that the waves of all strong oxidizing agents are indistinguishable, so that the polarogram can provide no indication of the presence of an unexpected strong oxidizing agent. With a wave whose rising portion does appear on the polarogram, however, one can compare both the half-wave potential and the shape of the rising portion of the wave obtained from an unknown with those on polarograms of authentic solutions containing only the one electroactive substance that is being determined; thus an unexpected impurity can rarely escape notice. In addition, the height of such a wave cannot be measured by an extrapolation technique, because the polarogram does not contain any portion of the residual-current curve. This, however, is a minor problem whose treatment was discussed on p. 159. When this problem can be ignored, it may be pointed out that deaeration is unnecessary if the wave height is to be measured at a potential at least as positive as +0.1 v. vs. S.C.E., for dissolved oxygen is not reduced at such positive potentials, although this should be checked in the development of any practical method because of the possibility that oxygen may yield a catalytic current.

The principal difficulties that arise in work with strong oxidizing agents result from their reduction by metallic mercury. The effect of this reduction on the wave height depends primarily on the nature of the supporting electrolyte. In a hydrochloric acid solution the mercury would be oxidized to solid mercurous chloride. As this is not reducible, the result is a decrease of the total concentration of reducible material in the solution, and the wave height decreases correspondingly. In a perchloric acid solution the mercury would be oxidized to mercurous ion, which is reducible. Depending on the diffusion coefficient of the substance being determined, this replacement of part of it by an equivalent concentration of mercurous ion may either increase, decrease, or have no effect on the wave height. To avoid changes of wave height, therefore, it is necessary to prevent contact between the solution and mercury in so far as this is possible. Mercury pool and other internal reference electrodes must accordingly never be used with such solutions.

Of course the oxidizing agent may react with the mercury that accumulates on the bottom of the solution compartment of a cell with an external reference electrode. Two expedients may be adopted to minimize the extent of the reaction. One is to keep the area of the mercury exposed to the solution as small as possible. Special care should be taken in cleaning the cell to ensure that mercury is completely removed from it after each polarogram is recorded; this also helps to prevent the accumulation of slightly soluble mercury compounds on the walls and in the frits. For the same reason, it is prudent, wherever it is possible, to employ supporting electrolytes containing perchlorate, acetate, citrate, and other anions that do not form precipitates with mercurous or mercuric ions in preference to those containing chloride, sulfate, and other anions that do form such precipitates. If deaeration is necessary, it should be completed before the dropping electrode is inserted; this is wise regardless of the nature of the solution but is doubly necessary here. Measurements should of course be made as rapidly as possible. If they must be prolonged, as in a kinetic study, it is helpful to use a cell in which a short length of 2–3-mm. i.d. glass tubing is sealed to the bottom of the solution compartment; collecting the mercury in this trap greatly decreases the rate of change of the composition of the bulk of the solution. The temptation to use a stopcock for this purpose should be resisted when the cell is immersed in a water thermostat, for electrical leakage paths from the sample to the thermostat liquid through the film of electrolyte between the ground surfaces of the stopcock can have very untoward effects.

One may also add to the cell a few drops of a protective liquid, which must be denser than and essentially immiscible with the solution, to form a layer on top of the mercury. Tri-*o*-cresyl phosphate, dimethyl phthalate, chloroform, and carbon tetrachloride have all been used in work with aqueous solutions, and there are other obvious possible choices such as ethylene dibromide. If all that is wanted is the height of the wave rising from zero applied e.m.f., there is little *a priori* ground for choice among these. One that is reducible, however, may interfere if the subsequent course of the polarogram is also of interest. Carbon tetrachloride is the most easily reducible: in many common aqueous supporting electrolytes its half-wave potential is around −0.35 v., and so its utility is rather limited. Chloroform, ethylene dibromide, and dimethyl phthalate are much more difficultly reducible, though the last of these should not be used in contact with media that can catalyze its hydrolysis because phthalic acid is much more easily reducible than the ester. No liquid suitable for this purpose in work with non-aqueous media is known, partly because of solubility problems and partly because the need for one is very rare.

Oxidation at the surface of a mercury droplet may be surprisingly rapid, and some hundredths of a second are ordinarily required for a droplet to fall from the capillary tip to the bottom of the cell. The composition of the solution may, therefore, be appreciably altered in prolonged measurements unless the capillary tip is so placed that the bottom of the drop is nearly in contact with the surface of the protective liquid when the drop reaches its maximum size. It is also wise to coat the bottom of the solution compartment with a water-repelling material to prevent the solution from gaining access to the mercury around the sides of the protective layer above it.

iii. Solutions That React with the Salt Bridge

The agar–potassium chloride bridges employed in H-cells may be attacked in any of several ways by many common constituents of polarographic solutions. That this necessitates more frequent replacement of the bridge is a minor disadvantage; far more important are the deleterious effects exerted on the polarograms obtained.

Agar is decomposed by very strongly alkaline solutions and also, though somewhat more slowly, by very strongly acidic ones; the rate of decomposition becomes appreciable if the concentration of hydroxyl ion in the sample solution exceeds about $2M$ or if that of hydrogen ion exceeds about $6M$. The products of decomposition act as maximum suppressors and often distort the polarograms. Oxidation of agar by powerful oxidizing agents yields products that give ill-defined waves, and the heights of these naturally vary with time as the oxidation proceeds. Dehydration and shrinkage of the gel occur when the sample solution contains so high a concentration of a salt or a non-aqueous solvent that the activity of water is much smaller than in the gel. They lead to contamination of the sample by the heavy metal ion present in the reference electrode, which alters the shape of the polarogram, and also to contamination of the reference electrode by the constituents of the sample solution, which alters its potential. Precipitation at the boundary between the sample solution and the bridge may occur if the former contains an ion that can react with chloride or potassium ion. When the reacting ion is the one being determined, as might be the case with silver ion or hexacyanomanganate(I), this may lead to a substantial change of the height of its wave and so to an error in the analysis. When it is a constituent of the supporting electrolyte, as is the case with perchlorate, the principal effect is the increase of cell resistance.

When a pure white agar bridge is exposed to a solution that attacks agar, it first becomes yellowish at the plane of contact, then the color spreads through the bridge toward the reference electrode and gradually deepens toward brownish, and eventually the gel liquefies and disintegrates. If the cell is so designed that the products of the reaction at the agar–solution interface can reach the vicinity of the capillary tip during the time needed to deaerate the solution and record its polarogram, which is true of the cells shown in Figs. 2.15 and 2.16, the bridge must be discarded as soon as the first discoloration appears. Its useful life can be increased by working rapidly so that it is not subjected to unnecessarily prolonged attack, and also by using two cells alternately, allowing one to stand with its solution compartment filled with water or saturated potassium chloride while the other is in use. It is also helpful to use an agar gel somewhat more concentrated than the usual 4% and to chill the clean empty cell before the first few drops of liquid gel are added to it; this prevents the liquid from seeping into the pores of the fritted disk that separates the cross-member of the cell from the solution compartment, and thereby serves to confine the agar to the cross-member. For anything more than occasional work with such solutions, however, it is far better to use a cell like the Carritt cell (48), in which contamination of the sample solution by the reaction products is very slow, or one of the Pecsok–Juvet (49) or Kalousek types, in which agar does not come into contact with the sample solution at all.

The dehydration and shrinkage of an agar bridge is so difficult to detect visually in its early stages that such bridges should not be brought into more than very brief and occasional contact with solutions having this effect. A Kalousek cell can be used with most non-aqueous solutions because these are less dense than saturated aqueous potassium chloride, but a cell having the shape shown in Fig. 2.17 should not be used with dense concentrated salt solutions for fear that convective mixing in the cross-member will cause contamination of the reference electrode and changes of its potential.

Precipitations occur so much more rapidly than attack on the agar that their effects can hardly be minimized by working rapidly. Nor can they be entirely obviated by moving the plane of contact away from the dropping electrode, as in a Carritt cell, for a high resistance is no less deleterious for occurring at a different place in the cell. This expedient does, however, eliminate changes in the composition of the solution around the capillary tip except in extraordinarily lengthy

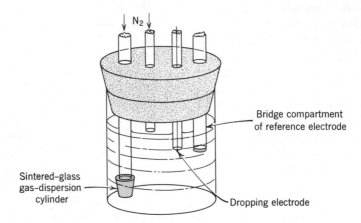

Figure 7.4. Simple polarographic cell for work with solutions that attack agar
or other constituents of salt bridges.

experiments. Occasional measurements can be made with such solutions in an ordinary H-cell if the sintered-glass disc between the
solution compartment and the bridge is washed very thoroughly with
a suitable solvent after each polarogram is recorded to prevent the
accumulation of precipitate from one experiment to the next. However, it is better to use some other salt instead of potassium chloride
in the bridge; then the reference electrode should also be changed so
that a truly stable potential will be secured. A mercury–mercurous
sulfate–saturated potassium sulfate reference electrode, together with
a 4% agar bridge containing $1F$ potassium sulfate, can be used for
work with solutions that react with chloride ion or whenever the
presence of chloride in the sample is undesirable, as it is in all work
at potential more positive than about $+0.1$ v. vs. S.C.E. A calomel
electrode may be prepared with saturated sodium or lithium chloride
and used with a 4% agar bridge containing $1F$ sodium or lithium
chloride for work with solutions containing more than about $1M$
perchlorate ion.

In all of these cases the writer strongly favors the use of a reference
electrode like that shown in Fig. 2.18, together with a cell like that
shown in Fig. 7.4. By appropriate choice of the reference electrode
and bridge solution, and by frequent renewal of the latter, routine

work is easily performed even with supporting electrolytes like concentrated perchloric acid, saturated sodium cyanide, and others that give rise to substantial difficulties in most other cells.

V. The Interpretation of the Wave Height

For the reasons described in Chap. 3, it is not possible to make *a priori* predictions of the relationship between wave height and concentration for any particular electroactive substance. Polarographic analyses must, therefore, be carried out by comparing the wave height of the unknown solution with wave height—concentration data obtained with known solutions. The comparison may be made in any of a number of ways. One, misleadingly called the "absolute" method, is based on the use of the diffusion current constant. Its essential characteristic is that different capillaries are used with the unknown and known solutions, and so it involves the errors inherent in the equations describing the relationship between the wave height and the capillary characteristics. Hence it is appreciably less accurate than the so-called "comparative" methods, in which the calibration data are obtained with the same capillary and under the same condition used to analyze unknowns. These methods require the preparation of standard solutions of the substance being determined, and for the highest accuracy most of them require that the calibration data be obtained anew whenever the capillary is changed. Routinely performed analyses are certainly best done by one of the comparative methods, for the additional work entailed is inappreciable when it is amortized over a large number of determinations. But the use of the absolute method saves enough time whenever the required value of the diffusion current constant can be gleaned from the literature that this method is widely preferred for analyses that are infrequently performed and that do not demand the very highest accuracy attainable.

A. THE "ABSOLUTE" METHOD

According to the Ilkovič equation, the concentration of an electroactive substance is related to its diffusion current by the equation

$$C = i_d / I m^{2/3} t^{1/6} \qquad (7.8)$$

To calculate the concentration C, it is evidently necessary to know the diffusion current constant I and to measure i_d, m, and t.

The literature value of I for lead ion in a supporting electrolyte containing $0.1F$ hydrochloric acid, $1F$ potassium chloride, and 0.02% gelatin is 3.79. Although, for the reasons set forth in Chap. 6 IV, this concentration of gelatin is probably much higher than is necessary or desirable, the analyst could not employ a different concentration without incurring grave danger that the value of I would no longer be applicable. On the basis of this datum, one might determine lead in a sample of impure metallic zinc by dissolving W grams of the sample in acid, evaporating just to dryness, taking up the residue in a total of V ml. of this supporting electrolyte, deaerating a portion of the solution in a polarographic cell, and measuring the diffusion current of lead ion. Suppose that this is 3.00 μamp., and that the values of m and t for the capillary employed are 2.00 mg./sec. and 4.00 sec., respectively. Because m and t vary with potential, they must be measured at the same potential as the diffusion current— e.g., at the half-wave potential if the diffusion current is measured by the technique illustrated by Fig. 3.15(c). Then the concentration of lead ion in the final solution is $3.00/(3.79)(2.00)^{2/3}(4.00)^{1/6} = 0.396$ mM, and the percentage of lead in the sample is $(0.396)(207.2)V/10^4W$.

In every such procedure it is essential that all of the experimental conditions be as nearly as possible identical with those used in measuring the diffusion current constant. It is tacitly assumed that the diffusion current constant obtained from the literature is valid for the capillary used in the analysis, and also that the diffusion current constant is not affected by the presence of the other constituents of the sample.

The first of these assumptions amounts to accepting the proposition that i_d is proportional to $m^{2/3}t^{1/6}$, as it is said to be by the Ilkovič equation. With rare exceptions, this is accurate to $\pm 3\%$ or better if, for both the capillary used to measure I and the capillary used in the analysis, t is between about 3 and 6 sec. while the drop weight mt is between about 6 and 15 mg. Adding an uncertainty of $\pm 3\%$ to the experimental errors certainly diminishes the overall accuracy that can be obtained, but the absolute method does yield results that are quite accurate enough for the majority of practical polarographic analyses. It does not seem likely that a substantial improvement could be effected by the use of the Koutecký equation, for there are too many cases in the literature in which different authors have obtained very different values for the constant A in eq. (3.19), often from the same experimental data. If the error of the Ilkovič equation is known to be abnormally large in the particular case at hand, if the above conditions are not satisfied, or if a greater accuracy must be obtained, a comparative method should be used instead.

TABLE 7.1.

Effects of Zinc Concentration on the Diffusion Current Constants of Lead and Cadmium Ions

The data were obtained in a supporting electrolyte containing 0.1F hydrochloric acid, 1F potassium chloride, and 0.02% gelatin (50). The significance of the ratios given in the last column is discussed in subsection B*iv* below.

$[Zn^{++}]$, g./ml.	I_{Pb}	I_{Cd}	I_{Pb}/I_{Cd}
0	3.79	3.46	1.09_5
0.05	3.40	3.02	1.12_6
0.10	3.09	2.77	1.11_6
0.20	2.50	2.35	1.06_4
		Mean:	$1.10_0 \pm 0.02_1$

The second assumption amounts to supposing that the wave height is diffusion controlled and that the other constituents of the sample do not alter the diffusion coefficient of the substance being determined as they might do by forming a complex or reacting with it in some other way, or by affecting the viscosity of the solution. Equation (7.8) does not apply to the heights of kinetic, catalytic, or adsorption waves, which should all be treated by means of standard curves as described in subsection B*i* below. The errors that may be incurred, even in a very simple case, by neglecting the effect of the remainder of the sample on the diffusion current constant are illustrated by Table 7.1. This shows that the diffusion current constants of both lead and cadmium ions are only about two-thirds as large in the presence of 0.2 g./ml. of zinc ion as in the pure supporting electrolyte. The changes of viscosity that are responsible for this behavior depend on the nature of the sample; in a determination of residual monomer in a polymeric material they might be much larger than they are in Table 7.1. Neglecting this phenomenon can obviously lead to very serious errors, especially if the percentage of the substance being determined is so low that a large sample must be taken to obtain a wave high enough for precise measurement. The problem must be taken into account whenever a minor or trace constituent is determined polarographically without separation from the major constituents of the sample.

Several approaches are available (51). The choice among them depends primarily on whether or not the proportions of the major constituents are so nearly the same in different samples that the use of a fixed weight of sample and a fixed volume of the final solution will yield solutions having essentially identical viscosities. If it will not, one should use either the standard addition or the pilot-ion technique. If it will, one can measure and employ a diffusion current constant appropriate to a single concentration of sample that is carefully reproduced in each analysis. For example, if 10.0 g. of zinc is always used to prepare 100 ml. of the final solution, the determination of lead might be accomplished by using the value $I_{Pb} = 3.09$ taken from Table 7.1. However, this is inconvenient if the percentage of the substance being determined may vary widely among different samples, in which case data like those in Table 7.1 may be used to establish an empirical relationship between the diffusion current constant and the sample concentration. The equation

$$I_{Pb} = 3.79 - 8c + 8c^2 \tag{7.9}$$

where c is the number of grams of zinc per milliliter of the final solution, reproduces the values in the second column of Table 7.1 with a mean error of only $\pm 0.45\%$. This is much smaller than the uncertainties inherent in the Ilkovič equation.

B. Comparative Methods

Comparative methods of polarographic analysis are more accurate than the absolute method, for the reasons mentioned above, and are more versatile as well. Some of them are applicable to kinetic, catalytic, and adsorption waves, for which diffusion current constants are meaningless, and to waves whose heights are not proportional to the concentrations of the substances responsible for them. Some of them serve for analyses in which variations of the composition or concentration of the sample produce substantial changes in the relationship between the diffusion current and the concentration of the substance being determined. Some of them even serve to compensate for variations of the temperature, capillary characteristics, and other factors that affect the diffusion current, and thereby greatly simplify practical polarographic analysis by rendering control of these factors unnecessary.

There are four principal comparative methods. They are discussed below in approximately their order of increasing complexity and increasing ability to compensate for variations of experimental conditions.

i. The Standard Curve Method

In the standard curve method one prepares a number of solutions, identical in composition with the solution to be finally prepared from the unknown but containing known concentrations of the substance being determined that cover the whole range of interest, records their polarograms, and measures their wave heights. These data are used to construct a standard curve that is then used to obtain the concentrations of unknown solutions from their wave heights. The polarograms of the known and unknown solutions must be secured under exactly identical conditions of temperature, pressure of mercury above the capillary, etc., and a new standard curve must be prepared whenever the capillary is changed.

An analyst wishing to apply this method to the determination of lead in zinc might proceed in the following way. Four 10.0-g. portions of pure lead-free zinc are dissolved in hydrochloric acid, and aliquots of a standard lead chloride solution containing successively 2.00, 5.00, 10.0, and 20.0 mg. of lead are added. The solutions are evaporated to dryness, the residues are taken up in the supporting electrolyte chosen, and each is diluted to exactly 100 ml. Polarograms of the resulting solutions give lead waves whose heights, converted to the same arbitrarily selected galvanometer or recorder sensitivity, are 24.6, 61.2, 122.2, and 244.2 mm. Plotting the wave height against the weight of lead gives a standard curve conforming to the equation

$$h = (12.2 \times \text{mg. Pb}) + 0.2$$

The zero intercept of 0.2 mm. might indicate either a trace of lead in one of the reagents or in the supposedly pure zinc, or a small systematic error in the measurement of the wave height.

Now suppose that a 10.0-g. sample of impure zinc is treated in exactly the same way and that the height of the lead wave is 20.0

mm. If the "blank" of 0.2 mm. is real, which is a question that the analyst must decide for himself, the weight of lead in the unknown is $(20.0 - 0.2)/12.2 = 1.62$ mg., and its percentage is 0.0162%. Unless the blank correction is so small that it can safely be neglected, its nature should be investigated by systematically varying the amounts of the different reagents employed. Negative blanks can, of course, result from traces of impurities that react with the substance being determined. It is all too common to force standard curves to pass through the origin; this reflects an entirely unrealistic approach to the problem of reagent purity, and in trace analysis it can lead to grossly erroneous results. It may be pointed out that the standard curve method is the only one in which interfering impurities in the reagents are automatically revealed. The user of any other method must check this question by special experiments.

Taylor (50) recommended that a portion of one of the known solutions be analyzed along with each unknown, and that any deviation of the wave height in the known solution from the value on the standard curve be employed to correct the wave height obtained with the unknown. This considerably increases the time and labor involved, but serves to minimize the effects of any differences of temperature, capillary characteristics, and other experimental variables from those employed in constructing the standard curve. If these conditions are controlled with sufficient care, the standard curve method is probably the most accurate one available (52).

Standard curves are usually constructed by plotting the wave height against the weight or concentration of the substance being determined or vice versa, as in Fig. 3.22(a). However, this is neither very accurate nor very convenient if the range of concentrations is appreciable, for the relative errors involved in constructing and using such a graph increase considerably as the concentration decreases. Moreover, such a plot can often even conceal significant deviations from proportionality between wave height and concentration: it would not be impossible to impose a straight line on the points in Fig. 3.22(a). It is much better to plot i_l/C against C, as in Fig. 3.22(b), and in routine analytical work it is still more convenient to plot C/i_l against i_l. If the weight of the sample and the final volume of solution are kept constant, one may similarly plot either W_X/i_l or % X/i_l against i_l, where W_X and % X are the weight and percentage of the substance being determined. Once i_l has been measured, such a graph yields the proportionality constant by which it must be multiplied to obtain the desired quantity. If the graph is plotted on semilog paper, the result is as accurate at low as at high concentrations.

Deviations from proportionality between wave height and concentration may arise from impurities in the reagents, from the use of extrapolation methods for measuring wave heights, from steps that are not pseudo-first-order in the mechanisms responsible for kinetic and catalytic waves, and from various other causes discussed elsewhere in this book. Methods in which the wave height is assumed to be proportional to concentration are then useless. Differential polarography can be employed: one of two synchronized dropping electrodes whose sensitivities are electrically matched is placed in the supporting electrolyte alone and the other is placed in the sample, the same potential on the plateau of the desired wave is applied to each, and a standard solution of the substance being determined is added to the first solution until the difference of current decreases to zero (53,54). However, this is so complex that the standard curve or, for occasional analyses, the standard sample (subsection *ii* below) methods have been far more widely used. In such cases it is especially important to construct the standard curve in accordance with the precept discussed in the preceding paragraph.

ii. The Standard Sample Method

This consists of measuring the wave height of a standard sample at the same time that the unknown is analyzed. Thus, one might carry a 10.0-g. sample of zinc known to contain 0.097% lead through the procedure described in subsection *i* above at the same time that a 10.0-g. sample of an unknown was being analyzed. If under identical conditions the heights of the lead waves were 40.0 and 46.3 mm. for the standard and unknown, respectively, the percentage of lead in the unknown would be simply $(46.3/40.0)(0.097) = 0.112\%$.

Such a technique is routinely used in the execution of classical procedures in many laboratories. In the analysis of technical materials one naturally prefers to use a standard whose composition is closely similar to that of the unknown, for this gives a more perfect compensation for any errors in the chemical steps that precede the polarographic measurements. However, the intent of the standard sample method is to minimize the effects of fluctuations in the capillary characteristics, temperature, and other experimental variables, either in circumstances where these are difficult or impossible to control or to obviate the trouble that is involved in controlling them. For this purpose synthetic samples serve as well as actual ones, or the standard may even have a quite different chemical composition (55): all that is needed is that the two wave heights be affected similarly by changes of the conditions.

In principle one could employ the standard sample method in cases where the wave height was not proportional to the concentration of the substance being determined by finding how much of that substance had to be added to an equal amount of the pure matrix to yield a wave having the same height as that obtained with the unknown. In practical work, however, this is rarely done. But it may again be stressed that proportionality between wave height and concentration should never be taken for granted; it must always be carefully checked during the development of any analytical method.

iii. Standard Addition Methods

There are three standard addition methods, all based on the increase of wave height produced by adding a known amount of the substance being determined. In the commonest of them, one first records the polarogram of an exactly known volume of the unknown solution, then adds a known volume of a standard solution of the substance being determined, and records the polarogram of the mixture (56). If V is the volume of the unknown solution, C_u its concentration, and i_1 its wave height, and if i_2 is the wave height obtained after adding v ml. of a standard solution whose concentration is C_s, one has

$$i_1 = kC_u \qquad (7.10)$$

and

$$i_2 = k(VC_u + vC_s)/(V + v) \qquad (7.11)$$

Dividing eq. (7.11) by eq. (7.10) to eliminate the constant of proportionality k and rearranging the result yields

$$C_u = i_1vC_s/[i_2v + (i_2 - i_1) V] \qquad (7.12)$$

It is obviously assumed that the wave height is proportional to the concentration of the substance being determined, and standard addition methods should not be used unless this is known to be so.

The size of the addition is important because it influences the relative error of the result. As was mentioned in Chap. 3 IV-A, there is an upper limit of concentration, which may vary considerably from one substance to another, above which the wave height of a substance is no longer proportional to its concentration. This limit, which we shall call C_{max}, must not be exceeded. Reinmuth (57) concluded that the optimum precision is usually obtained if the concentration is equal to C_{max} after the standard addition and if the standard addition roughly doubles the concentration, for this minimizes both the uncertainty in $(i_2 - i_1)$ in eq. (7.12) and the uncertainty contributed by the correction of i_1 and i_2 for the residual current. This implies that the original solution should be diluted or concentrated to a concentration of $C_{max}/2$ before the analysis is begun, which is an unattractive requirement in practice. If, on the other hand, C_u is considered to be fixed, the best result is obtained if the standard addition is large (58), though of course it must not be so large that C_{max} is exceeded. Very little is gained by making so large an addition that the concentration of the mixture exceeds about $10C_u$ even if this is much smaller than C_{max}.

In this method it is essential that the ratio k of wave height to concentration be unaffected by the addition of the standard solution. This may be much less trivial than it seems. Consider, for example, the determination of lead in zinc, which was discussed in subsection A above. If the concentration of zinc in the original solution is 0.1 g./ ml., eq. (7.9) predicts that the diffusion current constant (i.e., the value of k) of lead ion will be increased 2.1% by the addition of even enough standard aqueous lead solution to increase the volume of the solution, and decrease the concentration of zinc, 1%. Clearly it is best to add only a relatively small volume of a fairly concentrated standard solution. In extreme cases like this one, however, the standard solution should contain the same concentration of supporting electrolyte as the solution to which it is added, and the term "supporting electrolyte" here should be taken to include the major constituents of the sample as well as the nominal supporting electrolyte.

In another standard addition method, which might be called the "standard spike" method, two identical samples of the unknown are weighed out and a known weight of the substance being determined is added to one of them. Both are carried through the analytical procedure, their solutions are diluted to the same volume, and their polarograms are obtained under identical conditions. If w_u is the weight of the substance being determined in the un"spiked" sample and if w_s is the weight added to the other sample, one has

$$w_u = w_s i_1/(i_2 - i_1) \tag{7.13}$$

The total concentration of the spiked sample must not exceed $C_{\max}$. This is a more time-consuming method than the preceding one. Its advantage is that it eliminates uncertainties caused by dilution accompanying the standard addition.

The third kind of standard addition method, which might be called the double standard addition method, has two uses. One is to provide an approach to one facet of the wave-separation problem. From the fact, discussed in subsection I-Bi above, that two neighboring waves become less well separated as the concentrations become more widely disparate, it follows that a wave is sometimes difficult or impossible to discern on a polarogram of a complex sample although it could easily be seen and measured if the concentration of the constituent responsible for it were higher. Let V be the volume of such a solution and C_u the concentration of the constituent being determined. If just enough of this constituent is added, in the form of v_1 ml. of a solution in which its concentration is C_s, to produce a wave of measurable height i_2, one will have

$$i_2 = k(VC_u + v_1 C_s)/(V + v_1) \tag{7.14}$$

which is essentially identical with eq. (7.11). Now if v_2 ml. more of the standard solution is added, the wave height will become

$$i_3 = k[VC_u + (v_1 + v_2) C_s]/(V + v_1 + v_2) \tag{7.15}$$

Combining eqs. (7.14) and (7.15) yields

$$C_u = \frac{i_2(V + v_1 + v_2)(v_1 + v_2) - i_3 v_1(V + v_1)}{i_3(V + v_1) - i_2(V + v_1 + v_2)} \frac{C_s}{V} \tag{7.16}$$

This is less precise than a method in which i_1, the wave height in the original solution, could be measured directly, but enough time may be saved by avoiding a separation to reconcile the analyst to the loss.

Care must be taken to make the first addition as small as will barely serve to produce an acceptable wave. Small standard additions are most conveniently made by using a dropping bottle as a weight buret, measuring the density of the standard solution separately to permit converting the weights of the aliquots into their volumes. If C_u is taken as fixed, the second addition should be as large as possible, though again C_{max} must not be exceeded.

In a slightly different form, the double standard addition method also serves to compensate for changes in the diffusion current constant of the substance being determined resulting from changes of viscosity produced by the standard addition. This was discussed above in connection with Table 7.1, and it was pointed out that the quadratic eq. (7.9) describes the experimental results with a mean relative error of $\pm0.45\%$. A linear equation can be used instead; for example, the diffusion current constants of lead ion given in Table 7.1 are described by the equation

$$I_{Pb} = 3.76_5 - 6.5c \qquad (7.17)$$

with a relative mean deviation of ±1.0 per cent. At values of c much higher than 0.2 g./ml., this becomes grossly inferior to eq. (7.9) because it leads to negative values of I_{Pb}, which the latter cannot do. But if care is taken to avoid overstepping the previously established limits of its validity, an equation of the form of eq. (7.17) will often reproduce data on systems like this one with a precision commensurate with the errors of measurement.

It is convenient for the present purpose to describe the constant of proportionality k relating the wave height to the concentration of the substance being determined by the equation

$$k = k_1 - a(1 - c/c_1) \qquad (7.18)$$

where k_1 is the constant appropriate to the original solution, in which the concentration of the major constituent or of the supporting electrolyte is c_1, k and c are the corresponding values after a standard addition has been made, and a is a constant dependent on the experimental conditions. Originally

$$i_1 = k_1C_u \qquad (7.19)$$

After the addition of v_1 ml. of a standard solution, free from the major

constituent, in which the concentration of the substance being determined is C_s, the wave height i_2 is given by

$$i_2 = \left[k_1 - a\left(1 - \frac{c}{c_1} \right) \right] \frac{V_1 C_u + v_1 C_s}{V_1 + v_1} \qquad (7.20)$$

where V_1 is the volume of the original solution. The value of c is
given by

$$c = V_1 c_1 / (V_1 + v_1) \qquad (7.21)$$

so that

$$i_2 = \left[k_1 - a\left(\frac{v_1}{V_1 + v_1} \right) \right] \frac{V_1 C_u + v_1 C_s}{V_1 + v_1} \qquad (7.22)$$

Now v_2 ml. more of the standard solution is added and the total wave
height i_3 is measured. This may be described by an equation which
has the same form as eq. (7.22) and which may be combined with
eqs. (7.22) and (7.19) in such a way as to eliminate both k_1 and a.
The resulting expression,

$$\begin{aligned}
&[v_1 V_1 V_3{}^2 i_3 - (v_1 + v_2) V_1 V_2{}^2 i_2 + v_2 V_1{}^3 i_1] C_u{}^2 \\
&+ [v_1{}^2 V_3{}^2 i_3 - (v_1 + v_2)^2 V_2{}^2 i_2 + (2v_1 + v_2) v_2 V_1{}^2 i_1] C_s C_u \qquad (7.23) \\
&+ v_1 v_2 (v_1 + v_2) V_1 i_1 C_s = 0
\end{aligned}$$

where V_i is the total volume of the solution in which i_i is measured,
is readily solved for C_u. The computations are too lengthy to be
attractive in routine analysis, and hence the technique is virtually
confined to analyses so rarely performed that even more time would
be consumed in obtaining detailed calibration data, analyses of
samples of such widely varying compositions (e.g., polymers of different degrees of polymerization) that the appropriate standards would
be very numerous, or analyses in which the solution finally prepared
is very sensitive to air-oxidation or is otherwise unstable. In general,
however, it is better to prepare a standard solution that is identical
with the one being analyzed except for the addition of a known
increment of the substance being determined. Because this solution
will have the same viscosity as the one to which it is added, k will be
unaffected by the addition, so that the ordinary single standard
addition method can be used without difficulty. This is essentially

the principle of the standard spike method, but in this form it is much better adapted to the analysis of a large number of samples of similar composition.

The double unknown addition method involves manipulations and equations similar to those employed in the double standard addition method, but it serves a quite different purpose. It is intended to deal with the situation in which the wave height is not linearly dependent on the concentration at low concentrations, but becomes so at higher ones. This arises when the supporting electrolyte contains impurities that react with the substance being determined: for example, sulfate in the determination of lead, or residual oxygen in the determination of an easily air-oxidized material. To V_0 ml. of the supporting electrolyte one adds Δv ml. of a concentrated solution of the sample, in which the concentration of the substance being determined is C_u. In the resulting mixture, whose total volume is V ($= V_0 + \Delta v$) ml., the wave height is i_1 and the concentration of the substance being determined is C_1, which is less than $\Delta v C_u / V$ by some unknown amount because of the presence of the impurity. This first addition must be sufficiently large to consume the impurity completely. The value of i_1 may be described by eq. (7.10). Now an additional v_1 ml. of the solution of the sample is added. The wave height i_2 in the resulting mixture is described by eq. (7.14), which may be combined with eq. (7.10) in such a way as to eliminate C_1. The result is

$$C_u = \frac{(i_2 - i_1)\,V + i_2 v_1}{k v_1} \qquad (7.24)$$

The value of k must be known for the temperature, capillary characteristics, and other experimental conditions employed. If a pure supporting electrolyte cannot be obtained, or if the deviation from proportionality at low concentrations is due to some other cause, k can be evaluated by a modification of the same procedure. A standard solution of known concentration C_s is used. The value of i_1 is obtained as described above; then a number of additional aliquots of the standard solution are added and the total wave height i is measured after each addition. If the total volume of standard solution added is $(v + \Delta v)$, where Δv as above is the volume of the first aliquot, k is given by

$$k = \frac{(i - i_1)\,V + iv}{v C_s} \qquad (7.25)$$

The mean of several concordant values of k is employed in subsequent analyses.

iv. The Pilot-Ion Method

The pilot-ion method (59), sometimes called the "quotient of two waves" method, depends on the fact that the ratio of the heights of two diffusion-controlled waves is practically independent of such experimental variables as the temperature, the capillary characteristics, and the concentration and viscosity of the supporting electrolyte. Typical data bearing on the last of these points were shown in the last column of Table 7.1. Standard solutions are prepared that contain known concentrations of both the substance being determined and another substance, called the "pilot ion" despite the fact that it need not be ionic, and the ratio of their wave heights is measured. If a known concentration of the pilot ion is added to the solution being analyzed, the concentration of the substance being determined is easily calculated from the ratio of wave heights and the previously established calibration figure.

Suppose, for example, that a sample of zinc, which is free from cadmium or any other substance that would interfere with the measurement of the cadmium wave height, is to be analyzed for lead in the supporting electrolyte of Table 7.1. From the data given there, it is known that the height of the lead wave is 1.10 times that of the cadmium wave in a solution containing equal concentrations of lead and cadmium. That is,

$$\frac{i_{\text{Pb}}}{C_{\text{Pb}}} = 1.10 \frac{i_{\text{Cd}}}{C_{\text{Cd}}} \tag{7.26}$$

Suppose that enough cadmium is added to the solution to make its concentration $1.00\text{m}M$ and that the polarogram shows that the height of the lead wave is 0.55 times that of the cadmium wave. Rearranging equation (7.26) yields

$$C_{\text{Pb}} = \frac{1}{1.10} \frac{i_{\text{Pb}}}{i_{\text{Cd}}} C_{\text{Cd}} \tag{7.27}$$

from which the concentration of lead is evidently $0.50\text{m}M$.

If one is interested in the amount, rather than in the concentration, of the substance being determined, dilution to known volume is unnecessary. One need only know the amount of the pilot ion added;

the ratio of wave heights is independent of dilution over the whole range in which the wave heights of both substances are proportional to their respective concentrations.

Usually only a very small error is incurred if the ratio of wave heights measured in the calibration experiment (or calculated from literature values of the diffusion current constants) is employed in analyses performed with a different capillary or with the same capillary at a different pressure of mercury. In most other comparative methods, the calibration must be repeated whenever the capillary or the height of the mercury column above it is changed. It is true that the diffusion currents of different substances may not be affected in quite exactly the same ways if the capillary characteristics are changed; differences are, for example, predicted by the Koutecký equation. Nevertheless, the compensation is quite accurate enough for the great majority of practical analyses. It is occasionally stated that the concentration of the pilot ion must be kept constant or that a different calibration figure is needed for each concentration of the pilot ion, but this is not so as long as its wave height is proportional to its concentration. Changes of galvanometer or recorder sensitivity are entirely without effect. Temperature variations of as much as several degrees rarely cause appreciable errors because the temperature coefficients of the diffusion currents of most substances are nearly equal.

Because the height of a kinetic or catalytic wave is affected by capillary characteristics, temperature, and most other experimental variables in a quite different manner from that of a diffusion-controlled wave, the pilot ion method should not be used in determinations of substances yielding kinetic or catalytic waves.

The pilot ion must be a substance that is absent from the sample, that does not react with any possible constituent of the sample, and that gives a diffusion-controlled wave well separated from that of any constituent of the sample. If the sample is sufficiently complex, it may be difficult or even impossible to find a pilot ion that satisfies all of these requirements. With samples that give simple polarograms, however, there are usually many substances that can be used as the pilot ion. In general it is best to select one whose wave follows that of the substance being determined, so that one will not be confronted by a severe form of the wave-order problem if one sample happens to contain an unexpectedly small amount of that substance. The concentration of the pilot ion should then be large enough to ensure that the same difficulty will not arise even with the largest anticipated concentration of the substance being determined.

It is clear that the pilot-ion method permits the determination of several substances from the polarogram of a single solution containing a known concentration or amount of one pilot ion. For example, Fig. 3.20 was originally obtained while using thallous ion as a pilot ion in the simultaneous determination of silver, cadmium, nickel, and zinc in cyanide plating wastes. In such cases a different calibration figure is naturally required for each of the substances being determined. The wave of the pilot ion should be the last one on the polarogram, if possible, for the reason mentioned in the preceding paragraph; otherwise the concentration of the pilot ion must be chosen with care to avoid difficulties in measuring the height of a following wave.

The pilot-ion method is uniquely advantageous in rapid routine analysis because its compensation for variations of the experimental conditions, which the inexperienced polarographer in particular often finds troublesome to control, is usually so nearly perfect that quite accurate results can be obtained more rapidly than by any other polarographic technique.

v. Kinetic Methods

The applications of polarography in kinetic analysis have as yet been so infrequent that a definitive assessment of their utility is hard to make, and hence they will be very briefly summarized here. They may be divided into two classes. In one, the rate of a reaction is followed polarographically and correlated with the concentration of a reactant or the nature or efficacy of a catalyst or inhibitor. There have, for example, been a number of polarographic studies of the rates of consumption of oxygen by biological systems (60–62); recent work employing solid microelectrodes instead of dropping electrodes has been summarized by Longmuir (63). Such studies have been performed by recording the variation with time of the limiting current at a constant potential on the plateau of the first wave of oxygen. The same technique has been employed in methods for the evaluation of antioxidant activity (64).

Another, and perhaps more promising, technique consists of treating a mixture of two or more substances, which may yield overlapping waves or may not be reducible at all, with a reagent that reacts with them at different rates. The potential of a dropping electrode in the mixture is maintained constant at a suitable value, and the limiting current is recorded as the reaction proceeds. The potential may lie on the plateau of the wave of the reagent, on the plateau of the combined wave of the substances originally present, on the plateau of the combined wave of the products, or on the plateau of the wave of one of the reactants or products if these give waves at sufficiently different potentials. Interpretation of the data is facilitated if either the reagent or each of the substances being determined is present in large excess, for the equations needed to describe the reaction rate are thereby much simplified. For a pseudo-second-order reaction between a reagent and a single substance that can react with it,

$$-(dC/dt) = kC_{rgt}C_u \qquad (7.28)$$

where C_{rgt} is the concentration of the reagent, C_u is the concentration of the substance reacting with it, k is the pseudo-second-order rate constant, and C is the concentration of either of the reacting substances or, if the minus sign is omitted, of a product.

Consider the situation in which the unknown is present in large excess and in which the decrease of wave height of the reagent is followed. Equation (7.28) then becomes

$$-d(\ln i_{rgt})/dt = kC_u \qquad (7.29)$$

where i_{rgt} is the wave height of the reagent, which is assumed to be proportional to its concentration. Correction for the residual current is necessary in principle, but can often be ignored in practice if i_{rgt} is always much larger than the residual current. The value of k may be obtained by measuring the slope of a plot of log i_{rgt} versus time for a solution in which C_u is known; a similar measurement with an unknown solution yields the value of kC_u, from which C_u is easily calculated. Different vic-dihydroxy compounds, and probably amino acids as well, can be identified and determined in this fashion because they consume periodate at different rates (65). The procedure in this form is suitable for the determination of only one substance at a time, however. For a mixture of reacting substances, each present in large excess, one would have

$$-d(\ln i_{rgt})/dt = k_1C_1 + k_2C_2 + \cdots + k_nC_n \qquad (7.30)$$

The most rapidly reacting substance (or, more exactly, the one for which the kC product was largest) would be the only one that could be determined, and even this would be impossible unless the kC product for every other reactant were much smaller. It is useless to attempt to measure changes in the wave height of the reagent when it is present in large excess, for the total variation is then too small for accurate measurement.

Analyses of mixtures are, therefore, best performed by employing a large excess of a reagent that is not electroactive or that is difficultly reducible, with the dropping electrode at a potential where either all of the reactants being determined or all of the products yield their diffusion currents. A plot of the logarithm of the total wave height against time can then be dissected into several linear portions, from whose slopes and intercepts the successive reactants can be identified and determined by the familiar procedures of kinetic analysis. This serves, for example, for the identification and determination of different ketones in mixtures by virtue of the fact that they react with hydroxylamine at different rates to yield the more easily reducible ketoximes. Similarly, Δ^4-3-ketosteroids may be determined in the presence of $\Delta^{1,4}$-3-ketosteroids by observing the rate of appearance of semicarbazone (66). Most of the chemical procedures employed in indirect methods will probably be found to be applicable in one way or another. A very few examples are cited in Chap. 10 IV.

References

(1) H. Dehn, V. Gutmann, and G. Schöber, *Monatsh. Chem.*, **93**, 877 (1962).

(2) R. A. Day, S. R. Milliken, and W. D. Shults, *J. Am. Chem. Soc.*, **74**, 2741 (1952).

(3) W. Kemula and R. Sioda, *Bull. Acad. Polon. Sci., Sér. Sci. Chim.*, **10**, 507, 513 (1962); **11**, 395 (1963); *J. Electroanal. Chem.*, **7**, 233 (1964).

(4) J. F. Coetzee, G. P. Cunningham, D. K. McGuire, and G. R. Padmanabhan, *Anal. Chem.*, **34**, 1139 (1962).

(5) H. M. Koepp, H. Wendt, and H. Strehlow, *Z. Elektrochem.*, **64**, 483 (1960).

(6) I. V. Nelson and R. T. Iwamoto, *Anal. Chem.*, **33**, 1795 (1961); **35**, 867 (1963).

(6a) J. F. Coetzee, D. K. McGuire, and J. L. Hedrick, *J. Phys. Chem.*, **67**, 1814 (1963).

(7) A. Frisque, V. W. Meloche, and I. Shain, *Anal. Chem.*, **26**, 471 (1954).

(8)   Y. Israel, unpublished experiments (1962).
(9)   R. P. Bauman, *Absorption Spectroscopy*, Wiley, New York, 1962, pp. 403–413.
(10) L. Meites, *Anal. Chem.*, **27**, 1114 (1955).
(11) O. Manoušek and P. Zuman, *J. Electroanal. Chem.*, **1**, 324 (1960); *Collection Czechoslov. Chem. Communs.*, **27**, 486 (1962).
(12) G. W. C. Milner, in *Progress in Polarography*, P. Zuman and I. M. Kolthoff, eds., Interscience, New York, 1962, Vol. II, p. 609.
(13) H. H. Willard and J. A. Dean, *Anal. Chem.*, **22**, 1264 (1950).
(14) D. S. Turnham, *J. Electroanal. Chem.*, **7**, 211 (1964).
(15) H. Flaschka, S. E. Khalafalla, and F. Sadek, *Z. Anal. Chem.*, **156**, 169 (1957).
(16) J. J. Lingane, *Ind. Eng. Chem., Anal. Ed.*, **18**, 429 (1946).
(17) A. S. Landry, *Anal. Chem.*, **21**, 674 (1949).
(18) V. Šedivec, *Collection Czechoslov. Chem. Communs.*, **23**, 57 (1958).
(19) A. M. Hartley and D. J. Curran, *Anal. Chem.*, **35**, 686 (1963).
(20) A. A. Smales and H. N. Wilson, *J. Soc. Chem. Ind.*, **67**, 210 (1948).
(21) F. L. English, *Anal. Chem.*, **23**, 344 (1951).
(22) W. Discherl and H. U. Bergmeyer, *Biochem. Z.*, **320**, 46 (1949).
(23) P. J. Elving, B. Warshowsky, E. Shoemaker, and J. Margolit, *Anal. Chem.*, **20**, 25 (1948).
(24) W. A. Cannon, *Anal. Chem.*, **22**, 928 (1950).
(24a) K. Takiura and K. Koizumi, *J. Pharm. Soc. Japan*, **78**, 961 (1958); through *Electroanal. Abstr.*, **3**, no. 1/2, 46 (1965).
(25) M. Březina and P. Zuman, *Chem. Listy*, **47**, 975 (1953).
(26) R. E. van Atta and D. R. Jamieson, *Anal. Chem.*, **31**, 1217 (1959).
(27) A. D. Horton, P. F. Thomason, and M. T. Kelley, *Anal. Chem.*, **27**, 269 (1955).
(28) M. E. Hall, *Anal. Chem.*, **31**, 1219 (1959).
(29) W. J. Blaedel and J. W. Todd, *Anal. Chem.*, **32**, 1018 (1960).
(30) J. J. Lingane and H. Kerlinger, *Ind. Eng. Chem., Anal. Ed.*, **13**, 77 (1941).
(31) B. E. Gordon and L. C. Jones, *Anal. Chem.*, **22**, 981 (1950).
(32) W. J. P. Neish, *Rec. Trav. Chim.*, **72**, 105, 1098 (1953).
(33) W. Kemula, in *Progress in Polarography*, P. Zuman and I. M. Kolthoff, eds., Interscience, New York, 1962, Vol. II, pp. 397–409.
(34) W. Kemula, S. Brzozowski, and K. Butkiewicz, *Chem. Anal. (Warsaw)*, **3**, 489 (1958).
(35) V. I. Gnyubkin, A. A. Dobrinskaya, and M. B. Neiman, *Acta Physicochim. U.S.S.R.*, **10**, 701 (1939).
(36) N. H. Furman and C. E. Bricker, U.S. At. Energy Comm. *Rept. No. MDDC-691*, 1947; N. H. Furman, C. E. Bricker, and B. McDuffie, *J. Wash. Acad. Sci.*, **38**, no. 5 (May, 1948).
(37) L. Meites, *Anal. Chem.*, **27**, 977 (1955).
(38) P. D. Garn and E. W. Halline, *Anal. Chem.*, **27**, 1563 (1955).
(39) H. K. Ficker and L. Meites, *Anal. Chim. Acta*, **26**, 172 (1962).
(40) H. Catherino and L. Meites, *Anal. Chim. Acta*, **23**, 57 (1960).
(41) Y. Israel and L. Meites, *J. Electroanal. Chem.*, **8**, 99 (1964).
(42) L. Meites, *Anal. Chem.*, **27**, 416 (1955).

(43) M. T. Kelley and H. H. Miller, *Anal. Chem.*, **24**, 1895 (1952).

(44) G. Semerano and L. Riccoboni, *Gazz. Chim. Ital.*, **72**, 297 (1942).

(45) L. Airey and A. A. Smales, *Analyst*, **75**, 287 (1950).

(46) H. Flaschka, *Anal. Chim. Acta*, **4**, 242 (1950).

(47) L. Meites, *J. Chem. Education*, **27**, 458 (1950).

(48) D. E. Carritt, Ph.D. Thesis, Harvard University, 1947; L. Meites and T. Meites, *Anal. Chem.*, **23**, 1194 (1951).

(49) R. L. Pecsok and R. S. Juvet, Jr., *Anal. Chem.*, **27**, 165 (1955).

(50) J. K. Taylor, *Anal. Chem.*, **19**, 368 (1947).

(51) P. Rutherford and L. A. Cha, *Anal. Chem.*, **23**, 1714 (1951).

(52) V. Pliška, *Z. Anal. Chem.*, **191**, 241 (1962).

(53) S. Stankoviansky, *Chem. Zvesti*, **2**, 133 (1948).

(54) E. A. Kanevskii, *J. Appl. Chem. U.S.S.R.*, **17**, 514 (1944).

(55) J. T. Porter, II, *Anal. Chem.*, **29**, 1638 (1957).

(56) H. Hohn, *Chemische Analysen mit dem Polarographen*, Springer Verlag, Berlin, 1937, pp. 51–2.

(57) W. H. Reinmuth, *Anal. Chem.*, **28**, 1356 (1956); cf. also K. Eckschlager, *Collection Czechoslov. Chem. Communs.*, **27**, 1521 (1962).

(58) L. Meites, *Anal. Chem.*, **28**, 139 (1956).

(59) E. Forche, *Mikrochemie*, **25**, 217 (1938).

(60) H. G. Petering and F. Daniels, *J. Am. Chem. Soc.*, **60**, 2796 (1938).

(61) O. H. Müller, *J. Chem. Education*, **18**, 320 (1941).

(62) B. Chance, *Nature*, **69**, 215 (1952).

(63) I. S. Longmuir, *Record Chem. Progr.*, **24**, 3 (1963).

(64) J. W. Hamilton and A. L. Tappel, *J. Am. Oil Chemists' Soc.*, **40**, 52 (1963); *J. Nutrition*, **79**, 493 (1953).

(65) P. Zuman and J. Krupička, *Collection Czechoslov. Chem. Communs.*, **23**, 598 (1958).

(66) A. F. Krivis and G. R. Supp, *Anal. Chem.*, **35**, 141 (1963).

CHAPTER 8

OTHER VOLTAMMETRIC INDICATOR ELECTRODES

Much work has been devoted to the development of indicator electrodes that can be used instead of the dropping mercury electrode. This has sometimes reflected the special requirements of newly developed techniques, as when the streaming mercury electrode was designed for use in oscillopolarography; sometimes it has reflected the special nature of a novel system, as when the dropping molten bismuth electrode was devised for work with fused-salt systems at high temperatures. But for the most part it has been prompted by the existence of two unrelated limitations of the dropping electrode and has accordingly taken two somewhat different, though not completely divergent, directions.

The fact that metallic mercury is relatively easily oxidized renders mercury electrodes unsuitable for the study of cathodic and anodic processes occurring in any medium at potentials more positive than that at which the oxidation of mercury appears to begin. At best this is no more positive than about $+0.4$ v. vs. S.C.E., and in alkaline solutions or solutions of halides or other ions that react with mercurous or mercuric ion it is even less positive. Different strong oxidizing agents give waves that cannot be distinguished, while no waves at all can be obtained for the oxidation of weak reducing agents such as amines and phenols. Many other electrode materials have, therefore, been studied in attempts to extend the attainable range of potentials toward more positive values. These include platinum, gold, carbon in several different forms, and other difficultly oxidizable materials like boron carbide and tungsten hemipentoxide.

The other substantial limitation of the dropping mercury electrode is that the continuous variation of electrode area gives rise to relatively large condenser currents; together with the existence of capillary noise, these limit the sensitivity of the dropping electrode and the precision and accuracy that can be obtained in the analysis of dilute solutions. Different kinds of mercury electrodes having

411

constant areas have been devised to overcome these drawbacks. Among these the mercury pool and hanging mercury drop electrodes are especially noteworthy. The solid electrodes mentioned in the preceding paragraph naturally also have constant areas, but in addition they can be used in a variety of different configurations, such as rotated wires and discs, and these have pronounced influences on the reproducibilities of the results that can be obtained and on the ease with which they can be interpreted. At the same time, the advantages peculiar to some of these configurations can be combined with the advantages peculiar to mercury surfaces by depositing mercury onto an appropriate solid substrate.

There are thus a rather large number of voltammetric indicator electrodes available, and the discussion of them here is necessarily brief. More details can be found in recent reviews by Adams (1, 2), who has also compiled a valuable tabulation of the voltammetric properties of many inorganic and organic substances, in both aqueous and non-aqueous solutions, at solid electrodes of various types (3). Mechanical modifications of the dropping electrode, including multiple dropping electrodes connected in parallel and rotating and vibrating dropping electrodes, will not be discussed at all, partly for want of space and partly because they appear to have few if any advantages in practical work to compensate for their greater complexity.

I. Electrode Configurations

Two kinds of behavior can be distinguished with electrodes of fixed area, depending on whether the electrode and solution are stationary with respect to each other or not. If the electrode is rotated or if the solution is stirred, the supply of electroactive material at the electrode surface is constantly renewed, and hence the current at any fixed potential is ideally independent of electrolysis time as long as depletion of the bulk of the solution can be neglected. This is also the idealized behavior of the average current at a dropping mercury electrode. In each case it leads to current–potential curves having the familiar S shape of an ordinary polarogram. To be sure, complications may arise if a solid product accumulates on the electrode surface, or if the ratio of electrode area to solution volume or the efficiency of stirring is so high that the rate of bulk depletion becomes appreciable. With the dropping electrode the latter effect arises only under the unusual conditions described in Chap. 10 III; with solid electrodes it is much more likely to be encountered because much larger currents are usually involved. In general, however, the current-potential curves obtained with rotated electrodes or in stirred solutions obey equations very similar to those derived in Chap. 4.

The behavior of a stationary electrode in a quiet solution is quite different. At a constant potential the reduction or oxidation of an electroactive substance then depletes a layer of solution that extends farther and farther from the electrode surface into the bulk of the solution as time goes on, and the current decreases as a result. Of course this also occurs during the life of each drop at a dropping electrode, but there it is masked by the increase of current resulting from the growth of the drop. The depletion has a pronounced effect on the current-potential curve. Consider the current-potential curve for the reduction of an oxidizing agent O to its reduced form R, beginning at a potential so positive that the rate of reduction is negligible and proceeding toward more negative potentials. At first the principal effect is the increase of current resulting from an increase in the ratio of concentrations C_R^0/C_O^0 required to conform to the Nernst equation if the O–R couple is reversible, or from an increase in the rate of reduction of O if the couple is irreversible. When more negative potentials are reached, however, ions or molecules of O are reduced rapidly as they arrive at the electrode surface. The more negative the potential, the longer the electrolysis has lasted when it is reached, and the smaller is the rate of arrival of O at the electrode surface, so that the current tends to decrease as the potential becomes more negative. These two opposing effects cause the current first to pass through a maximum value called the peak current i_p, then decrease again; the curve has the form shown in Fig. 8.1. The peak current is proportional to concentration, and it also depends on the rate at which the electrode potential is varied. Increasing this rate decreases the thickness of the layer of solution that is depleted while the rising part of the wave is being scanned, and consequently increases the peak current. It is taken for granted that the recording is begun at a potential that precedes the start of the wave, and that the potential is scanned from this value toward the peak. This is called forward polarization. If the wave is cathodic, the potential of the electrode becomes more negative during the recording; if it is anodic, the potential becomes more positive. Backward polarization consists

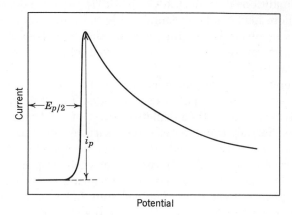

Figure 8.1. Schematic current–potential curve for a stationary microelectrode in a quiet solution, illustrating the definitions of the peak current i_p and the half-peak potential $E_{p/2}$.

of starting at a potential where the electrode reaction is fast—on an ordinary polarographic wave this would lie somewhere on the plateau —and scanning toward the foot of the wave. With a dropping mercury electrode, forward and backward polarization yield identical curves. This is also often true with electrodes that are rotated or used in stirred solutions, although differences may be observed with solid electrodes when the nature of the surface varies with potential. With stationary electrodes, however, meaningful and reproducible curves cannot be obtained except by forward polarization.

For linear diffusion to a plane electrode of area A square centimeters, the peak current obtained on forward polarization from the reversible reduction of O to a dissolved species R is described by the Randles–Ševčík equation (4,5)

$$i_p = 2.687 \times 10^5 n^{3/2} A D_O^{1/2} C_O v^{1/2} \qquad (8.1)$$

where i_p is the peak current in microamperes, C_O is the bulk concentration of O in millimoles per liter, and v is the scan rate in volts per second, while the other quantities have their ordinary polarographic significances. The derivation has been repeated several times (6–8) because Randles and Ševčík gave considerably different values of the numerical constant; the value above is that of Nicholson and Shain

(8), and it has been experimentally confirmed (9,10) within a per cent or two. The peak occurs at the potential given by (8)

$$E_p = E_{1/2} - (0.02850/n) \tag{8.2}$$

where $E_{1/2}$ is the polarographic half-wave potential in volts. The potential of the anodic peak on a voltammogram of the reduced species R is $28.50/n$ millivolts more positive than $E_{1/2}$. It is a little difficult to measure the peak potential precisely from a recorded curve, because the variation of current is not very great in the vicinity of the peak, and therefore Mueller and Adams (11) recommended the measurement of the half-peak potential $E_{p/2}$. This is defined as the potential where the current, after correction for the residual current, is half as large as at the peak, and it is measured in exactly the same way as the half-wave potential in polarography. For the reversible reduction of O to dissolved R the half-peak potential is given by (8)

$$E_{p/2} = E_{1/2} + (0.0280/n) \tag{8.3}$$

Conversely, the anodic half-peak potential of R is $28.0/n$ millivolts more negative than the half-wave potential. The fundamental criterion of reversibility is, therefore,

$$(E_{p/2})_c - (E_{p/2})_a = 56.0/n \text{ mv.} \tag{8.4}$$

Corresponding equations for the totally irreversible reduction of O have been obtained by several authors (8,12,13). The peak current is given by (8)

$$i_p = 2.985 \times 10^5 n(\alpha n_a)^{1/2} A D_0^{1/2} C_0 v^{1/2} \tag{8.5}$$

Although the numerical coefficient in eq. (8.5) is larger than that in eq. (8.1), smaller peak currents are obtained for irreversible processes than for reversible ones because αn_a is almost invariably smaller than n. It is evident that surface-active materials should be rigorously excluded or that their concentrations should be carefully controlled, for they are likely to affect the peak current by altering the value of αn_a. The peak potential is given by (8)

$$E_p = E^0 - \frac{0.05915}{\alpha n_a} \left[0.4565 + \log \frac{(\alpha n_a D_0 v)^{1/2}}{k_{s,h}} \right] \tag{8.6}$$

while the half-peak potential is described by

$$E_{p/2} = E_p + \frac{0.04771}{\alpha n_a} \tag{8.7}$$

Equivalent, but sometimes more convenient, expressions may be obtained by replacing E^0 and $k_{s,h}$ in eq. (8.6) by E^i and $k_{f,h}{}^i$, respectively; $k_{f,h}{}^i$ is the value of the heterogeneous rate constant $k_{f,h}$ at the potential E^i where the recording is begun, which must be well in advance of the start of the wave. As is also true in polarography, the slope of the rising part of the wave is smaller when the half-reaction is totally irreversible than when it is reversible, and decreases as the value of αn_a decreases.

Whereas the peak current is proportional to $v^{1/2}$ according to eqs. (8.1) and (8.5), the charging current is roughly proportional to v, as can be shown by differentiating eq. (3.1) if the differential capacity $\varkappa$ is taken as constant. For a reversible process one can obtain the approximate equation (14)

$$i_c/i_p = 0.023v^{1/2}/n^{3/2}C_O \tag{8.8}$$

where i_c is the charging current, by assuming typical values for $\varkappa$ and D_O. With $v = 0.003$ v./sec., $n = 1$, and $C_O = 0.01mM$, the charging current is nearly 15% of the peak current. It would be even larger for an irreversible process. The problem would not be very serious if $\varkappa$ were truly independent of potential, for then the charging-current curve would be flat and correction or compensation for it would be relatively simple. In fact, however, $\varkappa$ does vary with potential, and in such a way that the charging-current curve is not only not flat but also not exactly linear. Consequently the peak current cannot be found accurately by performing a linear extrapolation of the portion of the residual-current curve that precedes the rising part of the wave. Whenever the solution is so dilute that i_c/i_p is appreciable, the residual-current curve must be recorded separately so that the residual current at the peak potential can be subtracted from the total obtained in the presence of the electroactive substance. Delahay (15) proposed a differential procedure for performing the subtraction automatically. No matter how it is done, however, it involves some danger that the values of $\varkappa$ and the manner in which they vary with potential may be altered by the presence of the electroactive substance or its reduction product if either of these is surface-active.

Hence electrodes of this sort are rather ill-suited to work with very dilute solutions. It might appear from eq. (8.8) that their limits of detection could be improved by decreasing v. But convection becomes increasingly important as the scan rate decreases, and as a result the peak currents become less reproducible and deviate more and more from the theoretical values. Scan rates below about 0.002 v./sec. are rarely employed.

If the concentration of the electroactive substance is very much increased so that the charging current can be neglected, a different problem may arise. The iR drop through the cell and polarograph then becomes appreciable over most of the rising part of the wave, and produces variations of the rate of change of the electrode potential. The peak current decreases as a result. The error may be as large as 20 or 30%, increasing with increasing cell resistance. As it also increases with increasing peak current, the apparent value of i_p/C_O decreases as the concentration C_O increases. Approximate correction may be made $(10,16)$ by employing the equation

$$(i_p)_{\text{true}} = (i_p)_{\text{exptl}} \left[1 + \frac{(i_p)_{\text{exptl}}R}{\Delta E} \right]^{1/2} \qquad (8.9)$$

where $(i_p)_{\text{exptl}}$ is the measured peak current, R is the total resistance of the cell circuit, and ΔE is the difference between the applied voltage at the beginning of the rising part of the wave and that at the peak. If ΔE is expressed in millivolts the peak current must be expressed in milliamperes. Care must be taken to minimize the iR drop, for eq. (8.9) does not provide an exact correction and its error increases as the iR drop increases. It is better to use a three-electrode cell together with a circuit that provides a constant rate of change of potential rather than of voltage (10).

The above equations are strictly valid only for linear diffusion. This implies that the electrode is planar and that diffusion is restricted by a mantle as in Fig. 3.4. If the mantle is removed, so that the electrode merely protrudes into the bulk of the solution, the electro-active substance can diffuse toward its periphery from a larger volume of solution than would be involved in linear diffusion, and a larger peak current is obtained. This is usually called "unrestricted linear diffusion." The discrepancy increases as the scan rate decreases: if the scan is sufficiently rapid, even the behavior of a stationary wire electrode can be closely approximated by linear-diffusion equations. Explicitly (17), at a cylindrical electrode of radius r their error will not exceed 5% if

$$\tau \leq 0.003r^2/D_O \qquad (8.10)$$

where τ is the duration of the electrolysis in seconds. However, the more complicated equations for cylindrical diffusion are needed in the range of scan rates obtainable with an ordinary polarograph (6,17). Especially at slow scan rates, somewhat better precision can be obtained with linear than with cylindrical or spherical diffusion. In the first case it is possible to place the electrode in such a position as to stabilize the density gradient resulting from the flow of current (18), but this cannot be done with unrestricted linear diffusion or with cylindrical or spherical diffusion. On the other hand, a linear-diffusion electrode of exactly known area is a little difficult to construct and troublesome to use. For analytical purposes, therefore, most workers have gladly accepted the small deviations from theory and the small loss of precision that accompany the use of electrodes whose geometrical arrangements or configurations are such that mass transfer occurs by unrestricted linear diffusion. In fundamental work, however, it would be irrational to employ an electrode whose behavior cannot be described exactly. By the use of moderately fast scanning one can employ a wire or cylindrical electrode (6,17,19,20) or a spherical electrode, such as the hanging mercury drop, without appreciable difficulties due to convection. The hanging mercury drop electrode is discussed briefly in Sec. IV below. Here it may be said that Nicholson and Shain (8) have summarized the equations that describe the behavior of a spherical electrode and have also given diagnostic criteria and explicit equations useful in identifying and investigating a number of common types of chemical reactions coupled with electron-transfer processes.

The voltammogram obtained with a stationary electrode in a quiet solution contains successive peaks when two or more electroactive substances are present. If the scan is sufficiently slow or if the ratio of the electrode area to the volume of the electrolyzed phase is sufficiently high, the current on the tail of the first peak may decay nearly completely before the next peak begins, and then the second peak current can be measured with good accuracy and precision. However, the fact that convection becomes increasingly important at very low scan rates renders their use rather impractical unless the scan rate is so low and the volume of solution so small that essentially quantitative depletion is obtained before the next peak begins. In this event the convection is advantageous because it hastens the depletion, and the fluctuations of current that it produces are rendered harmless if a coulometric technique is employed to obtain the current–time integral under the peak (*21*). On the other hand, rapid decay of a peak is easily obtained in stripping voltammetry with a hanging mercury drop or a mercury-plated electrode, because the volume of the electrolyzed phase (the mercury itself) is very small. It is less easily obtained when the substance being determined is present in the solution phase, and the wave-order problem is then very much more severe than it is in polarography. This is illustrated by Fig. 8.2, where AC corresponds to the true value of i_p for the second peak while BC corresponds to the value likely to be obtained graphically. Except when a stripping procedure can be used, quantitative data are, therefore, difficult to obtain with mixtures unless neighboring peaks are fairly widely separated. As the height of the first peak can be measured without difficulty, the problem is significant only when the determination of two or more substances from a single voltammogram is contemplated. As far as the practical analyst is concerned, this defect of stationary electrodes in quiet solutions is at least counterbalanced by the fact that, for example, some substances giving overlapping waves at a dropping mercury electrode are easily resolved at a quiet mercury pool (*22*).

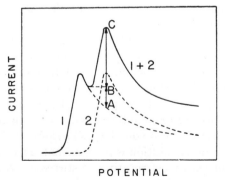

Figure 8.2. Schematic stationary-electrode voltammograms for two reducible substances A and B when present separately (dashed lines) and together (solid line) (*14*).

Incidentally, it may be mentioned that the shape of a recorded stationary-electrode voltammogram is drastically altered by overdamping the recorder. As the degree of damping is increased, the peak current decreases and the peak and half-peak potentials shift in the direction toward which the electrode potential is being changed. If the recorder is heavily overdamped the peak vanishes and a nearly level plateau is obtained. It is just conceivable that this might provide a way of dealing with the problem illustrated by Fig. 8.2 after careful calibration with known solutions. For any other purpose, however, it is far better to use a fast undamped recorder.

The phenomenon illustrated by Fig. 8.2 can also be made to arise with a rotated electrode or one employed in a stirred solution. It then reflects depletion of the bulk of the solution at a rate that is appreciable in comparison with the scan rate. This is so easily avoided by decreasing the area of the electrode, increasing the volume of the solution, increasing the scan rate, or decreasing the efficiency of stirring that it is of negligible practical importance. For analyses of mixtures for which stripping procedures cannot be devised, electrodes of these types have lower limits of detection than stationary electrodes in quiet solutions. When a stripping procedure is available, however— as it is in determinations of halides (*23–25*) or of many metals (*26–34*) —stationary electrodes, especially the hanging mercury drop, are peculiarly advantageous because the accumulation of deposited material in or on a very small electrode leads to extremely low limits of detection.

As was pointed out above, exact equations can be written for the peak and limiting currents at a plane linear-diffusion electrode. Equations for the current-potential curves obtained with reversible and irreversible couples are available as well (*4,5,8,12,17*). These make possible the objective evaluation of data obtained with any new system: diffusion coefficients and *n*-values can be calculated, the thermodynamics of reversible couples and the kinetics of irreversible ones can be studied, prior or intermediate rate-controlling chemical steps can be identified, and so on. The behavior of a stationary spherical electrode in a quiet solution is also amenable to exact description (*7,8,35–37*). But with most rotating or stirred electrodes the hydrodynamic complexities defy theoretical analysis. Equations that describe the limiting current have indeed been written for some such electrodes (*38,39*), but in general these either involve the Nernst

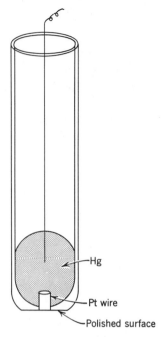

Figure 8.3.   Construction of a rotating platinum disc electrode.

diffusion-layer thickness, which for many electrode configurations is a parameter of very uncertain significance because it varies over the electrode surface, or are difficult to apply to experimental data because of the nonreproducibility of the convection that occurs.

For these reasons the rotating disc electrode (*40–52*) is assuming an increasing importance. A typical simple form of this electrode is shown in Fig. 8.3. Rotating disc electrodes have most often been made from platinum, but carbon paste (*53*) and graphite (*54,55*) have also been used.

Rotating a disc electrode causes liquid to flow from the bulk of the solution toward the center of the disc and thence outward toward its edges; the motion with respect to the surface of the disc is shown by Fig. 8.4. The surface velocity increases with increasing distance from the center, and does so in such a way that the current density is the same at every point. It is convenient to describe this current density

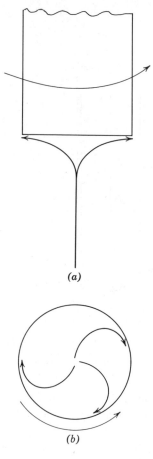

(a)

(b)

Figure 8.4. The motion of solution with respect to the surface of a rotating disc electrode: (a) side view, (b) bottom view.

by invoking a Nernst diffusion-layer treatment. According to Fick's first law

$$\left(\frac{dN}{dt} \right)_{x=0} = DA \left(\frac{\partial C}{\partial x} \right)_{x=0} \tag{8.11}$$

where $(dN/dt)_{x=0}$ is the number of moles of the electroactive substance that reach the electrode surface in each second, D is the diffusion coefficient of the electroactive substance, A is the area of the electrode in square centimeters, and $(\partial C/\partial x)_{x=0}$ is the concentration gradient at the electrode surface; x represents the distance from the electrode surface. One may define a parameter δ by the equation

$$\delta = \frac{C - C^0}{(\partial C/\partial x)_{x=0}} \tag{8.12}$$

where C and C^0 are the concentrations of the electroactive substance in the bulk of the solution and at the electrode surface, respectively. This may be visualized with the aid of Fig. 8.5, which corresponds to a point on the plateau of the wave, where $C^0 = 0$. Curve a shows the actual shape of the concentration profile while curve b represents the definition of δ according to eq. (8.12). Although δ is called the "thickness of the diffusion layer," it is clear that the name is inaccurate, for the depletion extends to distances substantially larger than δ. Nernst visualized δ as the thickness of a quiet layer of solution through which the electroactive substance diffuses after having been brought to its outer boundary by stirring, but this is also incorrect: in a stirred solution motion has been detected at values of x that are much smaller than δ (41,56). Care must be taken not to ascribe to δ a significance that it does not possess.

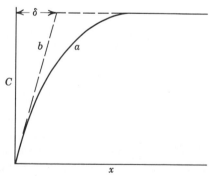

Figure 8.5. The concentration profile near the surface of an electrode at a potential on the plateau of a wave: (a) actual profile, (b) hypothetical profile showing the distance that corresponds to the value of δ defined by eq. (8.12).

According to Levich (48), the value of δ for a rotating disc electrode of virtually infinite area is given by

$$\delta = kD^{1/3}\nu^{1/6}\omega^{-1/2} \tag{8.13}$$

where ν is the kinematic viscosity of the solution, given by

$$\nu = \eta/d \qquad (8.14)$$

in which η is the viscosity in poises and d the density in grams per cubic centimeter, while ω is the angular velocity of the disc in radians per second, given by

$$\omega = 2\pi \mathbf{n} \qquad (8.15)$$

in which $\mathbf{n}$ is the number of revolutions per second. Gregory and Riddiford (43) gave the following expression for the quantity k in eq. (8.13):

$$k = 1.6125 + 0.5704(D/\nu)^{0.36} \qquad (8.16)$$

For water at 25° C. the value of ν is 8.96×10^{-3} cm.²/sec., so that if D has the typical value of 6×10^{-6} cm.²/sec. the second term in eq. (8.16) will be only about 2.5% as large as the first. Neglecting it, combining eqs. (8.11), (8.12), (8.13), and (8.16) with a description of the current

$$i = nF(dN/dt)_{x=0} \qquad (8.17)$$

and setting C^0 equal to zero to obtain an expression for the limiting current, one secures

$$i_l = 0.6201 n F A D^{2/3} C \nu^{-1/6} \omega^{1/2} \qquad (8.18a)$$

or, more conveniently,

$$i_l = 1.500 \times 10^5 n A D^{2/3} C \nu^{-1/6} \mathbf{n}^{1/2} \qquad (8.18b)$$

As usual, i_l is given in microamperes and C in millimoles per liter. Equations (8.18) fail at low values of ω or $\mathbf{n}$ (55), and have been modified (57) for use in this range, but they seem to be satisfactory as they stand if $\mathbf{n}$ is at least 3 revolutions per second. On the other hand, very high rates of revolution give rise to turbulence, which also leads to deviations from the theoretical equations. An upper limit can hardly be specified, because it is critically dependent on the construction of the electrode: if the axis of rotation is not exactly perpendicular to the surface of the disc or does not pass through its center, or if the disc is not perfectly plane, turbulence will become appreciable at much lower rates of revolution than it would with a perfectly constructed electrode. In general, however, rotating disk electrodes are most commonly used in the range $3 \leq \mathbf{n} \leq 30$ revolutions per second. The useful range of any particular electrode is best found experimentally by observing the behavior of the ratio $i_l/\mathbf{n}^{1/2}$ as $\mathbf{n}$ is varied; as the ratio varies with $\mathbf{n}$ when a prior or intermediate rate-controlling chemical step is involved in the half-reaction, a well-behaved electroactive substance such as ferricyanide ion should be employed. Mention may be made here of a report (50) that a uniform current density is not obtained when copper is deposited onto a rotating platinum disc electrode. It is not known whether this reflects the crystal growth of a deposited metal or the inhomogeneity of a platinum surface.

Equations (8.13) and (8.18) also fail if the disc is too small; an explicit criterion is that the ratio r/δ should exceed about 20, where r is the radius of the disc. In water, if $D = 6 \times 10^{-6}$ cm.^{2}/sec. and $\mathbf{n} = 10$ revolutions per second, eq. (8.13) gives a value of about 1.5×10^{-3} cm. for δ. This corresponds to a minimum radius of about 0.3 mm.

The applications of the rotating disc electrode have been both important and promising even though they have not been very numerous. They have included measurements of diffusion coefficients (53), of the rate constants of chemical reactions coupled with electron-transfer processes (44,46), and of the forward and backward hetero-geneous rate constants for electron transfer for couples having fairly high values of $k_{s,h}$ (50), among others. An explicit equation for the current-potential curve obtained with a reversible couple has been written only very recently (55); in most prior work the electrode has been used to measure the current at a fixed potential rather than to scan the entire wave.

As yet little can be said about the analytical utility of the rotating disc electrode. Its sensitivity, as defined in the discussion of equation (8.22) below, is typically of the order of 20 μamp./meq./l., which is smaller than for other rotating electrodes and electrodes used in stirred solutions. What is important in practice, however, is neither this value of i_l/nC nor its ratio to the residual current (which is often, though misleadingly, quoted as an index of practical sensitivity), but its ratio to the uncertainty in a measurement of the difference between the total current and the residual current. In principle, the reproducibilities of mass-transfer-controlled currents are not governed by quite the same factors as those of charging currents, but at very low concentrations the standard deviation of measurements of the total current approaches that of measurements of the residual current alone. Hence one may define the limit of detection as the concentration C^* at which the equation

$$nC^*(i_l/nC) = \sqrt{2}\,\sigma_{i_r} \qquad (8.19)$$

where σ_{i_r} is the standard deviation of measurements of the residual current, is just satisfied. Evidently the values of C^* will be somewhat different for different electroactive substances, and will be considerably higher for one whose limiting current must be measured at a potential where the residual current is large than for one whose wave occurs near the middle of the accessible range of potentials. To provide a basis for comparison, it may be said that σ_{i_r} is typically of the order of 0.003 μamp. for a dropping mercury electrode over most of the attainable range of potentials; it is much larger at potentials on the initial or final current rise, somewhat smaller near the electrocapillary maximum where i_r itself is small, and at any potential depends on the construction and cleanliness of the capillary. For a dropping electrode, according to the Ilkovič equation,

$$i_d/nC = 607\,D^{1/2}m^{2/3}t^{1/6} = (I/n)\,m^{2/3}t^{1/6} \qquad (8.20)$$

In Chap. 3 VI it was pointed out that many electroactive substances have diffusion current constants approximately equal to $1.5n$; on this basis, and with the typical value $m^{2/3}t^{1/6} = 3$ mg.$^{2/3}$sec.$^{-1/2}$, eqs. (8.19) and (8.20) may be combined to yield the estimate

$$C^* = 0.0010/n \text{ m}M \qquad (8.21)$$

for the limit of detection of ordinary polarography.

According to Adams et al. (53), the residual current at a typical rotating carbon-paste disc electrode is of the order of 0.02 μamp. over most of the accessible range of potentials. It is not known what fraction of this is due to the charging current, which could be decreased by decreasing the scan rate in accordance with eq. (3.1). One may make the conservative assumption that the relative standard deviation, σ_{i_r}/i_r, is the same for the rotating disc electrode as for the dropping mercury electrode despite the much greater hydrodynamic simplicity of the former. As σ_{i_r}/i_r is of the order of 0.05 or so for the

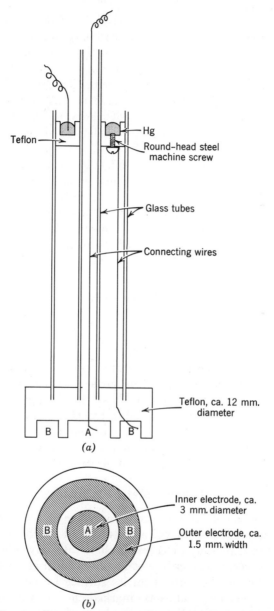

Figure 8.6.   Construction of an annular rotating disc electrode: (a) side view, (b) bottom view. Carbon paste is packed into the wells A and BB.

dropping electrode, this would give a limit of detection of perhaps $0.15/n$ micromolar for the rotating carbon-paste disc electrode, an order of magnitude better than that for the dropping electrode. The figure will be less favorable with platinum because of the effects of oxide formation and dissolution, which are discussed in Sec. II below. Few other electrode configurations give better limits of detection. Rotating wire electrodes, for example, have much larger values of i_l/nC, but these are more than counterbalanced by their higher values of σ_{i_r}.

The annular rotating disc electrode (48) is a promising tool for studies of the intermediates formed in complex reactions. One form of this electrode, intended for use with carbon paste and slightly modified from the original design of Adams et al. (53), is shown in Fig. 8.6. Its theory has been studied in some detail by Levich et al. $(45,58)$; only a brief indication of its utility can be given here. Suppose that an electrode reaction takes place by the "ECE" mechanism

$$A + n_1 e \rightarrow B$$
$$B \rightarrow C$$
$$C + n_2 e \rightarrow D$$

If the inner electrode is maintained at a potential where A is reduced to B, some B will fail to react at its surface because of the finite rate of the intermediate chemical step. This will be swept past the Teflon barrier separating the two electrodes, reacting to form C as it goes, and so some C will reach the surface of the outer electrode. If C is more easily reduced than A, its wave will be easy to discern on the current-potential curve for the outer electrode.

II. Noble-Metal Electrodes

Platinum wire indicator electrodes were the first solid electrodes to receive widespread use in voltammetry, and much more work has been done with platinum electrodes than with any other solid electrodes. However, platinum is not at all an ideal electrode material. An oxide film can be formed on its surface by either chemical or electrolytic oxidation, and exerts marked effects on its voltammetric behavior. Current-potential curves obtained with a platinum electrode depend on the pretreatment of the electrode and on such other factors as the direction of polarization. This section describes the behavior and use of platinum electrodes. Gold electrodes have characteristics so similar that they are included as well.

Platinum electrodes can be, and have been, constructed in any of a very large number of configurations: stationary plane electrodes for linear diffusion, stationary cylindrical and spherical electrodes for use in quiet solutions, rotating disc electrodes, electrodes for use in flowing solutions, and so on. By far the most widely used, however, has been the rotating wire electrode, which was introduced by Laitinen and Kolthoff (59), and a description of this will serve to summarize the problems common to all platinum electrodes regardless of their configurations.

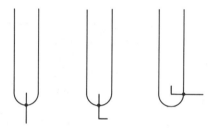

Figure 8.7.   Typical rotating platinum wire electrodes.

Typical rotating platinum wire electrodes are shown in Fig. 8.7. A 1- to 2-cm. length of 16- to 18-gauge wire is sealed through the end of a soft glass tube about 15 cm. long. The tube is partly filled with mercury, into which a platinum, tungsten, or nickel wire is dipped to provide electrical connection to the polarograph, and is rotated at a constant speed by a synchronous motor. A perfect platinum–glass seal is essential, for mercury will leak through one that is ever so slightly defective, and its oxidation will give rise to large anodic currents over most of the interesting range of potentials. A defective electrode should be discarded, for it is rarely possible to repair the seal after mercury has become trapped in it. It is also essential that the tube be accurately linear, for this minimizes the turbulence produced by rotating the electrode and improves the steadiness and reproducibility of the currents obtained. The currents depend on the rate of rotation, which also affects their reproducibility: the precision deteriorates if the rate of rotation is either too high or too low. A rate of 600 r.p.m.

is almost universally employed, though there is no real ground for preferring this to any other between about 200 and 1200 r.p.m. A convenient rotator (S-76485) is available from E. H. Sargent & Co., as are the electrodes themselves (S-30420 and S-30421).

The limiting current obtained with a rotating wire electrode depends on the concentration and diffusion coefficient of the substance responsible for the wave, on the value of n for the electrode reaction, and on the area and rate of rotation of the electrode (60,61). Unfortunately, the situation is so complicated hydrodynamically that an exact theoretical description of the limiting current seems impossible to obtain. Hence one can only write (62,63)

$$i_l = knC \qquad (8.22)$$

where k is a mass-transfer constant whose value depends on the identity of the electroactive substance, the identity and concentration of the supporting electrolyte, and the temperature, as well as on the area, geometry, and rate of revolution of the electrode. The sensitivity of the electrode is most conveniently described by the value of k, which is obviously equal to i_l/nC. A typical figure, for a 16-gauge wire 6 mm. long perpendicular to the axis of rotation at 600 r.p.m. in an aqueous solution of ordinary viscosity, is of the order of 200 μamp./meq./l. Such an electrode can be used for work down to about the micromolar level, or for amperometric titrations of solutions as dilute as about 0.01mM in favorable cases. However, the limit of detection of the electrode is not as much smaller than that of the dropping mercury electrode as would be inferred from the ratio of this figure to the comparable value, which would be about 5 μamp./ meq./l., for the latter. This is because the residual currents obtained with rotating platinum wire electrodes are both somewhat larger and, more importantly, considerably less reproducible than those obtained with dropping electrodes. In addition, the limiting currents obtained with rotating wire electrodes are affected by changes in the cell geometry, the pretreatment of the surface, and other factors difficult to control. A day-to-day precision of the order of ± 1 to 3% is about the best that has been achieved (39, 64) at concentrations around 0.1mM, although it is not difficult to secure better precision in a short series of experiments. To permit the examination of millimolar solutions without producing currents too large to be recorded on conventional polarographs, the sensitivity of the rotating wire electrode can be decreased to about 10 μamp./meq./l. by cutting off the exposed wire and using fine emery cloth to polish the stump flush with the surface of the glass (65).

Gold electrodes are more difficult to prepare because of the high coefficient of thermal expansion of gold. The original literature (66,67) must be consulted for details of construction. The mechanical problems can probably be circumvented by constructing a platinum electrode and gold-plating it (68), but nothing is known about any possible effects of variations of the thickness of the plate or of the manner in which it is deposited. Gold electrodes can be used to slightly more negative potentials than platinum electrodes because the overpotential for the evolution of hydrogen is larger on gold than on platinum. They are also more inert toward attack by some chemical oxidizing agents. But their other characteristics are so much like those of platinum electrodes that they have found very little practical use.

In supporting electrolytes whose ions are electrolytically inert, the range of potentials accessible to platinum electrodes is bounded by the potentials at which oxygen and hydrogen begin to be evolved at appreciable rates. These are approximately described by the equations

$$E_+ = 1.2 - 0.06\text{pH} \tag{8.23a}$$

$$E_- = -0.06\text{pH} \tag{8.23b}$$

where E_+ is the most positive and E_- the most negative potential accessible, both in volts versus S.C.E. The values depend on the sensitivity at which the current-potential curve is recorded, and that for E_+ also depends on the composition of the particular solution employed, so that these equations are no more than very rough guides to what can be expected. Mention may be made here of the growing custom of reporting the potentials at which the residual current differs by one microampere from an extrapolation of the intermediate linear part of the residual-current curve; this has the advantage of being objective and independent of the sensitivity employed, although the values will still depend on the electrode area. For gold electrodes the range is somewhat wider:

$$E_+ = 1.45 - 0.06\text{pH} \tag{8.24a}$$

$$E_- = -0.6 - 0.06\text{pH} \tag{8.24b}$$

except at pH values below about 2, where E_- is much less negative than eq. (8.24b) indicates. Moreover, the value of E_+ is misleading, for at least in some cases the gold oxide film formed at a potential roughly 0.6 v. less positive than E_+ acts as such an effective barrier to electron transfer that the electrode exhibits no voltammetric response between this potential and E_+ (67). For these two reasons the useful range of a gold electrode in $1F$ perchloric acid extends only from about $+0.85$ to -0.2 v. Chloride, cyanide, hydrazine, and other substances that facilitate the oxidation of platinum or gold or that are themselves oxidizable cause E_+ to shift toward a less positive value. The effect of chloride in acidic solutions is small with platinum but is nearly three quarters of a volt with gold. It is not known whether or how such substances affect the voltammetric response of a gold electrode at potentials where the oxide film prevents electron transfer in their absence.

Many important consequences result from the existence of oxide films on the surfaces of platinum and gold electrodes. The formation and reduction of the film give rise to anodic and cathodic residual currents. The nature of the electrode surface varies with potential and also depends on the prior history of the electrode. These variations usually affect the rates of electrode reactions, and in some cases may even alter their courses. The first detailed description of the effects of oxide formation and reduction on the residual-current curve was given by Kolthoff and Tanaka (69), and the first systematic studies of the properties and compositions of the oxide films were made soon thereafter by Lee, Adams, and Bricker (70) and by Anson and Lingane (71).

The direction of polarization has an important effect on the shape of the residual-current curve, as is illustrated by Fig. 8.8, where the arrows show the direction in which the potential was changed during the recording of each curve. Polarization toward increasingly positive potentials gives rise to an anodic wave; polarization toward increasingly negative potentials gives rise to a cathodic peak. The anodic wave reflects the formation of the oxide film. At sufficiently positive potentials this proceeds at a rate that is nearly constant and independent of potential, and so a plateau is observed. The cathodic peak reflects the reduction of the oxide film to metallic platinum. A peak is obtained even though the electrode is rotated, because there is only a limited amount of oxide present. The decay of current on the

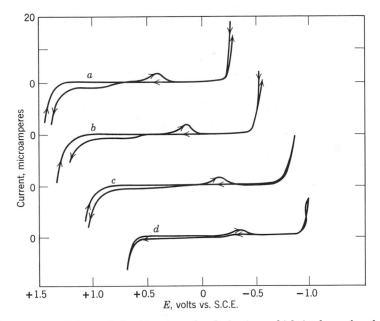

Figure 8.8. Effects of the direction of polarization, which is shown by the arrows on the curves, on the residual-current curves obtained with rotating platinum wire electrodes in (a) 0.1F perchloric acid, (b) an acetate buffer of pH 5, (c) a sodium borate solution of pH 9, and (d) 0.1F sodium hydroxide (66).

negative-potential side of the peak is due to the exhaustion of the oxide film, and the area under the peak is of course related to the amount of oxide present. Prolonged electrolysis at a potential on the plateau of the anodic wave causes the thickness of the film to approach a limiting value, which increases as the potential becomes more positive (72) and is typically of the order of a few hundred microcoulombs per square centimeter of projected electrode area. The shape of the peak is affected by the scan rate: the peak becomes wider as the scan rate increases. The anodic half-wave potential and the cathodic half-peak potential are not quite the same, because the half-reactions are irreversible, but their mean is in approximate agreement with the thermodynamic value for the potential of the hydrous platinum(IV) oxide–platinum couple, which is (73)

$$E = +0.80 - 0.06\text{pH} \tag{8.25}$$

In fact the situation appears to be even more complex than the fore-going discussion has implied: platinum(II) is found in the films as well as platinum(IV) (*71*), and both the cathodic and anodic patterns can be resolved into successive peaks whose positions and relative heights vary on changing the conditions under which the film is formed (*74*). Chemisorbed oxygen may be present instead of, or in addition to, the hydrous oxides as separate phases; in $0.1F$ sulfuric acid Visscher and Devanathan (*72*) concluded that the oxides begin to form only at potentials a quarter of a volt more positive than the value given by eq. (8.25). Chloride is found in the films formed at very positive potentials in chloride solutions, and the platinum(II): platinum(IV) ratios in such films are not the same as in chloride-free films (*75*).

Figure 8.9 shows the behavior of an electrode that has been allowed to stand at a potential so negative that hydrogen is evolved rapidly. Immediate polarization toward increasingly positive poten-tials yields an irregular residual-current curve with fairly large anodic currents, which are ascribed to the re-oxidation of adsorbed hydrogen. On the other hand, polarization from a very positive potential toward more negative ones gives first the cathodic peak due to dissolution of the oxide film formed at the start of the recording and then, at more

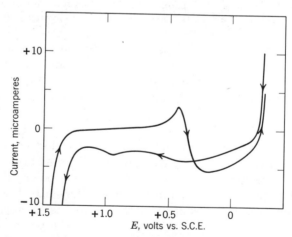

Figure 8.9.   Residual-current curves obtained with a rotating platinum wire electrode in air-free $0.1F$ perchloric acid after precathodization at -2.0 v. vs. S.C.E. Arrows show the direction of polarization (*66*).

negative potentials, an anodic current due to the re-oxidation of hydrogen. The shapes of these curves appear to reflect the fact that hydrogen is more rapidly oxidized at an oxide-free platinum surface than at one covered by a thick oxide film. Hence the anodic wave due to oxide formation is hardly visible on the curve obtained by polarization toward increasingly positive potentials, for the current due to the oxidation of hydrogen decreases as that due to the formation of oxide increases.

From the foregoing discussion it is evident that reproducible results cannot be obtained unless the pretreatment of the electrode is very carefully controlled. Kolthoff and Tanaka (69) recommended storing a platinum electrode in $6F$ nitric acid while it is not in use, thoroughly washing it with distilled water just before it is to be used, and then allowing it to stand at 0 v. vs. S.C.E. in air-free $0.1F$ perchloric acid until the current decays to a small and practically constant value, which typically requires 5 to 10 min. After this treatment the electrode is nominally "clean"—that is, free from both adsorbed hydrogen and surface oxides—although it is probably reasonable to doubt that it is completely so. How it should be used depends on both the range of potentials that is of interest and the direction of polarization that is to be employed. Reversing the direction of polarization often yields a significantly different curve, and so preliminary experiments are always needed to determine which direction is better suited to the purpose at hand. This is especially true when the region of interest includes the range over which the film is formed and destroyed.

It is convenient to divide the whole accessible range of potentials into two parts separated by the potential described by eq. (8.25). In addition, it must be recognized that forward and backward polarization may give quite different results, though for reasons that have nothing at all to do with the universal use of forward polarization in work with stationary electrodes in quiet solutions. Forward polarization is usually preferred because the electrode can be allowed to stand in the sample solution, with the starting potential applied to it, for as long as may be needed to reach equilibrium before the recording is begun. If a similar equilibration is attempted before backward polarization, however, the deposition or adsorption of the reaction product may foul the electrode surface and lead to curves that cannot be interpreted or reproduced. This is often the case in oxidations of amines and in other processes in which free radical polymerization can occur at the electrode surface, and also in the depositions of solid metals, in which even a monolayer of deposit can radically alter the nature of the surface. Fortunately there are only a few cases in which backward polarization is advantageous.

In work confined to potentials more negative than that described by eq. (8.25), the electrode can be used immediately after the pretreatment outlined above. Forward polarization can be used to obtain both cathodic and anodic waves in this region, and presents no problems except in dealing with materials so easily oxidized that the rising parts of their anodic waves occur very near the final current rise. To record such a wave by forward polarization it would be necessary to begin at a potential where hydrogen is fairly rapidly evolved, and the danger of doing this is made amply clear by Fig. 8.9. Backward polarization may then prove to be the lesser of two evils. As an anodic hydrogen wave does not seem to appear after brief slow evolution of hydrogen, however, difficulties do not arise when the recording is begun at a potential barely on the final current rise, and so forward polarization can be employed with the great majority of anodic waves.

In work at more positive potentials the oxide film should be allowed to form before the recording is begun. It reaches a nearly constant thickness on standing for 5 to 10 min. at a potential where only the residual current is obtained; at the end of this time the curve can be recorded with forward polarization. This preanodization improves both the limit of detection and the precision: the former because it decreases the residual current and the latter because it yields a more reproducible oxide film than can be obtained in any other way.

When the potential given by eq. (8.25) has to be crossed during the recording of the curve, the direction of polarization has to be selected by empirical trial. Substances like ferrous iron and hydrazine, which react chemically with a platinum oxide film, often give better defined and more reproducible waves when backward polarization is employed. To measure the limiting current of a substance whose half-wave potential is in this region, it is usually best to begin by allowing the electrode to stand in the supporting electrolyte alone at a potential known to be on the plateau. When the current has decayed to a small constant value, a concentrated stock solution of the electro-active substance should be added without disconnecting the electrode from the polarograph, and the current should then be measured as soon as stirring has rendered the solution homogeneous. Incidentally, it may be mentioned here that, since oxygen is not reduced over most of the range of potentials accessible with platinum electrodes, deaeration is usually unnecessary. One may use an H-cell, leaving the working-electrode compartment open to the air, or even a beaker with a reference electrode like that of Fig. 2.18.

Most commercially available polarographs are equipped for polarization in either direction. One that is equipped only for polarization toward increasingly negative potentials can be made to operate in the other direction simply by reversing the leads to the cell, so that the reference-electrode input terminal of the polarograph is connected to the platinum electrode. The sign of the potential being applied to the latter at any instant will then be opposite to that indicated by the instrument settings, and the sign of the recorded current will also be reversed. However, these are relatively trivial inconveniences.

Numerous other pretreatment procedures have been devised. The oxide film can be removed chemically by immersing the electrode in acidified ferrous sulfate or potassium iodide solutions, of which the former are preferable because iodine is strongly adsorbed onto platinum. Adsorbed hydrogen can be removed by treatment with air-saturated $0.1F$ perchloric acid or acidified ferric sulfate. An acidic solution containing both ferrous and ferric sulfates serves both purposes at once, and some workers prefer storing their electrodes in such a solution to pretreating them electrolytically just before use. Others prefer to oxidize the surface chemically with dichromate in sulfuric acid to remove adsorbed organic compounds, then to wash the electrode thoroughly with distilled water and allow it to stand in the sample solution for some time at the potential where the recording is to begin. This generally implies the use of forward polarization. Silver(II) in $6F$ nitric acid has been used instead of the acidic dichromate, and so has permanganate in concentrated sodium hydroxide, which should be followed by thorough washing with an oxalic acid solution to remove the manganese dioxide that precipitates. Still other workers have employed brief preanodization at a very positive potential, followed by electrolytic reduction of the resulting oxide film at a more negative potential; this gives very satisfactory results with gold electrodes (67). Yet others have employed several cycles of alternating preanodization and precathodization. There is no known

way to predict which of these techniques is likely to be the best suited
to any particular application that may be contemplated.

Mention has already been made of the effect of gold oxide films in
retarding electron transfer. Platinum oxide films also affect the
kinetics of electron-transfer processes, but (possibly because there
have been more investigations of platinum than of gold electrodes)
seem to do so in a less predictable way. A trace—something less than
a monolayer—of oxide has sometimes been said to accelerate electron
transfer (76–79), but it is generally agreed that a heavier deposit
almost always retards it. The thickness of the oxide film often exerts
drastic effects on the value of αn_a as well as on that of $Ak_{s,h}$, which
presumably means that the mechanism of the reaction is altered.
With hydrogen peroxide (80,81), hydrazine (65,82), and several
other substances (83) it appears that the increased rates of electron
transfer observed at electrodes apparently coated with oxide films are
actually due to the formation of very finely divided platinum—
essentially platinum black—on the electrode surface (84). This may
occur by the reaction of a chemical reducing agent with a film formed
by preanodization, or by the electrolytic reduction of a film formed
by the reaction of the metal with a strong chemical oxidizing agent.
Accordingly one could hardly expect an electrode that had never been
exposed to oxidizing conditions to manifest exactly the same behavior
as one that had been oxidized and then reduced just before use; even
though the surfaces of both were free from oxide, their structures
would be quite different. As platinum black is known to become less
active on standing, it follows that the characteristics of a platinum
surface that has been oxidized and then reduced will also depend on
the length of time that elapses between the reduction and the instant
when the electrode is used, and on the conditions to which the
electrode is exposed during this interval. Scrupulous attention to
experimental detail is absolutely essential in work with noble-metal
electrodes regardless of their configuration.

These difficulties can often be greatly mitigated by scanning only
a portion of the current-potential curve at a time, either that where
the surface remains free from oxide or that throughout which an oxide
film of substantial thickness is present. Even better results may be
obtained by using a manual polarograph. If the electrode is allowed
to stand for even a minute or two at each potential before the current
is measured, the surface will come to a much more nearly reproducible

state, the residual current will decay to a value much smaller than the transient one that would flow at the same potential during the recording of the curve, and both the precision and the limit of detection will be much improved. In the region of potentials over which an oxide film is present, its thickness will change as the potential changes, which complicates the thermodynamic and kinetic interpretation of the waves obtained, but in analytical work at least this is of little moment. Partly for this reason, rotating platinum wire electrodes have been much more widely used for amperometric titrations, in which the potential is kept constant throughout, than for voltammetry.

III. Other Solid Electrodes

Attempts to obviate the difficulties caused by the formation of oxide films on noble metals have led to the study and use of several other materials that have proved to be more inert. The most popular of these so far has been the graphite electrode, which is usually made from a rod of spectroscopic graphite having a diameter of about $\frac{1}{4}$ in. Because Lord and Rogers (66) reported disappointing results with a rotating graphite electrode, most experimenters have employed stationary graphite electrodes in quiet solutions, although they have also been used in stirred solutions with satisfactory results (85,86). Untreated electrodes give high and irregular residual currents; these are greatly decreased by thorough impregnation with wax, which also improves the precisions of measurements of limiting currents and half-wave or half-peak potentials. Ceresin wax is the most widely used, although castor wax gives smaller residual currents (85). The impregnation is best done by immersing the electrode in molten wax at 125° C., evacuating to a pressure of about 25 mm. of mercury for about ten minutes to remove as much entrapped gas as possible from the pores of the rod, then removing it from the wax, drying the surface, and coating it with Seal-All (Allen Products Co., Detroit 34, Michigan) (87). The Seal-All serves to insulate the cylindrical surface, so that only the end of the rod comes into contact with the solution. Consequently, mass transfer to the active surface occurs by unrestricted linear diffusion if the solution is unstirred. Some workers have preferred an epoxy resin to the Seal-All (88,89). One end of the rod is exposed by breaking it, by using a small manual lathe to remove a millimeter or so from its end, or by sanding with fine aluminum oxide paper. The last of these is the most economical, though it must be carefully done to avoid breaking the rather fragile rod and to ensure that the exposed plane is reasonably accurately perpendicular to the axis of the rod, which is necessary because variations of electrode area will be reflected by corresponding variations of the peak current, or of the limiting current if the solution is stirred. To prevent the accumulation of deposited or adsorbed material on the electrode surface, this treatment must be repeated just before each curve is recorded. Elving and Smith (90) further recommended immersing the freshly exposed surface in an aqueous 0.003% solution of Triton X-100 for a minute or two just before use. They found that the electrode was then thoroughly wetted by the solution of the sample, which is not true if this treatment is omitted, and that more reproducible currents were obtained because the effective area of the electrode was more reproducible. The experimenter employing this treatment should be aware of the danger that the adsorbed Triton will affect the value of αn_a for a totally irreversible process and thereby alter both the peak current and the half-peak potential.

To use the electrode it is only necessary to immerse its exposed end in the sample solution. There has been no proof that precathodization or preanodization, though essential with platinum, are necessary with graphite. As is true with any other electrode, dissolved air need not be removed from the solution unless the substance being investigated or its reduction or oxidation product is sensitive to air-oxidation, or unless measurements are to be made at potentials where oxygen is reduced. These eventualities are somewhat more likely to arise with graphite than with platinum electrodes, for the former are useful to much more negative potentials. They have been most used, however, at fairly positive potentials, which are the most interesting in solid-electrode voltammetry because they are inaccessible to mercury electrodes. Electrical connection to the rod is most easily made with an alligator clip.

Graphite is useful to both more positive and more negative potentials than platinum. Its range is from about +1.3 to −1.3 v. at pH values between 1 and 7, and from about +1.0 to −1.6 v. at pH 10; if an electrode is prepared as recommended above, it will give residual currents that are very small except near the extremes of this range. An electrode that has simply been dipped in or painted with molten wax cannot be used to quite as negative potentials, but the positive limit of its range will be about the same as for a thoroughly impregnated electrode. An electrode prepared by this simpler procedure gives larger and less regular residual currents, but these have little effect on its utility in exploratory work.

Morris and Schempf (87), who did not employ the treatment with Triton X-100 recommended above, obtained very reproducible results with graphite electrodes: their peak currents and half-peak potentials had mean deviations of only ±1.4% and ±2 mv., respectively. However, this is optimum rather than typical performance. In particular, it must be mentioned that electrodes prepared by repeatedly resurfacing a single graphite rod give distinctly more reproducible results than those prepared from different rods (90).

As can be seen from eq. (8.1), the sensitivity of a stationary electrode in an unstirred solution should be described by the parameter $i_p/n^{3/2}Cv^{1/2}$. In the units employed in eq. (8.1), this has a value of the order of 200 for an electrode $\frac{1}{4}$ in. in diameter: that is, i_p will be about 10 μamp. if n is 1, C is 1mM, and v is 0.002 v./sec. Under these conditions a limiting current of perhaps 500 μamp. might be obtained by stirring the solution efficiently.

It has already been mentioned that graphite electrodes, like the other electrodes included in this section, have been most widely used for studying processes that occur at relatively positive potentials. These have included the oxidations of such organic compounds as amines and phenols, the reductions of such substances as chlorine, dichromate, and permanganate, and the anodic stripping of such metals as silver and gold. They are preferable to noble-metal electrodes for these purposes because they give cleaner residual-current curves and more reproducible data. However, one should not expect to obtain identical data with electrodes prepared in different ways. For example, electrodes impregnated with different waxes have been reported (85) to give half-wave potentials (in stirred solutions) that differ by as much as 70 mv. for the oxidation of N,N'-di-sec-butyl-p-phenylenediamine under otherwise identical conditions. More often than not, in fact, the voltammetric characteristics of a substance depend on the electrode with which it is examined. Copper(II) in 2F hydrochloric acid gives a double wave at a glassy carbon electrode, but only a single wave at a pyrolytic graphite electrode. Hydrazine gives an anodic wave at a platinum electrode but not at a graphite electrode. The cathodic wave of p-benzoquinone and the anodic wave of p-benzohydroquinone have half-wave potentials that are identical at dropping mercury electrodes in nearly neutral solutions, but that differ by several tenths of a volt at graphite electrodes. In $0.1F$ sodium perchlorate the half-wave potential of the first wave of oxygen, which corresponds to reduction to hydrogen peroxide, is -0.05 v. vs. S.C.E. at a dropping mercury electrode, but is -0.4 v. at a rotating platinum wire electrode. Some of these effects can be attributed to electron-transfer mechanisms that involve bridging to or adsorption on the electrode surface, and in such cases the nature of the surface can be expected to have an important influence on the results obtained. At rotating electrodes or electrodes used in stirred solutions, the current density is considerably larger than at a dropping mercury electrode or at a stationary electrode used in an unstirred solution at a scan rate of the order of a few millivolts per second. A process that is rapid enough to appear reversible at electrodes of the latter class may demonstrate marked irreversibility at those of the former. As would be expected, the half-wave potentials of irreversible cathodic waves shift toward more negative values (while those of irreversible anodic waves shift toward more positive ones) on rotating the electrode or stirring the solution, and at the same time the waves become more drawn out.

Several authors (88–92) have described the fabrication and charac-teristics of pyrolytic graphite electrodes; the original literature should be consulted for details. As the behaviors of wax-impregnated graphite electrodes are generally assumed to be insensitive to electrolytic pretreatment, it seems worthwhile to note that this is untrue of pyrolytic graphite electrodes. Beilby et al. (89) found that the ferricyanide–ferrocyanide couple in $0.5F$ potassium chloride behaved irreversibly at electrodes that had been unused for a long time or that had been exposed to a very positive potential (e.g., $+1.5$ v. vs. S.C.E.) just before use. However, the couple behaved reversibly, and much more reproducible curves were obtained, if the electrode was allowed to stand in the supporting electrolyte for 15 min. at $+1.5$ v. and then for 5 min. at -0.3 v. before use. That such phenomena should be observed at an electrode that is more inert and less con-taminated with occluded impurities than ordinary graphite suggests that electrolytic pretreatment of an ordinary graphite electrode may be more germane to its behavior than is usually presumed. Some advantages have been claimed for glassy carbon electrodes (92a):

being isotropic, these need not be oriented in a particular way, unlike pyrolytic graphite electrodes, and they are said to require no pretreatment.

Boron carbide was first employed by Adams and co-workers (*10,11,93*) and is receiving increasing attention. It can be obtained from the Norton Company (Worcester, Massachusetts), most conveniently as cylindrical rods about ¾ in. long and $^3/_{16}$ in. in diameter. The electrical resistance of each rod should be tested before use; some rods have resistances so high (2–5×10^4 ohms) that they are unsuitable for the purpose. Mueller and Adams (*11*) contrived several ways of constructing a mantle to provide restricted linear diffusion, but for most voltammetric work it is easier to mount the electrode in a Teflon cylinder, about an inch in diameter and two or three inches long, through which an axial hole, having a diameter just smaller than that of the rod, has been drilled. A rod is broken in half, washed thoroughly with carbon tetrachloride and then with hot concentrated nitric acid, dried, and forced into the hole so that its unbroken end just protrudes above one face of the cylinder. It is then carefully ground, and finally polished with fine diamond powder, until it is just flush with the Teflon. Electrical connection is made by dipping a wire into a few drops of mercury placed in the well above the boron carbide. By forcing a glass tube of suitable size into the open end of the well, the electrode may be rotated, or it may be kept stationary while the solution is stirred or used as an unrestricted linear diffusion electrode in an unstirred solution. With an assembly that provided restricted linear diffusion, Mueller and Adams obtained peak currents precise to $\pm 1\%$ and half-peak potentials reproducible within a few millivolts, figures comparable with the best that have been obtained with wax-impregnated or pyrolytic graphite electrodes. Wax impregnation or other pretreatment is unnecessary with boron carbide, and so—at least under conditions where the electrode surface does not become fouled with adsorbed or deposited films—is the continual resurfacing traditional with wax-impregnated graphite electrodes. Boron carbide electrodes prepared in the above manner sometimes give high and erratic residual currents, but these can be decreased by polarization at $+1.0$ v. vs. S.C.E. in $1F$ nitric acid. In a brief investigation (*93a*) of the use of boron carbide electrodes in controlled-potential coulometry (Chap. 10 II), the quantity of electricity was found to depend on the electrode potential in a manner so anomalous as to suggest that the nature of a boron carbide surface may be considerably affected by its previous treatment.

Figure 8.6 showed an annular rotating disc electrode for use with carbon paste. The paste is made (94) by grinding pure powdered carbon or graphite with just enough Nujol or bromonaphthalene to give a workable consistency, and is packed as tightly as possible into a well as shown in the figure. Ordinary rotating disc electrodes can of course be assembled in the same fashion, and provide unrestricted linear diffusion when held stationary in quiet solutions. Carbon paste electrodes give appreciable cathodic residual currents at potentials where oxygen is reduced, presumably because of dissolved air in the solvent used to prepare the paste. Nevertheless, the reductions of a number of metal ions and difficultly reducible organic substances can be accomplished (95), and carbon paste electrodes can also be used for anodic stripping voltammetry (95a). At more positive potentials the residual currents are very small. The ranges of potential accessible with boron carbide and carbon paste electrodes are about the same as for wax-impregnated graphite electrodes. Carbon paste is too plastic to be used in some configurations, and it is also attacked by many organic solvents; both of these problems may be obviated by the use of carbon wax (95b) prepared by mixing 5 parts by weight of powdered graphite with 4 of molten ceresin wax and molding or machining the cooled mixture as desired.

Brief mention may be made of the rotating oxidized tungsten wire electrode (96). This is prepared by sealing a tungsten wire through the end of a Pyrex tube in one of the ways shown in Fig. 8.7. The exposed portion of the wire is cleaned by dipping it into fused sodium nitrite, and its surface is then oxidized for three hours in a current of air at 475°, which gives a tightly adherent film of tungsten hemi-pentoxide. The electrode is used in the same way as a platinum electrode. It gives residual currents that are small between about $+1.7$ and 0 v. vs. S.C.E. in $1F$ perchloric acid, about $+1.7$ and -0.2 v. at pH 7, and about 0 and -1.4 v. in $0.1F$ sodium hyhroxide. At potentials more positive than $+1.7$ v. in $1F$ perchloric acid, appreciable anodic currents arise from oxidation of the hemipentoxide to WO_3, but with care these can be reproduced closely enough to permit the electrode to be used to about $+3.1$ v. This is a value far more positive than can be obtained with any other known electrode in an aqueous solution. The behavior of an oxidized tungsten electrode is even more sensitive to the pretreatment, direction of polarization, and like variables than that of a platinum electrode is, for the hemi-pentoxide can be reduced to WO_2 as well as oxidized to WO_3. Nevertheless, these electrodes are uniquely well suited to work at very positive potentials in acidic and neutral media.

IV. Mercury Electrodes

For work at potentials where mercury is oxidized there is no real practical alternative to the use of a solid indicator electrode. Enough has been said in the two preceding sections, however, to show that it is not at all easy to secure a well characterized or even a satisfactorily reproducible solid surface. It is largely for this reason that no solid electrode yet devised yields as precise results as can be obtained with a dropping mercury electrode. Mercury electrodes of other types also

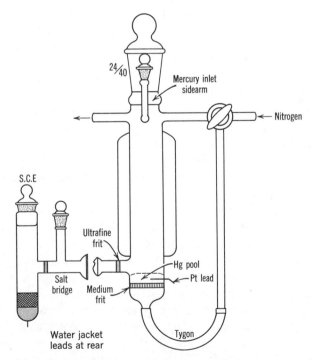

Figure 8.10.   Glass cell for voltammetry with a quiet mercury pool electrode in an unstirred solution (*22*).

have reproducible surfaces of known geometry, and may have
sensitivities and limits of detection much more favorable than those
of dropping electrodes.

Mercury pool electrodes have been most extensively investigated
by Cooke and his co-workers. For work with a quiet pool in an
unstirred solution, Streuli and Cooke (22) employed the cell shown
in Fig. 8.10. The glass must be thoroughly covered with Desicote to
prevent solution from creeping between the mercury and the cell
walls and especially from coming into contact with the platinum lead
wire. Other problems arise when glass cells are used in work with
extremely dilute solutions. Heavy metal cations are adsorbed onto
the glass, undoubtedly by an ion-exchange mechanism (97); this
decreases their concentration in the solution being studied and usually
results in the contamination of a subsequent solution. One consequence of this behavior is that a standard solution of a heavy metal
cation is often rather difficult to prepare in glass vessels if the concentration is much less than about $10^{-6}M$ (29); even at this level half of
the cation may be lost in a short time (98). Sometimes it is helpful to
acidify the solution strongly, but it is much better to convert such
cations to anionic complexes by the addition of such ligands as
citrate, tartrate, or ethylenediaminetetraacetate. Another approach
is to use a cell made from polystyrene or an acrylic plastic such as
Lucite, which are not wetted by water; the cell shown in Fig. 8.11 is
convenient for this purpose. In any event, attention should be paid
to the danger that hydrolytic precipitation of hydrous heavy metal
oxides may occur from dilute neutral unbuffered solutions of the
cations onto the cell walls.

Peaked current-potential curves are of course obtained with quiet
mercury pool electrodes. Streuli and Cooke (9) found that the peak
current was proportional to concentration for each of a number of
metal ions that were reversibly reduced to amalgams, the mean
deviation of i_p/C being about ± 2 to 3% for values of C between
0.005 and 0.1mM. The half-peak potentials were usually independent
of concentration over this range and, as expected from eq. (8.3), were
nearly equal to the polarographic half-wave potentials. For some
organic substances, though not for all, the ratio i_p/C decreased as the
concentration increased. This may simply reflect neglect of the
correction described by eq. (8.9).

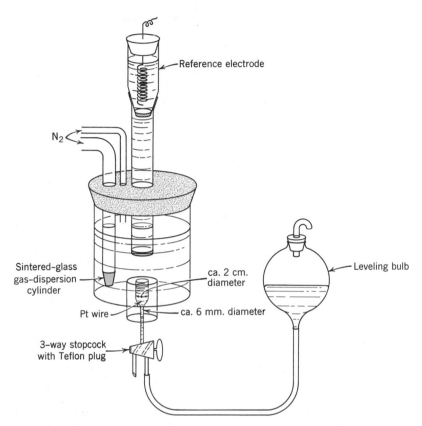

Figure 8.11.   Polystyrene or acrylic plastic cell for voltammetry with a quiet mercury pool electrode. When stirring is desired the reference electrode may be moved to one side and a propeller-type stirrer mounted above the pool.

Streuli and Cooke concluded that the ratio i_r/i_p of the residual current to the peak current was only about a tenth as large as the corresponding ratio, i_r/i_d, for a dropping electrode. Equation (8.8) may be consulted regarding the effects of changes in the experimental conditions on this comparison. If the relative uncertainties in measurements of the residual current were the same for the two electrodes, this would mean that the quiet mercury pool had a lower limit of detection about a tenth that of the dropping electrode under the conditions they employed. In fact, however, the limit of detection for

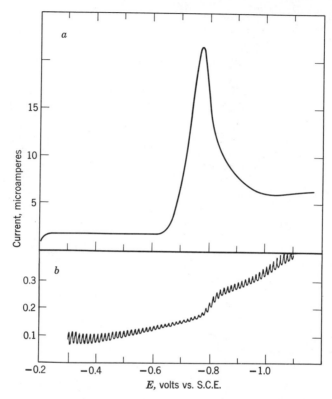

Figure 8.12. Current–potential curves for 0.01mM azobenzene in 0.1F lithium hydroxide containing 1% ethanol: (a) with a quiet mercury pool at a scan rate of 6.7 mv./sec., and (b) with a dropping mercury electrode (21).

the quiet pool is probably well below this, as may be inferred from Fig. 8.12. It is clear that the correction for the residual current will involve much less uncertainty on the quiet pool voltammogram than on the polarogram.

Of even greater interest is the fact (22) that many organic compounds behave quite differently at quiet mercury pool and dropping electrodes. For example, in 0.1F ammonia–0.1F ammonium chloride the half-wave potential of 1-nitroso-2-naphthol is −0.27 v. vs. S.C.E. at a dropping electrode, but the half-peak potential is −0.80 v. at a quiet pool. The half-wave potentials of nitrobenzene and of the first wave of *m*-dinitrobenzene are nearly the same in solutions having a pH of 3 and containing 10% ethanol at a dropping electrode, but at a quiet pool the wave of *m*-dinitrobenzene precedes that of nitrobenzene sufficiently to permit the determination of 0.005mM *m*-dinitrobenzene in the presence of 0.1mM nitrobenzene. Similarly, γ-hexachlorocyclohexane can be determined in the presence of a severalfold excess of heptachlorocyclohexanes (99), although at a dropping electrode their waves overlap to such an extent that the determination is impossible polarographically. These effects are due, of course, to side reactions occurring in the diffusion layer. Because no such reactions are possible in the reductions of most simple metal ions, these behave very similarly at the dropping electrode and the quiet pool. So do substances, such as quinones, whose reductions are straightforward. With nitro and nitroso compounds, oximes, carbonyl compounds, and others whose reductions take place by relatively complicated mechanisms, however, considerable differences can be expected if not as yet predicted. The quiet pool electrode may provide easy solutions to many problems of wave order and wave separation in which these substances are involved.

The use of the quiet pool in characterizing the products of electrode reactions is illustrated by Fig. 8.13, in which the curve labeled "reverse" shows an anodic peak for the product (presumably 9,10-anthracenediol-1,6-disulfonate) of the reduction that occurred during the first portion of the scan. This is closely akin to the useful technique of cyclic triangular-wave voltammetry (100,101).

Streuli and Cooke (9) reported that the final current rise began at a less negative potential at a quiet pool than at a dropping mercury electrode; the difference was usually several tenths of a volt. This is partly because the beginning of the final current rise at a dropping electrode is masked by the nearly linear increase of the charging current with potential: until the exponentially increasing faradaic current resulting from the reduction of the solvent or supporting electrolyte becomes an appreciable fraction of the charging current, it is likely to escape notice altogether. At the quiet pool, however, where the charging-current curve is nearly flat, the faradaic current becomes detectable at a much earlier stage. The problem becomes much more severe if the solution can come into contact with the platinum wire used for making electrical connection to the pool. At fairly negative potentials, where the interfacial tension between the

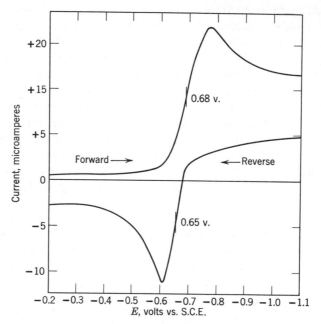

Figure 8.13. Current–potential curves obtained with a quiet mercury pool electrode for 0.06mM anthraquinone-1,6-disulfonate in 0.1F lithium hydroxide. The upper curve, obtained by forward polarization, shows only the cathodic peak. The lower one, obtained by backward polarization, does not show the cathodic peak for the reason described on p. 413, but does show an anodic peak for the product of the cathodic half-reaction (21). Reproduced by permission of *Analytical Chemistry*.

mercury and the solution is small, creeping of the solution around the sides of the mercury may be fairly pronounced in a glass cell even at low scan rates, and it becomes worse at high scan rates because these increase the rate of change of the radius of curvature of the electrode surface. Especially in work at potentials anywhere near the final current rise on a polarogram, useful results are much more likely to be secured in the cell of Fig. 8.11 than in that of Fig. 8.10.

The sensitivity of a pool electrode is greatly increased by stirring the solution (98). In the cells of Figs. 8.10 and 8.11, this is easily done by means of a propeller-type glass stirrer accurately centered above the electrode and rotated at a constant speed by a synchronous motor. The pitch of the propeller and its direction of rotation must be such that solution is forced downward onto the electrode surface; otherwise the currents are much less reproducible. Vortex formation and the transmission of vibration from the stirrer to the cell must also be avoided. The distance between the stirrer and the pool is very important: doubling it causes the limiting current to decrease 15 to 25%. A distance of 5 to 10 mm. is most convenient. The current increases linearly with the rate of revolution of the propeller over a range that depends on the shape and dimensions of the propeller and the geometry of the cell. A small two-bladed propeller rotated at 600 r.p.m. by a small synchronous motor gives satisfactory results, but it is probably better to employ a stirrer so large and so rapidly rotated that the current attains a constant value independent of further increases in stirring rate (102). As is characteristic of electrodes to which mass transfer occurs by convection rather than diffusion, the limiting current is virtually independent of the scan rate, but slightly smoother residual-current curves are obtained at lower scan rates. Different arrangements have been proposed by others (103,104).

The resulting sensitivity, i_l/nC, is of the order of 1000 μamp./ meq./l., which is roughly 200 times as large as that for a dropping electrode. It may be increased still further, to values between 50 and 100 ma./meq./l. (105), by increasing the area of the electrode to about 40 cm.^{2} and allowing the propeller to trail in the mercury–solution interface, as is done in controlled-potential electrolysis to maximize the mass-transfer coefficients. In view of the high sensitivities of quiet pool electrodes in stirred solutions, and the even higher ones of stirred pool electrodes, the very greatest care must be taken to exclude trace impurities. The residual current is very greatly increased by even a few parts per million of oxygen in the gas stream used for deaeration or of an electroactive heavy metal ion in the supporting electrolyte. Electrolytic purification of the supporting electrolyte (Chap. 7 IV-A) is strongly recommended; if this is not done, it is advisable to use as dilute a supporting electrolyte as possible while avoiding unduly large iR drops through the cell. The limit of detection is hard to estimate, but Fig. 8.14 shows that it is certainly far below that of the dropping electrode; under optimum conditions it may be as small as $10^{-8}M$.

Because the sensitivities of these electrodes are so high, depletion of the bulk of the solution proceeds at a significant rate, and this causes the limiting current to decay exponentially with time if the

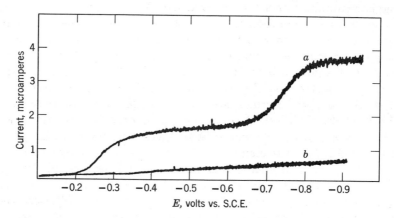

Figure 8.14. (*a*) Current–potential curve for 0.0002mM *p*-dinitrobenzene in 0.01F sodium acetate–0.01F acetic acid, obtained with a mercury pool electrode in a stirred solution; (*b*) residual-current curve (*90*). Reproduced by permission of *Analytical Chemistry*.

potential is kept constant at a value on the plateau. The limiting current $i_{l,0}$ at zero time may be related to the initial concentration C_0 by combining eqs. (8.11), (8.12), and (8.17); since

$$(\partial C/\partial x)_{x=0} = C_0/\delta \qquad (8.26)$$

on the plateau, because C^0 (the concentration at the electrode surface) is zero there, one obtains

$$i_{l,0} = nFDAC_0/\delta \qquad (8.27)$$

The value of δ in these equations cannot be described theoretically, as it can for the rotating disc electrode [cf. eq. (8.13)]; it has to be regarded as an empirical parameter, and very little can be said about it except that its value decreases on increasing the efficiency of stirring. One also has

$$dC/dt = -(i_l/nFV) \qquad (8.28)$$

which may be combined with eq. (8.27) to yield (*38*)

$$i_l = i_{l,0} \exp\left[-(DA/V\delta)\,t\right] \qquad (8.29)$$

Comparing eqs. (8.22) and (8.27) shows that the sensitivity k in the former is given by

$$k = FDA/\delta \qquad (8.30)$$

so that eq. (8.29) can be written

$$i_l = i_{l,0} \exp\left[-(k/FV)\,t\right] \qquad (8.31)$$

For $\delta = 0.003$ cm., eq. (8.31) yields $k = 1000$ amp./eq./cm.^{3} (or, in more convenient units, 1000 μamp./meq./l.), which is identical with the experimental value of Rosie and Cooke. Since $F = 10^5$ coulombs per equivalent very nearly, eq. (8.31) becomes approximately

$$i_l = i_{l,0} \exp\left(-0.01t/V\right) \qquad (8.32)$$

under these conditions, V being the volume of the solution in cubic centimeters. If this is, say, 25 cm.^{3}, as it was in the experiments of Rosie and Cooke, the limiting current should decrease approximately 0.04%/sec. A more detailed treatment was given by Lee (103).

This has two consequences. One is that the limiting current measured from a current-potential curve is slightly affected by the scan rate: the smaller the scan rate, the greater the extent to which the solution is depleted during the time required to scan the rising portion of the wave and reach the potential where the limiting current is measured. In a typical case Rosie and Cooke found that the limiting current decreased 4% on decreasing the scan rate from 100 to 20 mv./min. The effect obviously increases as k increases: voltammograms obtained with a large pool whose surface is efficiently stirred show peaks very like those obtained with stationary electrodes in quiet solutions (106), differing only in that the depletion extends throughout the solution instead of being confined to the diffusion layer. It is advisable to use as high a scan rate and as large a volume of solution as convenient.

The other is that, as is also true with the quiet pool electrode, the stirred pool can be used to study and characterize the products of electrode reactions. An example is shown in Fig. 8.15, in which the lower curve of each pair was obtained by electrolysis, at a potential on the plateau of the cathodic wave, until the current had decayed to half of its original value. In view of eq. (8.32), this must have required about half an hour under these conditions; a minute or two would

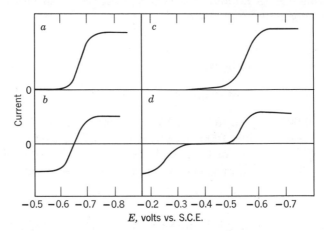

Figure 8.15. Current–potential curves for azobenzene, obtained with a mercury pool electrode in a stirred solution: (*a*) in 0.1*F* lithium hydroxide; (*b*) same, after reduction of half of the azobenzene at a potential on the plateau of its cathodic wave; (*c*) in 0.1*F* ammonia–0.1*F* ammonium chloride; (*d*) same as (*c*), after reduction of half of the azobenzene at a potential on the plateau of its cathodic wave (*90*). The difference between curves (*b*) and (*d*) reflects the influence of pH on the rate of the benzidine rearrangement.

suffice with a large pool whose surface was efficiently stirred. In the latter case one should obtain information very similar to that provided by backward polarization at a quiet pool, but in the former one may obtain quite different results because so much more time is available for decomposition of a metastable intermediate.

The limit of detection at a stirred mercury pool electrode is governed by the noise level in the residual-current curve, which may be seen from Fig. 8.14 to be appreciable. It reflects the turbulence produced by stirring, is more pronounced if the stirrer trails in the electrode–solution interface than if it is some distance above it, and is aggravated by any vibration transmitted from the stirrer shaft to the cell. It produces random fluctuations of the electrode area, and these in turn lead to both positive and negative surges of charging current. Much cleaner residual-current curves are obtained with the hanging mercury drop electrode, which was first used by Melik–Gaikazyan (*107*) and Gerischer (*108*) and which is much used in anodic stripping voltammetry (Chap. 10 V), where the limit of detection is lower at a hanging drop electrode than at any other. The hanging drop electrode gives more reproducible currents than most other stationary electrodes that have been devised, and its geometry is simple enough that exact descriptions of diffusion-controlled currents have been possible to obtain. Differences between observed currents and those calculated for diffusion-controlled processes can, therefore, be used to identify, and also to study the rates of, chemical reactions accompanying electrode reactions.

Hanging drop electrodes have been made in three ways. The drop may be hung onto a fine gold- or mercury-plated platinum wire sealed through, and barely protruding from, the end of a glass tube (29,108). A variant (109) is shown in Fig. 8.16. The surface of the 26- to 30-gauge platinum wire and the surrounding glass are polished flat, then a few tenths of a millimeter of the platinum is dissolved by hot aqua regia, and finally the platinum surface is covered with mercury by electrodeposition from an acidic fairly concentrated solution of mercurous perchlorate. When enough mercury has been deposited, its surface will be touched by that of a mercury drop brought up to the tip, and cohesion will then hold the drop in place. Electrical contact is thus made without danger of exposing a platinum or gold surface. A drop of known size is most conveniently obtained by means of a conventional dropping-electrode assembly for which the drop mass mt has been measured. A drop having an accurately known mass between about 6 and 25 mg. is obtained by collecting one to three droplets from the dropping electrode on a glass or Teflon scoop, which is then rotated to bring the drop in contact with the tip of the hanging drop assembly. A slightly modified cell suitable for work with as little as 0.5 ml. of solution has been devised (110).

Other experimenters (111–114) have employed syringe-type burets. By manipulation of a micrometer screw bearing on the plunger of the syringe, an accurately known volume of mercury may be forced through a capillary to form a droplet on its tip. As the cubical coefficient of thermal expansion of mercury is fairly large, about 0.018%/deg., this arrangement resembles a giant thermometer. If the total volume of mercury in the apparatus is 1 ml., the area of a 6-mg. drop will increase about 20% if the temperature rises one degree. The effect decreases as the size of the drop increases. But in any case the volume of the apparatus should be as small as possible and every precaution should be taken to minimize fluctuations of temperature.

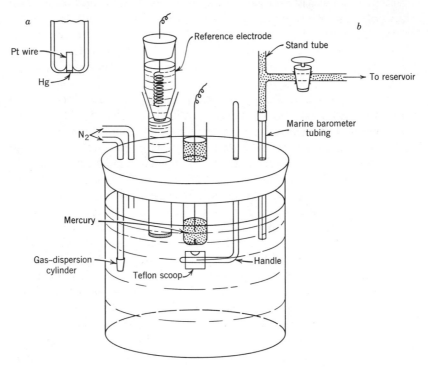

Figure 8.16.   (a) Support for hanging mercury drop electrode; (b) cell for use with hanging mercury drop electrodes.

Čermák (115) employed a much simpler arrangement, in which a stopcock between the stand tube and capillary of a conventional dropping-electrode assembly is closed at an instant when there is a droplet of suitable size on the capillary tip. Electrical connection to the droplet must, of course, be made by a wire located between the stopcock and the capillary.

The first two of these designs are suitable for quantitative work because they make it possible to obtain drops of known volumes and areas, but the third is not because it is impossible to control, and very difficult to measure, the drop size.

The hanging drop electrode is a stationary spherical electrode. Laitinen and Kolthoff (18) attempted to verify the theoretical equations for diffusion to a stationary spherical platinum microelectrode, and failed because they employed electrolysis times so long that the thickness of the depleted layer of solution around the electrode became substantial. Convection accordingly became very pronounced, and gave rise to high and irregular currents. Large deviations from the theoretical dependence of current on time begin to become apparent when the electrolysis time is even as long as 30 sec. (*115*) and are probably appreciable even at times well below this. Although lower scan rates can be employed in much qualitative work, quantitative work generally demands scan rates at least as high as 10 mv./sec. There are several polarographs manufactured abroad (including the Czechoslovakian LP 60 and the Japanese Shimadzu RP-2) that will provide such scan rates together with chart speeds high enough to yield curves of reasonable length, but the only American one that will do so is the Model FS Polarograph manufactured by E. H. Sargent & Co.

The current-potential curve obtained with a hanging drop electrode at suitably high scan rates is peaked, like that for a plane linear-diffusion electrode. In the latter case, the current decays exponentially toward zero as time goes on at potentials on the plateau, but at a spherical electrode there is a finite steady-state current even in the absence of convection, and so the slope is visibly smaller beyond the peak than it is with the plane electrode. At the same time, the peak current is larger at the hanging drop electrode than that given by eq. (8.1) for a plane electrode having the same area. The original literature (*7,8,35*) must be consulted for details; only a very abbreviated summary can be given here. For the reversible reduction of O to a dissolved species R, the peak current at a stationary spherical electrode of radius r cm. is described by the equation

$$ i_p = 2.687 \times 10^5 n^{3/2} A D_O^{1/2} C_O v^{1/2} \left[1 + \frac{0.269}{r} \left(\frac{D_O}{nv} \right)^{1/2} \right] $$

$$ (8.33) $$

if the quantity $D_O^{1/2}/rn^{1/2}v^{1/2}$ is small—that is, if r or v is large. This is the experimentally useful range: a very small drop of exactly known size would be very difficult to obtain, and low scan rates are useless because of the convection to which they give rise. Under typical conditions ($D_O = 6 \times 10^{-6}$ cm.^{2}/sec., $r = 0.05$ cm., $n = 1$ faraday/mole, and $v = 0.02$ v./sec.), the value of $D_O^{1/2}/rn^{1/2}v^{1/2}$ is about 0.3, and so the peak current at a hanging drop electrode is approximately 8% larger than at a plane linear-diffusion electrode of equal area. At very large values of this quantity the peak current increases more rapidly than eq. (8.33) predicts, the peak potential shifts to a value more negative than that described by eq. (8.2), and the peak width increases.

From eq. (8.33) it is evident that the parameter $i_p/n^{3/2}Cv^{1/2}$ provides only an imperfect description of the sensitivity of a hanging drop electrode because its value varies with $D_0^{1/2}/rn^{1/2}v^{1/2}$. Nevertheless, it can be said that, at scan rates of the order of 0.025 v./sec., the hanging drop electrode yields peak currents of the same order of magnitude as the diffusion currents obtained at the dropping mercury electrode. The limit of detection is about an order of magnitude lower for the hanging drop electrode, however, for it gives a cleaner residual-current curve. As is shown by eqs. (8.8) and (8.33), increasing the scan rate increases the sensitivity but also raises the limit of detection. Although the hanging drop electrode is better suited than the dropping electrode to work at concentrations between 0.01 and 0.001mM, it is not as well adapted to the analysis of mixtures for the reason explained in connection with Fig. 8.2.

This limitation can be at least partially circumvented by taking advantage of the fact that the current decays fairly rapidly at a potential just beyond a peak. After the first peak has been recorded, the electrode may be maintained at a constant potential slightly more negative than the peak potential (assuming the peak to be cathodic) for perhaps 15 to 20 sec. while the current decays, then the scan may be resumed for the recording of the second peak. The technique is better suited to qualitative than to quantitative work because of the danger that appreciable convection will develop. Martin and Shain (116) developed a differential procedure which is better though experimentally more complicated. Two hanging drop electrodes are used. One is placed in the sample and the other in a solution of the supporting electrolyte alone. The electrical circuitry is so designed that identical potentials are applied to the two electrodes at every instant, while the difference between the currents flowing through them is recorded as a function of their common potential. With the second electrode in a blank solution, this provides compensation for the residual current. The blank may then be titrated with a solution of the most easily reducible substance present in the sample until the first peak disappears from the differential curve; the height of the second peak can then be measured without difficulty. In this way it is possible to obtain a precision of about $\pm 2\%$ in determining 0.02mM cadmium ion in the presence of 1.0mM thallous ion.

Similar procedures can be used with an electrode of any type. The first technique would be more effective at a plane linear-diffusion electrode, partly because convection can be rendered negligible over a much longer period of time and partly because the current due to the first peak decays farther and more rapidly. With a large stirred pool electrode, where depletion of the whole solution is rapid and can be made quantitative (cf. Chap. 7 III-F) even though the difference of half-wave potentials may be relatively small, one could easily handle mixtures in which the concentrations were very disparate. When applied to the dropping electrode, the second technique is known as differential polarography, and this is considered briefly in Chap. 10 VIII.

Like the quiet and stirred mercury pool electrodes (cf. Figs. 8.13 and 8.15), the hanging drop electrode will probably prove to be of much use in studying the reversibilities and mechanisms of electrode reactions. The assessment of reversibility involves brief pre-electrolysis of a solution of, say, the oxidized form of a couple at a potential slightly more negative than the cathodic peak potential, then immediate backward polarization, and comparison of the half-peak potentials of the cathodic and anodic peaks. More detailed information can be obtained by employing a precisely defined triangular potential sweep. Substances that give rise to kinetic or adsorption waves, for example, in ordinary polarography behave quite distinctively in hanging-drop voltammetry. Under conditions where eq. (3.46) is valid, a voltammogram of the substance Y will be a smooth sigmoidal curve at a hanging drop electrode. A peak is not obtained because the concentration of Y at the electrode surface hardly varies during the scan. In a system in which an adsorption wave is obtained polarographically because the reduction product R is adsorbed onto the mercury surface (cf. Chap. 3 IX), backward polarization at a hanging drop electrode in a solution of the oxidized form O yields a curve on which both the slope of the rising portion of the anodic peak and the anodic peak current are abnormally large. The technique has been used for qualitative studies of reaction mechanisms (*101*,*117*) and for detecting the formation of intermetallic compounds in mixed amalgams (*118*). It can be regarded as a simpler form of oscillographic polarography, inferior to the latter in dealing with very fast reactions, but having the advantage of requiring much less complex electrical circuitry. Much additional information about the hanging drop electrode and its applications is given in a review by Kemula and Kublik (*119*).

Solid electrodes coated with mercury have been used for monitoring flowing streams in industrial process control and in chromato-polarography, for automatic amperometric titrations, for stripping analysis, and for some ordinary voltammetric work. Their use has generally stemmed from a desire to extend the favorable characteristics of residual-current curves at solid electrodes to the more negative potentials that can be obtained only with mercury. Silver has been used as the base metal (*120*), but the characteristics of an amalgamated silver electrode change with time (*121*), and therefore platinum is a much better choice. Electrodeposition of mercury onto a platinum electrode (*121,122*) usually does not give a satisfactorily adherent coating. If the platinum surface is plane, it suffices to abrade it under mercury (*123*). Otherwise it is best to clean the platinum by boiling it in $10F$ (60%) perchloric acid and then allowing it to stand in $1F$ perchloric acid or acidified sodium perchlorate solution for at least 10 min. at a potential where the oxide film is reduced but where hydrogen is not rapidly evolved. A potential of $+0.2$ v. vs. S.C.E. is suitable. Without interrupting the current, the electrode is then immersed in a pool of mercury at the bottom of the vessel in which the electrolysis has been performed (*124,125*).

The foregoing summary has described only a few of the very large number of mercury electrodes that have been proposed. Others include the streaming electrode, designed to provide a continuously renewed surface of constant area (*126–129*); membrane electrodes, designed to confine the diffusion layer to the thickness of a cellophane or similar membrane that separates the mercury from an efficiently stirred solution (*130*); and electrodes in which the mercury and solution are separated by a fritted glass disc that serves to provide restricted linear diffusion (*131,132*). The original literature must be consulted for information about these and others not mentioned here.

References

(1) R. N. Adams, "Solid Electrodes," in *Progress in Polarography*, P. Zuman and I. M. Kolthoff, eds., Interscience, New York, 1962, Vol. II, Chap. 23, pp. 503–13.

(2) R. N. Adams, "Voltammetry at Electrodes with Fixed Surfaces," in *Treatise on Analytical Chemistry*, I. M. Kolthoff and P. J. Elving, eds., Interscience, New York, 1963, Part I, Vol. 4, Chap. 47, pp. 2381–2416.

(3) R. N. Adams, in *Handbook of Analytical Chemistry*, L. Meites, ed., McGraw-Hill, New York, 1963, pp. 5–150 to 5–154.

(4) J. E. B. Randles, *Trans. Faraday Soc.*, 44, 327 (1948).

(5) A. Ševčík, *Collection Czechoslov. Chem. Communs.*, 13, 349 (1948).

(6) M. M. Nicholson, *J. Am. Chem. Soc.*, 76, 2539 (1954).

(7) W. H. Reinmuth, *J. Am. Chem. Soc.*, 79, 6358 (1957).

(8) R. S. Nicholson and I. Shain, *Anal. Chem.*, 36, 706 (1964); 37, 178, 191 (1965).

(9) C. A. Streuli and W. D. Cooke, *Anal. Chem.*, 25, 1691 (1953).

(10) T. R. Mueller and R. N. Adams, *Anal. Chem. Acta*, 23, 467 (1960).

(11) T. R. Mueller and R. N. Adams, *Anal. Chim. Acta*, 25, 482 (1961).

(12) P. Delahay, *J. Am. Chem. Soc.*, 75, 1190 (1953).

(13) II. Matsuda and Y. Ayabe, *Z. Elektrochem.*, 61, 489 (1957).

(14) P. Delahay, *New Instrumental Methods in Electrochemistry*, Interscience, New York, 1954, p. 131.

(15) *Ibid.*, p. 372.

(16) P. Delahay and G. L. Stiehl, *J. Phys. & Colloid Chem.*, 55, 570 (1951).

(17) T. Berzins and P. Delahay, *J. Am. Chem. Soc.*, 75, 555 (1953).

(18) H. A. Laitinen and I. M. Kolthoff, *J. Am. Chem. Soc.*, 61, 3344 (1939).

(19) M. M. Nicholson, *Anal. Chem.*, 31, 128 (1959).

(20) E. Morgan, J. E. Harrar, and A. L. Crittenden, *Anal. Chem.*, 32, 756 (1960).

(21) R. C. Propst, *Anal. Chem.*, 35, 958 (1963).

(22) C. A. Streuli and W. D. Cooke, *Anal. Chem.*, 26, 963 (1954).

(23) R. G. Ball, D. L. Manning, and O. Menis, *Anal. Chem.*, 32, 621 (1960).

(24) I. Shain and S. P. Perone, *Anal. Chem.*, 33, 325 (1961).

(25) W. Kemula, Z. Kublik, and J. Taraszewska, *Chem. Anal. (Warsaw)*, 8, 171 (1963).

(26) S. S. Lord, Jr., R. C. O'Neill, and L. B. Rogers, *Anal. Chem.*, 24, 209 (1952).

(27) G. C. Barker and I. L. Jenkins, *Analyst*, 77, 685 (1952).

(28) T. L. Marple and L. B. Rogers, *Anal. Chim. Acta*, 11, 574 (1954).

(29) R. D. DeMars and I. Shain, *Anal. Chem.*, 29, 1825 (1957).

(30) J. G. Nikelly and W. D. Cooke, *Anal. Chem.*, 29, 933 (1957).

(31) G. C. Barker, *Anal. Chim. Acta*, 18, 118 (1958).

(32) W. Kemula, Z. Kublik, and S. Glodowski, *J. Electroanal. Chem.*, 1, 91 (1959).

(33) M. M. Nicholson, *Anal. Chem.*, 32, 1058 (1960).

(34) S. Bruckenstein and T. Nagai, *Anal. Chem.*, 33, 1201 (1961).

(35) R. P. Frankenthal and I. Shain, *J. Am. Chem. Soc.*, 78, 2969 (1956).

(36) W. H. Reinmuth, *Anal. Chem.*, **33**, 185 (1961).

(37) I. Shain and J. Lewison, *Anal. Chem.*, **33**, 187 (1961).

(38) J. J. Lingane, *Electroanalytical Chemistry*, Interscience, New York, 1953, pp. 192–4.

(39) D. J. Ferrett and C. S. G. Phillips, *Trans. Faraday Soc.*, **51**, 390 (1955).

(40) V. G. Levich, *Acta Physicochim. U.S.S.R.*, **17**, 257 (1942); *Disc. Faraday Soc.*, **1**, 37 (1947).

(41) B. L. Bircumshaw and A. C. Riddiford, *Quart. Rev.*, **6**, 157 (1952).

(42) M. B. Kraichman and E. A. Hogge, *J. Phys. Chem.*, **59**, 986 (1955).

(43) D. P. Gregory and A. C. Riddiford, *J. Chem. Soc.*, **1956**, 3756.

(44) J. Koutecký and V. G. Levich, *Zh. Fiz. Khim.*, **32**, 1565 (1958).

(45) A. Frumkin, L. Nekrasov, V. G. Levich, and U. Ivanov, *J. Electroanal. Chem.*, **1**, 84 (1959).

(46) U. A. Pleskov, *Zh. Fiz. Khim.*, **34**, 523 (1960).

(47) J. D. Newson and A. C. Riddiford, *J. Electrochem. Soc.*, **108**, 695 (1961).

(48) V. G. Levich, *Physicochemical Hydrodynamics*, Prentice-Hall, Englewood Cliffs, N.J., 1962.

(49) W. Vielstich, *Z. Anal. Chem.*, **173**, 84 (1960).

(50) D. Jahn and W. Vielstich, *J. Electrochem. Soc.*, **109**, 849 (1962).

(51) G. R. Johnson and D. R. Turner, *J. Electrochem. Soc.*, **109**, 918 (1962).

(52) S. Azim and A. C. Riddiford, *Anal. Chem.*, **34**, 1023 (1962).

(53) Z. Galus, C. Olson, H. Y. Lee, and R. N. Adams, *Anal. Chem.*, **34**, 164 (1962).

(54) W. Geissler and R. Landsberg, *Z. Chem.*, **1**, 308 (1961).

(55) I. Fried and P. J. Elving, *Anal. Chem.*, **37**, 464, 803 (1965).

(56) A. Page and H. C. H. Townsend, *Proc. Roy. Soc. (London)*, **A135**, 656 (1932).

(57) L. P. Kholpanov, *Zh. Fiz. Khim.*, **35**, 1538 (1961).

(58) V. G. Levich and U. Ivanov, *Dokl. Akad. Nauk S.S.S.R.*, **126**, 505 (1959).

(59) H. A. Laitinen and I. M. Kolthoff, *J. Phys. Chem.*, **45**, 1061, 1079 (1941).

(60) T. Tsukamoto, T. Kambara, and I. Tachi, *Proc. 1st Intern. Polarogr. Congress, Prague, 1951*, Pt. I, p. 524.

(61) I. M. Kolthoff and J. Jordan, *J. Am. Chem. Soc.*, **76**, 3843 (1951).

(62) J. Jordan, *Anal. Chem.*, **27**, 1708 (1955).

(63) J. Jordan and R. A. Javick, *Electrochim. Acta*, **6**, 23 (1962).

(64) J. Jordan, R. A. Javick, and L. R. Jiminez, paper presented at the Pittsburgh Conference on Analytical Chemistry and Applied Spectroscopy, March, 1958.

(65) S. Karp and L. Meites, *J. Am. Chem. Soc.*, **84**, 906 (1962).

(66) S. S. Lord, Jr., and L. B. Rogers, *Anal. Chem.*, **26**, 284 (1954).

(67) F. Baumann and I. Shain, *Anal. Chem.*, **29**, 303 (1957).

(68) G. W. Miller, L. E. Long, G. M. George, and W. L. Sikes, *Anal. Chem.*, **36**, 980 (1964).

(69) I. M. Kolthoff and N. Tanaka, *Anal. Chem.*, **26**, 632 (1954).

(70) J. K. Lee, R. N. Adams, and C. E. Bricker, *Anal. Chim. Acta*, **17**, 321 (1957).

(71) F. C. Anson and J. J. Lingane, *J. Am. Chem. Soc.*, **79**, 4901 (1957); R. L. Every and R. L. Grimsley, *J. Electroanal. Chem.*, **9**, 165 (1965).

(72) W. Visscher and M. A. V. Devanathan, *J. Electroanal. Chem.*, **8**, 127 (1964).

(73) K. Nagel and H. Dietz, *Electrochim. Acta*, **4**, 161 (1961).

(74) A. Kozawa, *J. Electroanal. Chem.*, **8**, 20 (1964).

(75) D. G. Peters and J. J. Lingane, *J. Electroanal. Chem.*, **4**, 193 (1962).

(76) D. G. Davis, *Talanta*, **3**, 335 (1960).

(77) I. M. Kolthoff and E. R. Nightingale, *Anal. Chim. Acta*, **17**, 329 (1957).

(78) F. C. Anson, *J. Am. Chem. Soc.*, **81**, 1554 (1959).

(79) D. T. Sawyer and L. V. Interrante, *J. Electroanal. Chem.*, **2**, 310 (1961); D. T. Sawyer and E. T. Seo, *ibid.*, **3**, 410 (1962); **5**, 23 (1963); D. T. Sawyer and R. J. Day, *ibid.*, **5**, 195 (1963).

(80) A. Hickling and W. Wilson, *J. Electrochem. Soc.*, **98**, 425 (1951).

(81) J. J. Lingane and P. J. Lingane, *J. Electroanal. Chem.*, **5**, 411 (1963).

(82) A. J. Bard, *Anal. Chem.*, **35**, 1602 (1963).

(83) F. C. Anson and D. M. King, *Anal. Chem.*, **34**, 362 (1962).

(84) F. C. Anson, *Anal. Chem.*, **33**, 934 (1961).

(85) V. F. Gaylor, A. L. Conrad, and J. H. Landerl, *Anal. Chem.*, **29**, 224 (1957).

(86) V. F. Gaylor, A. L. Conrad, and J. H. Landerl, *Anal. Chem.*, **29**, 228 (1957).

(87) J. B. Morris and J. M. Schempf, *Anal. Chem.*, **31**, 286 (1959).

(88) F. J. Miller and H. E. Zittel, *Anal. Chem.*, **35**, 1866 (1963).

(89) A. L. Beilby, W. Brooks, Jr., and G. L. Lawrence, *Anal. Chem.*, **36**, 22 (1964).

(90) P. J. Elving and D. M. Smith, *Anal. Chem.*, **32**, 1849 (1960); W. R. Turner and P. J. Elving, *ibid.*, **37**, 207, 467 (1965).

(91) H. A. Laitinen and D. R. Rhodes, *J. Electrochem. Soc.*, **109**, 413 (1962).

(92) D. L. Manning and G. Mamantov, *J. Electroanal. Chem.*, **7**, 102 (1964).

(92a) H. E. Zittel and F. J. Miller, *Anal. Chem.*, **37**, 200 (1965).

(93) T. R. Mueller, C. E. Olson, and R. N. Adams, in *Advances in Polarography*, I. S. Longmuir, ed., Pergamon, London, 1960, Vol. I, p. 198.

(93a) W. R. Mountcastle, Jr., *Anal. Chim. Acta*, **32**, 332 (1965).

(94) R. N. Adams, *Anal. Chem.*, **30**, 1576 (1959).

(95) C. E. Olson and R. N. Adams, *Anal. Chim. Acta*, **29**, 358 (1963).

(95a) E. S. Jacobs, *Anal. Chem.*, **35**, 2112 (1963).

(95b) J. R. Covington and R. J. Lacoste, *Anal. Chem.*, **37**, 420 (1965).

(96) N. R. Stalica, Ph.D. Thesis, The Pennsylvania State University, 1963.

(97) J. C. Griess, Jr. and L. B. Rogers, *J. Electrochem. Soc.*, **95**, 129 (1949).

(98) D. J. Rosie and W. D. Cooke, *Anal. Chem.*, **27**, 1360 (1955).

(99) C. A. Streuli and W. D. Cooke, *Anal. Chem.*, **26**, 970 (1954).

(100) W. Kemula and Z. Kublik, *Nature*, **182**, 793 (1958); *Roczniki Chem.*, **32**, 941 (1958).

(101) C. Olson, H. Y. Lee, and R. N. Adams, *J. Electroanal. Chem.*, **2**, 396 (1961).

(102) I. M. Kolthoff, J. Jordan, and S. Prager, *J. Am. Chem. Soc.*, **76**, 5221 (1954).

(103) T. S. Lee, *J. Am. Chem. Soc.*, **74**, 5001 (1952).

(104) P. Arthur, J. C. Komyathy, R. F. Maness, and H. W. Vaughan, *Anal. Chem.*, **27**, 895 (1955).

(105) L. Meites, *Anal. Chim. Acta*, **18**, 364 (1958).

(106) P. B. Pinches, M. S. Thesis, Polytechnic Institute of Brooklyn, 1961.

(107) V. I. Melik-Gaikazyan, *Zh. Fiz. Khim.*, **26**, 560 (1952).

(108) H. Gerischer, *Z. Physik. Chem. (Leipzig)*, **202**, 302 (1953).

(109) J. W. Ross, Jr., R. D. DeMars, and I. Shain, *Anal. Chem.*, **28**, 1768 (1956).

(110) W. L. Underkofler and I. Shain, *Anal. Chem.*, **33**, 1966 (1961).

(111) J. E. B. Randles and W. White, *Z. Elektrochem.*, **59**, 669 (1955).

(112) W. Kemula and Z. Kublik, *Anal. Chim. Acta*, **18**, 104 (1958).

(113) R. Narayan, *J. Electroanal. Chem.*, **4**, 123 (1962).

(114) J. J. Vogel, *J. Electroanal. Chem.*, **8**, 82 (1964).

(115) V. Čermák, *Collection Czechoslov. Chem. Communs.*, **24**, 831 (1959).

(116) K. J. Martin and I. Shain, *Anal. Chem.*, **30**, 1808 (1958).

(117) M. Březina, *Collection Czechoslov. Chem. Communs.*, **24**, 4031 (1959).

(118) W. Kemula, Z. Galus, and Z. Kublik, *Nature*, **182**, 1228 (1958).

(119) W. Kemula and Z. Kublik, in *Advances in Analytical Chemistry and Instrumentation*, C. N. Reilley, ed., Interscience, New York, Vol. 2, 1963, p. 123.

(120) W. D. Cooke, *Anal. Chem.*, **25**, 215 (1953).

(121) K. W. Gardiner and L. B. Rogers, *Anal. Chem.*, **25**, 1393 (1953).

(122) T. L. Marple and L. B. Rogers, *Anal. Chem.*, **25**, 1351 (1953).

(123) S. A. Moros, *Anal. Chem.*, **34**, 1584 (1962).

(124) L. Ramaley, R. L. Brubaker, and C. G. Enke, *Anal. Chem.*, **35**, 1088 (1963).

(125) W. J. Blaedel and J. H. Strohl, *Anal. Chem.*, **36**, 1245 (1964).

(126) J. Heyrovský and J. Forejt, *Z. Physik. Chem.*, **193**, 77 (1943).

(127) A. Ríus, *Fundamentals and Applications of the Streaming Mercury Electrode*, Academy of Sciences of Madrid, Bermejo, Madrid, 1949.

(128) K. Györbíró, L. Poós, and J. Proszt, *Acta Chim. Acad. Sci. Hung.*, **9**, 27 (1956).

(129) J. R. Weaver and R. W. Parry, *J. Am. Chem. Soc.*, **76**, 6258 (1954); **78**, 5542 (1956).

(130) R. C. Bowers and A. M. Wilson, *J. Am. Chem. Soc.*, **80**, 2968 (1958); **81**, 1840 (1959).

(131) T. C. Franklin and J. Bradford, *Chemist-Analyst*, **52**, 118 (1963).

(132) J. Jordan and J. H. Clausen, paper presented at the XIXth International Congress of Pure and Applied Chemistry, London, July, 1963.

CHAPTER 9

AMPEROMETRIC TITRATIONS

A conventional amperometric or "polarometric" titration is a titration whose course is followed by measuring a current—almost always a limiting current—at a voltammetric indicator electrode. Depending on the potential of the electrode and the voltammetric characteristics of the chemical substances involved, the current may be proportional to the concentration of the substance being titrated, to the concentration of the excess of reagent, or to the concentration of one of the products of the reaction, or it may depend on two of these concentrations. The titration curve is a plot of the limiting current, corrected if necessary for the residual current and for dilution by the reagent, against the volume of reagent added. Ideally it consists of two straight lines intersecting at the equivalence point.

If the stoichiometry of the titration is known and reproducible, amperometric titrations are inherently more accurate and precise than ordinary polarographic or voltammetric analyses. Accuracies and precisions of a few tenths of a per cent are attainable in titrations of solutions having concentrations well above the limit of detection of the indicator electrode employed. The proportionality constant that relates the current to the concentration of the electroactive substance need not be known in an amperometric titration, so that no prior calibration is required. Amperometric titrations can be used to determine many substances, such as phosphate and sulfate, that are not electroactive; although such determinations can also be made by indirect methods (Chap. 7 II), amperometric titrations are usually less tedious and more precise.

I. Amperometric Precipitation Titrations. Theory of Amperometric Titration Curves

The shape of an amperometric titration curve depends on the substance being titrated, the reagent used, and the potential applied to the indicator electrode. Many different combinations are possible, but the features common to most titration curves can be explained

465

with the aid of a single example. We shall consider the titration of lead ion in a weakly acidic supporting electrolyte with standard potassium chromate, using a dropping electrode at a potential where both lead ion and chromium(VI) yield their diffusion currents. For the sake of simplicity we shall assume that the solubility of lead chromate is negligibly small in the medium employed, that the concentration of supporting electrolyte is so high that the migration current can be ignored, that chemical equilibrium is attained between the addition of each aliquot of reagent and the measurement of the current, and that the diffusion current of each ion is proportional to its concentration. The consequences of failure to satisfy these conditions will be examined in subsequent paragraphs.

If the initial volume of the lead solution is $V_{Pb}{}^0$ milliliters and if the initial concentration of lead ion in it is $C_{Pb}{}^0$ mM, there are $V_{Pb}{}^0 C_{Pb}{}^0$ micromoles of lead ion present initially. Up to the equivalence point, the addition of v_{Cr} milliliters of C_{Cr} mM chromate, containing $v_{Cr} C_{Cr}$ micromoles of chromate, will cause an equal number of micromoles of lead ion to precipitate, because the reaction is assumed to be complete; by the same token, the concentration of chromate will remain equal to zero throughout this region. The concentration of lead ion will be given by

$$C_{Pb} = \frac{V_{Pb}^0 C_{Pb}^0 - v_{Cr} C_{Cr}}{V_{Pb}^0 + v_{Cr}} \tag{9.1}$$

in which the numerator gives the number of micromoles of lead ion remaining in solution, while the denominator gives the total volume of the titration mixture. The current measured at any point is the sum of the residual current i_r and the diffusion current of lead ion, and is given by

$$i = i_r + k_{Pb} \frac{V_{Pb}^0 C_{Pb}^0 - v_{Cr} C_{Cr}}{V_{Pb}^0 + v_{Cr}} \tag{9.2}$$

where the proportionality constant k_{Pb} can be described by

$$k_{Pb} = \frac{(i_d)_{Pb}}{C_{Pb}} = 607 n_{Pb} D_{Pb}^{1/2} m^{2/3} t^{1/6} = I_{Pb} m^{2/3} t^{1/6} \tag{9.3}$$

according to the Ilkovič equation. Equation (9.2) can be written

$$(i - i_r) \frac{V^0_{Pb} + v_{Cr}}{V^0_{Pb}} = k_{Pb}C^0_{Pb} - \frac{k_{Pb}C_{Cr}}{V^0_{Pb}} v_{Cr} \tag{9.4}$$

so that a straight line having a negative slope is obtained when the left-hand side of this equation is plotted against v_{Cr}, the volume of reagent added.

Beyond the equivalence point, entirely similar arguments yield

$$C_{Cr} = \frac{v_{Cr}C_{Cr} - V^0_{Pb}C^0_{Pb}}{V^0_{Pb} + v_{Cr}} \tag{9.5}$$

and, finally,

$$(i - i_r) \frac{V^0_{Pb} + v_{Cr}}{V^0_{Pb}} = -k_{Cr}C^0_{Pb} + \frac{k_{Cr}C_{Cr}}{V^0_{Pb}} v_{Cr} \tag{9.6}$$

so that a straight line having a positive slope is obtained.

Consequently an amperometric titration curve is a plot of $(i - i_r)[(V^0 + v)/V^0]$ against v, where V^0 is the volume of solution titrated and v the volume of reagent added. The factor $(V^0 + v)/V^0$ serves as a correction for dilution by the reagent. If the reaction proceeds virtually to completion at every point during the titration, the plot consists of two straight lines which, as is shown below, intersect at the equivalence point. The slope of the line preceding the equivalence point depends on the value of k (the ratio of diffusion current to concentration) for the substance being titrated; that of the line following the equivalence point depends on the value of k for the reagent. In the titration of lead ion with chromate both k's are positive at potentials where both ions can be reduced, and therefore the plot is V-shaped. The same titration could be performed at a potential where chromate ion is reduced but lead ion is not, so that k_{Cr} would be positive while k_{Pb} was zero. Then the current would remain equal to the residual current until the equivalence point was reached, and the titration curve would be __/-shaped. If chromate ion were titrated with lead ion at the latter potential, the current would decrease until the equivalence point was reached and remain zero after it had been passed: the curve would be __-shaped. One might titrate lead ion with sulfide at a potential where lead ion gives a cathodic current while sulfide gives an anodic one, so that k_{Pb} would be positive while k_S was negative. The cathodic current would decrease to zero at the equivalence point, and the anodic current would increase thereafter: if the two k's were numerically equal, a single straight line intersecting the zero-current axis at the equivalence point would be obtained. More probably their values would differ slightly, and then the curve would consist of two straight lines intersecting each other (at a very obtuse angle) and the zero-current line at the equivalence point.

For the titration of lead ion with chromate, the point of intersection of the two line segments is described by equating the right-hand sides of eqs. (9.4) and (9.6). After rearrangement, one obtains

$$v_{Cr} = \frac{V^0_{Pb}C^0_{Pb}}{C_{Cr}} \qquad (9.7)$$

which is exactly the volume of reagent required to reach the equivalence point. This is true in all amperometric titrations: no matter what kind of chemical reaction may be involved, no matter what shape the titration curve may have, and no matter what the values of the k's may be, the line segments should always intersect at the equivalence point. This does not mean that amperometric titrations are inherently free from error: side reactions, coprecipitation phenomena, impurities, and other sources of error in volumetric procedures produce errors in amperometric titrations just as they do in titrations by any other technique.

Short cuts are often adopted to minimize the work that has to be done to construct an amperometric titration curve. If the solutions are sufficiently concentrated and if the currents are measured at points not too close to the equivalence point, the residual current will usually be only a negligible fraction of the total, and then it suffices to plot $i(V^0 + v)/V^0$ against v. If the reagent is about twenty or more times as concentrated as the solution being titrated, the dilution correction $(V^0 + v)/V^0$ will be so nearly equal to 1 throughout the titration that its variations will be smaller than the uncertainties in measuring the currents, and then one can simply plot i [or $(i - i_r)$, if the conditions in the preceding sentence are not fulfilled] against v.

Contrary to what has been assumed so far, the solubility of the precipitate formed in an amperometric titration is often far from negligible in comparison with the concentration of the solution being titrated. It is convenient to speak of the value of K_t, the conditional or formal equilibrium constant for the reaction that proceeds from left to right during the titration. Ringbom (1) has given an admirable discussion of the significance of K_t in titration procedures and has described a convenient procedure for evaluating it under any particular conditions from the tabulated values of the equilibrium constants of the individual reactions involved. In the absence of any side reaction that could consume either ion, K_t for the titration of lead ion with chromate would be simply the reciprocal of the solubility product of lead chromate, and would consequently be of the order of 10^{14}. If the titration is performed in an acetate buffer containing $0.1M$ acetate ion and having a pH of 5, this is decreased to about 10^9 by the formation of hydrogen chromate ion and the complexation of lead by acetate. Nevertheless, if even $1mM$ lead ion is present in the solution titrated, the solubility of lead chromate will remain negligibly small, thanks to the common-ion effect, until about half of the lead has been precipitated. As the equivalence point is approached, the solubility increases; it reaches a maximum at the equivalence point, and then it decreases again as excess chromate is added. In short, because K_t is finite, the concentrations of both lead and chromate ions exceed the values given by eqs. (9.1) and (9.5), but approach them more and more closely as the excess of either ion increases.

A more exact equation for the titration curve is needed to describe the result. Consider the titration of M^{n+} with X^{n-} at a potential where the former is reducible but the latter is not, so that the current is the sum of the residual current and the diffusion current of M^{n+}. The composition of the solution at any point is described by the equation (2)

$$[M^{n+}] = \frac{C_M^0 (1 - f)}{1 + rf} + \frac{1}{K_t [M^{n+}]} \tag{9.8}$$

The titration parameter f is defined by the equation

$$f = z v_X C_X / V_M^0 C_M^0 \tag{9.9}$$

where z is the number of moles of the substance being titrated that react with each mole of the reagent. In the present case $z = 1$. In any titration the value of f is proportional to the volume of reagent that has been added, and f becomes equal to 1 at the equivalence point. The dilution parameter r in eq. (9.8) is defined by

$$r = C_M^0/C_X \qquad (9.10)$$

As was mentioned above, it is customary in practical amperometric titrations for the reagent to be much more concentrated than the solution being titrated, so that r is always small. It is easily shown that, since z is 1,

$$1 + rf = (V_M^0 + v_X)/V_M^0 \qquad (9.11)$$

In a practical titration, where r is not known *a priori*, the dilution correction is always applied in the form $(V_M{}^0 + v_X)/V_M{}^0$, which is easily evaluated because both volumes are known at every point. In calculating titration curves, however, the form $(1 + rf)$ is much more convenient.

The second term on the right-hand side of eq. (9.8) represents the solubility of the precipitate. If the value of K_t is large, if $C_M{}^0$ is also large, and if f is not too close to 1, this term will be so much smaller than the first term that it can be neglected by comparison, and then one will obtain

$$(i - i_r)(1 + rf) = k_M C_M^0 (1 - f) \qquad (9.12)$$

for values of f less than 1. This is merely eq. (9.4) in a different guise. More generally, however, eq. (9.8) is a quadratic. Solving it for $[M^{n+}]$, multiplying this by the dilution correction $(1 + rf)$, and dividing the product by the initial concentration $C_M{}^0$ to normalize the curves obtained under different conditions, one has

$$\frac{[M^{n+}](1 + rf)}{C_M^0} = \frac{(i - i_r)(1 + rf)}{(i^0 - i_r)} \qquad (9.13)$$

$$= \frac{(1 - f) + [(1 - f)^2 + 4(1 + rf)^2/K_t(C_M^0)^2]^{1/2}}{2}$$

If $K_t(C_M{}^0)^2$ is very large, this becomes virtually identical with eq. (9.12) except in the immediate vicinity of the equivalence point, and in addition the curve is hardly affected by reasonable variations of r. It is when $K_t(C_M{}^0)^2$ is not very large—that is, when the initial con-

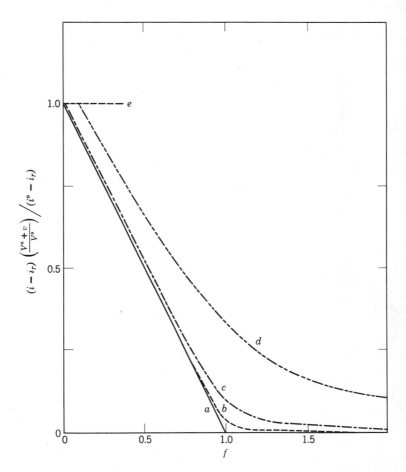

Figure 9.1. Calculated amperometric titration curves for the titration of M^{n+} with X^{n-} to yield the precipitate MX. Only M^{n+} is assumed to be electroactive at the potential employed, and the values of $K_t(C_M^0)^2$ are (a) ∞, (b) 10^3, (c) 10^2, (d) 10, and (e) 0. Curves (b)–(d) coincide with the horizontal dashed line (e) until precipitation has begun. The value of r is assumed to be 0.02, and the same assumption is made in Figs. 9.2–9.4.

centration of M is not much larger than the solubility of the precipitate at the equivalence point—that complications arise.

Typical calculated titration curves are shown in Figs. 9.1 and 9.2. Figure 9.1 pertains to titrations in which only M^{n+} is reducible at the

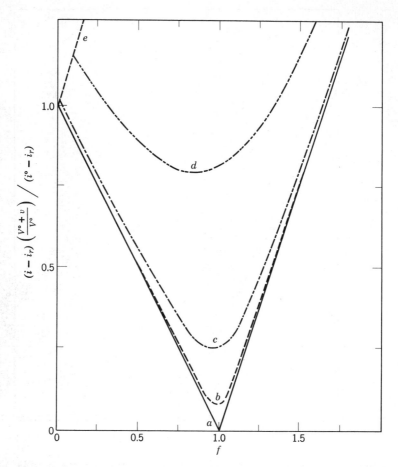

Figure 9.2. Calculated amperometric titration curves for the titrations of Fig. 9.1. Here it is assumed that both M^{n+} and X^{n-} are reducible, and that $k_X = 1.5\, k_M$.

potential selected. Figure 9.2, for comparison, pertains to titrations in which the reagent is reducible as well; each point in this figure was obtained by solving eq. (9.8) for $[M^{n+}]$, then calculating $[X^{n-}]$ from the equilibrium-constant expression

$$[M^{n+}][X^{n-}] = 1/K_t \tag{9.14}$$

and finally combining these concentrations with the equation

$$i - i_r = k_M[M^{n+}] + k_X[X^{n-}] \qquad (9.15)$$

after which the central term of eq. (9.13) is easily evaluated.

Curve a in each of these figures is the segmented curve described by eqs. (9.4) and (9.6). According to eq. (9.13), this corresponds to extremely large values of the product $K_t(C_M{}^0)^2$. Curves b show, however, that if this product is finite the curve actually consists of two nearly linear segments joined by a curve in the immediate vicinity of the equivalence point. As the product decreases, the width of the curved region increases, as is shown by curves c, but the two branches still approach linearity at points sufficiently far from the equivalence point, and the extrapolation can still be performed with little difficulty or error. It is apparent that measurements of the current in the vicinity of the equivalence point are of but little use in the construction of the titration curve. One consequence of this fact is that amperometric titrations can be performed much more rapidly than potentiometric ones: fewer points are needed to define the useful portions of the curve, and each can be obtained very rapidly because the excess of one of the reactants hastens the attainment of equilibrium. Of course the precision of the result depends on the length of the extrapolation: one should try to obtain points as close to the equivalence point as possible without infringing on the curved region. Most amperometric titrations are performed by making a few measurements well before the equivalence point (say, during the first 75 to 90% of the titration) and a few more well after it (say, when at least a 10 to 25% excess of reagent has been added). As few as three or four measurements in each region usually suffice.

A peculiarity of precipitation titrations, as opposed to those based on other kinds of reactions, is that their equilibria are not established until some finite volume of reagent has been added. Strictly speaking, therefore, the current measured in the original solution should not be used in the extrapolation to the end point. In Figs. 9.1 and 9.2 the curves actually follow lines e until the solution becomes saturated with the precipitate. Inspection of curves c and d in these figures shows that substantial errors may result from attempting to force the titration curve to pass through the point at $f = 0$. The problem could be overcome by saturating the solution with the precipitate before the titration is begun, but this is never done in practice.

If the value of $K_t(C_M{}^0)^2$ is very small, as it is for curves d of Figs. 9.1 and 9.2, the curvature due to the incompleteness of the reaction becomes extensive throughout the titration. It then becomes somewhat difficult to locate the end point by straightforward extrapolation. Other procedures are available for use in very severe cases.

One (3), which is strictly applicable only to titrations in which two ions having numerically equal charges react to form a precipitate, consists of drawing two parallel chords of the curve. The equivalence point is the point at which the line joining the midpoints of the chords intersects the zero-current axis. If the residual current has not been measured separately, or if the solution also contains a substance that contributes to the current at the potential selected but that does not react with the reagent, a similar but slightly different procedure is needed. After the above line has been drawn, another pair of parallel chords, having a slope as different as possible from that of the first pair, is constructed, and the midpoints of the second pair of chords are joined by a second straight line. The equivalence point is the point of intersection of the two extrapolated lines. The procedure is not applicable to complexometric or other titrations in which the product of the titration reaction remains dissolved, or to heterovalent precipitation titrations, and in addition its result will be sensibly affected by small variations in the shape of the curve drawn through the experimental points. In general it is much better to increase K_t as much as possible by suitable adjustment of the pH, ionic strength, temperature, and other appropriate variables. Titration curves for precipitation titrations are often much improved by the presence of 10 to 20% ethanol or some other non-aqueous solvent, although this may greatly increase the extent of coprecipitation.

An alternative procedure (4) consists of locating an approximate end point in the ordinary graphical way, then refining the estimate by successive algebraic approximations. The reference must be consulted for details. Though the procedure was devised for use with conductometric titrations, it is easily adapted to amperometric ones. It is more objective than the wholly graphical technique, but it is also much more laborious, and the algebra becomes excessively tedious for heterovalent precipitations.

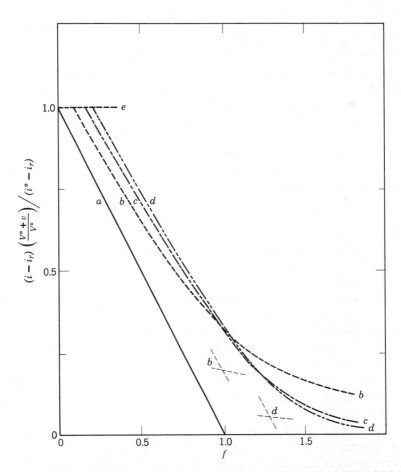

Figure 9.3.   Calculated amperometric titration curves for titrations of M^{n+} with X^{zn-} to yield the precipitate M_zX. Curve a would be obtained, regardless of the value of z, if the solubility of M_zX were exceedingly small; curve e describes the data prior to the onset of precipitation. The values of z for the other curves are (b) 1, (c) ½, and (d) ⅓, corresponding to MX, MX_2, and MX_3, respectively. Only M^{n+} is assumed to be reducible at the potential employed, and in each case it is assumed that $C_M^0/[M^{n+}]_{ep} = \sqrt{10}$. Curve b is identical with curve c of Fig. 9.1. The dashed lines show possible extrapolations of curves b and d.

Thus far it has been assumed that the precipitate is isovalent, so that it may be represented by the formula MX. When this is not the case, the titration curve becomes markedly asymmetrical unless the solubility of the precipitate is negligibly small, as is illustrated by Fig. 9.3. Curve b in this figure is identical with curve d of Fig. 9.1, and represents the isovalent titration curve under such conditions that the initial concentration of M^{n+} is just $\sqrt{10}$ times as large as its concentration at the equivalence point. Curves c and d are the calculated heterovalent titration curves under the same conditions. Their asymmetry has important practical consequences. The extrapolation of curve b shown in the figure is rather crude, but it yields an end point that differs less than half a per cent from the equivalence point. A similar extrapolation of curve d leads to an error of nearly $+30\%$. One could obtain a much more accurate result by drawing a straight line through the first few points on curve d after its departure from line e, then drawing a second line parallel to the first but passing through the initial point. A third line is drawn through the points obtained with very large excesses of the reagent; if the latter is not electroactive at the potential employed, this will be horizontal after proper correction for dilution is applied, and will coincide with the zero-current line if correction is made for the residual current and if there is no electroactive impurity present. The point of intersection of the second and third lines will nearly coincide with the equivalence point. To employ such a procedure one would need the courage born of desperation; it would again be much better to change the experimental conditions so as to increase K_t. It is probably unnecessary to say that the technique adopted for locating the end point should be evaluated by performing titrations with known solutions whenever any asymmetry can be detected in the titration curves obtained.

Figures 9.1 and 9.2 indicated that one must have $K_t(C_M^0)^2 \geq 10$ to obtain an easily interpretable titration curve in an isovalent precipitation titration. In such a titration the concentration of M^{n+} at the equivalence point is given by

$$[M^{n+}]_{ep} = 1/(K_t)^{1/2} \tag{9.16}$$

and so the above condition can be written in the more general form $C_M^0/[M^{n+}]_{ep} \geq \sqrt{10}$. Figure 9.3 shows that this is overoptimistic if the precipitate is heterovalent, but even then reasonable accuracy

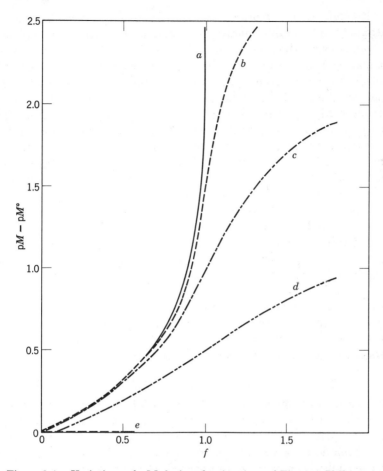

Figure 9.4. Variations of pM during the titrations of Fig. 9.1. If these titrations were followed with a M/M^{n+} indicator electrode at 25°, each pM unit would correspond to $59.15/n$ mv.

can be obtained by straightforward extrapolation if $C_M^0/[M^{n+}]_{ep} \geq 10$, which is equivalent to

$$C_M^0/z(K_t)^{1/(z+1)} \geq 10 \qquad (9.17)$$

In subsequent sections the above criteria will be applied to other kinds of titrations.

Although their accuracy and precision do deteriorate under extremely unfavorable conditions, amperometric titrations may still be useful even when potentiometric ones fail. This may be seen by comparing Figs. 9.1 and 9.2 with Fig. 9.4, which shows the potentiometric titration curves that would be obtained under exactly the same conditions with an indicator electrode responsive to the concentration of M^{n+}. For example, in the titration of a divalent metal ion under such conditions that n was 2 for the half-reaction at the potentiometric indicator electrode, the entire variation of potential over the whole portion of curve d shown in the Figure would be barely 28 mv., which is far too small to permit obtaining any useful estimate of the location of the equivalence point. On the other hand, curves d of Figs. 9.1 and 9.2, which pertain to exactly the same chemical conditions, indicate that an error much worse than a per cent or two could hardly result in the amperometric titration except from coprecipitation and other sources of error that are also neglected in Fig. 9.4.

If the substance being titrated is ionic, the currents measured near the beginning of the titration will include appreciable migration currents unless an excess of supporting electrolyte is present, and will, therefore, differ from the diffusion currents described by the foregoing equations. In the titration of a pure solution of lead nitrate with potassium dichromate, for example, the reaction is

$$2\,Pb^{++} + Cr_2O_7^{=} + H_2O = 2\,PbCrO_4 + 2\,H^+$$

As the titration proceeds, the concentration of lead ion decreases, while that of hydrogen ion increases and that of nitrate ion remains about the same. In accordance with eq. (3.8), the transference number of lead ion decreases, and the migration current decreases as a result. As the equivalence point is approached, the actual curve approaches the line segment that would have been obtained if an excess of supporting electrolyte had been present initially, as is shown by Fig. 9.5. After the equivalence point is passed, the migration current of dichromate ion is negligible because hydrogen and nitrate ions are present in considerable excess. There would be little difficulty or error in locating the end point; it would only be necessary to ignore the initial portion of the titration curve. However, difficulty would arise if $C_M^0/[M^{n+}]_{ep}$ were much smaller than it is here. One would then have to ignore a region of substantial width around the equivalence point; if one also has to ignore the initial portion of the curve, extrapolation to the end point will rest on a short and shaky foundation. Although it is possible in principle to perform an amperometric titration without adding a supporting electrolyte, this is rarely if ever advantageous; a supporting electrolyte is usually needed to define the stoichiometry of the reaction, to produce a suitable wave for the electroactive substance involved, or to mask another constituent of the sample. If for some reason a titration has to be performed without adding a foreign electrolyte, it is best to select a potential at which the reagent is electroactive while the substance being titrated is not. As in the titration of Fig. 9.5, the migration current of the reagent will then be suppressed by the electrolyte present at the equivalence point.

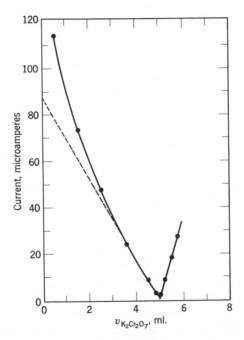

Figure 9.5. Influence of the migration current on an amperometric titration curve. The solid line was obtained on titrating 50 ml. of $0.01F$ lead nitrate with $0.05F$ potassium dichromate at -1.0 v. vs. S.C.E.; the dashed line shows the effect of suppressing the migration current by adding an excess of indifferent electrolyte to the lead nitrate solution before beginning the titration. By permission from *Polarography*, by I. M. Kolthoff and J. J. Lingane, Interscience, 2nd edition, 1952.

In the above treatment it has been assumed that chemical equilibrium was attained before each measurement of the current. Normally 15 to 30 sec. may elapse between the addition of an aliquot of reagent and the measurement of the resulting current. The titration mixture must be stirred until it is homogeneous; if the indicator electrode is a dropping electrode or any other electrode employed in a quiet solution, the stirring must be stopped and the convection allowed to die away before the measurement can be made. If the titration is performed at a potential where oxygen is reducible, an even longer time must be allowed for deaeration unless the reagent is freed from dissolved air or unless the solutions are so concentrated that the current due to the reduction of oxygen is negligibly small. Very many titration reactions will approach equilibrium very closely during the interval that must be allowed. This is particularly true because the immediate vicinity of the equivalence point is avoided, so that a substantial excess of one reactant is always present. If the current still drifts after the mixture has been stirred, deaerated, and allowed to become quiet, obvious recourses are available. One may wait until a steady current is obtained, alter the composition of the supporting electrolyte (or, in redox titrations, add a catalyst) to increase the rate of the reaction, or perform the titration at an elevated temperature if this does not unduly decrease the value of K_t. The effect of a slow approach to equilibrium on the end point of an automatic amperometric titration has been investigated for a number of representative systems (5).

It has also been assumed that the contribution of every substance to the measured current is proportional to its concentration. Unless this is so, the titration curve will consist of segments that are curved instead of linear, and extrapolation in the above fashion then becomes impossible. In principle the titration can still be made if $C_M{}^0/[M^{n+}]_{ep}$ is sufficiently high. If the titration curve is $\_\diagup$-shaped, one may titrate to the first permanent deflection of the galvanometer or recorder. If it is V-shaped, one may obtain points so close to the minimum on each side that the error of the extrapolation becomes negligible. But if $C_M{}^0/[M^{n+}]_{ep}$ is so small that the titration reaction is sensibly incomplete near the equivalence point, so that access to this region is forbidden, one must either modify the experimental conditions or perform the titration by a different technique.

Amperometric titrations were said above to be more rapid than potentiometric ones and to be useful under somewhat more adverse conditions. They are also somewhat more versatile. There are few if any potentiometric titrations that could not be performed amperometrically. Not all are feasible at a dropping mercury electrode: the titration of ferrous iron with permanganate in an acidic solution is one that would not be, for ferric iron and permanganate are oxidizing agents too powerful to be distinguished at a mercury electrode, while neither ferrous nor manganous ion would yield a wave in a strongly acidic solution. At a more inert electrode, such as gold, oxidized tungsten, or graphite, however, the titration could be easily performed at a potential where permanganate ion is reduced but ferric iron is not. On the other hand, some titrations that are feasible amperometrically are impossible potentiometrically because no suitable indicator electrode can be found. Two typical examples are titrations of amines with sodium nitrite and of aldehydes with 2,4-dinitrophenylhydrazine. But where amperometric and potentiometric titrations are equally feasible the potentiometric one will usually be the one capable of yielding the greater precision. This is because of the graphical error contributed by the customary procedure for locating the end point of an amperometric titration. Largely for this reason, precisions much better than $\pm 0.5\%$ have not often been claimed for amperometric titration even under favorable chemical conditions.

TABLE 9.1.

Precise Location of the End Point of an Amperometric Titration

100 ml. of 0.991mM bismuth(III) in 0.01F perchloric acid–0.1F sodium perchlorate was titrated with 21.38mF disodium dihydrogen ethylenediaminetetraacetate, using a dropping mercury electrode at -0.30 v. vs. S.C.E. The equivalence point was reached when 4.633 ml. of reagent had been added. The significances of the last three columns are given in the text.

v_{EDTA}, $(= x)$	$(i - i_r)\left(\dfrac{V^0{}_{Bi} + v_{EDTA}}{V^0{}_{Bi}}\right)$ microamps. $(= y)$	$\dfrac{y}{i^0 - i_r}$ $[= (1 - f)]$	f	v_{EDTA}/f $(= v^*)$
0	10.47	1	0	—
1.00	8.22	0.785 (0.806)	0.215 (0.194)	4.651 (5.154)
2.00	5.94	0.567 (0.582)	0.433 (0.418)	4.619 (4.784)
3.00	3.68	0.351 (0.361)	0.649 (0.639)	4.622 (4.694)
4.00	1.43	0.137 (0.140)	0.863 (0.860)	4.634 (4.651)
6.00	0.01	—	—	—
8.00	−0.01	—	—	—

The subjective errors inherent in the ordinary graphical procedure can be eliminated, however, by a relatively simple procedure that leads to appreciably more precise results. This is illustrated here for an $\diagdown$___-shaped curve by means of the data in the first two columns of Table 9.1, obtained in a titration of bismuth(III) with standard ethylenediaminetetraacetate. Equivalent procedures for most other kinds of titration curves can be devised without difficulty.

The ordinary titration curve is a plot of the values in the second column of Table 9.1 against those in the first, and is shown in Figure 9.6(a). Extrapolating such a plot to its point of intersection with the volume axis, five of the writer's colleagues and students obtained, in mean, 4.64 ± 0.02 ml. for v^*, the volume of reagent required to reach the end point. This purely graphical uncertainty exceeds $\pm 0.4\%$.

One objective technique for locating the end point might involve computing the least-squares values of the coefficients a and b in the "best" equation of the form $y = ax + b$, employing the familiar relations

$$a = \frac{n\Sigma xy - \Sigma x\Sigma y}{n\Sigma x^2 - (\Sigma x)^2}$$

and

$$b = \frac{\Sigma y - a\Sigma x}{n}$$

which here give $y = 10.47 - 2.262x$. Then the value of v^* can be computed from the equation $v^* = -a/b$, whence $v^* = 4.629$ ml.

The crippling disadvantage of this technique is its sensitivity to a single adventitious error: if, for example, the initial value of $(i - i_r)$ had been measured as 10.20 rather than as 10.47 μamp., one would have obtained $y = 10.42 - 2.208x$ and $v^* = 4.715$ ml., nearly 2% higher than the preceding value. This is too high a price to pay for objectivity, and what is most serious is that the least-squares calculation is practically powerless to reveal the error and its source.

A far better procedure, which is strongly recommended whenever the highest precision is wanted, is based on eq. (9.12). Another equation would of course be needed if the curve had a different shape from the one in question here. According to eq. (9.12),

$$f = \frac{v}{v^*} = \frac{\left(i - i_r \right)\left(\dfrac{V_{Bi}^0 + v_{EDTA}}{V_{Bi}^0} \right)}{(i^0 - i_r)}$$

from which a value of f, and thence a value of v^*, can be computed for each value of v. If the resulting values of v^* are plotted against v, a horizontal straight line would be obtained in the absence of chemical and experimental errors. In practice this is never quite true, and because the relative error in f tends to decrease as the equivalence point is approached it is the points nearest the end point that are the most useful. The recommended procedure is to extrapolate the curve to the point at which the values of v^* (on the ordinate axis) and v (on the abscissa axis) are identical. The extrapolation is facilitated by drawing the line $v^* = v$ and finding the point at which this intersects the experimental plot. The ordinate of this point, which represents the equivalence point, can be very precisely located. The procedure is illustrated by the last three columns of Table 9.1 and by Figure 9.6(b). It is easy to identify and discount points that are obviously erroneous, and the technique yields results that sacrifice none of the precision inherent in the data.

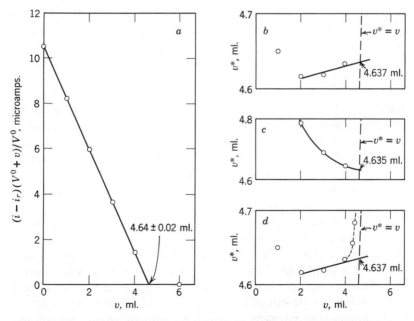

Figure 9.6. (a) Conventional amperometric titration curve for the titration of Table 9.1. (b) Curve obtained from the same data by the procedure recommended for the precise location of the end point. (c) Effect of an error in the measured initial current. (d) Effect of incompleteness near the end point.

It may appear that the result is susceptible to errors in the value of $(i^0 - i_r)$, but this is true to only a very limited extent. The values in parentheses in the last three columns of Table 9.1 would have been obtained with the erroneous value $(i^0 - i_r) = 10.20$ μamp.; this gave rise to an error of nearly $+2\%$ in the least-squares procedure. The plot obtained by the recommended technique is shown in Fig. 9.6(c): the extrapolation yields $v^* = 4.635$ ml., negligibly different from the value obtained from curve b.

If the titration reaction is sensibly incomplete near the equivalence point, the plot will resemble Fig. 9.6(d). In the writer's experience it is easier to identify and ignore the deviant points on such a plot than it is to do so on the conventional plot.

There are two kinds of interferences in amperometric titrations. Substances that consume the reagent, that coprecipitate, or that take part in induced reactions with the substance being determined, interfere in amperometric titrations as they do in titrations by any other technique. A different kind of interference arises from the presence of a substance that is reduced or oxidized at the potential where the titration is performed. Consider, for example, the titration of lead ion with an electrolytically inert reagent to give a precipitate of negligible solubility. If the diffusion current of lead ion in the original solution is 0.50 μamp. and if the residual current is 0.02 μamp., the total measured current will decrease from 0.52 μamp. initially to 0.02 μamp. at the equivalence point. However, if the solution is saturated with oxygen, and if the diffusion current of oxygen under these conditions is 3.00 μamp., the total current decrease only from 3.52 to 3.02 μamp. Because this is a much smaller relative change, the errors of measurement will be much more serious and the result will be considerably less precise. It is evident that no trouble would arise if oxygen were more difficultly reducible than lead ion: this is merely the wave-order problem in a slightly different form. It is also evident that interference from oxygen could be eliminated by deaerating the solution initially and after the addition of each aliquot of reagent, but if the interfering substance were ferric iron or persulfate it would be less easy to remove. One would need to resort to the techniques described in Secs. I-B ii and III of Chapter 7.

The lowest concentration at which an amperometric titration can be successfully performed depends on a number of factors. Side reactions may become more prominent at low concentrations, the titration reaction itself may become too slow for convenience, the effects of electroactive impurities become more prominent, and the curvature around the equivalence point increases as the reaction becomes less and less complete. Setting aside the first three of these problems, however, and assuming that K_t is so very high that the fourth can be ignored as well, it can be said as a general guide that the precision attainable in an amperometric titration will be roughly independent, under these favorable conditions, of the concentration of the solution titrated as long as this is at least 100 times as large as the voltammetric limit of detection of the electroactive substance involved. Then the precision of the titration will depend chiefly on the precisions with which the currents and volumes are measured— provided, of course, that the diffusion currents remain accurately proportional to concentration and that the chemistry of the titration remains straightforward. At lower concentrations, however, the precision deteriorates rapidly because the uncertainty in the correction for the residual current becomes increasingly important. If the initial concentration is smaller than about 10 times the limit of detection, an amperometric titration is unlikely to yield a satisfactory result. In other words, the concentration should preferably be at least $0.01\text{m}M$ if a dropping electrode is employed. Much more dilute solutions can be titrated with other indicator electrodes.

Amperometric titrations have often been employed to evaluate solubility products and other equilibrium constants. For example, if a reducible ion M^{n+} is titrated with an inert one X^{n-} to give the precipitate MX, and if the concentrations of both solutions are known the value of K_t under the conditions of the titration is easily obtained by appropriate use of eq. (9.13). Thus

$$K_t = \left(\frac{1}{C_M^0} \frac{i^0 - i_r}{i - i_r} \right)^2 \tag{9.18}$$

if i is the current at the equivalence point. If X^{n-} is also reducible, one can describe the equivalence point most compactly by writing

$$K_t = \left(\frac{k_M + k_X}{i - i_r} \right)^2 \tag{9.19}$$

Whether the precipitate is isovalent or heterovalent, the titration reaction can be represented by the equation

$$zM^{n+} + X^{zn-} = M_zX$$

The titration curve has a minimum if both M^{n+} and X^{zn-} are reducible, and at the minimum (2)

$$K_t = \left(\frac{z+1}{i - i_r} \right)^{z+1} \frac{k_X k_M^z}{z^z} \tag{9.20}$$

Comparing this with eq. (9.19) shows that, if $z = 1$, the minimum occurs at the equivalence point if $k_M = k_X$ but cannot do so otherwise (2). One can also calculate K_t from the concentrations of the ions at the point where precipitation begins; on each of the curves in Figs. 9.1–9.3, this is the point at which the first deviation from line e occurs. Equation (9.13) serves for the calculation of K_t from the current at any point after the onset of precipitation (5); the best precision is obtained at points not too far from the equivalence point.

II. Other Kinds of Amperometric Titrations

A. REDOX TITRATIONS

The titration curve obtained in an amperometric redox titration may have any of a fairly large number of shapes. The possibilities are more numerous than in a precipitation titration because there are four substances—the oxidized and reduced forms of each of the two couples involved—that may contribute to the current. Each of the four may give a cathodic current ($k > 0$) or an anodic one ($k < 0$), or may be electrolytically inert ($k = 0$), at the potential selected.

There are, however, two cases that are much more common than any others. In one of them, only one of these four substances yields a current, which may be either cathodic or anodic; in the other, the oxidized form of one couple yields a cathodic current while the reduced form of the other yields an anodic one.

Examples of the first case are furnished by the titration of vanadium(IV) with vanadium(II) in $1F$ sulfuric acid, using a dropping mercury electrode as the indicator electrode. The reaction can be described by the equation

$$VO^{++} + V^{++} + 2H^+ = 2V^{+++} + H_2O$$

In this medium vanadium(II) gives an anodic wave for which $E_{1/2}$ is −0.51 v. vs. S.C.E., vanadium(III) gives a cathodic wave having the same half-wave potential, and vanadium(IV) gives a cathodic wave for which $E_{1/2}$ is −0.85 v. At any potential more positive than about −0.4 v. one will obtain only the anodic diffusion current of vanadium(II); at potentials between about −0.6 and −0.75 v. one will obtain the cathodic diffusion current of vanadium(III); and at potentials more negative than about −0.95 v. one would obtain the sum of the cathodic diffusion currents of vanadium(III) and (IV). Titration curves obtained in the first two of these regions are shown in Fig. 9.7. The current at −0.2 v. remains very small until the

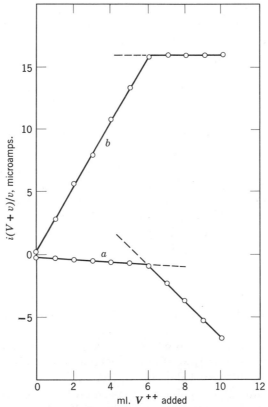

Figure 9.7.   Amperometric titration curves obtained on titrating 50.0 ml. of 3.00mM vanadium(IV) in 1F sulfuric acid with 25.0mM vanadium(II) at (a) −0.20 and (b) −0.65 v. vs. S.C.E.

equivalence point is reached, because vanadium(II) is nearly quantitatively consumed in reducing vanadium(IV) as long as any of the latter remains. The small negative slope in this region reflects the fact that the reaction between vanadium(II) and vanadium(IV) proceeds at a limited rate, so that some vanadium(II) remained unreacted when each measurement was made. After the equivalence point has been passed, the excess of vanadium(II) produces a substantial anodic current, which increases as more and more excess reagent is added. At -0.65 v. (curve b), the cathodic diffusion current of vanadium(III) increases up to the equivalence point as the titration reaction proceeds. Once the equivalence point is reached, however, the concentration of vanadium(III) can no longer increase appreciably, and therefore its diffusion current remains constant after correction for dilution is applied. Neither of these curves shows any appreciable curvature around the equivalence point, because the value of K_t is very large; under these conditions it is of the order of 10^{10}. If it were very much smaller, there would be some curvature like that in Figs. 9.1 and 9.2, but the algebraic relationships involved here and in the majority of other redox titrations are such that the curvature depends only on the value of K_t and not on the concentration of the solution titrated.

In the preceding section it was deduced that, in general, the ratio C^0/C_{ep}, where C^0 is the initial concentration of the substance being titrated and C_{ep} is its concentration at the equivalence point, should be at least 10 for easy and accurate location of the equivalence point of an amperometric titration. In a redox titration described by the equation $Ox_1 + Red_2 = Red_1 + Ox_2$, the ratio $[Ox_1]^0/[Ox_1]_{ep}$ will equal 10 if K_t is as small as 81. Explicitly,

$$C^0/C_{ep} = 1 + K_t^{1/2} \tag{9.21}$$

If each half-reaction involves n electrons, this value of K_t corresponds to a difference of $115/n$ mv. between their formal potentials. There is a still more general case, in which the reaction follows an equation of the form $aOx_1 + bRed_2 = cRed_1 + dOx_2$ and in which the products ad and bc have different values (6–8). Here the extent of the curvature around the equivalence point will depend on the concentration of the solution titrated as well as on the value of K_t.

The second kind of redox titration curve is exemplified by Fig. 9.7, which was obtained in a titration of iron(III) with vanadium(II) in a

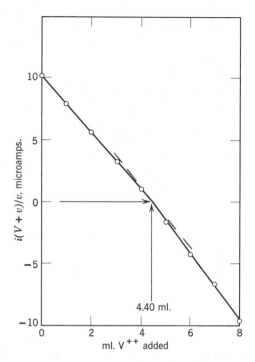

Figure 9.8. Amperometric titration curve obtained on titrating 50.0 ml. of 2.00mM iron(III) in 0.10F potassium citrate, pH 7.5, with 22.8mM vanadium(II) at −0.80 v. vs. S.C.E. The stoichiometric equivalence point lies at 4.39 ml.

neutral citrate medium. At −0.8 v. vs. S.C.E. iron(III) is reduced to iron(II) and gives a cathodic current, while vanadium (II) is oxidized to vanadium(III) and gives an anodic current. Up to the equivalence point, the current is cathodic and proportional to the concentration of iron(III) remaining unreduced; after the equivalence point it is anodic and proportional to the concentration of vanadium (II) in excess. As usual, the titration curve consists of two straight lines, but these have almost equal slopes (which would be exactly equal, according to the Ilkovič equation, if the absolute values of the products $nD^{1/2}$ were the same for the two electroactive substances), and the angle between them is, therefore, so obtuse that their point of intersection cannot be located very precisely. The best conventional technique is as follows. The titration curve is plotted in a suitable form: one may plot $(i - i_r)[(V^0 + v)/V^0]$ against v, one may plot $(i - i_r)$ against v if the reagent is so much more concentrated than the solution being titrated that the dilution correction is unimportant, or one may plot i against v if in addition the solution being titrated is so concentrated that no detectable deviation from linearity is produced by neglecting the residual current. Ignoring any curvature around the zero-current line, which might reflect either the incompleteness of the reaction or a slow approach to equilibrium in this region, one extrapolates first the cathodic and then the anodic branch of the curve to the point at which $(i - i_r) = 0$. Extrapolation of the cathodic branch yields the point at which, if the reaction were perfectly complete (which is very nearly the case in the region on which the extrapolation is based, because of the presence of excess iron(III) not yet reduced), the concentration of iron(III) would just become equal to zero. Extrapolation of the anodic branch yields the point at which, on the same assumption, the first trace of vanadium(II) was on the verge of appearing. Theoretically these points should coincide and each of them should represent the equivalence point. Often there is some small difference between them in an actual titration, which may be due to graphical errors or to the failure of one or another of the assumptions explicitly or implicitly involved. The magnitude of any such difference is a valuable indication of the reliability of their mean, which should be taken as the end point unless titrations with known solutions have shown that one extrapolation yields an erroneous result. Greater precision can be obtained by employing the considerations illustrated by Table 9.1 and Fig. 9.6(b).

It may perhaps be useful to point out that the potential of the indicator electrode is not a matter of indifference in an amperometric redox titration; not all of the imaginable types of titration curves are analytically useful. Consider, for example, the titration of iron(III) with vanadium(II) in a sulfuric acid solution. If the titration is performed at, say, -0.3 v. vs. S.C.E., where iron(III) yields a cathodic current and vanadium(II) an anodic one, the titration curve will resemble Fig. 9.8. But if it is performed at, say, -0.7 v., where only iron(III) and vanadium(III) can contribute to the measured current and where both of these yield cathodic currents, the situation will be quite different. Since K_t is extremely large, the portion of the titration curve preceding the equivalence point can be described by the equation

$$(i - i_r) \frac{V^0 + v}{V^0} = (i^0 - i_r) + (k_{V(III)} - k_{Fe(III)})f \quad (9.22)$$

The k's are not very different, because n is 1 for each ion while their diffusion coefficients are about the same, and so the slope of the line is nearly zero; the quantity on the left-hand side remains very nearly equal to $(i^0 - i_r)$ throughout this portion of the titration. Beyond the equivalence point one will have

$$(i - i_r) \frac{V^0 + v}{V^0} = k_{V(III)} C^0_{Fe(III)} = (i^0 - i_r) \frac{k_{V(III)}}{k_{Fe(III)}} \quad (9.23)$$

which is constant because neither the concentration of iron(III) nor that of vanadium(III) can vary after correction for dilution is applied, and which is again nearly equal to $(i^0 - i_r)$. The titration curve will be nearly if not quite a horizontal straight line, and the equivalence point will be quite impossible to locate. Only if the diffusion current constants of the two electroactive species were considerably different would such a titration be practical.

If a mercury indicator electrode is used in a titration with or of an oxidizing agent sufficiently powerful to oxidize metallic mercury, due attention should be paid to the considerations outlined in Chap. 7 IV-Bii. Usually it is better to use one of the more inert indicator electrodes described in Chap. 8. The rotating platinum wire electrode, in particular, has been very widely used in amperometric titrations. Mercury electrodes are, of course, especially advantageous in titrations with strong reducing agents because very negative potentials can be attained and because the electrode surface does not catalyze the oxidation of the reagent by water or hydrogen ion. The titrations of Figs. 9.7 and 9.8 would certainly be quite impossible with platinum electrodes.

B. COMPLEXOMETRIC AND CHELOMETRIC TITRATIONS

There are several ways in which amperometric techniques can be used to find the end point of a complexometric or chelometric titration. If the metal ion is electroactive and the complex or chelonate is fairly stable, it may be possible to find a potential at which the unreacted metal ion yields its limiting current while the reaction product is inert (9). For example, the titration of cupric ion with ethylenediaminetetraacetate may be performed with a dropping electrode at a potential where cupric ion is reduced but the chelonate is not. The titration curve then has the shape illustrated by Fig. 9.1; the current due to the reduction of unreacted cupric ion decreases as the equivalence point is approached, and becomes very small after it has been passed. Demanding that $C_M{}^0/[M^{n+}]_{ep}$ equal or exceed 10 is equivalent to demanding that the product $K_t C_M{}^0$ exceed about 90 if the titration reaction is $M^{n+} + Y^{p-} = MY^{n-p}$. This implies that such titrations would be feasible even if K_t were fairly small. But in that event the half-wave potentials of the simple and complex ions would be so nearly equal (in part because there would be so little free ligand present during the greater part of the titration) that it would be impossible to measure the wave height of the former. Even if K_t is large, complications may arise from the dissociation of the chelonate at the electrode surface and the reduction of the liberated metal ion. In Chap. 3 VII it was shown that the kinetic current thus produced is proportional to the quantity $k_f C_C / k_b{}^{1/2}$, where k_f is the first-order rate constant for the dissociation of the chelonate, k_b is the pseudo-first-order rate constant for the backward reaction, in which the metal ion and chelon recombine to form the chelonate, and C_C is the concentration of the chelonate at any point during the titration. The value of k_b can more properly be written

$$k_b = k_b'[Y^{p-}] \qquad (9.24)$$

where k_b' is the second-order rate constant for the recombination. The situation is complex, because there is so little free Y^{p-} in the bulk of the solution that its concentration at the electrode surface depends on the rate of dissociation of the chelonate and thus on the kinetic current, but this does not alter the qualitative conclusions. When a large excess of the chelon has been added, the value of k_b will become large, and hence the kinetic current decreases toward zero beyond the equivalence point. But when the excess of reagent is very small, as it is near the equivalence point, a larger kinetic current is obtained. The result is to increase the curvature around the equivalence point in the same way that a decrease of K_t would increase it. Hence the values of K_t and $C_M{}^0$ do not suffice to indicate whether a titration is feasible: to make such a decision one would need to know the values of k_f and k_b' as well. Usually the value of $K_t C_M^0$ must be some orders of magnitude larger than the value of 90 required by the simple criterion.

The same phenomenon or a related one may, of course, arise in other kinds of titrations as well. In a precipitation titration identical behavior would be produced by the dissolution of the precipitate at the electrode surface at an appreciable rate as its ions were reduced. Similarly, in a redox titration based on the reaction $Ox_1 + Red_2 = Red_1 + Ox_2$ and measurement of the diffusion current of Ox_1, appreciable kinetic currents will be obtained near the equivalence point unless the reverse reaction is quite slow. However, these situations appear to be very rare. A much more common complication in precipitation titrations arises from reduction of the suspended precipitate. For example, in the titration of silver or mercurous ion with chloride the current decays, not toward zero, but toward an appreciable and more or less constant value as a moderate excess of chloride is added (10,11). This necessitates adding a rather high concentration (0.05 to 0.1%) of gelatin, which is adsorbed onto the particles of the precipitate and prevents their reduction.

A second technique (12) is based on the measurement of the anodic current produced at a mercury electrode by the excess free chelon present after the equivalence point has been passed. The half-reaction responsible for the current can be written $Hg + H_x Y^{x-p} = HgY^{2-p} + xH^+ + 2e$. The technique can be used in titrations of metal ions, like lanthanum and zirconium, which are not electroactive under conditions suitable for their titrations, and of those, like the alkaline earth metal ions, which are reduced at potentials too negative for convenience or have otherwise undesirable voltammetric characteristics. A disadvantage is that halides must be excluded unless the titration is performed at a pH so high that the anodic wave of the chelon has a more negative half-wave potential than that of the halide.

A third procedure involves the use of a "polarographic indicator" (13). Consider the titration of a metal ion M^{n+} with a chelon Y^{p-}. For one or another of the reasons mentioned in the preceding paragraph, it may be difficult or impossible to measure the limiting current of unreacted M^{n+}, and at the same time it may not be feasible to measure the limiting current of the chelon. One may add a second substance that has voltammetric characteristics more favorable than those of M^{n+} and that does not react appreciably with the chelon until nearly all of the M^{n+} has been consumed. Zinc(II) may be used as the indicator in the titration of calcium ion with ethylenediaminetetraacetate in a strongly alkaline solution (14–16). The equilibria may be described by the equations

$$Ca^{++} + Y^{4-} = CaY^{=}; K = k_{Ca}$$
$$Zn(II) + Y^{4-} = ZnY^{=}; K = k_{Zn}$$

where the k's are the conditional formation constants of the respective chelonates. If k_{Ca} is much larger than k_{Zn}, the reagent will react with calcium ion almost exclusively until the equivalence point of the titration of calcium is reached. Thereafter, if k_{Zn} is also fairly large, the excess chelon will react almost quantitatively with the zinc, and consequently the limiting current of zinc will decrease linearly (after correction for dilution is applied) as more reagent is added. When an excess of ethylenediaminetetraacetate has been added, the current will become equal to the residual current because the concentration of free zinc(II) will be negligible and because the kinetic current of the zinc chelonate will also approach zero. The titration curve will be $\diagdown$-shaped. There are two equivalence points, located at the points of intersection of the sloping segment with the horizontal segments that precede and follow it. The first is the equivalence point of the titration of calcium; the curvature around it increases as the ratio k_{Ca}/k_{Zn} decreases. The second is the equivalence point of the titration of zinc; the curvature around it increases as k_{Zn} decreases. The amount of calcium in the sample can be found directly from the consumption of reagent at the first end point, and also from the consumption of reagent at the second end point if the amount of added zinc is known. Which of these two procedures will yield better results in any particular case will depend on the values of the conditional equilibrium constants involved. Titration to the first end point is normally preferable, but better results might be obtained by titration to the second if the ratio k_{Ca}/k_{Zn} were so small that the first end point could not be very precisely located.

By appropriate selection of the indicator one can titrate an ion giving a chelonate more stable than that of the indicator in the presence of others giving less stable ones (17). The same result can be obtained in direct titrations by adjustment of the pH or by masking (18). Ions giving chelonates too unstable for direct titrations can often be determined by back-titration (19).

Another technique that sometimes serves for amperometric titrations in which K_t is small is based on a difference between the diffusion coefficients of the free metal ion and the complex. This can be used for the titration of lead(II) in a strongly alkaline solution with tartrate. The stabilities of biplumbite ion and the lead tartrate complex are not very different, and so their half-wave potentials are about the same; it is impossible to measure the wave height of either ion alone. One can measure the sum of their limiting currents at a potential on the plateau of their combined wave. This decreases as tartrate is added, and reaches a constant value, equal to the diffusion current of the tartrate complex, after the equivalence point has been passed: the titration curve is __-shaped. As the chemical situation is exactly that described in Chap. 3 X until a considerable excess of reagent has been added, the utility of the technique in any particular case must be gauged by experiment. In any event the value of $K_t C_M{}^0$ must be large enough to obviate excessive curvature around the equivalence point.

C. Compensation and Diffusion-Layer Titrations

These are titrations that do not depend on the occurrence of a chemical reaction in the bulk of the solution titrated.

Compensation titrations are titrations in which the "reagent" and the "substance being titrated" give currents of opposite signs at some potential, but ideally do not react with each other at all. The end point of such a titration is the point where the cathodic current due to the reduction of one of them is just equal to the anodic current due to the oxidation of the other, so that the measured current is just equal to the residual current. There are two circumstances in which this may arise. One occurs when the electrode itself is oxidized in the anodic half-reaction, which is most likely to be possible if the electrode is made of mercury, aluminum (20), silver, or some other relatively base metal. The titration of oxygen with sulfide at a mercury electrode (21) is a typical example. In alkaline solutions sulfide gives an anodic wave corresponding to the half-reaction $Hg + S^= = HgS + 2e$. Oxygen gives a cathodic wave having a more positive half-wave potential at a dropping electrode and corresponding to the half-reaction $O_2 + 2H_2O + 2e = 2H_2O_2$. Because the cathodic half-wave potential of oxygen is more positive than the anodic half-wave potential of sulfide, the chemical reaction $Hg + S^= + O_2 + 2H_2O = HgS + 2H_2O_2$ will proceed at an appreciable rate at a mercury surface in contact with both oxygen and sulfide ion, but of course it cannot proceed at all in the bulk of the solution. If an alkaline solution of oxygen is titrated with sulfide, using a dropping mercury electrode at a potential that is on the plateau of each wave, the current at any point during the titration is given by

$$i = i_r + (i_d)_{O_2} + (i_d)_{S^=}$$
$$= i_r + I_{O_2}C_{O_2}m^{2/3}t^{1/6} + I_{S^=}C_{S^=}m^{2/3}t^{1/6} \qquad (9.25)$$

The values of I and i_d are positive for oxygen but negative for sulfide. The end point is the point where

$$I_{O_2}C_{O_2} + I_{S^=}C_{S^=} = 0 \qquad (9.26)$$

or, invoking the Ilkovič-equation descriptions of the diffusion current constants,

$$n_{O_2}D_{O_2}^{1/2}C_{O_2} = -n_{S^=}D_{S^=}^{1/2}C_{S^=} \qquad (9.27)$$

Because in general the diffusion coefficients of the substances involved will not be identical, the end point may differ substantially from the stoichiometric equivalence point. This is an important characteristic of both compensation and diffusion-layer titrations. Because the diffusion current constants of oxygen and sulfide may be affected differently by changes of the capillary characteristics, as well as of such variables as temperature and viscosity, the ratio $C_{O_2}/C_{S^=}$ may have different values at the end points of titrations performed with different capillaries or under different conditions. One can evaluate this ratio a priori with the aid of eq. (9.26) if the respective diffusion current constants are known for the capillary and experimental conditions to be employed. However, it is easier to obtain a precise value by performing preliminary titrations with known solutions.

Equation (9.25) can be written

$$i - i_r = m^{2/3}t^{1/6}\left(I_{O_2}C_{O_2}^0 \, \frac{V_{O_2}^0}{V_{O_2}^0 + v_{S^=}} + I_{S^=}C_{S^=}^0 \, \frac{v_{S^=}}{V_{O_2}^0} \, \frac{V_{O_2}^0}{V_{O_2}^0 + v_{S^=}} \right)$$

$$(9.28)$$

where $C_{O_2}^0$ is the concentration of oxygen in the solution being titrated and $C_{S^=}^0$ is the concentration of sulfide in the reagent. Since $I_{S^=}$ is negative, a plot of $(i - i_r)[(V_{O_2}^0 + v_S=)/V_{O_2}^0]$ versus $v_S=$ is a straight line having a negative slope. The end point, where the line crosses the volume axis, is easily found by interpolation.

The foregoing descriptions of the end point and the titration curve are based on the assumption that the reaction can proceed only at the electrode surface. Suppose, however, that the titration is performed in a cell having a large pool of mercury at the bottom, and that after each addition of sulfide the solution is stirred for a very long time before the current is measured. The reaction will then occur to some extent at the surface of the pool, and in the limit one will find that $(i - i_r) = 0$ at the point where just enough sulfide has been added to consume all of the oxygen in this reaction—that is, at the equivalence point. At the same time, the slope of the titration curve will change at this point for the reason described in connection with Fig. 9.7. If the reaction proceeds to any extent short of equilibrium anywhere except at the electrode surface, the end point will lie somewhere between the equivalence point and the point described by eq. (9.25), approaching the latter more closely as the titration is performed more rapidly. Compensation titrations that involve net chemical reactions (as many of them do) are impractical unless these are extremely slow.

A similar situation can arise even if the electrode does not participate chemically in the anodic half-reaction, as when tin(II) in an acidic tartrate solution is titrated with copper(II) (22). Thermodynamically the homogeneous reaction here is spontaneous, but it involves so large an activation energy that it does not occur at a measurable rate. Polarograms of the titration mixture therefore show both the cathodic wave of copper(II) and the anodic wave of tin(II). The end point is located in exactly the same fashion, and has exactly the same significance, as in the titration of oxygen with sulfide. Under typical conditions the ratio C_{Cu}/C_{Sn} is 1.020 at the end point: the difference between the end point and the equivalence point is small because the diffusion coefficients of the two tartrate complexes are nearly the same, and because the values of n for the half-reactions involving them are numerically equal.

In principle one could perform a compensation titration even if no net chemical reaction could occur at all. For instance, the iron(III)–iron(II) couple behaves reversibly at a dropping mercury electrode in a weakly acidic solution containing citrate, ethylenediaminetetraacetate, oxalate, or tartrate. In any of these media ferric iron could be titrated with ferrous iron at any potential on the rising parts of their waves, where ferric iron would give a cathodic current and ferrous iron an anodic one. Very careful control of the potential would be necessary to avoid sensible variations of the ratio $(i/C)_{Fe(III)}/(i/C)_{Fe(II)}$, which governs the location of the end point.

Diffusion-layer titrations are based on the considerations outlined in Chap. 3 X, and are exemplified by the titration of oxygen with a strong acid (23). The titration is performed with a dropping mercury electrode at a potential (e.g., -1.8 v. vs. S.C.E.) where both oxygen and hydrogen ion are reducible. A neutral but unbuffered supporting electrolyte should be used to suppress the migration current of hydrogen ion. As oxygen is reduced, hydroxyl ions are formed at the electrode surface by the half-reaction $O_2 + 2H_2O + 4e = 4OH^-$. As these diffuse away from the electrode surface they react with hydrogen ions diffusing toward it. Hydrogen ions are thus prevented from reaching the electrode surface until their flux equals that of hydroxyl ion, when $D^{1/2}_{H^+}C_{H^+} = 4D^{1/2}_{O_2}C_{O_2}$. Up to this point the value of $(i - i_r)$ remains constant after correction is applied for dilution; thereafter it increases linearly with the volume of acid added in excess. An accuracy and precision of the order of a few tenths of a per cent can be obtained. One could similarly titrate iodate with hydrogen ion (cf. Fig. 3.24). Selenium(IV) or tellurium(IV) could be titrated in an ammoniacal supporting electrolyte with copper(II) (24), because copper(II) would be precipitated in the diffusion layer by the selenide or telluride ion formed at the electrode surface.

Curvature around the end point of a diffusion-layer titration curve will occur whenever the reaction in the diffusion layer is sensibly incomplete, and this will be the case unless it has a very large equilibrium constant and is also very fast.

III. Apparatus and Techniques

Amperometric titrations are much simpler experimentally than other polarographic or voltammetric techniques. Simpler apparatus is needed because the current has to be measured at only a single potential. Fewer variables need be controlled because the exact value of the current at any point is unimportant: all that matters is how it varies as reagent is added. The temperature, the composition of the supporting electrolyte, the height of the mercury column above a dropping mercury electrode or the rate of rotation or stirring if another electrode is used, and other factors that are crucially important in other voltammetric techniques are, therefore, of little concern in amperometric titrations; it is only necessary to avoid significant variations during the course of any one titration.

Nearly all amperometric titrations are performed by measuring the current after the addition of each of a fairly small number of aliquots of reagent. If the titration is made at a potential where the reduction of dissolved oxygen would contribute to the measured current, it is usually necessary to remove any oxygen added with the reagent by bubbling inert gas through the cell for an appropriate length of time after each addition. Time can be saved by employing a microburet equipped with a three-way stopcock. This permits deaeration of the reagent solution at the same time as the solution being titrated. Some titrations can be performed in alkaline solutions containing sulfite or hydrazine, which react with dissolved oxygen, and then deaeration is unnecessary provided that neither the sample nor the reagent is air-oxidized. More elaborate precautions are needed if either solution is sensitive to air. Then the reagent must be deaerated, each aliquot of it should be added into a rapid stream of gas bubbling up through the titration mixture, and, if it is possible, the solution should be protected by sulfite or hydrazine as well as by an inert gas. In this connection it should be noted that some reagents whose stock solutions are hardly affected by oxygen may react with it very rapidly under the conditions of an amperometric titration. This is the case when hydrazine dihydrochloride is used to titrate copper(II) in an ammoniacal medium or when an acidic solution of stannous chloride is used for a titration in a strongly alkaline medium. Reagents like vanadium(II), chromium(II), and titanium(III), whose stock solutions are very sensitive to air-oxidation, may be prepared in and dispensed from reductor microburets (25,26) containing a few grams of heavily amalgamated zinc to ensure complete reduction.

Mixing after the addition of each aliquot of reagent is necessary even when deaeration is not. With rotating wire or stirred mercury pool electrodes, mixing is automatic, but with other indicator electrodes (including rotating disc electrodes) auxiliary stirring must be provided. A stream of inert gas can be used for stirring even if it is not needed for deaeration. Except with rotating wire and stirred pool electrodes, stirring must generally be stopped before the current can be measured. The time for which the stirring must be continued to ensure complete mixing, and the time that must be allowed to elapse after the cessation of stirring before a steady current is obtained, will vary with the design of the cell. They are most easily gauged by observing how their variations affect the current obtained after adding a similar volume of a stock solution of a metal ion to an appropriate volume of a supporting electrolyte. As was mentioned above, much longer times will have to be allowed in ordinary amperometric titrations if equilibrium is only slowly attained. In compensation titrations, however, long delays are harmful rather than beneficial, since the end point will be displaced if the reaction is allowed to occur to any appreciable extent in the bulk of the solution.

For amperometric titrations with a dropping mercury electrode, Laitinen and Burdett (27) designed a cell in which gas could be bubbled continuously through a solution without producing undue turbulence at the capillary tip. This was achieved by surrounding the capillary with a pair of slotted concentric baffles. Cells of this design are available from E. H. Sargent & Co. (S-29408). In the writer's laboratory they have been found to be unsuitable for automatic titrations, in which the reagent is added at a constant rate, for a gas stream fast enough to decrease the mixing time to a sufficiently low value produces very erratic currents (28). However, this is of little importance in manual titrations, in which a rather slow gas stream can be used without inconvenience. Cells suitable for amperometric titrations, using a dropping mercury electrode, of volumes of solution as small as 0.5 ml. have been designed (29,30), but any polarographic cell can be used.

Amperometric titrations can be performed with any voltammetric indicator electrode. Rotating platinum wire electrodes have been very widely used for titrations at potentials more positive than can be obtained with mercury electrodes, and the oxidized tungsten electrode (31) would extend the range still farther. Vibrating platinum electrodes (32,33) can be used for titrations of as little as 0.001 ml. of solution on a microscope slide (34). A mercury pool electrode has been used (35) in titrating metal ions with ethylenediaminetetraacetate; agitating the solution with a stream of nitrogen (whose flow rate need not be the same from one titration to the next) to increase the sensitivity, an accuracy and precision of the order of $\pm 1\%$ can be obtained with 0.2–0.5 micromolar solutions.

There are two reasons why relatively concentrated reagents should be employed in amperometric titrations. One, which was mentioned above, is to minimize the importance of the theoretically necessary correction for dilution. The other is to minimize variations in the concentration of the supporting electrolyte, which would affect the diffusion current constants of the substances that contribute to the measured current. Regardless of the shape of the titration curve, failure to correct for dilution always causes the end point found by the usual extrapolation procedure to occur a little earlier than it should. Changes in the concentration of the supporting electrolyte may displace the end point in either direction. The simplest case is that in which a solution containing a high concentration of a supporting electrolyte like sodium perchlorate is titrated with a very dilute reagent. The diffusion current constant of each electroactive species will increase as more reagent is added because of the decreasing viscosity, and as a result the end point will occur too late no matter which diffusion current is measured. The opposite effect would be produced if the reagent were much more viscous than the solution being titrated. More important but less generally predictable effects might result from the variations of pH produced by the addition of a substantial volume of strongly acidic or alkaline reagent to a poorly buffered solution.

Most amperometric titrations are performed with reagents having normalities at least 10 or 20 times as large as those of the solutions titrated. If the ratio is as high as 50, the dilution correction can be ignored in practical work, because then the error introduced by neglecting it will be smaller than the probable uncertainties of the measured currents. As the volume of solution titrated rarely exceeds 50 or 100 ml., the volume of reagent is usually of the order of a few milliliters. Consequently a microburet is usually employed to permit adequate precision to be obtained in the volume measurements. A syringe-type microburet in which the plunger is driven by a micrometer screw can also be used. In either case, the tip of the buret should be long enough to permit touching it to the surface of the solution in the cell after each addition of reagent; if this is not done, the droplet of reagent that may adhere to the buret tip might contain an appreciable fraction of the total volume delivered from the calibrated portion.

Several authors have devised equipment for automatic amperometric titrations (36–40). In their simplest form these involve addition of the reagent at a constant rate from a syringe-type buret actuated by a synchronous motor, and recording of the current-time curve obtained at a suitable fixed potential. A very concentrated reagent must be used because the dilution correction cannot be applied without replotting the curve. Efficient stirring is essential unless the rate of addition of reagent is extremely small, and such titrations are, therefore, hardly possible except at indicator electrodes that are used in stirred solutions, such as rotating or vibrating platinum or mercury electrodes and stirred mercury pools. Distorted curves and large titration errors are obtained with slow reactions; but these can be used to diagnose the mechanism and evaluate the rate constant of the rate-controlling step (28,41).

Except when it is used for this purpose, a recording polarograph has no advantage over a manual one for amperometric titrations. Stationary electrodes in quiet solutions, with which a recording instrument would be needed to obtain meaningful peak currents, are rarely if ever used in amperometric titrations. Consequently, if many amperometric titrations are to be performed, it is well worth purchasing a manual polarograph to free a recording one for other work. The electrical requirements are quite modest: the exact potential of the indicator electrode is rarely of much concern, for a variation of 50 or even 100 mv. is often without appreciable effect, and only the linearity of the current-measuring device is really important. There is no need for a polarizing circuit any more complex than that shown in Fig. 2.1; if the solutions are not too dilute, a condenser-damped microammeter serves very well for the current measurements.

Comprehensive reviews of the applications of amperometric titrations in practical analysis have been given by Kolthoff and Lingane (42), Laitinen (43), Doležal and Zýka (44–46), and Stock (47,48). A number of procedures critically selected on the basis of exacting criteria of fundamental importance, broad applicability, precision, and accuracy, have been summarized by Jordan and Clausen (49).

IV. Amperometric Titrations with Two Polarized Electrodes

The conventional amperometric titrations described in the foregoing sections are made in cells containing a reference electrode, whose potential is nearly or completely independent of the current, in addition to the indicator electrode. Applying a fixed potential difference across the electrodes fixes the potential of the indicator electrode, and the variations of cell current therefore reflect changes in the rate of mass transfer to the surface of the indicator electrode.

Qualitatively different curves are obtained in amperometric titrations with two polarized electrodes, also known as dual-electrode amperometric or biamperometric titrations. These are titrations in which the current-potential curve for each of the two electrodes changes as the composition of the titration mixture changes. It is easiest to discuss the case in which the two electrodes are identical, because then the behaviors of both can be explained with the aid of a single current-potential curve. In practical work it is by no means necessary for them to be identical: they may have different areas, the efficiencies of stirring at their surfaces may differ, and they may even be made from different materials. In this arrangement the difference between the potentials of the two indicator electrodes must be equal to the applied potential (neglecting iR drop through the cell), and the current flowing through the indicator cathode must be equal to (but have the opposite sign from) that flowing through the indicator anode. The current varies as the titration proceeds, and the shape of the titration curve depends on the reversibilities of the couples involved and on the magnitude of the potential difference applied.

Consider first a titration involving two reversible couples, such as the titration of azobenzene in an acidic solution with vanadium(II). If two exactly identical mercury indicator electrodes are used, each must obey the schematic current-potential curves shown in Fig. 9.9. At the start of the titration (curve a), azobenzene will be reduced at the cathode while mercury is oxidized at the anode. If the applied potential is small, the current flowing through the cell will be small because the slope of the current-potential curve is small at currents near zero. When part of the azobenzene has been reduced (curve b), the resulting hydrazobenzene can be oxidized at the anode, and consequently the anode potential will be much more negative than at the start. At the same time, the slope of the curve as it crosses the zero-current axis increases, and so a much larger current is observed. The current continues to increase until this slope reaches a maximum value, which occurs when the cathodic limiting current of the azobenzene remaining is just equal to the anodic limiting current of the hydrazobenzene produced. If (but only if) the rates of mass transfer of these substances to the two electrodes are identical, this will occur

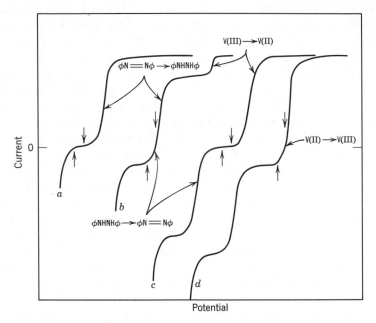

Figure 9.9.   Schematic current–potential curves at various stages of a titration of azobenzene with vanadium(II): (a) the initial solution, (b) after partial reduction, (c) at the equivalence point, and (d) after the addition of an excess of the reagent. The pairs of arrows indicate points that are separated by a fixed difference of potential and that correspond to equal anodic and cathodic currents. Successive curves are displaced along the potential axis for clarity, but the current axis is the same for all.

halfway to the equivalence point. Any difference between their diffusion coefficients, the electrode areas, or the efficiencies of stirring at the surfaces of the two electrodes will displace this point to one side or the other. Thereafter the current decreases again as the concentration of azobenzene falls, and it reaches a minimum value at or very near the equivalence point (curve c). As excess reagent is added the current increases again (curve d), vanadium(II) being oxidized at the anode while vanadium(III) is reduced at the cathode. The current is plotted against the volume of reagent to obtain a titration curve like that shown in curve a of Fig. 9.10. The practically linear portions that precede and follow the minimum are extrapolated to their point of intersection, and this is taken as the end point.

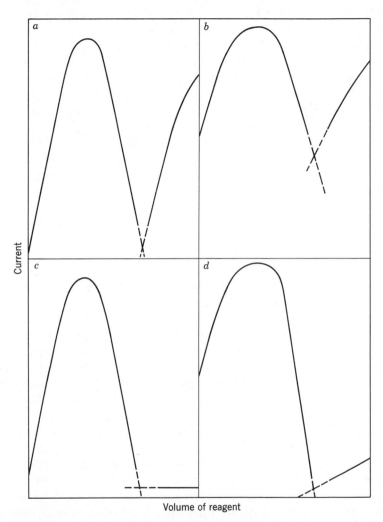

Figure 9.10. Schematic dual-electrode amperometric titration curves (*a*) for a titration in which both couples are reversible and the difference between the potentials of the electrodes is small, (*b*) same at a much larger applied potential, (*c*) for a titration in which the couple involving the substance being titrated is reversible while that involving the reagent is irreversible and the difference between the potentials of the electrodes is small, (*d*) same as (*c*) but at a much larger applied potential.

From the curves in Fig. 9.9 it is easily seen that applying a larger difference of potential across the two electrodes will increase the current at every point during the titration, and that the increase will be greatest near the start of the titration and around the equivalence point. Curve *b* of Fig. 9.10 would result. The angle between the two branches that are extrapolated to find the end point decreases as the applied potential increases, and this adversely affects the precision with which the end point can be found. Too small potential differences, on the other hand, give currents too small for convenient measurement even in the region of the maximum. Evidently some care must be taken in selecting the applied potential even though its exact value is not very critical. Values of 10 to 30 mv. are appropriate in titrations like these.

If one of the couples is irreversible the shape of the curve changes markedly. Consider the titration of azobenzene in dilute hydrochloric acid with chromous ion, using mercury electrodes. The cathodic half-wave potential of chromium(III) is so much more negative than the anodic one of chromium(II) that the slope of the current-potential curve around zero current will be very small after the equivalence point is passed. If the applied potential is small, the titration curve will have the form shown in curve *c* of Fig. 9.10. Before the equivalence point it will coincide with the corresponding portion of curve *a*, because the properties of the titrant couple are immaterial under these conditions, but after the equivalence point only a very small current can be obtained. This is the principle of the so-called "dead-stop end point" (*50*). If the titration is performed in the opposite direction, the current will remain small until the equivalence point is reached, then it will increase as excess azobenzene is added to the hydrazobenzene formed by the titration reaction. This is the "kick-off end point." Larger applied potentials can be used in such titrations than in those involving two reversible couples: in the region where the irreversible couple determines the current, even a fairly large potential can be applied without producing a sensible current, but an increase of potential increases the currents obtained from the reversible couple and thereby produces a sharper end point. This is illustrated by curve *d* of Fig. 9.10. Potentials as large as 500 mv. are occasionally used. Too large a value, however, gives rise to a substantial current at the end point and decreases the precision that can be obtained. The optimum value of the applied potential is best found from current-potential curves secured in the ordinary voltammetric way at various stages of the titration.

In principle these titrations can be made with electrodes of any kind, but stationary platinum wire electrodes in stirred solutions are much the most commonly used. Electrode areas of the order of 1 cm.[2] are typical. The desired potential can be obtained from a manual polarograph or from a simple voltage divider powered by a dry cell; in the latter case a microammeter could be used for the current measurements. Constancy of stirring rate is very important although it is not often emphasized, for the current depends on the efficiency of stirring.

Amperometric titrations with two polarized electrodes have sometimes been claimed to be more sensitive than those employing one polarized electrode, and partly for this reason they have been widely used in coulometric and other titrations in which high sensitivity is needed. The claim is unjustified, however: because the current measured at any point during a dual-electrode amperometric titration is generally much smaller than the limiting current of either of the electroactive substances that govern it, such titrations are actually less sensitive than single-electrode amperometric titrations performed under identical conditions. There is no question that dual-electrode amperometric titrations are very sensitive, but this merely reflects the extreme sensitivity that results from the use of a large electrode in a stirred solution.

The principles and applications of these titrations have been reviewed by Stock *(47,51)*, Delahay *(52)*, Lingane *(53)*, Kies *(54)*, and Davis *(55)*.

References

(1) A. Ringbom, *Complexation in Analytical Chemistry*, Interscience, New York, 1963.
(2) J. A. Goldman and L. Meites, *Anal. Chim. Acta*, **30**, 280 (1964).
(3) A. Langer and D. P. Stevenson, *Ind. Eng. Chem., Anal. Ed.*, **14**, 770 (1942).
(4) E. Grunwald, *Anal. Chem.*, **28**, 1112 (1956).
(5) I. M. Kolthoff and H. A. Laitinen, *Rec. Trav. Chim.*, **59**, 922 (1940).
(6) E. Bishop, *Anal. Chim. Acta*, **7**, 15 (1952).
(7) U. A. T. Brinkman, *Chem. Weekblad*, **59**, No. 2, 9 (1963).
(8) A. J. Bard and S. H. Simonsen, *J. Chem. Education*, **37**, 364 (1960).
(9) R. Přibil and B. Matyska, *Collection Czechoslov. Chem. Communs.*, **16**, 139 (1951).

(10) H. A. Laitinen and I. M. Kolthoff, *J. Phys. Chem.*, **45**, 1079 (1941).
(11) I. M. Kolthoff and C. S. Miller, *J. Am. Chem. Soc.*, **63**, 1405 (1941).
(12) G. Michel, *Anal. Chem. Acta*, **10**, 87 (1954).
(13) A. Ringbom and B. Wilkman, *Acta Chem. Scand.*, **3**, 22 (1949).
(14) R. Přibil and E. Vicenova, *Chem. Listy*, **46**, 16 (1952).
(15) H. A. Laitinen and R. F. Sympson, *Anal. Chem.*, **26**, 556 (1954).
(16) M. L. Richardson, *Talanta*, **10**, 103 (1963).
(17) G. Goldstein, D. E. Manning, and H. E. Zittel, *Anal. Chem.*, **34**, 358 (1962).
(18) C. N. Reilley, W. G. Scribner, and C. Temple, *Anal. Chem.*, **28**, 450 (1956).
(19) G. Goldstein, D. E. Manning, and H. E. Zittel, *Anal. Chem.*, **35**, 17 (1963).
(20) I. M. Kolthoff and C. J. Sambucetti, *Anal. Chim. Acta*, **21**, 17 (1959); **22**, 253, 351 (1960).
(21) I. M. Kolthoff and C. S. Miller, *J. Am. Chem. Soc.*, **62**, 2171 (1940).
(22) J. J. Lingane, *J. Am. Chem. Soc.*, **65**, 866 (1943).
(23) W. Kemula and S. Siekierski, *Collection Czechoslov. Chem. Communs.*, **15**, 1069 (1950).
(24) J. J. Lingane and L. W. Niedrach, *J. Am. Chem. Soc.*, **71**, 196 (1949).
(25) H. Flaschka, *Anal. Chim. Acta*, **4**, 242 (1950).
(26) L. Meites, *J. Chem. Education*, **27**, 458 (1950).
(27) H. A. Laitinen and L. W. Burdett, *Anal. Chem.*, **22**, 833 (1950).
(28) P. W. Carr, B.S. in Chem. Thesis, Polytechnic Institute of Brooklyn, 1965.
(29) M. A. Fill and J. T. Stock, *Analyst*, **69**, 178 (1944).
(30) J. T. Stock, *Analyst*, **71**, 583 (1946).
(31) N. R. Stalica, Ph.D. Thesis, The Pennsylvania State University, 1963.
(32) E. D. Harris and A. J. Lindsey, *Nature*, **162**, 413 (1948); *Analyst*, **76**, 647, 650 (1951).
(33) A. J. Lindsey, *J. Phys. Chem.*, **56**, 439 (1952).
(34) M. N. Petrikova and I. P. Alimarin, *Zh. Anal. Khim.*, **12**, 462 (1957).
(35) J. G. Nikelly and W. D. Cooke, *Anal. Chem.*, **28**, 243 (1956).
(36) J. M. Gonzalez Barredo and J. K. Taylor, *Trans. Electrochem. Soc.*, **92**, 437 (1947).
(37) A. L. Juliard, *Anal. Chem.*, **30**, 136 (1958).
(38) M. Murayama, U. S. Patent 2,834,654 (May 13, 1958).
(39) A. Liberti, *Ricerca Sci.*, **27**, Suppl. A, Polarografia, **3**, 21 (1957); A. Liberti and L. Ciavatta, *Met. Ital.*, **2**, 50 (1958).
(40) G. Milazzo, *J. Electroanal. Chem.*, **7**, 123 (1964).
(41) R. E. Cover and L. Meites, *J. Phys. Chem.*, **67**, 1528, 2311 (1963).
(42) I. M. Kolthoff and J. J. Lingane, *Polarography*, Interscience, New York, 2nd ed., 1952, Vol. II, pp. 913–953.
(43) H. A. Laitinen, *Anal. Chem.*, **28**, 666 (1956); **30**, 657 (1958); **32**, 180R (1960); **34**, 307R (1962).
(44) J. Doležal and J. Zýka, *Polarometricke titrace*, Statni Nakladatelstvi Tech. Literatury, Prague, 1961.
(45) J. Zýka, in *Progress in Polarography*, P. Zuman and I. M. Kolthoff, eds., Interscience, New York, 1962, Vol. II, p. 649.
(46) A. Berka, J. Doležal, and J. Zýka, *Chemist-Analyst*, **53**, 122 (1964); **54**, 24 (1965).

(47) J. T. Stock, *Anal. Chem.*, **36**, 355R (1964).

(48) J. T. Stock, *Amperometric Titrations*, Interscience, New York, 1965.

(49) J. Jordan and J. H. Clausen, in *Handbook of Analytical Chemistry*, L. Meites, ed., McGraw-Hill, New York, 1963, pp. 5–155 to 5–163.

(50) C. W. Foulk and A. T. Bawden, *J. Am. Chem. Soc.*, **48**, 2045 (1926).

(51) J. T. Stock, *Metallurgia*, **37**, 220 (1948).

(52) P. Delahay, *New Instrumental Methods in Electrochemistry*, Interscience, New York, 1954, pp. 258–264.

(53) J. J. Lingane, *Electroanalytical Chemistry*, Interscience, New York, 2nd ed., 1958, pp. 280–295.

(54) H. L. Kies, *Anal. Chim. Acta*, **18**, 14 (1958).

(55) D. G. Davis, in *Handbook of Analytical Chemistry*, L. Meites, ed., McGraw-Hill, New York, 1963, pp. 5–164 to 5–167.

CHAPTER 10

RELATED TECHNIQUES

The foregoing chapters have described the theory, execution, and some of the applications of voltammetric measurements at dropping mercury and other indicator electrodes. This chapter is devoted to a number of more or less closely related techniques. Some of these have been chosen because of their utility in the polarographic laboratory, others because they illustrate further applications of the ideas previously described.

I. Controlled-Potential Electrolysis

When the indicator electrode in a voltammetric cell is maintained at a potential on the plateau of a wave, the electroactive substance responsible for the wave is reduced or oxidized as rapidly as it arrives at the electrode surface. Its concentration in the bulk of the solution decreases, and therefore the wave height decreases as well. With most voltammetric indicator electrodes the bulk concentration decreases so slowly that the wave height remains nearly constant over long periods of time. For example, if 25 ml. of a solution of an electroactive substance for which $I = 4.0$ and $n = 2$ is electrolyzed at a potential on the plateau of its wave with a dropping electrode for which $m^{2/3}t^{1/6} = 2.5$, the rate of decrease of the bulk concentration will be only 0.8%/hr. For some purposes it is very advantageous that this depletion is so slow. Polarograms of stable solutions can be recorded over and over again without sensible change. Variations of wave height with time are easily correlated with the rates of chemical reactions occurring in the bulk of the solution.

There are, however, many purposes for which it is desirable to perform quantitative electrolyses in reasonable lengths of time; one important one was discussed in Chap. 7 III-F. To do this one must use a large electrode, usually either a mercury pool or a cylinder of platinum gauze, in an efficiently stirred solution. Because the processes that occur at the electrode-solution interface under any given conditions are chiefly dependent on the potential of the electrode,

511

voltammetric data can easily be used to find the potential that is best suited to carrying out any desired electrode reaction, and the results of such electrolyses are in turn very useful in interpreting the voltammetric observations.

The most frequent application of controlled-potential electrolysis at solid electrodes has been to electrogravimetric determinations of metals (1–3). For other purposes mercury electrodes have been much more extensively used, because the optimum conditions for the performance of controlled-potential electrolyses are most easily deduced from voltammetric data, which have been much scarcer for solid than for mercury electrodes. In this discussion it is convenient to stress the use of mercury electrodes and correlations with polarographic data. However, similar uses of solid electrodes and similar correlations with voltammetric data are equally possible, and are appearing in the literature with increasing frequency.

The electrolysis of stirred solutions with large mercury cathodes, employing nearly constant electrolysis currents, is a familiar technique of separation. In the analytical laboratory it is often used to separate elements such as iron, chromium, cobalt, copper, and nickel, which are deposited into the mercury from acidic solutions, from others such as aluminum, titanium, tungsten, and vanadium, which remain in the solution. Such constant-current separations depend on the fact that the potential of the mercury electrode must always assume a value determined by the composition of the solution at the instant under consideration. If a solution of copper(II) in dilute sulfuric acid is electrolyzed with a mercury cathode, and if the current is smaller than the limiting current of cupric ion, the potential must lie somewhere on the rising part of the copper(II) wave. Later in the electrolysis, when some of the cupric ion has been reduced, its limiting current will be smaller, and hence the electrode potential must become more negative. Eventually the potential will approach the plateau of the wave. Because the current is constant and is being entirely consumed by the reduction of copper(II), the rate of decrease of concentration will be constant, but the rate of change of the potential will increase as the plateau is approached because the slope of the wave is smaller at potentials on its shoulder than at those on its rising part. These phenomena are illustrated by Fig. 10.1. When the limiting current of the copper(II) remaining unreduced becomes smaller than the constant current being forced through the cell, the reduction of copper(II) can no longer occur rapidly enough to consume all of the current. Some other process must begin, and in the case represented by Fig. 10.1 this will be the reduction of hydrogen ion. The potential of the electrode will undergo a rapid change from a value on the shoulder of the copper(II) wave to one on the rising part of the hydrogen-ion wave. Thereafter it will continue to become more negative as the last of the copper(II) is reduced and as hydrogen ion is consumed, but in even moderately dilute acid the concentration of hydrogen ion would be so high that it would hardly be affected for a long time. Indeed, if the anode is immersed in the same solution, hydrogen ion will be produced as rapidly at its surface as it can be consumed at the cathode. Hence the shift of potential must halt on the rising portion of the wave of hydrogen ion. The limiting potential depends on the composition of the solution and on the current density; in $1F$ sulfuric acid it is typically in the vicinity of -1.4 v. vs. S.C.E. This is sufficiently negative to deposit iron, cobalt, and many other metals, but those whose half-wave potentials are appreciably more

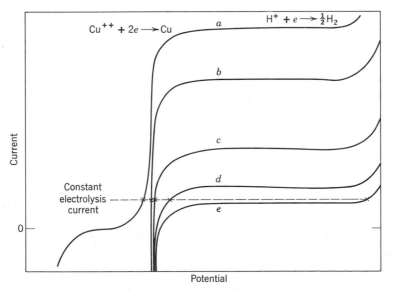

Figure 10.1.   Schematic current–potential curves at various stages of a constant-current electroreduction of copper(II) from a stirred acidic solution with a mercury electrode. The anodic currents on curves b–e are due to the re-oxidation of the copper amalgam.

negative than this value will be unaffected. A typical potential–time curve is shown in Fig. 10.2. Ferric and cupric ions are reduced together during the first 30 min. or so. Thereafter their concentrations are too small to sustain the entire current, and the reduction of cadmium ion begins. The electrode potential remains for some time at values on the rising part of the wave of cadmium ion, whose half-wave potential in this medium is about −0.6 v.; then, when most of the cadmium has been reduced as well, it assumes values on the rising part of the nickel wave, and so on until it is eventually stabilized by the reduction of hydrogen ion.

The selectivity of this procedure is modest because it divides electrode reactions into only two groups: those that do and those that do not occur at appreciable rates at the potential finally attained. Far higher selectivity can be attained by maintaining the potential of the electrode constant at some intermediate value, and this is the fundamental idea of controlled-potential electrolysis. It is clear from Fig. 3.20, for example, that silver could be quantitatively deposited and

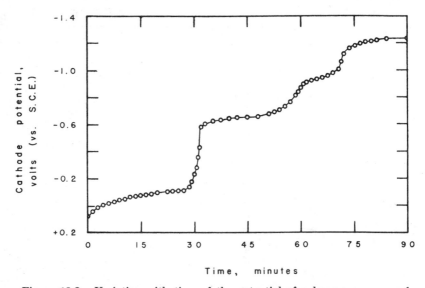

Figure 10.2. Variation with time of the potential of a large mercury pool cathode during the electrolysis, with a constant current of 0.260 amp., of 100 ml. of $1F$ sulfuric acid containing approximately 2.5 millimole each of iron(III), copper(II), cadmium(II), and nickel(II). After 180 min. the potential was only 0.045 v. more negative than after 90 min.

separated by thallium by electrolysis at a mercury electrode whose potential was kept constant at, say, −0.30 v. vs. S.C.E. under these conditions; silver and thallium could be deposited together and separated from cadmium at, say, −0.7 v., and so on. In either case the reduction would proceed as rapidly as the reducible ions reached the electrode surface because the potential lies on the plateau of the wave. Similar selectivity can be achieved in cases where stepwise reduction or oxidation is possible, as witness Fig. 3.21: electrolysis with a mercury cathode whose potential is kept constant at, say, −0.38 v., which is on the plateau of the first wave, would yield copper(I) quantitatively. The positions of the equilibria ultimately attained in such processes can be predicted from polarographic data as was shown in Chap. 7 III-F. With rare exceptions, a potential suitable for a controlled-potential electrolysis can be chosen by obtaining a polarogram of the solution with which one has to deal, and selecting a potential near the midpoint of the plateau of the wave that corresponds to the desired reduction or oxidation.

The potential thus chosen will usually be near the mean of the half-wave potential of this wave and the one that follows it on the polarogram, and so the choice can usually be guided by tables of polarographic data. The optimum value actually depends on the difference between the half-wave potentials (as in the separation of cadmium from zinc discussed on p. 373, where the difference is large and the optimum potential is considerably more negative than their mean), on the reversibilities of the two waves (if the first wave is totally irreversible the electrolysis may be, and if the second one is totally irreversible it should be, performed at a potential more positive than the mean of their half-wave potentials), and on the natures of the two processes [because of the volume terms that are needed in equations like eq. (7.7)], but these are usually minor effects. Suffice it to say that the optimum potential can usually be assessed *a priori* if enough polarographic information is available, or (in view of what was said on p. 449) by evaluating the results of electrolyses performed at different potentials.

As the electroactive species is consumed in a controlled-potential electrolysis the current must decrease. If only one such species is present, if its reduction proceeds in a single step devoid of chemical complications, and if the product does not yield an anodic current at the potential employed, as will be true whenever the electrolysis is performed on the plateau of a wave, the current at every instant will be described by eq. (8.29), which can be written (4)

$$i_t = i^0 e^{-\beta t} = \beta n F V C^0 e^{-\beta t} \tag{10.1}$$

where the first-order electrolytic rate constant β is given by

$$\beta = DA/V\delta \tag{10.2}$$

and has the units of sec.$^{-1}$; the current i_t will be given in milliamperes if V is expressed in liters and the initial concentration C^0 is expressed in millimoles per liter. According to eq. (10.1) the current decreases exponentially with time, and the degree of completion t seconds after the start of the electrolysis is given by

$$(C^0 - C_t)/C^0 = 1 - e^{-\beta t} \tag{10.3}$$

More generally, both the value of β and the degree of completion that can be obtained depend on the potential of the working electrode, and do so in different ways for reversible and irreversible reactions (5). No matter how much the electrolysis is prolonged, the degree of completion can never exceed the figure deduced from the considerations that lead to eq. (7.7).

In most work it is advantageous for β to be as large as possible. In view of eq. (10.2), this can be achieved by maximizing the ratio of electrode area to solution volume and, much more importantly, by using very efficient stirring to minimize the diffusion-layer thickness δ. In voltammetry with mercury pool electrodes in stirred solutions (Chap. 8 IV) relatively inefficient stirring is employed for the sake of minimizing fluctuations of the current, but in controlled-potential electrolysis such fluctuations are far less significant. A rapidly rotating propeller-type stirrer half immersed in the mercury-solution interface has usually proven satisfactory. Typically this yields a value of β that is of the order of 0.003 to 0.005 sec.$^{-1}$, which corresponds to 99.9% completion in 40 to 25 min. On this basis it has sometimes been said that controlled-potential electrolysis is too slow for use in the routine laboratory, but this is untrue. By the use of either ultrasonic agitation (6) or a large four-bladed paddle-type stirrer rapidly rotated in the electrode–solution interface (7), values of β even as high as 0.05 sec.$^{-1}$ have been obtained. This corresponds to 99.9% completion in only 2.5 min.

Even if β is only 0.003 sec.$^{-1}$ fairly large currents are obtained; according to eq. (10.1) the initial current would then be 30 mamp. for the electrolysis of 100 ml. of a 1mM solution of an electroactive substance that underwent a one-electron reduction or oxidation. The voltage V that must be applied across the cell is given by eq. (2.12):

$$V = E_a - E_c + iR \qquad (10.4)$$

In polarographic work it is usually possible to employ a two-electrode cell in which the electrolysis current flows through a reference electrode, because the iR drop through the cell is usually so small that the applied voltage is nearly identical with the difference between the potentials of the electrodes, and also because the potential of a properly designed reference electrode is virtually unaffected by the flow of a few microamperes of current through it. In controlled-potential electrolysis the situation is quite different: the iR drop may be as large as 100 v., or even larger in work with non-aqueous solutions, and several amperes may flow through the electrolysis circuit.

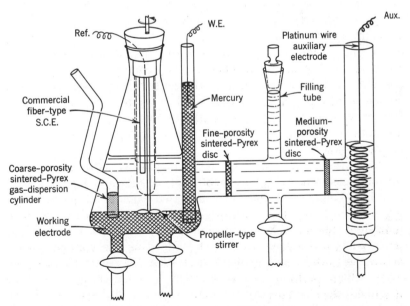

Figure 10.3. Double-diaphragm cell for controlled-potential electrolysis with mercury working electrode and isolated auxiliary electrode.

Unless the solution being electrolyzed is extremely dilute, which is unusual, it is therefore necessary to employ a three-electrode cell.

A typical cell (8) is shown in Fig. 10.3. Slight modifications (9) are desirable for very prolonged experiments with air-sensitive solutions. The electrolysis current flows through the mercury-pool working electrode and an auxiliary electrode which may be either a helix of platinum wire as shown or a graphite rod. In the former case it is usually advisable to add a little hydrazine or hydroxylamine to the auxiliary-electrode compartment to prevent anodic attack on the platinum. In some applications of controlled-potential electrolysis it is feasible to place the working and auxiliary electrodes in the same solution, and a beaker can then be used as the electrolysis cell. Diaphragm cells like the one shown here are, however, much more widely useful. They serve to prevent the products formed at the auxiliary electrode from reaching the working electrode, where they might consume current or react with the desired product, and also to prevent the cyclic oxidation and reduction that would sometimes occur if the latter came into contact with the auxiliary electrode. The cell resistance depends on the supporting electrolyte employed, but rarely exceeds 100 ohms. Care should be taken to allow the cell to stand for a while before use with an electrolyte solution in the center compartment, for the resistance of a dry fritted disc is very high. Exclusion of air from the working-electrode compartment is generally desirable, and is accomplished by the continuous passage of a rapid stream of nitrogen or other gas, which must be scrupulously freed from every trace of oxygen, especially in coulometric work with small amounts of material, into the solution through the fritted-glass gas-dispersion cylinder.

The working-electrode potential is monitored with the aid of a reference electrode. This may be of the type shown in Fig. 2.18, or it may be a commercial fiber-type saturated calomel electrode except when the solution being investigated might react with saturated potassium chloride to form a precipitate in the pores of the fiber. The potential is maintained constant by adjusting the voltage applied across the working and auxiliary electrodes. A great many potentiostats, which perform this adjustment automatically, have been described; the characteristics of many of them have been summarized by Lingane (10), while those of several that are commercially available have been tabulated by Rechnitz (3). There are two principal types: electronic and electromechanical. The electronic instruments have shorter response times, better nominal precision of control of the potential, and smaller current outputs. In studying the rates of very fast electrode reactions the rapid response of an electronic potentiostat is essential, but in work with stirred mercury-pool electrodes it may actually be disadvantageous. The area of such an electrode and the apparent thickness of the diffusion layer fluctuate considerably when the electrode-solution interface is stirred violently. An instrument too fast to ignore these fluctuations but too slow to track them with complete fidelity may produce variations of the working-electrode potential that far exceed the nominal precision of control. On the other hand, variations of ±10 mv. or so from the desired potential are extremely unlikely to have any observable effect on the results obtained.

Controlled-potential electrolysis has found many important applications. Only a brief summary of these can be given here; more extensive reviews are available (11,12) and should be consulted for further details. Its use in effecting separations prior to polarographic analyses was described in Chap. 7 III-F, and its use in removing electroactive impurities from supporting electrolytes was described in Chap. 7 IV-A. It has also often been employed to prepare solutions for polarographic or voltammetric examination: after one or more controlled-potential electrolyses that serve to convert the substance of interest into the desired form as well as to remove interfering electroactive substances, an indicator electrode may be inserted directly into the working-electrode compartment and the voltammogram recorded. Electroactive species that are very sensitive to air-oxidation can be prepared and studied with great ease. Solutions of −2 selenium and tellurium (13), +3 and +5 tungsten (14), +1 manganese (15), and the lower oxidation states of rhenium (16), ruthenium (17,18), and osmium (19), among others, have been prepared in this way. The peculiar virtue of the technique is that it not only gives an essentially quantitative yield of the desired product, but does so without introducing foreign reducing or oxidizing agents. The extreme selectivity that can be achieved is of special importance when the desired product can undergo further reduction or oxidation. By the controlled-potential electroreduction of 9-(o-iodophenyl)acridine (I) one can obtain a nearly quantitative yield of the dihydro derivative (II), whereas chemical reducing agents powerful enough to reduce the starting material at all are powerful enough to effect further reduction to III (*20*).

Analytical methods based on these considerations, and applicable even to very complex samples, are relatively easy to design. Uranium can be determined by electrolysis of a solution in $1F$ hydrochloric acid at -1.1 v. vs. S.C.E., which converts it to the $+3$ state. A dropping electrode is inserted into the solution after the electrolysis is complete, and a polarogram is recorded. The working electrode itself could be used as the indicator electrode unless some metal has been deposited into it that would interfere with the desired wave. The half-wave potential of the anodic wave of uranium(III) is -0.90 v., and the wave height can be measured without difficulty. Copper, lead, nickel, and many others do not interfere because they are deposited at -1.1 v. and removed from the solution; aluminum, manganese, and many others are not removed from the solution but do not yield anodic waves; chromium and vanadium are reduced to their $+2$ states and do give anodic waves, but these have half-wave potentials so much less negative than that of uranium(III) that they also do not interfere. If it were desired to determine chromium in the presence of uranium, the solution resulting from this first electrolysis could be further electrolyzed at a different potential, at which uranium(III) would be quantitatively oxidized while chromium(II) remained unaffected. Great specificity may be obtained (*21*).

Because foreign reducing or oxidizing agents need not be added, the solution resulting from a controlled-potential electrolysis is well suited to the identification of the product by any of a wide variety of chemical or physical techniques. Nonvolatile organic products can usually be isolated by solvent extraction, and their physical properties or infrared or mass spectra obtained. Ultraviolet and visible spectra can usually be obtained directly without isolating the product from the final solution. To avoid possible air-oxidation of the product, and to permit following the progress of a complex reaction, the solution in the working-electrode compartment may be circulated through a spectrophotometric cell during the electrolysis. If the working-electrode compartment is sealed, volatile products can be detected and the rates at which they appear can be measured by means of a gas buret (*21a*), or samples of the gas phase above the solution might be analyzed by gas chromatography or another appropriate technique. One can, of course, examine the product voltammetrically by inserting an indicator electrode into the working-electrode compartment when the electrolysis is complete. To monitor the course of the reaction so that transient intermediates can be identified, it is better to circulate the solution through an external voltammetric cell, for it is difficult to obtain satisfactory voltammograms in a controlled-potential electrolysis cell unless the indicator and reference electrodes are shielded so that the electrolysis current does not produce an iR drop in the solution between them.

The most common application of these techniques has been in elucidating the products and n-values of half-reactions that occur in voltammetry. For example, mercaptobenzothiazole gives an anodic wave at a dropping mercury electrode, and the techniques outlined in Chap. 3 VI show that the oxidation involves one electron per molecule. This might correspond to either of two possible products: the disulfide [2 RSH → RSSR + $2H^+$ + $2e$] or the mercurous salt [2 RSH + 2Hg → $(RS)_2Hg_2$ + $2H^+$ + $2e$]. On controlled-potential electrolysis the latter is obtained (*22*). Because the certainty with which n can be evaluated from diffusion-current data diminishes rapidly for n-values above about 4, identification of the product is of very great value in interpreting waves having large diffusion current constants. Electrolyses are easily performed with 1–10 millimoles of material, and hence it is often possible to identify even minor amounts of the products of side reactions. Some very complex processes have been studied in this way (*23–25*).

However, a word of warning is essential here, for it has too often been assumed that the same products must be obtained in controlled-potential electrolysis as in voltammetry under the same conditions. In fact they are often different, for a step too slow to occur to any noticeable extent on the time scale implicit in a voltammetric measurement will tend to be forced to completion during a controlled-potential electrolysis. This is especially true if a second-order reaction is involved and if, in his zeal to obtain a substantial amount of the product, the chemist employs a much more concentrated solution in his electrolytic experiments than in his voltammetric ones. Two examples will suffice to illustrate the point. At a dropping electrode the reduction of p-(dimethylamino)azobenzene from an alkaline solution consumes two electrons and yields the hydrazo compound, but controlled-potential electrolysis at a mercury working electrode at the same potential in the same supporting electrolyte involves a four-electron reduction to aniline and N,N-dimethyl-p-phenylene-diamine (*26*). The reduction of α-furildioxime cannot consume more than six electrons at a dropping electrode, but in controlled-potential electrolysis it consumes eight, and 1,2-bis(2-furyl)ethylenediamine is the only product obtained (*27*). It is wise to record the current-time curve during the controlled-potential electrolysis. If a plot of log i vs. t, which is most easily obtained by using a recorder with a logarithmic scale, is linear, or if it becomes so after appropriate background corrections (*28*) have been applied, complications like these can be discounted. Otherwise further inquiry into the mechanism is advisable.

If the overall mechanism involves any slow chemical step that is followed by, or that competes with, an electron-transfer reaction, much information about the nature and rate of the chemical step can be obtained by observing the manner in which the current decays during the electrolysis (*29–34*). In one common case, the product of the electrolysis reacts with water, hydrogen ion, or some other substance (e.g., chlorate) whose concentration is large and essentially constant, regenerating the starting material or some other electroactive species. Instead of decaying to zero in accordance with eq. (10.1), the current then decays to a constant value that is proportional to the rate of this reaction (*9*,*28*,*33*,*35*). This would give a catalytic current (Chap. 3 VIII) in polarography, but because the catalytic current would be accompanied by the diffusion current of the starting material it could not be measured as precisely as the steady-state current at the end of an electrolysis. In another common case, an intermediate can undergo a slow chemical transformation of some kind (e.g., rearrangement or loss of water) and the product of this transformation can then be further reduced. This so-called ECE mechanism is observed, for example, with p-nitrosophenol (*36–39*):

NO–[C$_6$H$_4$]–OH $\xrightarrow{+\,2H^+ + 2e}$ NHOH–[C$_6$H$_4$]–OH $\xrightarrow{-\,H_2O}$ NH=[C$_6$H$_4$]=O $\xrightarrow{+\,2H^+ + 2e}$ NH–[C$_6$H$_4$]–OH

as well as with p-nitroaniline, α-furildioxime, vanadium(II), and numerous others. The polarographic limiting current is partly kinetic (40,41), but if the rate of the chemical step is either too small or too large the deviation from diffusion-controlled behavior will be too small to be evaluated precisely and may be too small to be detected. The electrolytic technique can be used over a considerably wider range. Depending on the relative values of the mass-transfer constants for the two electroactive species and the rate constant for the chemical step, a plot of log i vs. t can assume any of several forms (34); procedures have been devised for evaluating these constants and have been applied to several examples. Numerous other mechanisms have been considered, and the original literature should be consulted for details.

II. Coulometry at Controlled Potential

Suppose that a solution is subjected to controlled-potential electrolysis under the conditions assumed in eq. (10.1)—on the plateau of a reversible wave, or on either the plateau or the rising part of a totally irreversible one—and that the potential of the working electrode and the composition of the solution are such that neither the supporting electrolyte nor any other constituent of the solution is reduced or oxidized to any appreciable extent. Then the current will be due entirely to the reduction or oxidation of the substance responsible for the wave. If the overall reaction is simply $A \pm ne \rightarrow B$, the current will decay exponentially toward zero as the concentration of this substance decreases, and the number of coulombs consumed will approach the limit described by integration of eq. (10.1):

$$Q_\infty = \int_0^\infty i \; dt = nFVC^0 = nFN^0 \qquad (10.5)$$

where N^0 is the number of moles of the electroactive substance present at the start of the electrolysis. This is equivalent to Faraday's law, and is the fundamental equation of coulometry at controlled potential (42,43).

The methodology of coulometry at controlled potential is essentially identical with that of controlled-potential electrolysis; there are only two differences. Provision must be made for the integration of the electrolysis current, and greater care must be taken to avoid the oxidations or reductions of other substances during the electrolysis, or to correct for the extents of such side reactions if they cannot be eliminated. When the potential of the working electrode is sufficiently negative to reduce oxygen, rigorous deaeration of the solution is essential. Diaphragm cells are needed to eliminate any possible cyclic reactions that would contribute to the current. Care must be exerted in choosing the potential of the working electrode to minimize the extents of undesired electrode reactions. The reduction of hydrogen ion or water proceeds at a finite rate even at potentials considerably more positive than the value at which the final current rise appears to begin on a polarogram, and correction for the rate of this reduction is often needed. In work with very small amounts of material, even the quantity of electricity consumed in charging the double layer at the surface of the working electrode has to be taken into account. Apparatus for current integration is briefly surveyed in subsequent paragraphs.

Equation (10.5) can be put to two uses: the evaluation of n if N^0 is known, and the evaluation of N^0 if n is known. For the first of these purposes it is far superior to the techniques described in Chap. 3 VI because it does not involve any uncertain assumptions about the diffusion coefficient of the electroactive species. It can, therefore, be used no matter how high the value of n may be; values as high as 36 (for the six-electron reduction of each of the six nitro groups in dipicrylamine) have been measured without difficulty. The technique has served to illuminate the voltammetric characteristics of a host of inorganic and organic substances. Where the n-value by itself does not suffice to identify the product unambiguously, its measurement can be supplemented by physical or chemical identification after the electrolysis is complete. In such cases knowledge of the n-value renders the identification simpler and more certain by decreasing the number of possible products that have to be considered.

The accuracy and precision required for this purpose are usually modest: neither confusion nor error is likely to arise if n is smaller than about 6 and the relative error in its measurement does not exceed $\pm 5\%$. This is the one application of controlled-potential coulometry for which chemical coulometers can still be recommended. Very much the most convenient of these are the hydrogen–oxygen coulometer (43), in which a gas buret is employed to measure the volume of gas evolved by the passage of the electrolysis current between two platinum electrodes in a potassium sulfate solution, and the hydrogen-nitrogen coulometer (44), which is similarly constructed but which employs a hydrazine sulfate solution. In each of these the volume of gas evolved by the passage of one coulomb is about 0.168 ml. at S.T.P., but depends to some extent on the current density. In the hydrogen–oxygen coulometer it decreases as the current density decreases, chiefly because some dissolved oxygen is reduced at the cathode, and perhaps also because there is some oxidation of hydrogen at the anode. In the hydrogen–nitrogen coulometer it must decrease at high current densities because of side reactions that occur during the oxidation of hydrazine. Relative errors below about $\pm 0.5\%$ are difficult to achieve with these coulometers, and they are ill-suited to work with less than about 0.1 meq. of electroactive material. Electronic and electromechanical current integrators, which are capable of precisions of $\pm 0.1\%$ or better and which are sensitive enough for use on the nanoequivalent level, are far more widely used in analytical work.

Controlled-potential coulometric measurements of n are performed in the following way. Suitable volumes of supporting electrolyte are placed in the different compartments of a cell like the one shown in Fig. 10.3, and the solution in the working-electrode compartment is deaerated with a stream of purified nitrogen or some other oxygen-free gas while being stirred with a propeller- or paddle-type stirrer. Meanwhile a little hydrazine is added to the auxiliary-electrode compartment to prevent anodic attack on the electrode, evolution of chlorine, oxidation of organic anions in the supporting electrolyte, and other undesirable processes. When deaeration is judged to be complete, an appropriate volume of mercury is added to the working-electrode compartment, the stirrer is adjusted to provide efficient agitation of the mercury-solution interface, and the potentiostat is adjusted to maintain the mercury at the desired potential. In the great majority of cases this will lie on the plateau of the polarographic wave that is of interest. Care must be taken, however, to avoid encroaching on the rising part of a subsequent wave, especially if it is totally irreversible. If the wave of interest is totally irreversible, it is often advantageous to select a potential on its rising portion; this prolongs the electrolysis by decreasing the rate of the desired process, but it decreases the rates of processes responsible for subsequent waves as well and does so to a much larger extent, and therefore provides more effective separations. The pre-electrolysis is then allowed to proceed undisturbed for some minutes to remove traces of reducible impurities. Normally the initial current is of the order of a few milliamperes, and the current decays in the same exponential manner as in an ordinary controlled-potential electrolysis. The current may decay to a negligibly small value or to a steady finite one. If it decreases to less than, say, 0.01% of the initial current expected during the subsequent electrolysis, it may be ignored; otherwise, in careful work, its value should be noted so that appropriate correction for it can be made.

The potentiostat is then disconnected from the cell and a known volume of a stock solution of the substance being investigated is added to the working-electrode compartment. If this oxidizes mercury, the stirrer should be turned off before it is added and allowed to remain off until the electrolysis is almost complete. The mixture is thoroughly deaerated while a coulometer or current integrator in series with the working electrode is read. Then the potentiostat is turned on again and the electrolysis is allowed to proceed without further attention until it has proceeded virtually to completion. This may require as little as 5 to 10 min. if the reaction is chemically straightforward and the stirring very efficient, or as much as several hours if an extremely slow chemical step is involved. As in the pre-electrolysis, the current may decay to a negligible value or to an appreciable one. If it becomes less than about 0.01% of the initial current it may be ignored, and the value of n may be taken as the ratio of the number of millifaradays consumed to the number of millimoles, N^0, of the electroactive substance taken. If it decays to an appreciable value that is identical with the one obtained at the end of the pre-electrolysis, n may be computed from the equation

$$n = (Q_t - i_{f,c}) t/N^0 \tag{10.6}$$

where Q_t is the number of millifaradays accumulated during t seconds of electrolysis and $i_{f,c}$ is the steady final current in millifaradays per second. If the steady final current is an appreciable fraction of the initial one and is also appreciably larger than the current at the end of the pre-electrolysis, correction should be applied for the extent of the catalytic process that must be involved. Though this is often essential in analytical work, it is rarely so in evaluations of n because much larger errors can be tolerated.

As was mentioned in Sec. I, controlled-potential electrolysis and polarography will give different n-values if the mechanism involves a slow intermediate chemical step. In the ECE mechanism

$$A \xrightarrow{\;+\; n_1 e\;} B \xrightarrow[\text{chemical}]{\text{slow}} C \xrightarrow{\;+\; n_2 e\;} D$$

for example, the reduction at the dropping electrode will proceed no farther than B if the chemical step has a half-time much longer than the drop time, and so it will involve only n_1 electrons, whereas exhaustive electrolysis will yield the sum $(n_1 + n_2)$. Another common mechanism is

$$A + n_1 e \rightarrow B$$
$$2B \rightarrow A + C$$

in which C is electrolytically inert; this describes the reduction of uranium(VI) in acidic media and that of p-(dimethylamino)azobenzene in alkaline ones. Here the polarographic n-value will be n_1 while the coulometric one will be $2n_1$. On the other hand, the coulometric value may be smaller than the polarographic one if the mechanism is

$$A + n_1 e \rightarrow B$$
$$2B \rightarrow C$$
$$B + n_2 e \rightarrow D$$

in which both C and D are inert. The majority of coulometric measurements of n have been performed with something like 1 meq. of starting material in 50 to 100 ml. of solution, which corresponds to concentrations well above those likely to be employed in polarography. This is unnecessary, and in this case it is undesirable as well, for it greatly increases the relative extent of the dimerization. In this situation a non-integral value of n is usually obtained: it approaches $(n_1 + n_2)$ at low concentrations and n_1 at high ones, and varies with the initial concentration. For this reason the n-value obtained in the reduction of picric acid from $1F$ hydrochloric acid, which is 18.00 ± 0.01 if the initial concentration of picric acid is below a value that depends on the rate of stirring but is typically about 1mM, decreases below 17 at higher concentrations (*45*). Increasing the rate of stirring would decrease the n-value because it removes the intermediate more rapidly from the electrode surface into the bulk of the solution, where only the dimerization can occur. Or the intermediate free radical B might attack the solvent, regenerating A, or take part in some other catalytic step. Increasing the efficiency of stirring would then have the opposite effect: it would militate against both the further reduction and (by decreasing the concentration of B in the diffusion layer) the dimerization, and the n-value would rise as the catalytic step became more prominent. The reduction of benzophenone is the classical example of this general mechanism, and it has been found to exhibit several of these complexities (*7*).

When the n-value obtained coulometrically is integral and independent of initial concentration and stirring rate, and when a plot of log i vs. t shows that there is no conspicuously slow step involved, it can be confidently concluded that this value corresponds to the same overall process that is responsible for the polarographic or voltammetric wave obtained under the same conditions. Stress has been laid here on the difficulties that may arise because the matter seems so simple at first glance. There are indeed many processes for which meaningful n-values can be obtained by performing a single coulometric experiment in which both the initial concentration and the rate of stirring are chosen almost at random. But it is always prudent to vary both of these parameters to make sure that complications are not involved.

The most important characteristic of coulometry at controlled potential as an analytical technique is that it is capable of far better accuracy and precision than can be obtained from voltammetry. Polarographic analyses accurate and precise to a few tenths of a per cent can be and have been made, but only under optimum conditions and after lengthy and painstaking calibration, and even this figure cannot yet be attained in solid-electrode voltammetry. In coulometric work, accuracies and precisions of the order of $\pm 0.1\%$ are more nearly the rule than the exception. There have been numerous practical applications. Uranium can be determined in reactor fuel elements and a wide variety of other materials (*46*,*47*) by measuring the quantity of electricity consumed in reducing it from the +6 to the +4 state in dilute sulfuric acid or a citrate buffer; other substances that might interfere can be removed by solvent extraction. Chromium has been determined in ferro-alloys (48) by reducing it to the +2 state; this has to be done at potentials so negative that hydrogen is rapidly evolved, which would necessitate a very large correction to the total quantity of electricity consumed, and hence it is preferable to measure the quantity of electricity required to reoxidize the chromium to the +3 state, a process in which very few other elements interfere. Gold may be determined by measuring the quantity of electricity consumed in depositing it onto a platinum electrode (49). Trichloroacetic acid may be assayed by measuring the quantity of electricity consumed in the half-reaction $Cl_3CCOO^- + H^+ + 2e \rightarrow Cl_2HCCOO^- + Cl^-$; dichloroacetate and monochloroacetate do not interfere (50). Many other examples might be cited: some quite straightforward, others involving one or more preliminary controlled-potential electrolyses to remove interfering substances or convert them into innocuous forms while converting the desired substance into a form suitable for the coulometric measurement. Conditions suitable for the execution of a large number of practical analyses have been summarized elsewhere (3,51).

Controlled-potential coulometric analysis is most often used to determine quantities ranging from about 10 meq. to about 1 μeq. The upper limit depends chiefly on the voltage and current that can be obtained from the potentiostat: high output currents are needed in work with concentrated solutions, and high output voltages are needed as well because of the large iR drops encountered. The lower limit depends chiefly on the precision with which the correction described by eq. (10.6) can be measured and applied. In stripping analysis it is sometimes possible to determine as little as a few nano-equivalents (52), and in this case the lower limit is determined chiefly by the precision with which the quantity of electricity consumed in charging the electrical double layer can be measured. Chemical side reactions that consume electroactive intermediates will naturally have adverse effects on both the precision and the sensitivity.

Electronic or electromechanical current integrators are needed to attain the accuracy, precision, and sensitivity of which the technique is inherently capable. An instrument is commercially available (Analytical Instruments, Inc., Wolcott, Conn.) in which the shaft of a tachometer generator is caused to rotate at a rate proportional to the iR drop across an input resistor in series with the working electrode. Integration is accomplished by employing a mechanical counter to count the revolutions of the generator shaft, and the servo loop parameters are so adjusted that the counter reads directly in milli-faradays (8). By operational-amplifier circuitry, the iR drop across a precision resistor in series with the cell may be used to charge a precision capacitor; the potential across the capacitor may be read on a digital voltmeter (or, less conveniently, on an ordinary precision potentiometer) and is proportional to the quantity of electricity that has flowed through the cell (53). The same effect may be produced more compactly by presenting the iR drop across the precision resistor to an integrating digital millivoltmeter. A voltage-frequency converter may be used to obtain a train of pulses whose frequency at any instant is proportional to the current flowing through a precision resistor; integration is performed by an electronic counter (54,56). Many other expedients have been adopted.

Corrections are often needed for the effects of other processes that contribute to the total measured quantity of electricity. These include the charging of the electrical double layer at the electrode surface, the reduction or oxidation of a major constituent of the solvent or supporting electrolyte (e.g., water or hydrogen ion), the reduction or oxidation of traces of electroactive impurities, the re-reduction or -oxidation of starting material regenerated by a reaction between the product and some electrolytically inert constituent of the solution, and the induced reduction of water or hydrogen ion. Most of these have obvious analogs in polarography. The original literature must be consulted for discussions of these processes and of the manners in which corrections for them should be applied (9,11,12,28,33,52,57).

Polarographic data usually serve as reasonably reliable guides to the selection of conditions for controlled-potential coulometric analyses. Employing the considerations outlined in Chap. 7 I, one seeks a solvent and supporting electrolyte in which the substance being determined gives a well-defined wave when it is present alone, and one that is well separated from the waves of other constituents of the sample. Prior waves do not interfere because they can be eliminated by pre-electrolysis. To save time one would normally choose a potential on the plateau of the desired wave, and this is necessary to obtain a quantitative result if the wave is reversible. If it is totally irreversible, however, a potential on its rising part may be chosen to provide better separation from a closely following wave. Thus the wave-separation problem is a little less pressing than in polarography, but systems that yield very ill-defined polarographic waves are rarely amenable to precise coulometric analysis.

However, the fact that a substance yields a well-defined wave does not guarantee that its coulometric behavior will be acceptable; experiments with known amounts of it are essential. Situations giving rise to non-integral n-values should generally be shunned in practical analysis despite their utility in studies of reaction mechanisms, though those involving second- or higher-order side reactions may be used if the concentration of the substance being determined can be prevented from exceeding a safe upper limit. It was mentioned in Chap. 8 IV that voltammograms at stirred mercury pool electrodes are not always simply related to polarograms obtained under the same conditions, for intermediates may suffer quite different fates in stirred solutions than in quiet ones. Exactly the same thing is true at the stirred electrodes used in controlled-potential electrolysis and coulometry. This or some other complication should be suspected whenever the coulometric and polarographic (cf. Chap. 3 VI) n-values differ appreciably, or whenever the former is found to vary with experimental conditions that do not affect the latter (57).

Controlled-potential coulometry is sometimes described as an "absolute" technique because eq. (10.5) does not involve such factors as the capillary characteristics, temperature, and viscosity, which affect polarographic wave heights and which make it essential to establish the relationship between wave height and concentration by experimental measurements under rigorously defined conditions before embarking on polarographic analyses. With systems that obey eq. (10.5)—which include those involving consecutive steps as well as those that occur in a single step—it is certainly true that an integral n-value will be obtained and that there is no need for an empirical calibration figure. Exactly the opposite is true, however, whenever cyclic or competing steps are involved, for the ratio Q_∞/N^0 then becomes dependent on the initial conditions. Changes of temperature may affect the coulometric results with such systems by altering the rates of the chemical side reactions; changes of viscosity, like those of stirring rate, may affect the results by altering the distributions of reactive intermediates between the diffusion layer and the bulk of the solution. Many side reactions that occur to extents too small to be detected polarographically become prominent in coulometric experiments, not only because the mass-transfer situations are different, but also because the much greater inherent precision of coulometric measurements casts a much more searching light on small deviations from straightforward behavior. To describe controlled-potential coulometry as a simple or absolute technique is to overestimate its utility in practical analysis and to underestimate its utility in elucidating the chemical processes that may accompany electrode reactions.

III. Coulometry at Voltammetric Indicator Electrodes

The preceding section discussed the evaluation of n by the quantitative reduction of a known amount of electroactive substance, using large working electrodes in efficiently stirred solutions to hasten the attainment of virtual completion. The same end may be served by incomplete reduction at a voltammetric indicator electrode. This is experimentally advantageous because the iR drop is relatively small: the potential of the indicator electrode can be "controlled" by a polarograph, an ordinary two-electrode voltammetric cell can be used, and there is no need for a potentiostat or an auxiliary electrode.

Two techniques are available. One involves an implicit integration of the current-time curve; experimentally, it is the rate of decay of the limiting current that is measured. The other involves explicit integration; a coulometer, current integrator, or some other device is used to measure the quantity of electricity needed to consume some measured fraction of a known amount of starting material. The latter technique has been called "millicoulometry" or "polarocoulometry."

In the first technique the argument is based on the equation

$$i_l - i_r = kC = -nFV \frac{dC}{dt} \tag{10.7}$$

where $(i_l - i_r)$ is the average wave height in microamperes, C the concentration of the electroactive substance in millimoles per liter, and V the volume of solution in milliliters. After integration and rearrangement one obtains $(58,59)$

$$\log (i_l - i_r) = \log (i_l^0 - i_r) - \frac{4.501 \times 10^{-6} kt}{nV} \tag{10.8}$$

Plotting $\log (i_l - i_r)$ vs. t gives a straight line, from whose slope n can be calculated if k and V are known. The value of k is easily calculated from the ratio of the initial wave height to the initial concentration.

Equation (10.7) is merely eq. (10.1) in a different guise, and eq. (10.8) is completely analogous to eq. (10.5). In view of what was said in the preceding section, it may be emphasized that the present technique, like controlled-potential coulometry, will yield misleading results whenever cyclic or competing reactions are involved. In controlled-potential coulometry, intermediates are driven away from the electrode surface and into the bulk of the solution by stirring, and in the bulk of the solution they may react with the starting material, the final product, the solvent, or each other. Precisely the same fates await intermediates that are present in the diffusion layer around a mercury drop when the drop falls.

When a dropping electrode is to be used, about 0.2 ml. of a solution containing a known concentration of the electroactive substance is placed in a microcell and deaerated with a very slow stream of inert gas. Because the volume is small and must be accurately known, the cell must be dry when the solution is added to it, and spraying of solution onto the cell walls cannot be tolerated. An external reference electrode is essential because cyclic reduction and oxidation often occur if an internal one is used. The limiting current is measured and the dropping electrode is allowed to remain at a potential on the plateau of the wave for perhaps 20 min. Then the solution is stirred briefly with a slow stream of gas and the limiting current is measured again, together with the time that has elapsed since the electrolysis was begun. This is continued until the current has fallen to perhaps half of its initial value. Since k is proportional to n, the total time required is nearly the same no matter what electroactive substance is involved, and is directly proportional to the volume of solution taken; an hour or two is typical. Each of the measured currents is corrected for the separately measured residual current, and the value of n is obtained graphically or, if the currents have been very precisely measured, algebraically by using eq. (10.8).

With a dropping electrode this does not give very accurate results. There are various sources of error, which have been enumerated and discussed by Weaver and Whitnack (60). One of the most important is the depletion of the solution around the capillary tip. During the intervals between measurements, the concentration falls off more rapidly there than it does in the bulk of the solution, because stirring by the falling drops is not very efficient. Hence the current is always smaller than it would be if the solution were homogeneous, and this leads to too large a value of n. Typically the result is 10% too high (58,59). The error is of little moment if n is 1 or 2, but the technique is virtually useless if it is as large as 4.

This error may be avoided by explicit integration of the current–time curve. One may use a current integrator in series with the electrolysis cell (58); a microcoulometer (61) may also be used, but the quantities of electricity involved are so small that this involves some difficulties of manipulation. The initial limiting current is measured as above and the electrolysis is allowed to proceed while the current is integrated; after an hour or two the solution is stirred briefly and the limiting current is measured again. Measurements may be made more frequently if desired, and stirring is necessary before each is made, but there is no need to stir during the intervals between them. The quantity of electricity consumed, in microfaradays, is given by

$$Q = \left(\frac{i_l^0 - i_l}{i_l^0 - i_r} \right) nVC^0 + 1.036 \times 10^{-5} i_r t \qquad (10.9)$$

where i_r is the residual current in microamperes and t is the duration of the electrolysis in seconds. Various expedients have been devised to eliminate the need for a current integrator. DeVries and Kroon (62) employed a second polarographic cell, containing a known volume of a standard solution of a substance for which n is known, in series with the one containing the substance of interest; the quantity of electricity flowing through the circuit can be deduced from the decrease of the limiting current in the reference cell by means of eq. (10.9). Further simplification can be effected by a pilot-ion technique (63) in which the substance being investigated and a reference substance, for which n is known, are present in the same solution, the electrolysis being performed at a potential where the sum of their diffusion currents is obtained. The reference substance must be chosen with great care, for errors usually result if it, its reduction product, or any intermediate formed during its reduction can react with the substance of interest or its reduction product. The second wave must be totally irreversible; otherwise its product is likely to react with the substance giving the first wave. But this is not a sufficient condition for success, because other kinds of side reactions are also possible. As in the polarographic pilot-ion technique (Chap. 7 V-Biv), many possible errors are nearly or completely eliminated. In yet another technique, a constant current of i microamperes is passed through the cell, across which a large capacitor must be connected to minimize the excursions of potential that occur near the beginnings of the drop lives (64); after electrolysis for t seconds, the value of Q required in eq. (10.9) is simply

$$Q = 1.0364 \times 10^{-5}it \qquad (10.10)$$

As the value of i must not exceed the limiting current at the end of the electrolysis, this technique considerably increases the duration of each experiment.

Many other voltammetric indicator electrodes are better suited to such determinations of n than the dropping electrode. Because k is always small at the dropping electrode, electrolyses are inordinately slow unless extremely small volumes of solution are used, and as a result sensible errors are incurred if even a few microliters are lost by spraying onto the cell walls. Electrodes that are rotated or used in stirred solutions give much larger values of k, and consequently much larger volumes of solution can be employed; cell design is facilitated, the manipulations become less exacting, electrolyses can be carried more nearly to completion in reasonable lengths of time, and more precise results become easier to obtain. By employing eq. (10.9), Rosie and Cooke (65) obtained values of n having precisions of about $\pm 2\%$ with mercury pool electrodes in stirred solutions, and similarly precise results should be available with rotating wire or disc electrodes. Explicit integration of the current would be essential with stationary electrodes employed in quiet solutions, because of the irregular fluctuations of current produced by convection on prolonged electrolysis. In such a case the electrolysis would be interrupted after it has proceeded to a sufficient extent, the solution would be stirred, and the peak current would be recorded in the same way as for the initial solution; the data would be interpreted by employing eq. (10.9), in which the second term on the right-hand side could almost always be neglected.

In all of these techniques it is taken for granted that the wave height of the substance of interest is proportional to its concentration over the range of concentrations involved in the electrolysis. They should not be used unless this has been shown to be true.

IV. Other Voltammetric Current–Time Curves

If the volume of solution is sufficiently large, the rate of electrolytic depletion caused by electrolysis with a dropping mercury electrode becomes very small. Variations of wave height with time then reflect the formation or consumption of electroactive material by a chemical reaction in the bulk of the solution, and can be employed in studying reaction kinetics or in performing kinetic analyses.

Ordinarily one selects a potential at which only one of the reactants or products yields a limiting current. A known volume of supporting electrolyte solution containing a known concentration of one reactant is placed in a polarographic cell and thoroughly deaerated. The residual current must be measured and corrected for unless it is certain to be negligibly small, and it is therefore convenient, whenever it is possible, to begin by placing a solution of a non-electroactive reactant in the cell so that the residual current can be measured at this point. A known volume of a stock solution of the other reactant is added rapidly while a very rapid stream of gas is passed through the solution in the cell to provide stirring and to remove any oxygen that may be dissolved in the solution being added. When stirring and deaeration are complete, the gas stream is diverted over the surface of the mixture, and the current is measured at appropriate intervals.

If the reaction is not too fast, its progress is easily followed with a manual polarograph. Because the periodic variations of current that reflect the growth and fall of the drops are superimposed on the variation that reflects the production or disappearance of the electro-active substance, it is impossible to make meaningful measurements at exactly predetermined instants. However, this could hardly introduce a significant error unless the half-time is quite short, in which event it is better to use a recording instrument as described below. It is much easier to measure the current at very nearly a predetermined time than to try to record both the current and the exact time at which it was measured. One may record the maximum deflection that occurs most nearly at the predetermined time, or the mean of the last maximum occurring before that time and the first minimum occurring after it if average currents are preferred.

If the dropping electrode is replaced by a rotating electrode or an electrode used in stirred solutions, this problem does not arise. Instead one may encounter a difficulty that reflects the much greater rates of electrolytic depletion at such electrodes: the limiting current decreases at a sensible rate even when the electroactive substance is not being consumed chemically. Gross errors may result if the chemical reaction is very slow. The obvious course is to leave the indicator electrode disconnected from the polarograph except while the current is being measured. Even with a dropping electrode, although the rate of bulk depletion is certainly negligible if the volume of solution exceeds 25 ml. or so unless the chemical reaction is excessively slow, depletion around the capillary tip becomes substantial on prolonged electrolysis. Again the dropping electrode may be disconnected from the polarograph between measurements, or the reaction mixture can be stirred briefly before each measurement is made.

Faster reactions are more easily studied by means of a recording polarograph whose bridge-drive mechanism is disabled so that it provides a steady potential. The current–time curve is then recorded directly. Reactions having half-times as short as 30 sec. can be followed, though some difficulty may arise with dropping electrodes because of the length of time that is consumed by stirring and de-aerating the mixture and allowing the turbulence to die down before the first meaningful measurements can be made. It is helpful to deaerate the second reagent before it is added, so that time need not be wasted in removing oxygen from the mixture. Special vessels have been designed for this purpose (66,67), but the microburet recommended in Chap. 7 IV-Bi for work with easily air-oxidized solutions serves as well and is more precise. A still better expedient is to replace the dropping electrode with a rotated wire electrode or a mercury pool electrode in a stirred solution. Some voltammetric indicator electrodes have been specially designed for work in rapidly flowing solutions (68,69), and these can be used in conjunction with classical flow techniques to study much faster reactions (70).

Unless the reaction is very slow, attempts to record complete polarograms while it is in progress are likely to produce more confusion than enlightenment. However, if it is so slow that excessive distortion does not result from changes of concentration during a recording, complete polarograms may permit two or more concentrations to be followed or may provide valuable information about the appearance and disappearance of electroactive intermediates. The former purpose can also be served by the device shown in Fig. 2.13. The latter is better served for faster reactions by single-sweep oscilloscopic polarography, which is also known as cathode-ray polarography and (although no explicit relation between current and time is involved) as potential-sweep chronoamperometry, and which is equivalent to stationary-electrode voltammetry at the dropping electrode. A fairly rapid potential sweep is begun at a predetermined instant during the latter part of a drop life, and the resulting current–potential curve is presented on the face of a cathode-ray tube. The area of the drop is very nearly constant while the sweep is taking place, and curves of the expected peaked form are obtained (71,72). As the sweep is synchronized with the formation of the drop, a curve is obtained every few seconds, so that intermediates in even quite fast reactions can be detected and followed. A commercially available instrument, the "Polarotrace," is manufactured by Southern Analytical, Ltd. (Camberley, Surrey, England) and is sold for $6500 by the Standard Scientific Supply Corporation (New York).

The applications of these techniques have included studies of the kinetics and mechanisms of such reactions as the reduction of iron(III) by sulfur dioxide in acidic media (73), the reaction between ferricyanide and antimony(III) in alkaline media (74), the oxidations of several vic-dihydroxy compounds by periodate (75), the coupling of diazonium salts with phenols and other compounds (76), the hydrolysis of pyridoxal-5-phosphate (77), and many others. They have also been used to study bacterial and tissue respiration (78) and lipid antioxidant activity (79). Applications to kinetic analysis (Chap. 7 V-Bv) have not yet become numerous, but polarographic measurements of reaction rates have been used to determine ketosteroids (80) and to analyze some mixtures of vic-dihydroxy compounds.

V. Stripping Analysis

In conventional voltammetric analysis one measures a limiting or peak current that depends on the rate at which the substance being determined reaches the indicator electrode, and that also includes a residual current. As the concentration of this substance decreases, the rate at which it reaches the electrode surface decreases, but the residual current remains the same. The residual current becomes a larger and larger fraction of the total current measured, and the limit of detection is reached when the two become indistinguishable.

If the substance being determined is deposited onto the indicator electrode at potentials on the plateau of the wave, prolonged electrolysis at such potentials will cause its reduction or oxidation product to accumulate at the electrode surface. As the accumulation proceeds, the supply of deposited material at the electrode surface may become very much larger than that of the substance being determined was initially. If the deposited substance can be re-oxidized or -reduced, it will yield a correspondingly larger limiting or peak current; both the sensitivity and the limit of detection are considerably improved. This is the principle of a family of techniques called stripping analysis.

There are two kinds of stripping analysis. Anodic stripping is used to determine metal ions that are reduced to the metallic state during the preliminary electrolysis, and is based on the anodic currents obtained when the metals are reoxidized. Cathodic stripping is used to determine halides, thiols, and other substances that give anodic waves at metallic electrodes; if the half-reaction yields an insoluble salt that adheres to the electrode surface, a cathodic current is obtained from the reduction of the salt that accumulates there. Cathodic stripping has also been used to evaluate the thicknesses of tarnish films on such metals as iron, copper, and silver (81,82), and both cathodic and anodic stripping have been used to investigate the adsorption of electroactive substances onto inert electrodes. The following discussion is devoted primarily to the use of anodic stripping in the determination of metal ions because this application has been much the most extensively studied and used.

As applied to the dropping mercury electrode, stripping analysis takes the form of oscillopolarography (p. 586), although the classification is a little forced because prolonged deposition is hardly possible and this prevents the accumulation of material that is the heart of stripping analysis. Stationary electrodes, including hanging mercury drop electrodes, mercury pools, and solid electrodes of various materials, are much more suitable. Stripping analyses have been performed in many different ways, which can be discussed most easily by dividing them into two groups: those in which the preliminary deposition is quantitative, and those in which it is not.

Perhaps the simplest technique is that in which a quantitative deposition is followed by quantitative stripping of the deposited material. Curve a of Fig. 10.4 shows the current–potential curve obtained with a large stirred mercury pool electrode in a solution containing zinc(II). If the potential of the electrode is maintained at

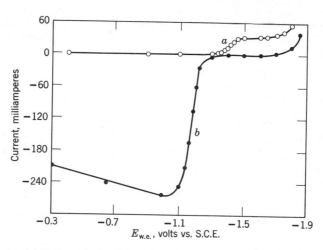

Figure 10.4. Current–potential curves obtained with a large stirred mercury pool electrode for (*a*) the reduction of 0.6m*M* zinc(II) from 2*F* ammonia–1*F* ammonium citrate, and (*b*) the re-oxidation of the amalgam prepared by quantitative deposition of the zinc in 50 ml. of this solution into 25 ml. of mercury at −1.45 v. vs. S.C.E. (*52*).

a value on the plateau of the cathodic wave, zinc ions will be reduced as rapidly as they reach the electrode surface, and quantitative reduction to zinc amalgam will result if sufficient time is allowed. Curve *b* shows the current–potential curve for the amalgam electrode thus obtained. At any potential on the plateau of the anodic wave, zinc atoms are rapidly re-oxidized, and the quantity of zinc present in the original solution can be deduced from a measurement of the quantity of electricity consumed in the quantitative re-oxidation. This serves for the determination of 10 μg. of zinc with an accuracy and precision of the order of ±0.1%, while 0.07 μg. of zinc can be determined with an accuracy and precision of roughly ±10%. Although it is the amount and not the concentration of the substance being determined that is important in such a procedure, it may be noted, to facilitate comparison with other results cited below, that 0.07 μg. of zinc would be contained in about 100 ml. of a $1 \times 10^{-8}M$ solution.

A disadvantage of this technique is that the electrode area must be relatively large to effect quantitative deposition in a reasonable length of time. The rate of reduction of hydrogen ion or water may often be small at the potential employed for the stripping, but as it is proportional to the area of the electrode it is unlikely to be negligible in dealing with a very small amount of material. As the stripping proceeds, this "continuous faradaic" current (28) becomes a larger and larger fraction of the current being integrated, and the latter part of the integration must, therefore, proceed under such conditions that the stripping current is only a small part of the whole. A similar difficulty arises from the fact that the quantity of electricity required to change the potential of the electrode from the value employed during the deposition to that employed during the stripping is also proportional to the area of the electrode.

On the other hand, quantitative deposition is feasible even with a small electrode if the volume of solution is small. Rogers et al. (83) designed a cell in which as little as 0.02 ml. of solution could be electrolyzed at a platinum working electrode, and employed it for the determination of silver by anodic stripping. Instead of measuring the quantity of electricity consumed in the stripping process at a potential on the plateau of the anodic wave, one may record the anodic current–potential curve after the deposition is complete. An example is shown in Fig. 10.5, together with the corresponding residual–current curve. At a solid electrode little significance can be attached to the peak current (84), and the area between the two curves must be measured instead. Rogers et al. were able to determine 2.5×10^{-12} mole of silver in 0.02 ml. of solution with an accuracy and precision of about $\pm 5\%$; this corresponds to a roughly $1 \times 10^{-7} M$ solution.

In general, however, it is better and more convenient to use an electrode of small area in a substantial volume of solution. Quantitative deposition would then require an inordinate length of time, and hence it is preferable to deposit only some reproducible fraction of the starting material. This is done by maintaining the electrode at a potential on the plateau of the cathodic wave for a measured length of time while stirring the solution at a constant rate, which must be accurately reproduced in successive experiments. Stirring is necessary even with a stationary electrode such as the hanging mercury drop, for wide and erratic fluctuations of current would result from natural convection if the solution were unstirred. Momentary fluctuations of stirring efficiency are much less important than in voltammetric work with stirred electrodes, for all that is important is the average stirring efficiency over the whole duration of the deposition step. Unless the

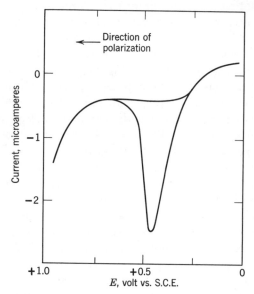

Figure 10.5. Current–potential curves for the anodic stripping of 5.6 ng. of silver from a platinum electrode into dilute nitric or sulfuric acid and for the supporting electrolyte alone (*83*). The scan rate was 50 mv./sec.

electrode is intended for work in stirred solutions, however, the stirrer should be stopped and the solution allowed to become quiet before the subsequent measurement is begun. The quantity of metal deposited is proportional to the concentration of metal ion in the solution, and also to the deposition time if this is not too great (*85*); a reasonable criterion is that no more than one or two per cent of the metal ion should be deposited. Prolonged deposition from a dilute solution is preferable for very brief deposition from a concentrated one, for some additional deposition occurs at the start of the subsequent recording and is difficult to take into account.

The quantity of metal thus deposited onto a solid electrode is best measured as shown in Fig. 10.5. The polarization rate must not be too high, for if it is the residual current will be undesirably large and there is also some danger that the potential may become positive enough to initiate some other anodic process before the entire peak has been recorded. It is not difficult to analyze mixtures if the deposition can be carried out at such a potential that the substance being determined is the only one deposited. But if several substances are deposited together, the formation of an alloy or solid solution would make it impossible to strip any of them quantitatively without interference from the others. The technique has been applied to determinations of nickel (*86*) by anodic stripping from a platinum electrode into a thiocyanate solution, and to determinations of halides (*87*,*88*) by cathodic stripping after anodic deposition onto a silver or stationary mercury electrode. Carbon-paste and wax-impregnated graphite electrodes have also been employed (*88a*).

Both controlled-potential and constant-current coulometric procedures for the determination of metals by anodic stripping from platinum electrodes have generally given low results (*88b*). The causes of these errors have been investigated, and ways of correcting for them have been devised, by Bixler and Bruckenstein (*88c*).

Mercury electrodes have two advantages over solid ones for the determination of metals by anodic stripping. One is that amalgams do not pose the problems arising from the variable activity of very

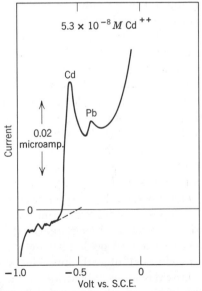

Figure 10.6. Anodic stripping voltammogram obtained with a small mercury pool electrode in a stirred solution originally containing $5.3 \times 10^{-8} M$ cadmium(II) after pre-electrolysis for 35 min. at -1.0 v. vs. S.C.E. (*89*).

thin layers of solid metals. This permits the measurement of the height of an anodic peak instead of the area under it, which is not only more convenient but also much more sensitive. The other is that, if a mixed amalgam is sufficiently dilute, its different constituents can be re-oxidized independently, a separate peak being obtained for each. This permits mixtures to be analyzed much more easily than with solid electrodes. The principle is illustrated by Fig. 10.6. After the lead and cadmium had been deposited together during the electrolysis at -1.0 v., the current–potential curve was recorded for the mixed amalgam by polarization toward increasingly positive potentials. The Sargent Model FS Polarograph is especially intended for this purpose. The peak current of cadmium is easily measured, whereas the area under the cadmium peak could be obtained only by using a polarization rate so small that the current due to the oxidation of cadmium could decay virtually to zero before a potential was reached at which the oxidation of lead could begin. Subject to the conditions outlined above, and at a constant rate of polarization during the recording of the peak, the quantity $i_p/C_M t$ should be constant, C_M being the concentration of metal ion in the solution and t the deposition time. This has been confirmed with hanging mercury drop electrodes for solutions as dilute as $10^{-9} M$ (90–95); at this level an accuracy and precision of the order of $\pm 3\%$ can be obtained after deposition for 60 min., and the limit of detection may be as small as $10^{-11} M$. Mercury-plated electrodes have been used to prevent the deposited metal from diffusing away from the electrode surface while retaining the advantages that result from amalgam formation, but have the defect that the value of $i_p/C_M t$ depends on the thickness of the mercury film (96–98). Anodic stripping voltammetry at mercury electrodes has been comprehensively reviewed by Barendrecht (99).

An important characteristic of stripping procedures is that, if all of the couples involved are reversible, the anodic peaks on the stripping curve occur in the opposite order from the cathodic peaks on the voltammogram of the solution being analyzed: in Fig. 10.6 the cadmium peak precedes the lead peak, although the cathodic peak of lead ion would precede that of cadmium ion. With such couples, stripping analysis provides an easy solution to the wave-order problem. If one or both of the couples is irreversible, however, no such generalization can be made: in dilute chloride media the half-peak potential of zinc ion is less negative than that of cobaltous ion, but the cobalt couple is so irreversible that cobalt does not give an anodic peak, and hence the zinc peak occurs first on the anodic voltammogram as well as on the cathodic one.

The chief obstacle to the analysis of mixtures by anodic stripping techniques is the formation of intermetallic compounds in mixed amalgams (100–108), which has the voltammetric effects shown in Fig. 10.7: the reaction between nickel and zinc not only decreases the peak current of zinc but also gives rise to a new peak reflecting the oxidation of the intermetallic compound. As the concentrations rise the effect becomes more pronounced: under conditions such that the oxidation of zinc from an amalgam is rapid and quantitative when it is present alone, no stripping current whatever can be detected if a 10^5-fold excess of copper is present as well. Curves like those in Fig. 10.7 reveal the existence of such compounds in many amalgams containing two deposited metals, and compound formation with mercury may also occur in those containing only one. As yet very little can be said about the formulas and stabilities of these compounds. In part this is because no less than 60 hr. are required for equilibrium to be reached in one system that is not obviously atypical, so that the

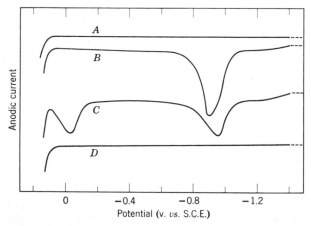

Figure 10.7. Anodic stripping voltammograms obtained with hanging mercury drop electrodes in 01.*F* potassium chloride after deposition for 2 min.: (A) the residual-current curve, (B) with 0.5m*M* zinc(II), (C) with 0.5m*M* zinc(II) and 0.5m*M* nickel(II), (D) with 0.5m*M* nickel(II) (*104*). The scan rate was 6.7 mv./sec. The peak near −0.1 v. on curve C is attributed to the oxidation of a nickel–zinc compound.

relative peak heights obtained after shorter times are quite irrelevant to the ultimate position of the equilibrium. The slowness of these reactions is very fortunate for polarographic purposes, because if they were fast the half-wave potential of a metal ion would be altered by the presence of another whenever the two deposited metals reacted in the mercury phase. In addition, the amalgams may be extremely complex: there are at least five different species of zinc in amalgams containing excess cobalt (*108*). One practical solution to the problem is to employ amalgams so dilute that intermetallic compound formation is negligible, but this is not always feasible: if a sample contained much copper but very little zinc, deposition would have to be fairly prolonged to obtain an amalgam containing enough zinc to give a measurable peak, and meanwhile so much copper would be deposited that most of the zinc might be bound by compound formation. In such a case one might first remove most of the copper by controlled-potential electrolysis at a separate stirred-pool electrode before beginning the deposition of zinc for the stripping analysis. Ternary compounds appear to form in some systems and to be even more troublesome, but next to nothing is known about them as yet.

The practical applications of stripping analysis have included determinations of metals (*94*,*109–112*) and halides (*87*,*88*,*113*,*114*) in reagent-grade chemicals, of metals (*115–117*) and halides (*118*) in natural waters, of lead in urine (*119*,*120*), and of copper in steels (*120a*). A comprehensive review by Shain (*121*) should be consulted for further information.

VI. Coulometric Titrations

Constant-current coulometric analysis is based on the behavior shown in Fig. 10.1. A solution containing the substance of interest is electrolyzed with a precisely controlled current between a generator electrode and an auxiliary electrode. The generator electrode is the one where the desired half-reaction takes place; the auxiliary electrode is the other current-carrying electrode and, as in controlled-potential electrolysis, is usually isolated by a diaphragm to prevent side reactions and cyclic processes, though it is more convenient to eliminate these by adding a depolarizer to the solution when a suitable one can be found. As is evident from Fig. 10.1, the reduction or oxidation of the substance being determined cannot proceed to completion with 100% current efficiency; some other process must begin to consume current before the first one is complete. Hence one cannot simply measure the time for which the constant current must flow to bring about the reduction or oxidation quantitatively.

The difficulty can be avoided by adding a substance, called a reagent precursor, whose reduction or oxidation will consume any current that is not consumed by the substance being determined, and which is reduced or oxidized to give a product, called a reagent, that reacts with the substance being determined to give the same product that is formed from the latter at the electrode surface. In the determination of ferric iron, one might add titanium(IV) as the reagent precursor. The half-reaction $Fe^{+++} + e = Fe^{++}$ will be the only one that occurs at the generator cathode as long as the limiting current of ferric iron exceeds the constant current employed. When they become equal, the reduction of titanium(IV) to titanium(III) must begin in order to consume the current that is not consumed by the direct reduction of ferric ions. The reagent thus produced reacts with the remaining ferric ions in the bulk of the solution. One faraday of electricity serves to reduce one mole of ferric iron, no matter whether the reduction proceeds directly at the electrode surface or chemically in the bulk of the solution by the mediation of the reagent. The chemical situation is essentially identical with that encountered when ferric iron is titrated with a standard solution of titanium(III), and the technique is therefore called "coulometric titration."

One important element of this identity is the necessity of locating an end point, for the reduction of titanium(IV) in this example would continue to consume electricity long after the iron(III) had been quantitatively reduced. The end points of coulometric titrations can be located by any of a large number of techniques, among which potentiometry, pH measurements, single- and dual-electrode amperometry, and spectrophotometry have been the most often used. Potentiometry is the least satisfactory of these, partly because potentials conforming to the Nernst equation are often not obtained at the low concentrations employed, and partly because the necessary large excess of reagent precursor often decreases the slope of the titration curve around the equivalence point. The time for which a known constant current must flow to reach the end point is found as in an ordinary volumetric titration, the number of microfaradays consumed is calculated from eq. (10.10), and the quantity of substance titrated is obtained from eq. (10.5). The constant current employed is usually of the order of a few milliamperes; not quite 200 sec. are needed to reach the equivalence point of a titration of 10 μeq. of material if the current is 5 mamp. Many constant-current generators have been described, and the characteristics of many of them are described by Lingane (*121*), as are those of a number of devices for automatic coulometric titrations employing potentiometric and spectrophotometric end points (*122*). Of the constant-current generators available commercially the best, in the writer's opinion, are those manufactured by Metrohm AG Herisau (the E211 "Coulometer") and by the Leeds and Northrup Company.

Nearly every reagent employed in volumetric analysis can be produced at a generator electrode and used for coulometric titrations, and so can many others whose solutions are far too unstable for volumetric use. Strong oxidizing agents such as cerium(IV), manganese(III), silver(II), and chlorine and the other halogens can be produced at platinum or other solid electrodes and used in determinations of reducing agents. Electrolytically generated bromine serves for determinations of phenols, aryl amines, and many unsaturated compounds; electrolytically generated iodine serves for the determination of water as in the classical Karl Fischer titration. Strong reducing agents such as chromium(II), copper(I), the iron(II)–ethylenediaminetetraacetate complex, titanium(III), and tin(II) can be generated at mercury electrodes and used in determinations of oxidizing agents. Acid–base titrations can be performed with platinum generator electrodes; one mole of hydrogen ion is produced at the anode, and one mole of hydroxyl ion is produced at the cathode, for each faraday used. Essentially non-aqueous acid–base titrations have been performed in acetonitrile (*123,124*) and in acetone (*125*) containing a little water as the reagent precursor. Chelometric titrations may be performed with ethylenediaminetetraacetate liberated by the reduction of the mercury(II) chelonate (*64*) or some other stable chelonate (*126*) at a mercury electrode; other chelons can be generated similarly, as can a number of other chelating agents, including thioglycolic acid and 2-hydroxyethanethiol (*127*). Halides, thiols, thioureas, and numerous others can be determined by precipitation with anodically generated mercurous or silver ion; the argentimetric determination of thiols (*128*) is widely used in the analysis of petroleum products, while that of chloride in biological materials (*129*) has been adopted as a standard procedure by the American Association of Clinical Chemists. Cyanide and chelons can be similarly determined. Details of these and many other applications, together with references to the original literature, are given by Lingane (130) and Farrington (131).

Enough has been said to demonstrate the intimate relationship between coulometric and volumetric titrations. The differences between them stem largely from the fact that the reagent is generated *in situ* in coulometric titrations. This makes it possible to use reagents like silver(II) and chlorine in aqueous solutions and diphenyl radical monoanions in N,N-dimethylformamide (132), and others whose solutions are much too unstable for volumetric use. It eliminates the difficulties of preparation and storage that afflict the use of standard solutions of air-sensitive reagents like chromium(II) and titanium (III). It eliminates the necessity of restandardizing reagents at frequent intervals. Its most important consequence is that coulometric titrations are much more suitable for determinations of very small amounts of material: on the microequivalent scale, where the problems of reagent stability and standardization become acute in volumetric work, coulometric titrations are usually much simpler and more accurate. Actually the two techniques are complementary rather than competitive. Coulometric titrations are not very well suited to work on the milliequivalent level, partly because the high currents that would be needed to permit completing them in reasonable lengths of time are somewhat difficult to obtain with suitable precision, and partly because absurdly high concentrations of the reagent precursors would usually be needed to obtain 100% current efficiency. It is with amounts below about 10 μeq. that coulometric titrations come into their own.

The success of a coulometric titration depends on many factors that also govern the success of volumetric procedures, such as the stoichiometry and rate of the reaction between the substance being determined and the reagent, the effects of other constituents of the sample, the precision with which the end point can be located, and the degree of correspondence between the end point and the equivalence point. It also depends on the achievement of 100% current efficiency for the overall process. A necessary (though insufficient) requirement is that the electrolysis current must not exceed the limiting current that would be obtained with the reagent precursor alone by using the generator electrode as a voltammetric indicator electrode. In that event, yet another process would have to occur at the generator electrode to consume the current that is not consumed by either the substance being determined or the reagent precursor, and the danger is that the product of this additional process—which would most often be hydrogen at a generator cathode or oxygen at a generator anode—would not react in the bulk of the solution with the substance being determined. Coulometric titrations are usually performed with generator electrodes—platinum or silver wire, foil, or gauze, or mercury pools—having areas of a few square centimeters, and with magnetic stirring to increase the limiting currents and to bring reagent generated at the electrode surface into contact with unreacted material in the bulk of the solution. Limiting currents at solid electrodes in solutions thus stirred are typically of the order of 0.5 mamp./cm.^{2}/meq./l., and this figure (133) provides a convenient estimate of the lowest concentration of reagent precursor at which useful results can be obtained. An end-point time of at least 200 sec. is usually desirable to minimize timing errors; if 10 μeq. of material is present, it is easily calculated from eq. (10.10) that the current should be about 5 mamp., and if the area of the generator electrode is 1 cm.^{2} this means that the concentration of the reagent precursor must not be less than about 10 meq./l. It will become apparent from the following paragraphs that much higher concentrations are often needed.

Strictly speaking, it is never possible to obtain a current efficiency of 100% in a coulometric titration, though fortunately this can often be very closely approached. There are two sources of error, and the accuracy and sensitivity of a coulometric titration depend on the care that is taken to minimize their effects. The titration of iron(II) with cerium(IV) generated by the oxidation of cerium(III) at a platinum anode will serve as a typical example.

At the positive potentials that the generator anode will assume during this process, the oxidation of water will proceed at appreciable rates. No error would result if the resulting oxygen were quantitatively re-reduced by ferrous ions, but this is not the case. The oxidation of water therefore results in the consumption of more electricity before the end point than is equivalent to the ferrous iron present. The magnitude of the error being incurred at any instant depends on the potential of the generator anode. If the electrolysis current is sufficiently small, the potential will remain for some time at values on the rising part of the anodic ferrous wave, as in the situations illustrated by Figs. 10.1 and 10.2. During this interval the rate of oxidation of water will be extremely small. Later in the titration the potential of the generator anode will shift to much more positive values on the rising part of the anodic wave of cerium(III), and the rate of oxidation of water will then be much larger.

Estimates of the maximum error thus produced can be obtained (134–136) from a residual-current curve of the supporting electrolyte alone and a voltammogram of the reagent precursor in the supporting electrolyte, both obtained by using the generator electrode as a voltammetric indicator electrode. For example, it might be found that a particular electrode assumes a potential of +1.50 v. vs. S.C.E. in 1F sulfuric acid containing 0.025F cerium(III) sulfate when an anodic current of 5 mamp. is passed through it, and that the residual current due to the oxidation of water is 0.10 mamp. at the same potential in 1F sulfuric acid alone. Then the current efficiency for the generation of cerium(IV), which is given by

$$\text{current efficiency} = 100[1 - (i_r/i)] \text{ per cent} \qquad (10.11)$$

is 98% under these conditions. If the potential of the generator anode remained at this value throughout the titration, an error of +2% would result. One could also evaluate the current efficiency by electrolyzing the solution of the reagent precursor with a constant current for a measured length of time that was too short to affect its concentration appreciably, then determining the amount of cerium(IV) produced, but this is much more troublesome.

Except when the substance being determined cannot be directly reduced or oxidized at the generator electrode, which is unusual, the error arising from this cause in an actual titration will be smaller than the value thus calculated. This is because the potential of the generator anode cannot assume as positive values in the presence of ferrous ion as it does in its absence, so that the current due to the oxidation of water will be smaller and the current efficiency higher than the above calculation implies. Moreover, this example is somewhat extreme: much smaller errors would be incurred in generating an oxidizing (or reducing) agent of more moderate strength. If the electrolysis current is only a small fraction of the initial limiting current of ferrous ion, the rate of oxidation of water will remain negligible until just before the equivalence point is reached. It is hardly practical to employ a very small generating current, because this prolongs the titration unduly, but the same objective is attained by increasing the area of the generator electrode and the efficiency of stirring. The first of these expedients increases the currents that would result at any fixed potential from all three of the oxidizable substances (ferrous ion, cerous ion, and water) present, and increases them all in the same proportion. Because the current is held constant, the potential is forced to assume a less positive value at the larger electrode, and the result is to render the oxidation of water relatively less important and thus to increase the overall current efficiency. The second expedient also increases the overall current efficiency because stirring increases the rates at which ferrous and cerous ions reach the electrode surface but has little or no effect on the rate of oxidation of water. Very large increases of stirring efficiency are difficult to effect, but the same result is produced by increasing the concentration of the reagent precursor. If the concentration of cerium(III) sulfate were increased to $0.25F$ in the above example, a current of 50 mamp. would be needed to attain a potential of $+1.50$ v., and then the current efficiency for reagent generation would be 99.8%.

It is now appropriate to return to the statement, which was made in an earlier paragraph, that the electrolysis current must not exceed the limiting current of the reagent precursor. In fact it must be considerably smaller. This is partly because the efficiency of stirring fluctuates appreciably from one instant to the next, so that a current smaller than the limiting current of the reagent precursor at one moment may exceed it at another. Even if a reasonable margin of safety is allowed, however, the fact that the slope of a voltammetric wave decreases after the half-wave potential has been passed means that increasing the current beyond this point increases the rate of the undesired process more rapidly than that of the desired one. Better current efficiency is very often obtained if the potential of the generator electrode remains near the foot of the wave of the reagent precursor than if it can approach the plateau. This is another reason why the concentration of reagent precursor should be as large as possible.

One might conclude from the foregoing argument that the current efficiency for reagent generation is always improved by decreasing the current, but this is not so. The ratio i_r/i in eq. (10.11), which governs the current efficiency, is given by

$$\frac{i_r}{i} = \frac{(nk_{f,h}^0 C)_{H_2O}}{(nk_{f,h}^0 C)_{Ce}} \exp \left\{ [(\beta n_a)_{H_2O} - (\beta n_a)_{Ce}] FE/RT \right\} \quad (10.12)$$

in which the β's are the anodic transfer coefficients and the n_a's are the numbers of electrons involved in the rate-determining anodic steps. If the product βn_a is larger for the oxidation of cerium(III) than for the oxidation of water, i_r/i will decrease, and the current efficiency will increase, as the potential becomes more positive—that is, as the current increases, provided that it remains so small that the concentration of cerium(III) at the electrode surface does not differ importantly from its concentration C in the bulk of the solution. Eventually, on the rising part of the anodic cerium wave, the concentration of cerium(III) at the electrode surface does begin to decrease, and consequently the value of i_r/i will increase, so that the current efficiency decreases, as the electrode potential is made still more positive by increasing the current still farther. By virtue of these two opposing effects the current efficiency for reagent generation must pass through a maximum, and this is exactly what was observed by Lingane et al. (135). On the other hand, if βn_a is larger for the oxidation of water than for the oxidation of the reagent precursor, the current efficiency will decrease continuously as the current increases from very small values, so that the best results would be obtained by the use of very small generating currents. Finally, with identical values of βn_a the current efficiency is constant and independent of current as long as this is too small to have a sensible effect on the concentration of the reagent precursor at the electrode surface; at potentials on the rising part of the voltammetric wave the current efficiency begins to decrease as the current rises.

It should not be inferred that the residual current is always minimized by employing an electrolysis current that is smaller than the initial limiting current of the substance being determined. If cerium(IV) were being titrated with electrolytically generated ferrous ion, the residual current would be appreciable for as long as the potential remained on the rising part of the cathodic wave of cerium(IV), and then would decrease as the potential shifted to less positive values on the rising part of the ferric wave. It would be advantageous to employ a current exceeding the limiting current of cerium(IV) in the initial solution. Here as well as in the preceding case one is trying to minimize the length of time for which the electrode remains at very positive values, where water is most rapidly oxidized. In a titration involving a powerful reducing agent the primary concern would be the length of time for which the electrode remained at very negative values.

Moreover, there are circumstances in which large errors may result from the use of a current that is not very much larger than the initial limiting current of the substance being determined. The coulometric titration of aniline with electrolytically generated bromine (137) is based on the reactions

$$6Br^- = 3Br_2 + 6e$$

so that each mole of aniline is equivalent to six faradays. But if aniline is oxidized and the oxidation product is then brominated the overall n-value may be quite different, and an accurate result could not be obtained unless the current consumed by the oxidation of bromide were many times as large as that consumed in the direct oxidation of aniline.

Another source of error arises from the consumption of electricity in changing the potentials of the double layers at the generator and indicator electrodes. If the titration is performed discontinuously by opening the electrolysis circuit whenever a measurement is made— which is the procedure almost always adopted in practical analytical work—the total quantity of electricity thus consumed will depend on the areas of the electrodes and on the differences between their zero-current potentials at the start of the titration and at the end point. Typically both of these electrodes might be made of platinum and the sum of their areas might be 2 cm.^{2}, the average differential capacity of the double layer might be 30 $\mu f./cm.^2$, and the zero-current potentials might vary 0.5 v. during the titration. Then 30 micro-coulombs, or 0.31 nanofaraday, will be consumed. This would often be small enough to neglect: with 10 $\mu eq.$ of material it would represent an error of only 0.03%. But Cooke, Reilley, and Furman (*138*) performed coulometric titrations of as little as 3 nanograms of manganese (as permanganate) with electrolytically generated ferrous ion; this is equivalent to only 30 microcoulombs, or to roughly 50 ml. of a $1 \times 10^{-9}M$ solution. On this scale the charging quantity of electricity could hardly be ignored.

The error is best eliminated by pretitration, in which the generator and indicator electrodes are brought to the end-point potential in the titration medium before the sample is added. Suppose that this is done prior to a titration of cerium(IV) with electrolytically generated ferrous ion. When the cerium(IV) is added the potentials of the electrodes will shift to more positive values. The quantity of electricity consumed in these shifts will have been supplied by the reduction of an equivalent amount of cerium(IV), and the additional quantity of electricity that will then have to be supplied to reduce the rest of the cerium(IV) and restore the end-point potentials will be exactly equivalent to the total amount of cerium(IV) added.

Additional complications may arise from the formation and re-reduction of oxide films on platinum electrodes. Much larger quantities of electricity may be consumed in these processes than in double-layer charging. A second important purpose of pretitration is to bring the electrode surfaces to the same condition that they will have at the end point.

Pretitration also serves the very important function of removing interfering impurities from the reagents employed. The concentrations of the supporting electrolytes and reagent precursors employed in coulometric titrations are so much higher than those of the substances titrated that even traces of impurities can produce very large errors. In most cases the pretitration is best done by adding a small amount of the substance being determined to the mixture of reagent precursor and supporting electrolyte, and titrating to or slightly beyond the end point. The sample is added and titrated in the same way to the same end point, and the calculation is based on the quantity of electricity consumed between the two end points. This is most satisfactory when the location of the end point is independent of the quantity of material being titrated, as it is in strong acid–strong base, precipitation, and some redox titrations. In such cases it is often possible, after completing the titration of one sample, to add another to the same solution and continue the electrolysis, so that the first titration serves as a pretitration for the second, and so on. As the quality of the end point sometimes deteriorates after several successive titrations, this procedure must always be tested by experiments with known samples. Less perfect compensation is obtained when the position of the end-point is concentration-dependent, as it is in weak acid–strong base titrations and many others. Especially in titrations of small amounts of material, where small variations in the charge of the double layer or in the nature and thickness of the oxide film may correspond to large relative errors, exactly the same generating current should be used in the pretitration as in the titration itself.

VII. Chronopotentiometry

Chronopotentiometry consists of passing a constant current through a stationary indicator electrode in an unstirred solution and observing the manner in which the potential of the electrode varies with time. Curves are obtained that have the same form as Fig. 10.2, differing from it only in that they reflect the depletion of the electroactive substance in the diffusion layer rather than throughout the solution.

A typical chronopotentiogram, obtained with a small mercury pool in a perchloric acid solution containing copper(II) and cadmium(II), is shown in Fig. 10.8. The short horizontal line at the left-hand side of the Figure corresponds to the zero-current potential. When the flow of current is started, the potential shifts toward more negative values on the rising part of the copper wave. The shift is rapid at first, then slows as the concentration of copper(II) decreases while the concentration of copper(0) increases at the electrode surface until the point of maximum poising capacity is reached, and thereafter accelerates again as the concentration of copper(II) becomes still smaller. Eventually the flux of copper(II) at the electrode surface becomes too small to consume all of the current, and the potential shifts rapidly to values at which cadmium(II) is reduced. The time (in seconds) required to reach the point of maximum slope is the "transition time" τ. For linear diffusion to a plane electrode this is approximately described by the Sand equation (*139*)

$$i\tau^{1/2} = \frac{1}{2}(\pi^{1/2}nFD^{1/2}AC) \qquad (10.13)$$

where i is the current in microamperes, A is the area of the electrode in square centimeters, and C is the bulk concentration of the electro-active substance in millimoles per liter. The equation is approximate in that double-layer charging is ignored.

On more prolonged electrolysis cadmium ions are more and more completely removed from the diffusion layer, and a second transition time is observed. Because the reduction of copper(II) continues while that of cadmium(II) is taking place, the difference between the two transition times is longer than the single transition time that would have been observed if the cadmium had been present alone. In a mixture of two substances the first transition time τ_1 is given by eq. (10.13) while the sum of the two transition times, $(\tau_1 + \tau_2)$, obeys the equation (140)

$$i[(\tau_1 + \tau_2)^{1/2} - \tau_1^{1/2}] = \tfrac{1}{2}(\pi^{1/2} n_2 F D_2^{1/2} A C_2) \qquad (10.14)$$

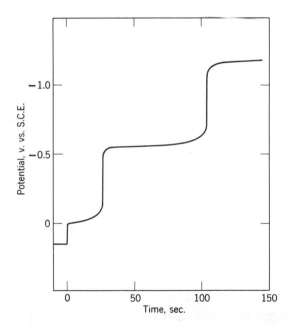

Figure 10.8. Chronopotentiogram obtained with a mercury electrode having an area of approximately 1 cm.² for a solution containing 10mM copper(II) and 10mM cadmium(II) in 2F perchloric acid, using a current of 0.50 mamp.

More generally $(141,142)$,

$$i[(\tau_1 + \tau_2 + \cdots + \tau_n)^{1/2} - (\tau_1 + \tau_2 + \cdots + \tau_{n-1})^{1/2}] \\ = \tfrac{1}{2}(\pi^{1/2} n_n F D_n^{1/2} A C_n) \tag{10.15}$$

An important special case is that of a stepwise reduction or oxidation involving n_1 electrons in the first step and n_2 in the second. Assuming that the n_1-electron reduction product has the same diffusion coefficient as the starting material, one may substitute the description of τ_1 provided by eq. (10.13) into eq. (10.14) and divide the result by eq. (10.13) to obtain

$$(\tau_1 + \tau_2)/\tau_1 = (n_1 + n_2)^2/n_1^2 \tag{10.16}$$

Hence, if $n_1 = n_2$, the total transition time is four times the first transition time; this is strikingly different from the corresponding voltammetric behavior.

Equations for the potential–time curves obtained in chronopotentiometry have been derived for a number of kinds of electrode reactions. For the reversible reduction of one dissolved substance, O, to another, R, one obtains, at $25°$ (143),

$$E = E^0 - \frac{0.05915}{n} \log \frac{f_R D_O^{1/2}}{f_O D_R^{1/2}} - \frac{0.05915}{n} \log \frac{t^{1/2}}{\tau^{1/2} - t^{1/2}} \tag{10.17}$$

which may be compared with eq. (4.6) for the corresponding voltammetric wave. When $t^{1/2} = \tau^{1/2}/2$—that is, when $t = \tau/4$—the last term vanishes, and defining the potential at this point as the quarter-transition-time potential $E_{\tau/4}$ permits the equation of the chronopotentiometric curve to be written in the form

$$E = E_{\tau/4} - \frac{0.05915}{n} \log \frac{t^{1/2}}{\tau^{1/2} - t^{1/2}} \tag{10.18}$$

The quarter-transition-time potential should be identical with the voltammetric half-wave potential obtained with an indicator electrode of the same material, and should be the same for the anodic as for the cathodic process. The slope of a plot of E vs. $\log t^{1/2}/(\tau^{1/2} - t^{1/2})$ should be equal to $-0.05915/n$ volt for the cathodic process and to $+0.05915/n$ volt for the anodic process. The equation analogous to eq. (4.45) is

$$E_{3\tau/4} - E_{\tau/4} = -(0.0479/n) \text{ volt} \tag{10.19}$$

for the cathodic process. After the value of n has been deduced from transition-time data in much the same way as it is deduced from wave-height data in voltammetry, assessments of reversibility can be based on these equations in much the same way as they are based on the corresponding voltammetric equations.

For a totally irreversible cathodic process that includes just one rate-determining step in which n_a electrons are involved, one obtains (144)

$$E + 0.2412 = \frac{0.05915}{\alpha n_a} \log \frac{2k^0_{f,h}}{\pi^{1/2}D_O^{1/2}} + \frac{0.05915}{\alpha n_a} \log (\tau^{1/2} - t^{1/2})$$
(10.20)

where E is the potential in volts vs. S.C.E. At the quarter-transition-time potential this becomes

$$E_{\tau/4} = -0.2412 + \frac{0.05915}{\alpha n_a} \log \frac{0.564 k^0_{f,h} \tau^{1/2}}{D_O^{1/2}}$$
(10.21)

which may be compared with eq. (4.60). Values of αn_a may be obtained from the slopes of plots of E vs. $\log (\tau^{1/2} - t^{1/2})$, or from the equation

$$E_{3\tau/4} - E_{\tau/4} = - (0.0327/\alpha n_a) \text{ volt}$$
(10.22)

and $k^0_{f,h}$ may then be evaluated from eq. (10.21) after the necessary value of D_O has been deduced from transition-time data. Variations of $E_{\tau/4}$ with the composition of the supporting electrolyte can thus be used to elucidate the stoichiometry of the half-reaction through the rate-determining step. This is less satisfactory than the corresponding polarographic technique, however, for chronopotentiometric measurements of $E_{\tau/4}$ have generally been appreciably less accurate and precise than polarographic measurements of $E_{1/2}$. In some cases this may be because an appreciable iR drop is included in the potentials measured in chronopotentiometry; in others it may be because the response of the recorder is not perfectly linear, so that a substantial uncertainty arises because the chart width must correspond to half a volt or more to permit recording the entire transition; in still others it may be because the response time of the recorder is too large a fraction of the transition time to permit obtaining a faithful record.

At any rate, it is clear that the elementary theory of chronopotentiometry, as described thus far, is very closely akin to that of polarography. One important difference is that chronopotentiometric transition times can often be measured more precisely than polarographic limiting currents, and there is the additional advantage that the relative error in τ is halved in computing C because of the form of eq. (10.13). Of some analytical importance is the fact that the transition time is increased by the prior reduction of a substance more easily reduced (or the prior oxidation of a substance more easily oxidized) than the one being determined, as follows from eq. (10.14). If a solution contains C_1 millimoles per liter of a more easily reducible or oxidizable substance in addition to C_2 millimoles per liter of the substance being determined, and if the values of $nD^{1/2}$ are the same for the two substances, the ratio τ_2/τ_1 approaches $2C_2/C_1$ as C_1 is increased while C_2 remains constant. Morris and Lingane (145) employed this principle in determining hydroxylamine in the presence of larger concentrations of hydrazine.

Three-electrode cells are required in chronopotentiometry: in addition to the indicator electrode, there must be an auxiliary electrode to carry the current and a reference electrode for use in monitoring the potential of the indicator electrode. Isolation of the auxiliary electrode is unnecessary unless successive chronopotentiograms are to be obtained with the same solution, in which case the solution must be stirred after each recording to destroy the concentration gradients set up at the indicator electrode. If the quantity of electricity used in the transition is large and the volume of solution small, the product formed at the auxiliary electrode during the first recording may be present at a concentration high enough to cause difficulty in the second. Both for this reason and to minimize the bulk depletion of the substance of interest, the ratio of the area of the indicator electrode to the volume of the solution should be kept small in such experiments.

Transition times should be rather short in chronopotentiometry because the theoretical equations are founded on the assumption that there is no convective mixing in the diffusion layer. Transition times as short as a few milliseconds have been measured oscilloscopically (144,146), and are needed in studying very fast processes, but the roughness of a solid electrode becomes more prominent as τ decreases and the diffusion layer becomes thinner, and the correction for double-layer charging that must be applied unless the solution is fairly concentrated becomes more important. For most purposes pen-and-ink recording is more satisfactory as well as more convenient. At the other extreme, convection is almost impossible to eliminate in electrolyses lasting for more than two or three minutes. Most workers have tended to employ transition times in the neighborhood of 20 sec. Care must be taken to guard against vibration, which disturbs the diffusion layer, increases the transition time, and may even affect the value of $E_{\tau/4}$; the difficulty of doing this increases as the transition time becomes longer.

It usually suffices to connect a recording potentiometer directly to the indicator and reference electrodes. So that the transition time can be measured with reasonable precision, the chart speed should be at least 5 mm./sec. The period of the recorder must not exceed 1 sec. full-scale, and even faster response is preferable. The input impedance of the recorder should be at least 0.1 megohm, so that it will draw only a negligible current from the indicator electrode. If the resistance of the reference electrode is large, if the electrolysis current is low, or if very precise values of the potential are needed, it is advisable to interpose an amplifier between the cell and the recorder. The Leeds and Northrup Type 7664 pH meter is very convenient for this purpose. The necessary constant current, which is most often of the order of 10 mamp., may be provided by a constant-current generator of nearly any of the designs intended for coulometric titrations. The Metrohm E211 "Coulometer" (available from Brinkmann Instruments, Inc., Westbury, New York) is especially convenient because a current accurately equal to any desired value up to about 30 mamp. is easily obtained. One often wants to investigate the effect of a small change of current, or to make a slight adjustment so as to bring the transition time into a convenient range for accurate measurement; if the current can only be varied by successive factors of 2 or 3, as is the case with most other commercially available instruments, much inconvenience is often encountered.

The areas of the indicator electrodes employed in chronopotentiometric experiments are usually of the order of 1 cm.^{2}. Mercury-pool and platinum-foil electrodes have been the most widely used. A cell like the one shown in Fig. 8.11, to which an auxiliary electrode must be added, is convenient for use with a mercury pool; polystyrene or methacrylic plastic cells are preferable to glass ones, for equations assuming linear diffusion cannot be used if the surface of the pool is far from plane unless the transition time is quite short. An explicit criterion $(147,148)$ is that the quantity $D^{1/2}\tau^{1/2}/r_0$, where r_0 is the radius of curvature of the electrode, should not exceed about 0.07. At a hanging mercury drop, if $D = 6 \times 10^{-6}$ cm.^{2}/sec., this corresponds to a drop mass of at least 2.2 mg. if $\tau = 1$ sec., or at least 300 mg. if $\tau = 25$ sec. The latter is much too large to be practical; one must either employ very short transition times or interpret longer ones by equations that take spherical diffusion into account. For many purposes an unshielded platinum foil electrode can be used; although the transition times deviate from the above predictions because linear diffusion is not obtained, so that the product $i\tau^{1/2}$ increases as the current decreases, the discrepancy is small if the area of the electrode is at least 1 cm.^{2} and if the transition time does not exceed about 20 sec. $(148a)$. For unrestricted linear diffusion to an unshielded circular plane electrode of radius r cm., the transition time has been found to obey the equation

$$i\tau^{1/2} = \tfrac{1}{2}(\pi^{1/2}nFD^{1/2}AC)[1 + 0.98(D\tau)^{1/2}/r]$$

and on this basis it has been suggested $(148a)$ that values of the "chronopotentiometric constant" $i\tau^{1/2}/AC$ for such electrodes are best obtained by extrapolating to $\tau^{1/2} = 0$. Davis and Ganchoff (149) pointed out that values of $i\tau^{1/2}$ proportional to concentration can be obtained by adjusting the current in such a way as to yield the same transition time in each experiment. As this cannot provide an exact compensation for the effects of convection, which is a real danger under such circumstances, it is better in general to use an electrode of the type shown in Fig. 10.9. This can be attached, by a short length of Tygon tubing, to a piece of 7-mm. glass tubing, which should be straight (so that diffusion proceeds upward toward the disk) if the solution becomes less dense at the electrode surface as the electrolysis proceeds, but should be bent through 180° (so that diffusion proceeds downward) in the opposite case. In this way linear diffusion is ensured and the density gradient is stabilized, and values of $i\tau^{1/2}$ having standard deviations as small as ±0.2% over a range of transition times from 7 to 145 sec. can be obtained.

One effect of convection or vibration is to prevent the occurrence of any transition if the current becomes too small. It is well worth while to experiment with each new system to find the current at which

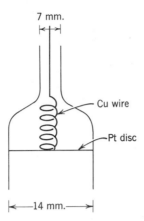

Figure 10.9. Construction of a platinum electrode providing linear diffusion and suitable for use with either upward or downward diffusion, according to Bard (148).

the transition vanishes. A reasonable margin of safety appears to be provided by using a current at least 25% higher than this in subsequent experiments.

There have been some analytical applications of chronopotentiometry (145,149–152), but it cannot be regarded as a very promising analytical technique: although it is capable of good precision under favorable conditions, its limit of detection is considerably inferior even to that of polarography. This is largely due to the influences of double-layer charging and, at solid electrodes, oxide formation. The argument may be put in the following form. Consider the chronopotentiogram of a substance for which $n = 1$, $D = 6 \times 10^{-6}$ cm.^{2}/sec., and $C = 0.1$mM. If the area of the indicator electrode is 1 cm.^{2}, eq. (10.13) gives $i\tau^{1/2} = 20.94$ μamp.-sec.$^{1/2}$. If $\tau = 20$ seconds, a current of 4.68 μamp. is required, and the quantity of electricity consumed in the reduction of the substance being determined is, therefore, $i\tau = 93.6$ microcoulombs. Suppose that the potential at the transition time is 0.5 v. more negative than at the start of the electrolysis and that the average differential capacity of the double layer is 30 μf./cm.^{2}; then 15 microcoulombs must be consumed in charging the double layer. This is nearly 14% of the total quantity of electricity consumed, so that the correction is much larger than it would be in stationary-electrode voltammetry under the same conditions. Equa-

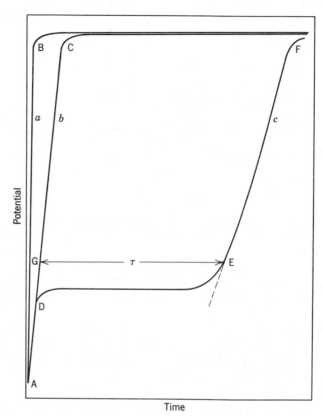

Figure 10.10. Schematic chronopotentiograms for a pure supporting electrolyte at (*a*) a relatively high current density and (*b*) a much lower current density, and for (*c*) a solution containing a reducible substance under the same conditions as (*b*). Segment EF is not quite linear, nor is it exactly parallel to AC.

tion (8.8) showed that the charging current becomes increasingly important as the rate of change of potential increases, and the correction for the charging current is large in this example simply because the rate of change of potential (25 mv./sec., on the average) is larger than it usually is in stationary-electrode voltammetry.

Worse yet, this argument understates the difficulty. Very little of the total quantity of electricity consumed in charging the double layer is consumed near the quarter-transition-time potential, because the rate of change of potential is small there. Most of it is consumed just after the start of the electrolysis and just before the transition time. The practical consequences of these facts are illustrated by Fig. 10.10. Curve a shows schematically the chronopotentiogram that would be obtained with a mercury electrode in a pure supporting electrolyte, in which the current is entirely consumed by double-layer charging until a very negative potential is reached. Because of the films of oxide, chemisorbed oxygen, and adsorbed hydrogen that can exist on the surfaces of platinum electrodes, the curves obtained with them are much more complex. The slope of segment AB of this curve is described by the equation

$$dE/dt = -(i/\kappa A) \qquad (10.23)$$

and it would be constant if κ were independent of potential. On this assumption curve b would be obtained at a much lower current i', and the slope of AC would be simply i'/i times that of AB. Curve c would be obtained under the same conditions as curve b but in the presence of a reducible substance O. In the region AD this will coincide with curve b because the current is entirely consumed by double-layer charging in each case. At point D the reduction of O begins to proceed at an appreciable rate; the segment DE represents the interval during which the concentration of O is being decreased at the electrode surface, and at point E this becomes very small. In the region EF most of the current is consumed by double-layer charging, but part of it is consumed by the reduction of O diffusing toward the electrode surface under the influence of the concentration gradient established during the interval DE. Hence the current available for charging the double layer in the region EF is smaller than in the absence of the reducible material, and the result is that the slope of EF is smaller than that of AC. Moreover, the fraction of the current consumed by the reduction of O decreases as time goes on and the solution becomes depleted farther and farther away from the electrode surface: the slope of EF is not constant, but increases slightly as t increases. In practice, however, EF usually appears nearly linear. Because the slopes of EF and AC are different, the accurate evaluation of τ is impossible. One widely used procedure is to extrapolate AD and EF, locate the point E at which the curve just merges with EF, and measure the distance GE. Whatever procedure is adopted, the result does not exactly correspond to the theoretical transition time, and empirical calibration with known solutions is essential. Decreasing the current makes matters worse by increasing the discrepancy between the slopes of AC and EF and by increasing the curvature of EF.

In general, the difficulty of measuring τ begins to become acute even at concentrations around 0.1mM. In a few favorable cases, Reilley et al. (*141*) obtained curves that were not too distorted with 0.01mM solutions. But the general experience is that the technique becomes increasingly unsatisfactory as the concentration decreases below about 0.5mM.

An algebraic correction based on the same principle as the graphical one described above was devised by Lingane (*153*) and Bard (*154*), who have generalized it to include corrections for other background processes in addition to double-layer charging. The total quantity of electricity B (in microcoulombs) consumed in extraneous processes while the potential is changing from A to E along curve c of Fig. 10.10 can be represented by

$$B = -\bar{\kappa}A\Delta E + Q_{ox} + nF\Gamma \qquad (10.24)$$

where κ is the mean differential capacity of the double layer over the range of potentials ΔE between the start of the recording at A and the end of the transition at E, Q_{ox} is the quantity of electricity consumed in forming or reducing the layer of oxide film or chemisorbed oxygen if a solid indicator electrode is used, and Γ is the number of micromoles of electroactive substance adsorbed on the electrode surface. Both Q_{ox} and Γ are of course proportional to the area of the electrode. The total quantity of electricity consumed at point E is given by

$$i\tau = \frac{\pi^{1/2}nFD^{1/2}AC\tau^{1/2}}{2} + B \qquad (10.25)$$

which becomes indistinguishable from eq. (10.13) as the ratio of the first term on the right-hand side to the second increases. The value of B can be obtained from the intercept, while that of C could be obtained from the slope, of a plot of $i\tau$ vs. $\tau^{1/2}$. This is useful in studying the extent of adsorption or film formation, but of course it is powerless to deal with the increasing difficulty of locating point E as the concentration and current decrease. One technique of mitigating that problem consists of employing a current that increases with time

(*142,155–157*), but it is not yet known whether or how much the limit of detection can be improved by this expedient. If the current is proportional to the square root of time, τ becomes proportional to the concentration of electroactive substance under conditions where B is negligible, and the values of τ for successive transitions become additive.

For these reasons chronopotentiometric experiments are generally performed at concentrations between about 1 and 10mM. Because these are higher than the concentrations used in most polarographic work, electrical migration of charged electroactive substances toward the indicator electrode is much more likely to be appreciable in chronopotentiometry than the migration current is in polarography. Corrections for electrical migration have been described by Morris and Lingane (*158*).

According to eq. (10.25), the value of $i\tau^{1/2}$ increases as τ decreases (that is, as i increases) when some of the electroactive species is adsorbed onto the electrode surface. Exactly similar variations of the ratio of wave height to $h_{corr}^{1/2}$ are observed for adsorption waves in polarography (Chap. 3 IX). In polarography the behavior of this ratio as h_{corr} is varied serves to distinguish among diffusion-controlled, adsorption, and kinetic or catalytic waves; in chronopotentiometry the behavior of $i\tau^{1/2}$ as τ is varied serves the same purpose. Whereas the value of $i\tau^{1/2}$ is independent of i or τ for a diffusion-controlled process, and increases with decreasing τ or increasing i when adsorption is involved, it decreases with decreasing τ or increasing i in processes that give rise to kinetic or catalytic waves in polarography. For example, if the reaction scheme is

$$Y \underset{k_b}{\overset{k_f}{\rightleftharpoons}} O \xrightarrow{\;+\;ne\;} R$$

one obtains, on assuming that Y and O have the same diffusion coefficient D (*144,159*)

$$i\tau^{1/2} = \frac{\pi^{1/2}nFD^{1/2}AC}{2} - \frac{\pi^{1/2}A}{2K(k_f + k_b)^{1/2}}\,i \qquad (10.26)$$

where $K = k_f/k_b$, if $(k_f + k_b)\,\tau$ exceeds about 4. If $(k_f + k_b)$ is not too large, the limiting value of $i\tau^{1/2}$ described by

$$\lim_{i \to \infty} i\tau^{1/2} = \frac{\pi^{1/2}nFD^{1/2}AC}{2[1 + (1/K)]} \tag{10.27}$$

will be very nearly attained at currents small enough to be employed experimentally. Equation (10.27) then provides the value of k_f/k_b, and the individual values of the two rate constants can be obtained from data at lower currents by employing eq. (10.26).

For the catalytic mechanism

$$O + ne = R$$

$$R + Z \xrightarrow{k_f} O$$

if $k_f C_Z^0 \tau$ is appreciable while the reaction between R and Z is slow enough and the excess of Z large enough to permit equating the concentration C_Z^0 of Z at the electrode surface to its concentration C_Z in the bulk of the solution—conditions very similar to those which lead to eq. (3.59)—one obtains (160)

$$\left(\frac{\tau}{\tau_d}\right)^{1/2} = \frac{2}{\pi^{1/2}} \frac{(k_f C_Z \tau)^{1/2}}{\text{erf } (k_f C_Z \tau)^{1/2}} \tag{10.28}$$

where τ_d, the transition time that would be obtained for the diffusion-controlled process in the absence of the catalytic step, is described by eq. (10.13). The quantity in the denominator is the error function, which is tabulated for various values of the argument in numerous reference works. If $k_f C_Z \tau$ is very small, τ/τ_d is nearly 1; on increasing $k_f C_Z \tau$, either by increasing C_Z or by decreasing the current, the catalytic process becomes relatively more important and τ/τ_d increases.

Many other kinds of mechanisms have been considered. The manner in which $i\tau^{1/2}$ is affected by changes of the current and the concentration of electroactive substance can often be used to elucidate the nature of the process and to evaluate the rate constants of the chemical steps involved. Several excellent reviews of the kinetic applications of chronopotentiometry are available (161–164) and should be consulted for details.

Although ordinary chronopotentiometry is best suited to the investigation of the forward reaction, there are a few circumstances in which it can furnish information about the fate of the product. If, for example, the reversible reduction of O to R is followed by the chemical transformation of R into some other species, the quarter-transition-time potential will be less negative than the value described by eq. (10.17) but will approach it as a limit on increasing the current *(160)*. If the starting material O is reversibly reduced to give a precipitate, equation (10.18) will not be obeyed, and again $E_{\tau/4}$ will vary with the current under otherwise fixed conditions; the phenomena are very similar to those discussed in Chap. 4 II.

Such approaches are useless if the electron-transfer step is irreversible, and in general transformations of the product are better followed by current-reversal chronopotentiometry. This involves the instantaneous reversal of the current at the transition time τ_f for the forward process. If the product R is electroactive it will be re-oxidized and there will be an anodic transition τ_r seconds after the reversal of current. If the process is simply $O + ne = R$, and if the R remains dissolved (either in the solution or, if a mercury electrode is used, in the mercury), the value of τ_r is exactly one-third that of τ_f *(140,165)*. On the other hand, if the R precipitates onto the electrode surface none of it is lost by diffusion, and then $\tau_r = \tau_f$ *(164)*. Many other schemes have been discussed *(166–172)*.

Current-reversal chronopotentiometry should be a useful technique for assessing the reversibility of a half-reaction because it eliminates the necessity of preparing both the oxidized and reduced forms of the couple. For example, a definitive assessment of the reversibility of a metal ion–metal amalgam couple cannot be made polarographically without examining the behavior of the dropping metal amalgam electrode, which is not easy to do. In current-reversal chronopotentiometry it would be unnecessary to prepare the amalgam separately, for it would be formed *in situ* while the cathodic transition was being observed.

As is shown by eq. (10.17), the quarter-transition time for the forward process (which, for the sake of convenience, is assumed to be the cathodic one) is equal to the polarographic half-wave potential described by eq. (4.18a). The potential–time curve for the reverse transition with a reversible couple is described, if the reduced form R remains dissolved, by the equation *(140)*

$$E = E^0 - \frac{0.05915}{n} \log \frac{f_R D_O^{1/2}}{f_O D_R^{1/2}}$$

$$+ \frac{0.05915}{n} \log \left[\frac{\tau_f^{1/2}}{(\tau_f + t_r)^{1/2} - 2t_r^{1/2}} - 1 \right] \quad (10.29)$$

where τ_f is the transition time for the forward process and t_r is the time that has elapsed since the reversal of current. The first two terms on the right-hand side of this equation are again equal to the reversible polarographic half-wave potential according to eq. (4.18a), but the third term does not vanish at this point. When it does, so that $E = E_{1/2} = E_{\tau_f/4}$, it is easily shown that one must have $t_r = 0.07160\tau_f$. Since $\tau_r = \tau_f/3$, as was stated above, this corresponds to $t_r = 0.215\tau_r$. Thus the potential at which the forward transition is 25% complete is reached when the reverse transition is only 21.5% complete. Hence the quarter-transition-time potentials are not exactly the same in current-reversal chronopotentiometry even when the half-reaction is reversible. However, substituting $t_r = \tau_r/4 = \tau_f/12$ into eq. (10.29) and combining the result with eq. (10.17) yields, for the difference between these two potentials,

$$E_{\tau_r/4} - E_{\tau_f/4} = 3.76/n \text{ millivolts} \qquad (10.30)$$

This is too small to be detected experimentally, and so the practical criterion of reversibility in current-reversal chronopotentiometry is equality of the forward and reverse quarter-transition-time potentials.

If the couple is totally irreversible, and if the product R of the forward transition remains dissolved, the potential–time curve for the reverse transition is described by the equation

$$E = -0.2412 + \frac{0.05915}{(1 - \alpha)\, n_a} \log \frac{\pi^{1/2} D_{\mathrm{R}}^{1/2}}{2k_{b,h}^0}$$
$$- \frac{0.05915}{(1 - \alpha)\, n_a} \log \left[(\tau_f + t_r)^{1/2} - 2t_r^{1/2} \right] \qquad (10.31)$$

where, as usual in descriptions of current–potential curves for irreversible processes, E is referred to the N.H.E. Hence

$$E_{\tau_r/4} = -0.2412 + \frac{0.05915}{(1 - \alpha)\, n_a} \log \frac{1.912 D_{\mathrm{R}}^{1/2}}{k_{b,h}^0 \tau_f^{1/2}} \qquad (10.32)$$

It cannot be taken for granted that the values of α and n_a are the same for the forward and reverse processes, for these may occur along different paths; for each couple the matter must be tested by experiment. When they are, their values can be combined with those of $k_{f,h}^0$ obtained from the quarter-transition-time potential of the forward process by eq. (10.21) and of $k^0{}_{b,h}$ obtained from the quarter-transition-time potential of the reverse process by eq. (10.32), together with the equation

$$k_{s,h} = k^0_{f,h} \exp(-\alpha n_a FE^0/RT) = k^0_{b,h} \exp[(1 - \alpha)n_a FE^0/RT]$$
(10.33)

to obtain values of $k_{s,h}$ and the standard potential E^0 of the couple.

Other ways of varying the current during chronopotentiometric experiments have also been considered theoretically. In current-cessation chronopotentiometry (170,171), the current is simply turned off at a transition time. This is uninteresting if only a single electroactive substance is present, for then the potential simply decays exponentially toward its original value. If two electroactive species A and B are present, two transitions are observed while the current flows and the transition times are described by eq. (10.14); shutting off the current at the second transition should yield a third τ_3 seconds later, and $\tau_3 = \tau_2{}^2/4\tau_1$ if all of the species involved are soluble and have equal diffusion coefficients and if the reaction between the stronger oxidizing agent A and the reduced form of B is rapid and quantitative. Otherwise it might be possible to obtain information about the rate of this reaction. Cyclic chronopotentiometry (172), in which the current is reversed at each of several alternating forward and reverse transitions, should furnish information analogous to that obtainable by other cyclic techniques (cf. Sec. IX).

VIII. Differential and Derivative Voltammetry

Differential voltammetry was originally devised by Semerano and Riccoboni (173). Two indicator electrodes at the same potential in different solutions are used, and the difference between the currents flowing through them is recorded as a function of their common potential. A simple circuit that will serve the purpose is shown in Fig. 10.11, where the magnitude of the potential drop E_R indicated by the recorder is given by

$$E_R = i_1 R_1 - i_2 R_2$$
(10.34)

A solution of the supporting electrolyte alone may be placed in cell 2 and an identical solution containing an electroactive substance may

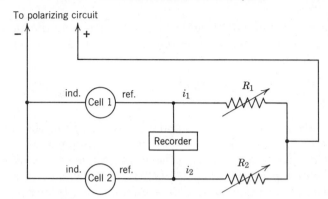

Figure 10.11.   Schematic diagram of a simple circuit for differential voltammetry.

be placed in cell 1. If the two indicator electrodes are exactly identical, the variation of i_2 with potential will be exactly the same as the variation of the residual current included in i_1. Hence, if R_1 and R_2 are equal, E_R will be proportional to the current due to the electroactive substance alone, and the resulting plot of E_R against indicator-electrode potential will provide an automatic correction for the residual current. This can be used to compensate for the final current to improve the shape of a cathodic wave occurring at potentials so negative that its plateau is too short to be measured on an ordinary voltammogram.

Compensation can be achieved, not only for the residual current, but also for the current on the plateau of a prior wave. A portion of the cadmium–zinc solution yielding the polarogram shown in Fig. 3.19 might be placed in cell 1 while the supporting electrolyte was placed in cell 2. Then, with the polarizing circuit adjusted to provide a potential on the plateau of the cadmium wave, enough of a concentrated solution of cadmium ion might be added to cell 2 to decrease E_R to zero. A difference between the concentrations of cadmium ion in the solutions, between the areas of two stationary or solid indicator electrodes, or between the values of m for two dropping electrodes can be compensated by suitable adjustment of the ratio R_1/R_2. A plot of E_R against indicator-electrode potential would then show only the zinc wave.

Both of the foregoing applications are termed "subtractive" voltammetry. In "comparative" voltammetry the same technique is employed to a different end: in the preceding example it would involve measuring the volume of standard cadmium solution that would have to be added to a known volume of supporting electrolyte in cell 2 to produce equal currents in the two cells at a potential on the plateau of the cadmium wave. If the two electrodes have identical characteristics, the concentrations of cadmium ion will then be the same in the two cells. This would permit the unknown concentration of cadmium ion in cell 1 to be evaluated more precisely than would be possible by ordinary techniques.

Differential polarography, in which dropping electrodes are used as the indicator electrodes, involves some difficulty, for unless the cycles of drop growth and fall are exactly synchronized the difference of current will undergo wide periodic fluctuations even though the two electrodes yield the same average current. Kolthoff and Lingane called this the "beaded string" effect. Several authors attempted to mitigate it by using a number of dropping electrodes in each solution, but with only indifferent success, for a great many are needed to give a current that is nearly constant from one instant to the next. Acceptable curves might possibly be obtained by using a fritted-glass disc instead of a large number of capillaries (174). However, the most common expedient has been to use an electromagnetic device to apply a mechanical shock to the two capillaries simultaneously at regular intervals shorter than the normal drop times (175–178). The fluctuations can also be greatly decreased by thorough filtering of the electrical signal presented to the recorder (179), and this approach is much to be preferred.

Premature mechanical detachment of the drop from the capillary tip can be effected in other ways (180,181), and devices for this purpose (182) are available from several manufacturers of polarographs. Their use permits ordinary polarograms to be recorded much more rapidly than is possible with conventional drop times, because significant features of the curve are not lost in the drawn-out traces obtained for individual drops, and is also said to facilitate measurement by decreasing the amplitudes of the oscillations and by eliminating the variation of drop time with potential. However, confining the measurement to the first part of the normal drop life, where the charging current is greatest and the faradaic current smallest, considerably raises the limit of detection. To the writer it does not seem prudent to add further mechanical complications to those that already beset the dropping electrode.

It is generally asserted that the two capillaries used in differential polarography must have nearly identical values of m as well as of t. This would mean that, after equal values of t has been obtained in one of the ways mentioned above, the heights of the two mercury columns would have to be adjusted until the values of m became equal. On the face of it, this is so tedious that differential polarography is rarely if ever used in practice. However, the assertion is quite fallacious: for any practical purpose it is immaterial whether the values of m are equal or not. Consider, for example, the determination of zinc in the solution of Fig. 3.19 by subtractive polarography. The residual current in each cell is proportional to $m^{2/3}$ according to eq. (3.5). The diffusion current of cadmium ion in each cell is proportional to $m^{2/3}$ according to eq. (3.15); even according to the Koutecký equation (3.20), if $D = 6 \times 10^{-6}$ cm.^{2}/sec. the ratio $i_d/m^{2/3}$ varies only 1.5% as m changes by a factor of 2. The same thing is true of the heights of kinetic waves according to eq. (3.46), of catalytic waves according to eq. (3.59), and of adsorption waves according to eq. (3.64). Whatever the source of the current being compensated, it is nearly or exactly proportional to $m^{2/3}$. Any difference between the two m-values can, therefore, be nearly or exactly compensated by adjusting R_1 and R_2 so that $R_2/R_1 = m_1^{2/3}/m_2^{2/3}$. The values of m need not be known or measured; it suffices to place identical solutions in the two cells and adjust R_1 and R_2 until E_R becomes zero. It appears that the practical difficulty of differential polarography has been somewhat overestimated.

There have been a number of variations on this theme. One of them is related to single-sweep oscillographic polarography, which was mentioned briefly in Sec. IV. Two synchronized dropping electrodes having drop times of about 7 sec. are employed; near the end of the drop life a rapid potential sweep is applied to both, and the difference of current is displayed on the face of a cathode-ray tube (*183*). An instrument designed for this purpose, the Differential Cathode Ray Polarotrace 1660, is manufactured by Southern Analytical Ltd. (Camberley, Surrey, England) and distributed by the Cincinnati Division of the Bendix Corporation. Another variation, differential voltammetry with hanging drop electrodes, was mentioned in Chap. 8 IV.

Derivative voltammetry (*184–186*) consists of recording the rate of change, di/dt, of the current flowing through a voltammetric cell against the potential E of the indicator electrode, which is varied at a constant rate dE/dt. The value of di/dE is small at potentials preceding the wave, increases to a maximum at the half-wave potential if the wave obeys either eq. (4.9) or eq. (4.59), and then decreases again to a very small value on the plateau. By differentiating either of these equations one obtains the following expression for the maximum value of di/dE:

$$\left(\frac{di}{dE} \right)_{\max} = - \frac{\nu F}{RT} \frac{i_d}{4} \qquad (10.35)$$

where ν is equal to n if the wave is reversible, or to αn_a if it is totally irreversible and involves a single rate-determining step. As it is di/dt and not di/dE that is actually recorded, it is more revealing to write

$$\left(\frac{di}{dt} \right)_{\max} = - \frac{\nu F}{RT} \frac{i_d}{4} \frac{dE}{dt} \qquad (10.36)$$

The maximum deflection of the galvanometer or recorder occurs at the half-wave potential. It is proportional to the diffusion current (and hence to the concentration of the electroactive substance responsible for the maximum) and increases as the rate of polarization increases. It is larger for a reversible wave than for an irreversible one involving the same overall number of electrons, and it increases as n or αn_a increases.

The simplest practical technique of recording a derivative voltammogram consists of connecting a condenser having a high capacitance in series with the galvanometer or the resistor across which the recorder is connected. As in differential polarography, difficulty arises when a dropping electrode is used, for heavy damping is required to smooth out the variations of di/dt that accompany the growth and fall of the drops. This introduces a lag into the recording, displaces the peak away from the half-wave potential, and decreases the maximum value of di/dt (187,188). Efficient filtering (179) of the derivative signal is again much to be preferred. Several commercial polarographs are equipped with circuitry for derivative polarography.

Two reversible two-electron waves whose half-wave potentials differ by as little as 50 mv. can be distinguished on an ordinary polarogram only by a trained eye. On a derivative polarogram two rather easily identifiable peaks are obtained. This is very useful for

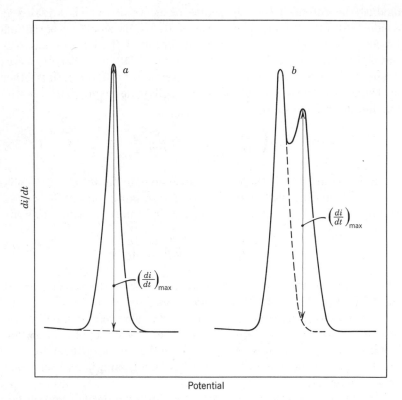

Figure 10.12.   Schematic derivative voltammograms obtained with (a) a single reducible substance, illustrating the measurement of the peak height, and (b) a mixture of two such substances giving overlapping peaks, showing that the more difficultly reducible substance is more readily detected than determined.

qualitative purposes, but is less so for quantitative ones. Peak heights in derivative polarography have to be measured by a base-line technique. If there is only one wave on the polarogram, the derivative curve has the typical shape shown in curve *a* of Fig. 10.12, and the height of the peak can be measured with little trouble or uncertainty. The same shape would be obtained if the wave is well separated from a prior one having a well-defined plateau, as is the zinc wave in Fig. 3.19. Although the peak becomes less and less well defined as the height of the prior wave increases, at any particular ratio of wave heights it is much more likely to yield accurate and precise results than the compensation technique described in Chap. 3 V. Trouble arises when the waves are poorly separated, so that the derivative polarogram has the shape shown in curve *b* of Fig. 10.12. Just as in the similar situation shown in Fig. 8.2, the height of the second peak is difficult to measure, and the error involved in measuring it increases as the wave becomes more irreversible and the width of the peak increases or as the ratio of wave heights becomes more unfavorable. Moreover, the slope of the base line increases as the concentration of the more easily reducible constituent increases, and the result is that the measured peak height for the substance being determined depends not only on its concentration but also on the concentration of the more easily reducible substance. Quantitative measurements are easier than they would be on an ordinary polarogram, but are not as much better as has sometimes been implied.

IX. Cyclic and Pulse Techniques

This section briefly reviews a number of techniques that may be regarded as offshoots of stationary-electrode voltammetry, whose theory was discussed in Chap. 8 I. In oscillographic or cathode-ray polarography (*189–193*), a rapid linear voltage sweep is applied to a dropping electrode near the end of the drop life, and the resulting current–potential curve is displayed on the screen of an oscilloscope. Because the area of the drop is nearly constant during the sweep, the shape of the curve and the height of the peak conform fairly closely to the descriptions given in Chap. 8 I. A rather high sensitivity is attained because of the large rate of change of potential that is needed to minimize variations of drop area and deviations from linear-diffusion equations, but this in turn gives rise to rather large charging currents in accordance with eq. (8.8). If the value of κ were independent of potential and if the area of the drop were truly constant, the charging current would be constant throughout the sweep, and correction or compensation for it would be very simple. As neither of these requirements is quite satisfied, the charging current does vary appreciably, with the effect shown in Fig. 10.13. In theory it would be best to subtract the residual current, measured separately under identical conditions, from the total current at the peak, but what is generally done instead in practice is to measure the vertical distance between the peak of the curve and a linear extrapolation of the

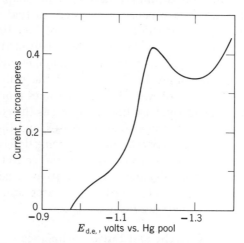

Figure 10.13. Single-sweep oscillographic ("cathode-ray") polarogram of 0.003mM zinc(II) in 1F ammonia–1F ammonium chloride. By permission from *The Principles and Applications of Cathode-Ray Polarography*, by R. C. Rooney, Southern Analytical Ltd., Camberley, Surrey, England, 1962.

residual-current curve that precedes the rising portion of the peak. As the actual course of the residual-current curve cannot be exactly linear, careful calibration with known solutions is essential when small concentrations are in question. The problem is especially severe in the vicinity of the electrocapillary maximum potential, where the variation of κ is most pronounced. Nevertheless, the limit of detection is typically one or even two orders of magnitude lower than in conventional polarography (*192,194*); for the reasons given in Chap. 8 I the improvement is smaller for irreversible waves than for reversible ones. Numerous practical analytical applications of the technique have been made (*195–201*) with dropping electrodes.

The cyclic analog of oscillographic polarography (*202–204*) employs a continuous succession of linear sweeps, each followed by a rapid return to the starting potential—a so-called "sawtooth" wave—and is of much less interest or importance. The aim is to measure the largest peak current obtained during the drop life. Difficulty arises, however, from the fact that the drop time is not reproducible when the sweeps are not synchronized with the formation of the drop. Hence it is necessary to photograph the traces obtained with a number of successive drops and to select only the one showing the largest peak current for measurement, but this is only a partial solution to the problem: the area of the drop at the corresponding instant is equally important and is much more difficult to evaluate precisely. Another difficulty arises with processes so irreversible that the reaction occurring during one sweep is not reversed at the beginning of the next; then the successive sweeps deplete the layer of solution surrounding the drop, and the significance of the maximum peak current becomes uncertain. The problem can be avoided when the backward reaction does occur at not too positive potentials by maintaining the electrode at such a potential for some time, during which the current is not presented to the oscilloscope, between successive sweeps. An interval of 0.02 sec. usually suffices. There is certainly no advantage over the use of a single sweep begun at a precisely predetermined instant after the fall of the preceding drop.

A more interesting technique (*72,205–207*) employs a cyclic triangular wave as shown in Fig. 10.14(c). The forward sweep gives the same curve that would be obtained with a sawtooth wave at the same stage of the drop life. At the start of the reverse sweep dE/dt changes sign and so does the charging current, but the current due to the reduction of the electroactive species remains positive because the potential is still on the plateau of its wave. The faradaic current continues to decay as time goes on. If the electrode reaction is sufficiently fast, the substance formed by reduction during the forward sweep will begin to be reoxidized as the rate of the forward reaction begins to decrease, so that an anodic peak will be obtained in the same range of potentials as the cathodic one. More accurately, the anodic and cathodic half-peak potentials will differ by $56/n$ millivolts, the anodic one being the more negative. This is in accordance with eq. (8.3), which is applicable here although the electrode is spherical because the sweep is so rapid that the diffusion layer is very thin. If the half-reaction is slow, a wave reflecting the cessation of the reduction process will appear during the reverse sweep and will be followed by an anodic peak at a more positive potential; in an extreme case, of course, there may be no anodic peak at all.

Because fast sweeps are employed, many electron-transfer processes fast enough to appear reversible in ordinary polarography will appear to be irreversible in these techniques. As the sweep speed increases, the slowness of the electron-transfer step becomes more and more

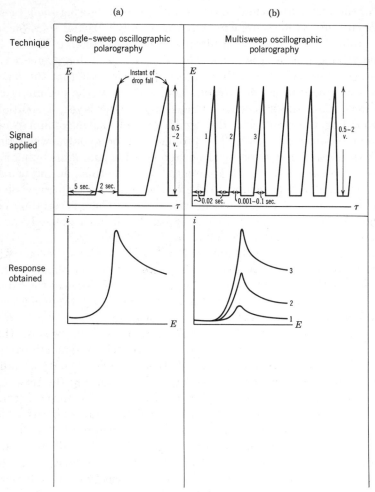

Figure 10.14. Summary of the signals applied and the responses obtained in a number of cyclic and pulse techniques. This figure is continued on the next 5 pages.

pronounced, and the deviations from Nernstian behavior become more marked. On the other hand, the processes discussed in Chap. 4 VI, in which a fast electron-transfer step is followed by a slow chemical transformation of the product into a form that is not electroactive, appear to be irreversible in ordinary polarography because the stable form of the product does not give an anodic wave

(c)   (d)

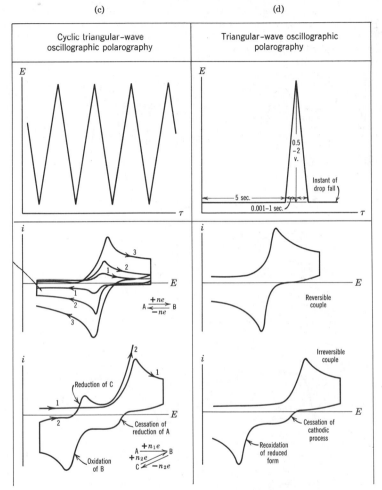

Figure 10.14 *(continued)*. Summary of the signals applied and the responses obtained in a number of cyclic and pulse techniques.

having the same half-wave potential as the cathodic wave of the starting material. If the sweep rate is high, such a process may appear to behave reversibly because the inactivation can then occur to only a limited extent, and the deviations from reversible behavior decrease as the sweep rate increases up to the point where the finite speed of the electron-transfer step becomes perceptible.

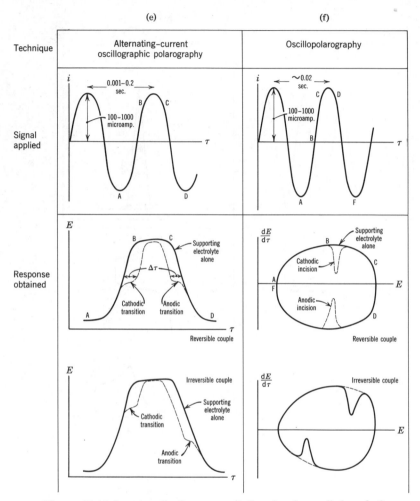

Figure 10.14 (*continued*). Summary of the signals applied and the responses obtained in a number of cyclic and pulse techniques.

For quantitative purposes a cyclic triangular wave suffers from the same disadvantages as a sawtooth when a dropping electrode is used, and a simpler and more easily interpretable curve is obtained with a single triangular impulse initiated at a predetermined instant after the birth of a drop (*208*). The advantage of the cyclic techniques is that a reactive intermediate formed at the drop surface can be

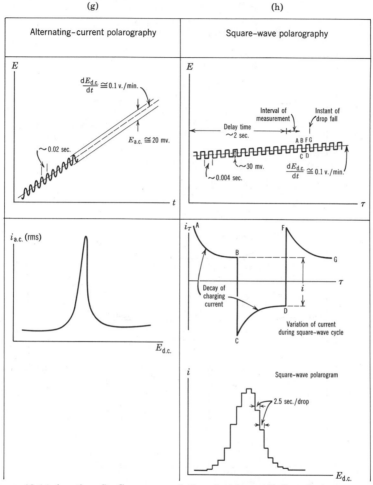

(g)   (h)

| Alternating-current polarography | Square-wave polarography |

Figure 10.14 (*continued*). Summary of the signals applied and the responses obtained in a number of cyclic and pulse techniques.

detected during the second and subsequent sweeps. A single triangular impulse would yield information about the re-oxidation of an intermediate formed during the forward sweep but not about the re-reduction of one formed during the reverse sweep.

The manner in which a polarographic cell responds to the application of an alternating current or voltage depends primarily on the

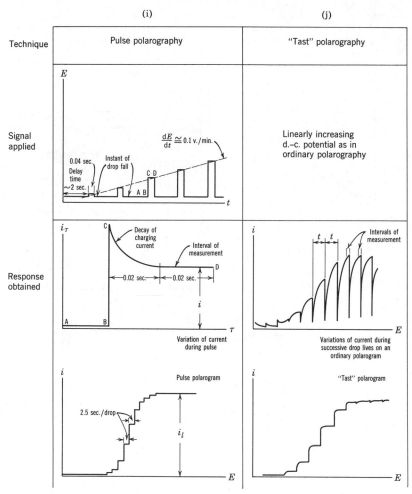

Figure 10.14 (*continued*). Summary of the signals applied and the responses obtained in a number of cyclic and pulse techniques.

amplitude of the stimulus employed. Alternating currents of large amplitude were most systematically investigated by Heyrovský and co-workers (*209–211*). A constant alternating current of the order of 300 μamp. is obtained by applying an alternating voltage of 300 v. across the cell and a 1-megohm resistor in series with it. A d.-c. bias voltage is added to prevent the anodic portion of the a.-c. cycle from

(k)

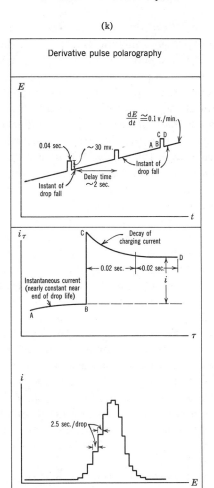

Figure 10.14 (*continued*). Summary of the signals applied and the responses obtained in a number of cyclic and pulse techniques.

driving the electrode to potentials so positive that mercury is oxidized. Square-wave rather than sinusoidal currents may be employed (*212*). In early work the potential of the indicator electrode was presented to the vertical-deflection amplifier of an oscilloscope having a time-based sweep, and the resulting patterns had the shapes illustrated in Fig. 10.14(*e*). To avoid the changes that would result from the growth of the drop, a streaming mercury electrode was employed; other expedients include the use of a hanging drop electrode or a small mercury pool (in which case a larger current would be appropriate) and the application to a dropping electrode of a short train of impulses begun at a precisely predetermined instant after the birth of each drop. As the potential is driven to more negative values during the cathodic half of the cycle, an inflection resembling a chronopotentiometric transition is produced by the reduction of an electroactive species, and the delay $\Delta\tau$ thus produced increases with increasing concentration, although it does not obey eq. (10.13) because the current is not constant during the transition. A similar anodic transition is obtained during the reverse half of the cycle unless the electron-transfer step is extremely irreversible. For a reversible or quasireversible process the cathodic and anodic inflections occur in the same range of potentials and have approximately equal values of $\Delta\tau$, despite what was said in Sec. VII above about the inequality of the transition times in current-reversal chronopotentiometry, because here the reduction is continued for a comparatively long time after the cathodic transition time, and the reduced form continues to accumulate at the electrode surface during this interval. For a quasireversible process the anodic value of $\Delta\tau$ decreases as the frequency of the alternating current decreases because an increasing fraction of the reduced material is transformed into the inactive form. For an irreversible process there is, of course, some difference between the transition potentials, which increases as the value of $k_{s,h}$ decreases. As in chronopotentiometry, and for the same reasons, the inflections become more and more poorly defined as the concentration decreases below roughly 1mM.

Oscillopolarography (*213*) involves the addition of an RC differentiating circuit to obtain a plot of $dE/d\tau$ vs. E instead of one of E vs. τ. During a transition the value of $dE/d\tau$ decreases, passes through a minimum, and then increases again; the transitions appear as incisions, as shown in Fig. 10.14(f). The potential at the peak of the incision, where $dE/d\tau$ is smallest, is very nearly equal to the polarographic half-wave potential. According to eqs. (4.6) and (10.17) the two would be exactly equal for a reversible wave if the current remained constant instead of varying sinusoidally and if the differential capacity of the double layer were independent of potential throughout the transition. For an irreversible process the discrepancy is greater but can still be ignored in view of the rather modest precision that can be attained in measuring the potential at the peak of an incision. For a reversible half-reaction the value of $dE/d\tau$ at the peak of the incision is given approximately by the equation (214–217)

$$\frac{dE}{d\tau} = i\omega^{1/2} \cos \alpha \Big/ \left[\frac{n^2F^2}{4RT} (D_O^{1/2}C_O + D_R^{1/2}C_R) + \kappa\omega^{1/2} \right] \quad (10.32)$$

where ω is the angular frequency and i the amplitude of the alternating current, α is the phase angle at the peak, C_O and C_R are the bulk concentrations of the oxidized and reduced forms of the couple, respectively, and the other symbols have their usual significances. One consequence of this equation is that the depth of the incision is not proportional to the concentration of the substance responsible for it; in analytical applications careful standardization with known solutions is essential. Another is that the conveniently accessible range of concentrations is rather limited: typically, if the concentration is below about $0.1\mathrm{m}M$ the incision is too shallow for precise measurement, while if the concentration exceeds about $1\mathrm{m}M$ the incision is so deep that it is hardly affected by a further increase of concentration. Even within this range the attainable precision is rarely better than $\pm 5\%$, somewhat poorer than can be secured by ordinary polarography.

More important than the analytical applications of the technique are its uses in assessing the reversibilities and elucidating the mechanisms of electrode reactions. As the cathodic and anodic incisions appear at the same potential and have approximately the same depth for reversible processes or for quasireversible ones in which the first- or pseudo-first-order rate constant of the chemical step is much smaller than the frequency of the alternating current, reversibility is easily evaluated. The rates of moderately fast electron-transfer processes can be studied by varying the frequency: for example, the reduction of zinc ion to zinc amalgam appears to be reversible at a frequency around 0.3 sec.$^{-1}$ but displays marked irreversibility when this is increased to 50 sec.$^{-1}$. The application of a single cycle or the use of a streaming mercury electrode provides information about the reversibility of the initial electron-transfer step; as in triangular-wave oscillographic polarography, the use of a dropping or stationary electrode often permits the detection of electroactive intermediates that accumulate at the electrode surface during several cycles of polarization before the one for which the trace is photographed. The shapes of the incisions and the manners in which they are affected by frequency, temperature, and the addition of surface-active agents can be used to distinguish among diffusion-controlled, kinetic, and adsorption processes (*211,218*). The adsorption or desorption of a surface-active substance affects the values of κ in the range of potentials over which it occurs, and thus gives rise to peaks or incisions; this permits the determination of such substances even though they cannot be reduced or oxidized, and it also makes possible studies of their adsorption isotherms (*219*).

Alternating current ("a.-c.") polarography (*220–229a*) consists of superimposing a small alternating voltage, typically having an amplitude of 10 to 20 mv., on a linearly increasing d.-c. potential applied to a polarographic cell, and plotting the alternating current against the d.-c. potential. At the foot of the ordinary polarographic wave the alternating current is entirely due to the charging and discharging of the double layer and is therefore relatively small. On the plateau the electroactive species is consumed as fast as it reaches the electrode surface at any time during the alternating voltage cycle, and the alternating current is again due solely to variations in the potential of the double layer. On the rising part of the wave the alternating current depends on the reversibility of the half-reaction. If the electron-transfer step is instantaneous, a certain equilibrium is attained at the drop surface at an instant when the alternating voltage is zero. As it becomes more negative, the rate of reduction increases rapidly because the d.-c. wave is steep, and at the same time the rate of oxidation decreases rapidly; a large increase of the net cathodic current is obtained. As the instantaneous value of the alternating voltage becomes more positive these changes are reversed and the current becomes much more anodic. The greatest variations of the composition of the layer of solution around the drop occur at the half-wave potential, and consequently the maximum alternating current is observed at that potential. On the other hand, if the process is not perfectly reversible the reduction product will be only partially reoxidized during the anodic half of the cycle; if it is totally irreversible there can be practically no reoxidation at all. In addition, the fact that the slope of the d.-c. wave is smaller causes the cathodic component of the current to vary less during the cycle than it does when the process is reversible. For both of these reasons, the value of the alternating current at the peak is much smaller for irreversible waves than for reversible ones, and this permits the technique [most conveniently in a modified form in which the polarization resistance and the pseudocapacity, which in series constitute the faradaic impedance of the cell, are measured separately by means of an a.-c. bridge (222,230–233)] to be used in studying the rates of quite fast electron-transfer processes. A detailed description of the theory is not possible here; the monograph by Breyer and Bauer (229) and a review by Delahay (234) should be consulted for further information and additional references to the original literature.

From the above summary, however, it is clear that the charging and discharging of the double layer contribute to the current over the entire peak. The limit of detection is, therefore, rarely much below about 0.01mM, though it may be as low as 10^{-4}mM if the electroactive substance is adsorbed onto the electrode surface, as appears to be the case with many organic substances. As in oscillopolarography, the adsorption of a substance like camphor or a long-chain n-alkanol onto the electrode surface over a narrow range of potentials alters the double-layer capacity and gives rise to an a.-c. peak even though the capacity wave on the ordinary polarogram (Chap. 3 XI) may be too small and too drawn out to detect; measurements of such peaks are called "tensammetric" (225,229). The limit of detection can be improved, usually to about 0.001mM, by using an a.-c. bridge (235, 236) or phase-selective circuitry (237) or by measuring the second harmonic (238–241). The "Univector" polarograph (242) manufactured by the Cambridge Instrument Co. Ltd. employs the second of these principles.

Much improvement is effected, though at the cost of much instrumental complexity, by the use of square-wave polarography (243–256). A linearly increasing d.-c. potential is applied to a dropping electrode; on it is superimposed a train of square waves having a frequency of about 225 sec.$^{-1}$ and an amplitude of about 30 mv. On the rising part of the d.-c. wave, the same phenomena occur during the cathodic half of a cycle as occur in a.-c. polarography. However, because the potential is essentially constant during this interval the charging current decays rapidly toward zero, whereas the faradaic component of the increase of current decays much more slowly because the concentration profile previously established in the diffusion layer must be readjusted, and this involves the relatively slow process of mass transfer. When the potential is suddenly changed to a more positive value to initiate the anodic half of a cycle, the anodic charging current decays rapidly, and this decay is followed by an interval during which the change of concentration gradient effected during the cathodic half of the cycle is reversed by the re-oxidation of the reduced species. The difference between the currents flowing near the ends of successive half-cycles during a short interval near the end of the drop life (which must be reproducible from one drop to the next to avoid variations of drop area) is recorded against the d.-c. potential, as shown in Fig. 10.14(h). Because the charging current is negligible during the interval of measurement, the limit of detection is very low: roughly 2×10^{-4}mM for a reversible one-electron process, or 4×10^{-5}mM for a reversible two-electron one. As in a.-c. polarography, the reversibility of the half-reaction is important: for a totally irreversible half-reaction the limit of detection is rarely better than 0.001mM. It is essential for the cell resistance to be as low as possible, for the time required for the charging current to decay to any given fraction of its initial value is proportional to the resistance of the cell circuit. Unless this resistance is very small, the charging current will still be appreciable while the measurement is being made. It is, therefore, necessary to use fairly concentrated supporting electrolytes. Taken together with the very low limit of detection, this means that the problem of reagent purity is far more troublesome than in most polarographic work.

In pulse polarography ($257,258$) a single square-wave voltage impulse having a duration of about 40 msec. is applied to each drop at a predetermined instant after its birth, and the amplitudes of the successive pulses are increased linearly with time. The charging current decays rapidly after the initial change of voltage. Since the duration of the pulse is much longer than in square-wave polarography a much longer time can be allowed for the charging current to decay, and the resistance of the cell is much less important, so that considerably more dilute supporting electrolytes can be employed. The relatively slowly decaying faradaic current that continues to flow during the second 20 msec. of the pulse is recorded against the pulse amplitude. The resulting curve has the same shape as an ordinary polarographic wave, and the limit of detection is improved to a level that is probably of the order of 10^{-5}mM. Especially noteworthy is the fact that the limit of detection must be very nearly the same for irreversible processes as for reversible ones. An important corollary is that the height of the wave, which is the quantity ultimately measured for analytical purposes, is no more sensitive to adventitious traces of surface-active materials than is the case in ordinary polarography.

A very similar effect is obtained in "tast" ("touch") polarography (259–264). A simple linear potential sweep is used, but the current is presented to the recorder only for a short interval just before the fall of each drop, and the recorder pen is then immobilized until the corresponding interval during the life of the next drop. The characteristics of the "tast" polarograph manufactured by Atlas-Werke AG (Bremen, Germany) are summarized in Table 2.1.

Techniques like a.-c. polarography and square-wave polarography, in which the measured response passes through a maximum at a potential on the rising part of the d.-c. wave and then decreases toward zero on the plateau, are able to cope with wave-order problems that would be very difficult to handle in ordinary polarography. In square-wave polarography, for example, it is possible to determine one electroactive substance in the presence of a 10^5-fold larger concentration of another that yields a prior wave. The limit depends on the difference between the half-wave potentials of the two waves and on whether or not they are reversible. At the same time, closely spaced waves are easier to distinguish because the instrumental response to the first may decay considerably before the second begins. These advantages are retained in pulse polarography, although the curves obtained have the same shape as ordinary polarograms, because it is only the difference of current resulting from the application of the pulse that is recorded. With the solution of Fig. 3.19, for example, the pulse polarogram might be obtained by applying pulses rising from a steady applied potential of -0.8 v. vs. S.C.E.; because cadmium ions are already being reduced as rapidly as they reach the electrode surface at this potential, there would be no increase of faradaic current until the reduction of zinc ion began. In "tast" polarography, however, the entire cell current is presented to the recorder, and the zinc wave would again appear as only a small increase of current atop the large cadmium wave. Nevertheless, the situation is less unfavorable in "tast" polarography than in ordinary polarography. As the current does not change very much in the interval during which it is recorded in "tast" polarography, the oscillations are very much smaller than on an ordinary polarogram, so that a much smoother base line is obtained for the extrapolation that must be performed to measure the height of the zinc wave. Moreover, because the current is recorded at the same drop age for every drop, variations of drop time with applied potential are irrelevant, and the distortion thus caused on an ordinary polarogram and shown in curve *b* of Fig. 3.19 would not appear.

A second kind of pulse polarography (*257*) might perhaps be called derivative pulse polarography because it yields curves that are essentially the derivatives of those obtained by the technique previously described. A single square-wave voltage pulse having a duration of about 40 msec. is again applied to each successive drop at a predetermined instant after the fall of its predecessor, but the pulses have a constant amplitude of perhaps 50 mv. and are superimposed on a relatively slow linear d.-c. potential sweep. During the first half of the pulse the charging current decays as described above; during the second half the increase of current is recorded. The resulting increase of faradaic current produced by a fixed change of potential is plotted against the d.-c. potential, and a peak is obtained at the inflection point of the d.-c. or pulse polarogram. The height of the peak is proportional to the slope di/dE of the polarogram, which is described by eq. (10.30). This is smaller for irreversible waves (for which $\nu = \alpha n_a$) than for reversible ones (for which $\nu = n$), and consequently the sensitivity and limit of detection are poorer for irreversible waves. For a substance that undergoes a reversible two-electron reduction the limit of detection is probably of the order of $10^{-6}mM$, roughly an order of magnitude lower than in "ordinary" pulse polarography. On the other hand, increasing-amplitude pulse polarography is better suited to work with irreversible waves because the height of the peak obtained in the derivative technique is affected by any change in the experimental conditions that results in a variation of αn_a.

The characteristics of all of these techniques are briefly summarized for convenient reference in Fig. 10.14.

Instruments for square-wave polarography and for pulse and derivative pulse polarography are commercially available, from Mervyn Instruments (St. Johns, Woking, Surrey, England) and Southern Analytical Ltd. (Camberley, Surrey, England), respectively. The Southern Analytical Ltd. pulse polarograph is distributed in the United States by the Cincinnati Division of the Bendix Corporation. Unfortunately these instruments are necessarily very complex; they are, therefore, very expensive and in addition the time between successive breakdowns is too short to make the use of these techniques feasible as yet except in the very near proximity of a sophisticated instrument-maintenance group.

References

(1) J. J. Lingane, *Electroanalytical Chemistry*, Interscience, New York, 2nd ed., 1958, pp. 351–415.

(2) J. A. Page, in *Handbook of Analytical Chemistry*, L. Meites, ed., McGraw-Hill, New York, 1963, pp. 5–170 to 5–184.

(3) G. A. Rechnitz, *Controlled-Potential Analysis*, Macmillan, New York, 1963; *cf.* also P. F. Lott, *J. Chem. Education*, **42**, A261, A361 (1965).

(4) Ref. 1, pp. 225–228.

(5) L. Meites, *J. Electroanal. Chem.*, **7**, 337 (1964).

(6) A. J. Bard, *Anal. Chem.*, **35**, 1125 (1963).

(7) S. Karp, Ph.D. Thesis, Polytechnic Institute of Brooklyn, 1966.

(8) L. Meites, *Anal. Chem.*, **27**, 1116 (1955).

(9) Y. Israel and L. Meites, *J. Electroanal. Chem.*, **8**, 99 (1964).

(10) Ref. 1, pp. 308–339.

(11) L. Meites, in *Physical Methods of Organic Chemistry* (vol. I of "Technique of Organic Chemistry"), 3rd ed., A. Weissberger, ed., Interscience, New York, 1960, pp. 3281–3333.

(12) L. Meites, *Record Chem. Progress*, **22**, 80 (1961).

(13) J. J. Lingane and L. W. Niedrach, *J. Am. Chem. Soc.*, **71**, 196 (1949).

(14) J. J. Lingane and L. A. Small, *J. Am. Chem. Soc.*, **71**, 973 (1949).

(15) S. A. Moros and L. Meites, *J. Electroanal. Chem.*, **5**, 90 (1963).

(16) C. L. Rulfs and P. J. Elving, *J. Am. Chem. Soc.*, **73**, 3284 (1951).

(17) D. D. DeFord, W. G. Hime, and L. Meites, unpublished work (1955).

(18) G. A. Rechnitz, *Inorg. Chem.*, **1**, 953 (1962).

(19) R. E. Cover and L. Meites, *J. Am. Chem. Soc.*, **83**, 4706 (1961).

(20) J. J. Lingane, C. G. Swain, and M. Fields, *J. Am. Chem. Soc.*, **65**, 1348 (1943).

(21) H. A. Catherino and L. Meites, *Anal. Chim. Acta*, **23**, 57 (1960).

(21a) D. M. King and A. J. Bard, *Anal. Chem.*, **36**, 2351 (1964); *J. Am. Chem. Soc.*, **87**, 419 (1965).

(22) A. Sartori and A. Liberti, *J. Electrochem. Soc.*, **97**, 20 (1950).

(23) P. J. Elving and C. E. Bennett, *J. Am. Chem. Soc.*, **76**, 1412 (1954); *J. Electrochem. Soc.*, **101**, 520 (1954).

(24) P. J. Elving, I. Rosenthal, and A. J. Martin, *J. Am. Chem. Soc.*, **77**, 5218 (1955).

(25) D. L. Smith and P. J. Elving, *J. Am. Chem. Soc.*, **84**, 1312, 2741 (1962).

(26) H. A. Laitinen and T. J. Kneip, *J. Am. Chem. Soc.*, **78**, 736 (1956).

(27) R. I. Gelb and L. Meites, *J. Phys. Chem.*, **68**, 2599 (1964).

(28) L. Meites and S. A. Moros, *Anal. Chem.*, **31**, 23 (1959).

(29) D. H. Geske and A. J. Bard, *J. Phys. Chem.*, **63**, 1057 (1959).

(30) A. J. Bard and J. S. Mayell, *J. Phys. Chem.*, **66**, 2173 (1962).

(31) A. J. Bard and E. Solon, *J. Phys. Chem.*, **67**, 2326 (1963).

(32) L. Meites, *J. Electroanal. Chem.*, **5**, 270 (1963).

(33) S. A. Moros and L. Meites, *J. Electroanal. Chem.*, **5**, 103 (1963).

(34) R. I. Gelb and L. Meites, *J. Phys. Chem.*, **68**, 630 (1964).

(35) G. A. Rechnitz and J. E. McClure, *Talanta*, **10**, 417 (1963); *Anal. Chem.*, **36**, 2287 (1964).
(36) A. C. Testa and W. H. Reinmuth, *J. Am. Chem. Soc.*, **83**, 784 (1961).
(37) G. S. Alberts and I. Shain, *Anal. Chem.*, **35**, 1859 (1963); R. S. Nicholson and I. Shain, *Anal. Chem.*, **37**, 190 (1965).
(38) M. Suzuki, *J. Electrochem. Soc. Japan*, **22**, 112 (1954).
(39) L. Holleck and R. Schindler, *Z. Elektrochem.*, **60**, 1138 (1956).
(40) J. Koutecký, *Collection Czechoslov. Chem. Communs.*, **18**, 183 (1953).
(41) I. Tachi and M. Senda, in *Advances in Polarography*, I. S. Longmuir, ed., Pergamon, London, 1960, Vol. II, p. 454.
(42) J. J. Lingane, *Ind. Eng. Chem., Anal. Ed.*, **18**, 429 (1946).
(43) J. J. Lingane, *J. Am. Chem. Soc.*, **67**, 1916 (1945).
(44) J. A. Page and J. J. Lingane, *Anal. Chim. Acta*, **16**, 175 (1957).
(45) T. Meites and L. Meites, *Anal. Chem.*, **28**, 103 (1956).
(46) G. L. Booman and W. B. Holbrook, *Anal. Chem.*, **31**, 10 (1959).
(47) W. D. Shults and P. F. Thomason, *Anal. Chem.*, **31**, 492 (1959).
(48) L. Meites, *Anal. Chim. Acta*, **18**, 364 (1958).
(49) J. E. Harrar and F. B. Stephens, *J. Electroanal. Chem.*, **3**, 112 (1962).
(50) T. Meites and L. Meites, *Anal. Chem.*, **27**, 1531 (1955).
(51) Y. Israel and L. Meites, in *Handbook of Analytical Chemistry*, L. Meites, ed., McGraw-Hill, New York, 1963, pp. 5–195 to 5–204.
(52) L. Meites, *Anal. Chim. Acta*, **20**, 456 (1959).
(53) M. T. Kelley, H. C. Jones, and D. J. Fisher, *Anal. Chem.*, **31**, 488, 956 (1959); *Talanta*, **6**, 185 (1960).
(54) R. Ammann and J. Desbarres, *Bull. Soc. Chim. France*, 1012 (1962); *J. Electroanal. Chem.*, **4**, 121 (1962).
(55) A. J. Bard and E. Solon, *Anal. Chem.*, **34**, 1181 (1962).
(56) E. N. Wise, *Anal. Chem.*, **34**, 1181 (1962).
(57) M. Spritzer and L. Meites, *Anal. Chim. Acta*, **26**, 58 (1962).
(58) S. Bogan, L. Meites, E. Peters, and J. M. Sturtevant, *J. Am. Chem. Soc.*, **73**, 1584 (1951).
(59) G. A. Gilbert and E. K. Rideal, *Trans. Faraday Soc.*, **47**, 396 (1951).
(60) R. D. Weaver and G. C. Whitnack, *Anal. Chim. Acta*, **18**, 51 (1958).
(61) J. Proszt and L. Poós, *Periodica Polytech.*, **1**, 25 (1957).
(62) T. DeVries and J. L. Kroon, *J. Am. Chem. Soc.*, **75**, 2484 (1953).
(63) R. E. Cover and L. Meites, *Anal. Chim. Acta*, **25**, 93 (1961).
(64) C. N. Reilley and W. W. Porterfield, *Anal. Chem.*, **28**, 443 (1956).
(65) D. J. Rosie and W. D. Cooke, *Anal. Chem.*, **27**, 1360 (1955).
(66) R. Dabard and J. Tirouflet, in *Advances in Polarography*, I. S. Longmuir, ed., Pergamon, London, 1960, Vol. I, p. 291.
(67) D. C. Taylor and D. M. Smith, *Chemist-Analyst*, **53**, 117 (1964).
(68) J. Jordan and R. A. Javick, *Electrochim. Acta*, **6**, 23 (1962).
(69) W. J. Blaedel, C. L. Olson, and L. R. Sharma, *Anal. Chem.*, **35**, 2100 (1963).
(70) H. Berg and H. Kapulla, *Z. Elektrochem.*, **64**, 44 (1960).
(71) J. E. B. Randles, *Trans. Faraday Soc.*, **44**, 322, 327 (1948).
(72) A. Ševčík, *Collection Czechoslov. Chem. Communs.*, **13**, 349 (1949).
(73) A. Blumberg, Ph.D. Thesis, Yale University, 1953.

(74) L. Meites and R. H. Schlossel, *J. Phys. Chem.*, **67**, 2397 (1963).

(75) P. Zuman and J. Krupička, *Collection Czechoslov. Chem. Communs.*, **23**, 598 (1958).

(76) F. C. Snowden and H. T. Page, *Anal. Chem.*, **22**, 969 (1950).

(77) P. Zuman and O. Manoušek, *Collection Czechoslov. Chem. Communs.*, **26**, 2314 (1961).

(78) I. S. Longmuir, *Record Chem. Progress*, **24**, 2 (1963).

(79) J. W. Hamilton and A. L. Tappel, *J. Nutrition*, **79**, 493 (1963).

(80) A. F. Krivis and G. R. Supp, *Anal. Chem.*, **35**, 1411 (1963).

(81) U. R. Evans and L. C. Bannister, *Proc. Roy. Soc.* (London), **A125**, 370 (1929); U. R. Evans and H. A. Miley, *Nature*, **139**, 283 (1937).

(82) W. E. Campbell and U. B. Thomas, *Trans. Electrochem. Soc.*,**76**, 303 (1939).

(83) S. S. Lord, Jr., R. C. O'Neill, and L. B. Rogers, *Anal. Chem.*, **24**, 209 (1952).

(84) M. M. Nicholson, *J. Am. Chem. Soc.*, **79**, 7 (1957).

(85) L. N. Vasileva and E. N. Vinogradova, *Zavodskaya Lab.*, **28**, 1427 (1962).

(86) M. M. Nicholson, *Anal. Chem.*, **32**, 1058 (1960).

(87) I. Shain and S. P. Perone, *Anal. Chem.*, **33**, 325 (1961).

(88) Kh. Z. Brainina, E. M. Royzenblatt, and V. B. Belyavskaya, *Zavodskaya Lab.*, **28**, 1047 (1962).

(88a) S. P. Perone, *Anal. Chem.*, **35**, 2091 (1963); E. S. Jacobs, *ibid.*, **35**, 2112 (1963).

(88b) J. E. Harrar and F. B. Stephens, *J. Electroanal. Chem.*, **3**, 112 (1962); L. R. Duncan, personal communication (1962); A. R. Nisbet and A. J. Bard, *J. Electroanal. Chem.*, **6**, 332 (1963).

(88c) J. W. Bixler and S. Bruckenstein, *Anal. Chem.*, **37**, 791 (1965).

(89) J. G. Nikelly and W. D. Cooke, *Anal. Chem.*, **29**, 933 (1957).

(90) R. D. DeMars and I. Shain, *Anal. Chem.*, **29**, 1825 (1957).

(91) W. Kemula, Z. Kublik, and S. Glodowski, *J. Electroanal. Chem.*, **1**, 91 (1959).

(92) L. Jansovsky, *Chem. Tech.* (*Berlin*), **13**, 519 (1961).

(93) Z. Kublik and S. Glodowski, *Chem. Anal.* (*Warsaw*), **7**, 583 (1962).

(94) H. Specker, G. Schiewe, and H. Trüb, *Z. Anal. Chem.*, **190**, 144 (1962).

(95) A. G. Stromberg, *Zavodskaya Lab.*, **29**, 387 (1963).

(96) W. Kemula, Z. Galus, and Z. Kublik, *Bull. Acad. Polon. Sci., Sér. Sci. Chim.*, **7**, 723 (1959).

(97) R. Neeb, *Z. Anal. Chem.*, **171**, 321, 330 (1959); **180**, 161 (1961).

(98) S. Bruckenstein and T. Nagai, *Anal. Chem.*, **33**, 1201 (1961).

(99) E. Barendrecht, *Chem. Weekblad*, **60**, 345 (1964).

(100) A. S. Russel, P. V. F. Cazelet, and N. M. Irvin, *J. Chem. Soc.*, 841 (1932).

(101) M. T. Kozlovskii and S. P. Buchman, *Izv. Akad. Nauk Kazakh S.S.R., Ser. Khim.*, No. 120, **5**, 14 (1953).

(102) A. I. Zebreva and M. T. Kozlovskii, *Zh. Fiz. Khim.*, **30**, 1553 (1956).

(103) G. N. Babkin and M. T. Kozlovskii, *Izv. Vysshikh Ucheb. Zavdnii, Khim. i Khim. Tekhnol.*, 129 (1958).

(104) W. Kemula, Z. Galus, and Z. Kublik, *Bull. Acad. Polon. Sci., Sér. Sci. Chim.*, **6**, 661 (1958); **7**, 613, 723 (1959); *Nature*, **182**, 1228 (1958).

(105) W. Kemula and Z. Galus, *Bull. Acad. Polon. Sci., Sér. Sci. Chim.*, **7**, 553 (1959); *Roczniki Chem.*, **33**, 1431 (1959); **34**, 251 (1960).

(106) W. Kemula, Z. Kublik, and Z. Galus, *Nature*, **184**, 56 (1959).

(107) F. von Sturm and M. Ressel, *Z. Anal. Chem.*, **186**, 63 (1962).

(108) H. K. Ficker and L. Meites, *Anal. Chim. Acta*, **26**, 172 (1962).

(109) T. L. Marple and L. B. Rogers, *Anal. Chim. Acta*, **11**, 574 (1954).

(110) S. I. Sinyakova and I. V. Markova, *Zavodskaya Lab.*, **27**, 521 (1961).

(111) H. Specker and H. Trüb, *Z. Anal. Chem.*, **186**, 123 (1962).

(112) W. Kemula and S. Glodowski, *Chem. Anal. (Warsaw)*, **8**, 369 (1963).

(113) T. Kuwana and R. N. Adams, *Anal. Chim. Acta*, **20**, 51, 60 (1959).

(114) R. G. Ball, D. L. Manning, and O. Menis, *Anal. Chem.*, **32**, 621 (1960).

(115) Z. Kublik, *Acta Chem. Hung.*, **27**, 79 (1961).

(116) M. Ariel and U. Eisner, *Bull. Res. Council Israel*, Sect. A, **11A**, 184 (1962); *J. Electroanal. Chem.*, **5**, 362 (1963).

(117) M. Ariel, U. Eisner, and S. Gottesfeld, *J. Electroanal. Chem.*, **7**, 307 (1964).

(118) W. Kemula, Z. Kublik, and J. Taraszewska, *Chem. Anal. (Warsaw)*, **8**, 171 (1963).

(119) W. Kemula and Z. Kublik, *Nature*, **189**, 57 (1961).

(120) P. Zuman and M. Březina, *Leybolds Polarogr. Ber.*, **3**, 224 (1955).

(120a) S. Gottesfeld and M. Ariel, *J. Electroanal. Chem.*, **9**, 112 (1965).

(121) Ref. 1, pp. 499–511.

(122) Ref. 1, pp. 528–532.

(123) C. A. Streuli, *Anal. Chem.*, **28**, 130 (1956).

(124) R. B. Hanselman and C. A. Streuli, *Anal. Chem.*, **28**, 916 (1956).

(125) C. A. Streuli, J. J. Cincotta, D. L. Maricle, and K. K. Mead, *Anal. Chem.*, **36**, 1371 (1964).

(126) H. H. Stein, Ph.D. Thesis, Northwestern University, 1956.

(127) B. Miller and D. N. Hume, *Anal. Chem.*, **32**, 524, 764 (1960).

(128) F. A. Leisey, *Anal. Chem.*, **26**, 1607 (1954).

(129) E. Cotlove and H. H. Nishi, *Clin. Chem.*, **7**, 285 (1961).

(130) Ref. 1, pp. 536–616.

(131) P. S. Farrington, in *Handbook of Analytical Chemistry*, L. Meites, ed., McGraw-Hill, New York, 1963, pp. 5–187 to 5–195.

(132) D. L. Maricle, *Anal. Chem.*, **35**, 683 (1963).

(133) Ref. 1, p. 490.

(134) A. J. Fenton and N. H. Furman, *Anal. Chem.*, **29**, 221 (1957).

(135) J. J. Lingane, C. H. Langford, and F. C. Anson, *Anal. Chim. Acta*, **16**, 165 (1957).

(136) J. J. Lingane and J. H. Kennedy, *Anal. Chim. Acta*, **15**, 465 (1956).

(137) R. P. Buck and E. H. Swift, *Anal. Chem.*, **24**, 499 (1952).

(138) W. D. Cooke, C. N. Reilley, and N. H. Furman, *Anal. Chem.*, **24**, 205 (1952).

(139) H. J. S. Sand, *Phil. Mag.*, **1**, 45 (1901).

(140) T. Berzins and P. Delahay, *J. Am. Chem. Soc.*, **75**, 4205 (1953).

(141) C. N. Reilley, G. W. Everett, and R. H. Johns, *Anal. Chem.*, **27**, 483 (1955).

(142) T. Kambara and I. Tachi, *J. Phys. Chem.*, **61**, 1405 (1957).

(143) Z. Karaoglanoff, *Z. Elektrochem.*, **12**, 5 (1906).

(144) P. Delahay and T. Berzins, *J. Am. Chem. Soc.*, **75**, 2486 (1953); *cf.* C. D. Russell and J. M. Peterson, *J. Electroanal. Chem.*, **5**, 467 (1963).

(145) M. D. Morris and J. J. Lingane, *J. Electroanal. Chem.*, **8**, 85 (1964).

(146) L. Gierst, Thesis, University of Brussels, 1952; L. Gierst and A. Juliard, *J. Phys. Chem.*, **57**, 701 (1953).

(147) G. Mamantov and P. Delahay, *J. Am. Chem. Soc.*, **76**, 5323 (1954).

(148) A. J. Bard, *Anal. Chem.*, **33**, 11 (1961); *cf.* also H. B. Mark, Jr., *Anal. Chem.*, **36**, 958 (1964).

(148a) P. J. Lingane, *Anal. Chem.*, **36**, 1723 (1964).

(149) D. G. Davis and J. Ganchoff, *J. Electroanal. Chem.*, **1**, 248 (1960).

(150) M. M. Nicholson and J. H. Karchmer, *Anal. Chem.*, **27**, 1095 (1955).

(151) R. N. Adams, J. B. McClure, and J. H. Morris, *Anal. Chem.*, **30**, 471 (1958).

(152) J. D. Voorhies and N. H. Furman, *Anal. Chem.*, **31**, 381 (1959).

(153) J. J. Lingane, *J. Electroanal. Chem.*, **1**, 379 (1960); *cf.* also D. H. Evans, *Anal. Chem.*, **36**, 2027 (1964).

(154) A. J. Bard, *Anal. Chem.*, **35**, 340 (1963).

(155) I. Senda, *Rev. Polarogr. (Kyoto)*, **4**, 89 (1956).

(156) H. Hurwitz and L. Gierst, *J. Electroanal. Chem.*, **2**, 128 (1961); H. Hurwitz, *ibid.*, **2**, 142, 328 (1961).

(157) R. W. Murray, *Anal. Chem.*, **35**, 1784 (1963); *J. Electroanal. Chem.*, **7**, 242 (1964).

(158) M. D. Morris and J. J. Lingane, *J. Electroanal. Chem.*, **6**, 300 (1963); M. D. Morris, *ibid.*, **8**, 1 (1964).

(159) H. Matsuda, *J. Am. Chem. Soc.*, **82**, 331 (1960).

(160) P. Delahay, C. C. Mattax, and T. Berzins, *J. Am. Chem. Soc.*, **76**, 5319 (1954).

(161) P. Delahay, *New Instrumental Methods in Electrochemistry*, Interscience, New York, 1954, pp. 179–216.

(162) H. Gerischer, *Z. Elektrochem.*, **59**, 604 (1955).

(163) P. Delahay, *Ann. Rev. Phys. Chem.*, **8**, 229 (1957); *Record Chem. Progr.*, **19**, 83 (1958).

(163a) O. Dračka et al., *Collection Czechoslov. Chem. Communs.*, **24**, 3523 (1959); **25**, 323, 338 (1960).

(164) W. H. Reinmuth, *Anal. Chem.*, **32**, 1514 (1960).

(165) P. Delahay and C. C. Mattax, *J. Am. Chem. Soc.*, **76**, 874 (1954).

(166) D. H. Geske, *J. Am. Chem. Soc.*, **81**, 4145 (1959).

(167) O. Dračka, *Collection Czechoslov. Chem. Communs.*, **26**, 2144 (1961).

(168) C. Furlani and G. Morpurgo, *J. Electroanal. Chem.*, **1**, 351 (1960).

(169) R. M. King and C. N. Reilley, *J. Electroanal. Chem.*, **1**, 434 (1960).

(170) A. C. Testa and W. H. Reinmuth, *Anal. Chem.*, **32**, 1512, 1518 (1960); **33**, 1320, 1324 (1961); T. O. Rouse, Ph.D. Thesis, University of Minnesota, 1961.

(171) W. E. Palke, C. D. Russell, and F. C. Anson, *Anal. Chem.*, **34**, 1171 (1962).

(172) H. B. Herman and A. J. Bard, *Anal. Chem.*, **35**, 1121 (1963).

(173) G. Semerano and L. Riccoboni, *Gazz. chim. ital.*, **72**, 297 (1942).

(174) M. B. Neiman, A. V. Ryabov, and E. M. Sheyanova, *Dokl. Akad. Nauk S.S.S.R.*, **68**, 1065 (1949).

(175) E. D. Coleman, U. S. Patent 2,343,885 (1944); O. Kanner and E. D. Coleman, U. S. Patent 2,361,295 (1944).

(176) S. Stankoviansky, *Chem. Zvesti*, **2**, 133 (1948).

(177) V. A. Tsimmergakl, *Zavodskaya Lab.*, **15**, 1370 (1949).

(178) L. Airey and A. A. Smales, *Analyst*, **75**, 287 (1950).

(179) M. T. Kelley and D. J. Fisher, *Anal. Chem.*, **28**, 1130 (1956); **30**, 929 (1958); **31**, 1475 (1959).

(180) E. M. Skobets and N. S. Kavetskii, *Zavodskaya Lab.*, **15**, 1299 (1949).

(181) D. A. Berman, P. R. Saunders, and R. J. Winzler, *Anal. Chem.*, **23**, 1040 (1951).

(182) S. Wolf, *Angew. Chem.*, **72**, 449 (1960).

(183) H. M. Davis and J. E. Seaborn, in *Advances in Polarography*, I. S. Longmuir, ed., Pergamon, London, 1960, Vol. I, p. 239; H. M. Davis and H. I. Shalgosky, *ibid.*, Vol. II, p. 618; H. M. Davis and R. C. Rooney, *J. Polarogr. Soc.*, **8**, 25 (1962).

(184) J. Heyrovský, *Chem. Listy*, **40**, 222 (1946); **43**, 149 (1949); *Analyst*, **72**, 229 (1947); *Anal. Chim. Acta*, **2**, 537 (1948).

(185) M. P. Lévêque and F. Roth, *J. Chim. Phys.*, **46**, 480 (1949).

(186) J. Vogel and J. Říha, *J. Chim. Phys.*, **47**, 5 (1950).

(187) J. J. Lingane and R. Williams, *J. Am. Chem. Soc.*, **74**, 790 (1952).

(188) T. Jäckel, *Z. Anal. Chem.*, **173**, 59 (1960).

(189) J. E. B. Randles, *Trans. Faraday Soc.*, **44**, 344 (1948).

(190) J. E. B. Randles and L. Airey, *Analyst*, **72**, 301 (1950).

(191) F. C. Snowden and H. T. Page, *Anal. Chem.*, **22**, 969 (1950).

(192) H. M. Davis and J. E. Seaborn, *Electronic Eng.*, **26**, 314 (1953).

(193) G. F. Reynolds and H. M. Davis, *Analyst*, **78**, 314 (1953).

(194) D. J. Ferrett, G. W. C. Milner, H. I. Shalgosky, and L. J. Slee, *Analyst*, **81**, 506 (1956).

(195) G. F. Reynolds, H. I. Shalgosky, and T. J. Webber, *Anal. Chim. Acta*, **8**, 558, 564 (1953); **9**, 91 (1953); **10**, 192 (1954).

(196) B. J. McNulty, G. F. Reynolds, and E. A. Terry, *Analyst*, **79**, 190 (1954).

(197) R. C. Rooney, *Analyst*, **83**, 83, 546 (1958); *Talanta*, **2**, 190 (1959).

(198) A. F. Williams and D. Kenyon, *Talanta*, **2**, 79 (1959); **3**, 160 (1959).

(199) J. S. Hetman, *Talanta*, **3**, 127 (1959); **5**, 267 (1960); *Anal. Chem.*, **32**, 1699 (1960); *Anal. Chim. Acta*, **22**, 394 (1960).

(200) E. Booth and E. A. Terry, *Anal. Chim. Acta*, **22**, 82 (1960).

(201) G. F. Reynolds and E. A. Terry, *J. Polarogr. Soc.*, **7**, 2 (1961).

(202) P. Delahay, *J. Phys. & Colloid Chem.*, **54**, 402 (1950).

(203) P. Delahay and G. L. Stiehl, *J. Phys. & Colloid Chem.*, **55**, 570 (1951).

(204) P. Delahay and G. Perkins, *J. Phys. & Colloid Chem.*, **55**, 586 (1951).

(205) R. Bieber and G. Trümpler, *Helv. Chim. Acta*, **30**, 971 (1947).

(206) J. W. Loveland and P. J. Elving, *J. Phys. Chem.*, **56**, 250 (1952).

(207) P. Delahay, *J. Am. Chem. Soc.*, **75**, 1190 (1953).

(208) P. Valenta, *Collection Czechoslov. Chem. Communs.*, **25**, 853 (1960); P. Valenta and J. Volke, *Chem. Listy*, **54**, 1279 (1960).

(*209*) J. Heyrovský and J. Forejt, *Z. Physik. Chem.*, **193**, 77 (1943).
(*210*) J. Heyrovský, F. Sorm, and J. Forejt, *Collection Czechoslov. Chem. Communs.*, **12**, 11 (1947).
(*211*) J. Heyrovský, *Disc. Faraday Soc.*, **1**, 212 (1947).
(*212*) E. Schmidt, *Electrochim. Acta*, **8**, 23 (1963).
(*213*) J. Heyrovský and R. Kalvoda, *Oszillographische Polarographie mit Wechselstrom*, Akademie-Verlag, Berlin, 1960.
(*214*) T. Kambara, *Leybolds Polarogr. Ber.*, **2**, 59 (1954).
(*215*) H. Matsuda, *Z. Elektrochem.*, **60**, 617 (1956).
(*216*) R. Kalvoda and J. Macků, *Collection Czechoslov. Chem. Communs.*, **20**, 254, 257 (1955); **21**, 493 (1956).
(*217*) K. Micka, *Z. Physik. Chem. (Leipzig)*, **206**, 345 (1957).
(*218*) J. Heyrovský, *Collection Czechoslov. Chem. Communs.*, **18**, Suppl. II, 58 (1954).
(*219*) E. Paleček and D. Kaláb, *Chem. Listy*, **57**, 13 (1963).
(*220*) C. MacAleavy, Belgian Patent 443,003 (1941); French Patent 886,848 (1942).
(*221*) B. Breyer and F. Gutmann, *Australian J. Sci.*, **8**, 21, 163 (1945); *Trans. Faraday Soc.*, **42**, 645, 650 (1946); **43**, 785 (1947); *Disc. Faraday Soc.*, **1**, 19 (1947).
(*222*) J. E. B. Randles, *Disc. Faraday Soc.*, **1**, 11 (1947).
(*223*) B. V. Ershler, *Disc. Faraday Soc.*, **1**, 269 (1947); *Zh. Fiz. Khim.*, **22**, 683 (1948).
(*224*) D. C. Grahame, *J. Electrochem. Soc.*, **99**, C370 (1952).
(*225*) B. Breyer and S. Hacobian, *Australian J. Sci. Res.*, **5A**, 500 (1952); *Australian J. Chem.*, **6**, 186 (1953); **7**, 225 (1954); *Anal. Chim. Acta*, **16**, 497 (1957).
(*226*) B. Breyer, *Australian J. Sci.*, **16**, 109 (1953).
(*227*) B. Breyer, H. H. Bauer, and S. Hacobian, *Australian J. Chem.*, **7**, 305 (1954); **8**, 312, 322 (1955).
(*228*) B. Breyer and H. H. Bauer, *Australian J. Chem.*, **8**, 472 (1955); **9**, 1, 437 (1956).
(*229*) B. Breyer and H. H. Bauer, *Alternating Current Polarography and Tensammetry*, Interscience, New York, 1963.
(*229a*) W. L. Underkofler and I. Shain, *Anal. Chem.*, **37**, 218 (1965).
(*230*) J. E. B. Randles, *Trans. Faraday Soc.*, **48**, 828 (1952).
(*231*) J. E. B. Randles and K. W. Somerton, *Trans. Faraday Soc.*, **48**, 937, 951 (1952.)
(*232*) K. J. Vetter, *Z. Physik. Chem.*, **199**, 285 (1952).
(*233*) H. H. Bauer and P. J. Elving, *Anal. Chem.*, **30**, 334, 341 (1958).
(*234*) Ref. 144, pp. 146–178.
(*235*) E. Niki, *Rev. Polarogr. (Kyoto)*, **3**, 75 (1955).
(*236*) T. Takahashi and E. Niki, *Talanta*, **1**, 245 (1958).
(*237*) G. Jessop, British Patent 640,768 (1950).
(*238*) J. van Cakenberghe, *Bull. Soc. Chim. Belges*, **60**, 3 (1951).
(*239*) H. H. Bauer, *J. Electroanal. Chem.*, **1**, 256 (1960).
(*240*) R. Neeb, *Z. Anal. Chem.*, **186**, 53 (1962); **188**, 401 (1962).

(241) D. E. Smith and W. H. Reinmuth, *Anal. Chem.*, **33**, 482 (1962).

(242) J. W. Haves and H. H. Bauer, *J. Electroanal. Chem.*, **3**, 336 (1962).

(243) G. C. Barker and I. L. Jenkins, *Analyst*, **77**, 685 (1952).

(244) J. Koutecký, *Collection Czechoslov. Chem. Communs.*, **21**, 433 (1953).

(245) D. J. Ferrett, G. W. C. Milner, and A. A. Smales, *Analyst*, **79**, 731 (1954).

(246) T. Kambara, *Bull. Chem. Soc. Japan*, **27**, 523 (1954).

(247) D. J. Ferrett and G. W. C. Milner, *Analyst*, **80**, 132 (1955); **81**, 193 (1956).

(248) G. C. Barker, *Anal. Chim. Acta*, **18**, 118 (1958).

(249) H. Matsuda, *Z. Elektrochem.*, **62**, 977 (1958).

(250) R. E. Hamm, *Anal. Chem.*, **30**, 450 (1958).

(251) F. von Sturm, *J. Polarogr. Soc.*, **2**, 28 (1958); *Z. Anal. Chem.*, **166**, 100 (1959); **173**, 11 (1960).

(252) M. Kaukewitsch and F. von Sturm, in *Advances in Polarography*, I. S. Longmuir, ed., Pergamon, London, 1960, Vol. II, p. 551.

(253) H. Schmidt, *Z. Instr.*, **67**, 301 (1959); *Z. Anal. Chem.*, **173**, 73 (1960).

(254) F. von Sturm and M. Ressel, *Microchem. J.*, **5**, 53 (1961); *Z. Anal. Chem.*, **186**, 63 (1962).

(255) B. Ya. Kaplan and I. Sorokovskaya, *Zavodskaya Lab.*, **28**, 1053 (1962).

(256) G. Geerinck, H. Hilderson, C. Van Hulle, and F. Verbeek, *J. Electroanal. Chem.*, **5**, 48 (1963).

(257) G. C. Barker and A. W. Gardner, *Z. Anal. Chem.*, **173**, 79 (1960).

(258) V. I. Boduy, I. V. Kotlova, and U. S. Lyapikov, *Zavodskaya Lab.*, **28**, 1042 (1963).

(259) E. Wåhlin, *Radiometer Polarogr.*, **1**, 113 (1952).

(260) E. Wåhlin and A. Bresle, *Acta Chem. Scand.*, **10**, 935 (1956).

(261) A. Bresle, *Acta Chem. Scand.*, **10**, 943, 947, 951 (1956).

(262) K. Kronenberger, H. Strehlow, and A. W. Elbel, *Leybolds Polarogr. Ber.*, **5**, 62 (1957).

(263) A. W. Elbel, *Z. Anal. Chem.*, **173**, 70 (1960).

(264) P. O. Kane, *J. Polarogr. Soc.*, **8**, 10 (1962).

TROUBLE-SHOOTING IN POLAROGRAPHIC CIRCUITS

Polarographic equipment is sufficiently complex to be prone to a number of troubles. Some of these are subtle enough to escape the notice of the beginner; others can arise in so many different ways that they are difficult to localize. This Appendix is intended to help the beginner to recognize and correct the most common symptoms of trouble in polarographic work. The directions are written for, and the illustrative curves were obtained with, a visible-recording instrument of the resistance-potentiometer type. A few of the directions can be followed only with such instruments, but most are also possible with photographically recording and with manual ones. In applying them to a manual polarograph it is advisable to plot the current–potential curves directly as the data are obtained. The steps are necessarily sequential, and it is, therefore, assumed that any defect found in one step has been corrected and that the curve in question has been re-recorded before the next step is undertaken.

I. Checking the Polarograph

Connect a 1-megohm precision ($\pm 0.1\%$) resistor across the cell terminals of the polarograph, standardize the recorder against its standard cell, and make the following instrument settings:

Initial potential: 0 v. $\Big\}$ or polarization range: 0 to -2 v.
Span potential: -2 v.
Damping: none or minimum
Sensitivity: 2 μamp. full scale
Recorder pen: barely above zero on the chart (mark its position)

and record the current–potential curve. A satisfactory curve is shown in Fig. A-1.

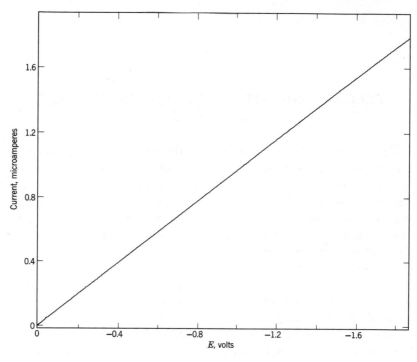

Figure A-1.

A. If the recorder simply draws the horizontal zero-current line [Fig. A-2(a)]:

1. Check the above settings and make sure that the function-selector switch was correctly set, that the bridge-drive motor was operating, and the clutch or other bridge-drive mechanism was engaged. Check the 1-megohm resistor with an ohmmeter.

2. Connect a precision potentiometer or a vacuum-tube or other high-resistance voltmeter across the 1-megohm resistor, set the bridge to 50% of full scale, and read the voltage across the resistor.

a. If this is zero, connect the potentiometer or voltmeter across the output terminals (one end and the slider) of the bridge and read the voltage there.

i. If this is also zero, turn the polarograph off and use an ohmmeter to measure the resistances between the slider and each of the two ends of the bridge.

(a) If either resistance is infinite, the bridge is defective and must be replaced.

(b) If each is 100 ohms or less (but not zero), check the continuity of the wiring between the initial-potential source and the bridge.

(c) If either resistance is zero, check for a short in the appropriate part of the circuit or in the bridge itself.

ii. If the bridge output is 1 v., check the continuity of the wiring in the cell circuit.

b. If the applied potential is 1 v., disconnect the leads to the recorder input. Connect a 1.5-v. dry cell, a 1-megohm resistor, and a 1000-ohm resistor in series and connect the recorder input leads across the 1000-ohm resistor, with due attention to polarity. (If a galvanometer is employed for current measurements, connect its leads to a 1.5-v. dry cell and a 10-megohm resistor in series with it. If a microammeter is employed, connect its leads to a 1.5-v. dry cell and a 1-megohm resistor in series with it.)

i. If no deflection is obtained, the recorder is defective; consult the service manual provided by the manufacturer.

ii. If a deflection corresponding to an input of 1.5 mv. (0.15 μamp. with a galvanometer, or 1.5 μamp. with a microammeter) is obtained, check for a short in the sensitivity and damping switches.

B. If the pen deflects toward negative currents, an odd number of pairs of connections in the cell circuit have the wrong polarity.

C. Examine the initial portion of the curve.

1. If it is linear right from the start but if the zero intercept does not coincide with the zero-current position of the pen [Fig. A-2(b)], the electrical and mechanical zeros of the bridge do not coincide. This can be tested more sensitively

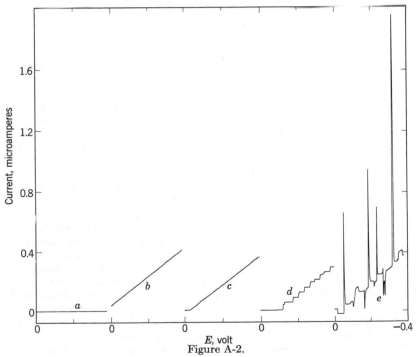

Figure A-2.

by replacing the 1-megohm resistor with a smaller one and re-recording the first part of the curve.

2. If a short horizontal portion precedes the beginning of the rise [Fig. A-2(c)], there is a lag in the bridge drive. In either of these cases, check the mechanical assembly of the bridge and its driving mechanism. If no defect is found, remove the 1-megohm resistor across the cell terminals, connect a precision potentiometer in its place, set the bridge to zero, and measure the potential being applied across the cell terminals. The zero-point error of a typical ten-turn helical potentiometer is of the order of 0.1%, which corresponds to an error of 2 mv. if the span potential is 2 v. Calibration is essential if this error would be significant.

D. Examine the uniformity of the rising portion of the curve. Optimum behavior is reflected by a perfectly smooth straight line. Very small and uniform steps are, however, obtained with many instruments in normal operation. They result from the finite width of the dead zone of the recorder and from the finite resolutions of the bridge and the recorder slide wire.

1. If the curve rises continuously but in a markedly stepwise manner [Fig. A-2(d) is grossly exaggerated for clarity]:

a. Check and, if necessary, advance the setting of the gain control in the recorder amplifier, and check the characteristics of the tubes.

b. Especially if the non-uniformity is confined to certain portions of the curve, clean the recorder slide wire and its sliding contact.

c. Check the mechanical assembly of the pen drive.

d. If a galvanometer is employed for current measurements, check its suspension.

e. Check the uniformity of the bridge-drive mechanism by connecting a vacuum-tube or other high-resistance voltmeter across the output terminals of the bridge and observing the manner in which the voltmeter reading increases as the bridge rotates. If it is noticeably non-uniform, check for slippage and stiction in the mechanism, and especially in the dial attached to the shaft of the bridge.

2. If the curve is grossly irregular [Fig. A-2(e)], disconnect the 1-megohm resistor from the cell terminals and record the curve again. The result should have the shape shown in Fig. A-2(a).

a. If similar irregularities are observed and if a recorder is employed for measurement of the current, short the leads to the recorder input and record the curve once again.

i. If the irregularities still persist, consult the recorder service manual.

ii. If they disappear on shorting the recorder input, they are probably due to a.-c. pickup in the damping network. If they appear only when the 1-megohm resistor is connected across the cell terminals, they probably reflect a.-c. pickup elsewhere in the circuit. Grounding the chassis and operating the polarograph from an isolation transformer are occasionally, but only occasionally, helpful; it is far better to dissect the circuit into its component modules, locate the source of the trouble with the aid of an a.-c. voltmeter or oscilloscope, and repair the defect.

b. If similar irregularities are observed and if a galvanometer is employed for current measurements, disconnect the leads to the galvanometer but do not short them, and observe the behavior of the light spot on open circuit. Short-term irregularities ranging from a barely visible trembling of the spot to sharp random displacements are due to excessive vibration, and can be cured only by vibration-proofing; cf. Chap. 2 V. A slow drift that ceases after the instrument has been turned on for some time is occasionally produced by changes in the position of the filament in the galvanometer lamp as it warms up, and can usually be cured by replacing the bulb. Persistent slow drifts back and forth may be due to drafts. If the spot is stable on open circuit, consult the preceding paragraph.

E. Measure the slope of the curve and compare it with the expected value, which is 1.00 μamp./v. With a few instruments, precise comparison requires that the iR drop across the recorder be taken into account: if, for example, a recorder having a sensitivity of 1 mv./in. gives a pen deflection of 9.0 in. when the nominal applied potential is -1.800 v., the voltage across the 1-megohm resistor is actually only -1.791 v. Whether the slope differs appreciably from the expected

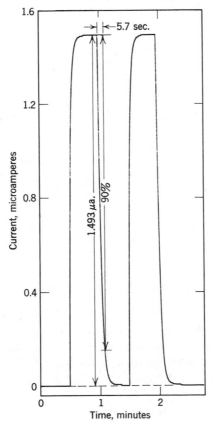

Figure A-3.

value or not, set the bridge to provide approximately −1.5 v. across the cell terminals and the 1-megohm resistor, and measure this voltage E with a precision potentiometer while current flows through the resistor. With the bridge stationary and the chart running continuously, alternately make and break the connection in the cell circuit several times by means of the function-selector switch, waiting each time until a steady pen deflection is obtained. Measure the average deflection (Fig. A-3) and also the period of the recorder (say, for 90% deflection). Compare the current corresponding to this average deflection with the expected value, which is E microamperes.

1. If the slope of the recorded curve disagrees with the expected value while the deflection produced by a known steady current agrees with it, check the span potential, the bridge-drive mechanism, and the linearity of the bridge.

2. If both the slope and the steady deflection are in error and if their errors are the same, check the standard cell in the recorder and the sensitivity resistors.

3. If the slope agrees with the expected value while the steady deflection disagrees with it, there are two compensating errors and all of the above points should be checked.

4. If the period is significantly longer than that specified by the manufacturer, advance the setting of the gain control on the recorder amplifier and check the characteristics of the tubes.

F. Check the action of the upscale and downscale compensation controls, including the smoothness of motion of the pen as they are rotated and the precision with which the pen can be set to any desired point on the chart.

G. The action of the linear compensation circuit, if one is provided, is most easily checked by observing whether it can be set in such a way as to yield a perfectly smooth horizontal line under the conditions used to obtain Fig. A-1.

H. The damping circuit is best checked by repeating the manipulations described in E above at each of the available settings. The steady deflection should be independent of damping and the period should vary in accordance with the manufacturer's specifications.

I. The initial and span potential circuits can be checked by using a precision potentiometer to measure the voltage across the cell terminals with the bridge set at zero and at full scale.

II. Checking the Dropping-Electrode Assembly and the Cell

Dissolve 0.114 g. of $CdCl_2 \cdot 2.5H_2O$ or 0.128 g. of $CdSO_4 \cdot 8/3H_2O$ in 1000 ml. of $1.0F$ hydrochloric acid and mix thoroughly. Clean the solution compartment of the cell, place a suitable volume of this 0.5mM cadmium solution in it, and deaerate for a suitable time. Make the following settings of the polarograph:

Initial potential: +0.1 v.
Span potential: −2 v.
Damping: none or minimum

Sensitivity: 20 μamp. full scale
Recorder pen: about 10% upscale (mark its position)

and set the function-selector switch to "standby." When deaeration is judged to be complete, divert the gas stream so that it passes over the surface of the solution, lower the capillary (with mercury flowing

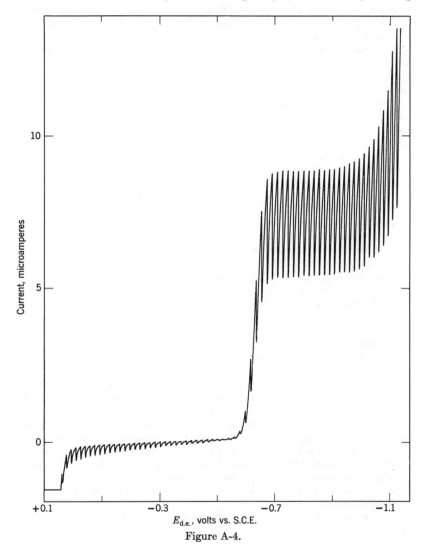

Figure A-4.

through it) into the solution, adjust the height of the mercury reservoir so that the drop time is about 5 sec., and record the polarogram. A satisfactory curve is shown in Fig. A-4.

A. If the recorder simply draws the horizontal zero-current line [Fig. A-2(a)], make sure that mercury is flowing through the capillary. If it is not, replace the capillary and obtain another curve by the same procedure. If it is, disconnect the lead to the dropping electrode and connect it to one end of a piece of platinum or silver wire several inches long. Immerse about an inch of the other end of the wire in the cadmium solution in the cell and record the curve again.

1. If the recorder again draws only the zero-current line, there is a defect either in the cell or in the electrical connections between the cell and the polarograph. Set the bridge to provide about -1.0 v., disconnect the lead wires from the cell, and connect them to a vacuum-tube or other high-resistance voltmeter.

a. If the voltmeter reading is zero, use an ohmmeter to check the continuity of each of the lead wires and to check for a short between them. If the lead wires are found to be satisfactory, check for an open connection or short in the input plug and jack.

b. If the voltmeter reading is -1.0 v., the trouble lies in the cell. If a calomel electrode of the type shown in Fig. 2.15 is used as the reference electrode, check the resistance through the column of mercury and platinum wire in the connecting tube, and make sure that the platinum wire makes contact with the mercury in the calomel electrode. Check for fritted discs that have dried out or become clogged with precipitate, for grease on the central stopcock of a Kalousek cell, and other possible causes of an infinite cell resistance.

2. If measurable currents are obtained, there is a defective connection in the dropping-electrode assembly. Check the connecting tube used to make contact between the lead wire and the mercury in the reservoir, and check for an air bubble in the mercury column, especially in the plug of a stopcock if one is used.

B. Observe the height of the wave. If the sensitivity was incorrectly set, if the value of m is abnormally high or low, or in certain other circumstances, the curve may have one of the forms illustrated in Fig. A-5. The pen may go off scale before the plateau is reached (curve a) if the sensitivity is too high, if m is unusually large, or if the solution is contaminated with other reducible substances; the wave height may be too small for convenient measurement (curve b) if the sensitivity is too low, if m is unusually small, or if the solution or gas stream is contaminated with some substance that removes cadmium ion. An improperly chosen sensitivity causes the oscillations at -0.3 v. to be much wider (as on curve a) or narrower (as on curve b) than they are in Fig. A-4. The value of m may be checked as described in Chap. 2 IV; for typical capillaries it should be between 1 and 2 mg./sec. when t is 5 sec. as prescribed above. The possible presence of contaminants is best checked by discarding the solution after checking it for a possible precipitate, cleaning the cell thoroughly with special care to avoid leaving traces of detergents on its walls, and obtaining the polarogram of a second portion of the cadmium solution.

Obtain a polarogram showing the entire plateau and giving an easily measurable wave height.

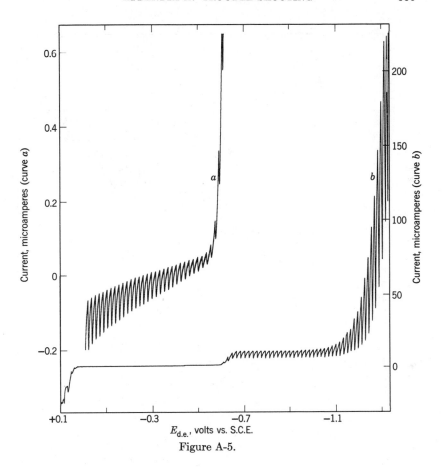

Figure A-5.

C. Observe the half-wave potential and general shape of the wave, and compare the curve with Fig. A-4. If the half-wave potential is around −0.6 v., if the plateau is essentially flat, and if the individual oscillations on the plateau have the shapes shown in Fig. A-4 (where the current increases slowly as a drop grows and decreases rapidly as it falls), go on to **D** below. If the half-wave potential is around −0.2 v., if the plateau has a distinct positive slope, and if the oscillations on the plateau show that the current decreases slowly as a drop grows and increases rapidly at the instant of fall, as in Fig. A-6—all three elements are important—the polarity is reversed. Make sure that the lead wires are properly connected to the cell and to the input terminals of the polarograph. If there is no defect in the external wiring, an even number of pairs of connections in the cell circuit of the polarograph (e.g., both the internal connections to the input jack and the d.-c. leads to the recorder input) must be reversed.

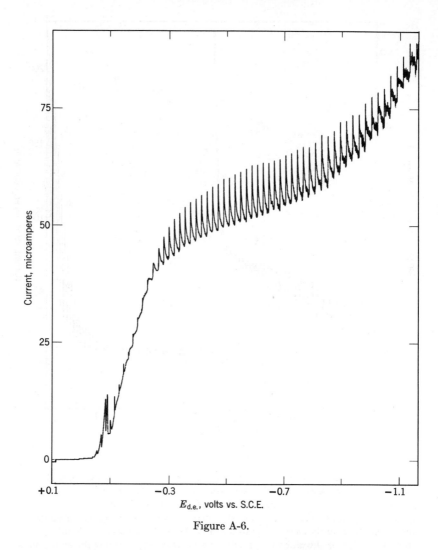

Figure A-6.

D. Irregular oscillations, like those in Fig. A-7, are usually especially prominent on the plateau and reflect vibration or other mechanical causes of malfunction of the dropping electrode. Two extreme kinds of behavior can be distinguished. Stirring of the solution, or vibration of low frequency and large amplitude, tends to increase the current while having little if any visible effect on the drop time, which is reflected on a polarogram by the spacing of the traces due to successive drops. This may be observed at *a* in the figure. On the other hand, a dirty capil-

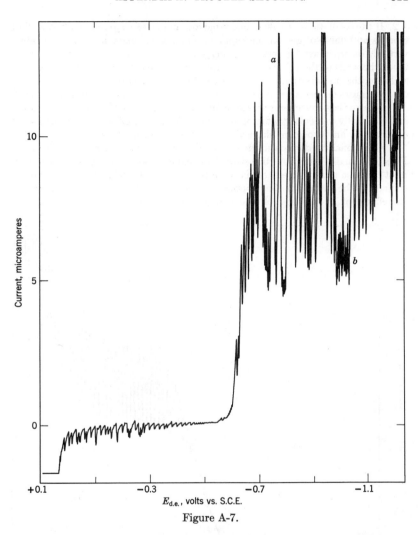

Figure A-7.

lary or one subjected to vibration of relatively high frequency tends to give abnormally small currents and short drop times, as at *b* in the figure.

1. If the oscillations are abnormally wide and the currents abnormally high, make sure that the stream of gas used for deaeration is passed over the surface of the solution while a polarogram is being recorded. Make sure that the dropping-electrode assembly is mounted on a solid support frame and that room or cabinet doors and drawers are not slammed during the recording. Excessive traffic through the polarographic laboratory should not be countenanced.

2. If the oscillations are abnormally narrow and closely spaced, make sure that there is no bubble of gas on the capillary tip. The capillary must be accurately vertical, its tip must be accurately perpendicular to its axis, and it must not touch the walls of the cell. It is often necessary to turn off the thermostat stirrer and any other motors operating near the cell before beginning a recording. If none of these causes is operative, the capillary is probably dirty and should be changed.

3. More or less continuous vibration may also be produced by heavy machinery and by nearby vehicular traffic; in either case it may be difficult or impossible to eliminate by any expedient short of moving the laboratory to a better location.

4. Occasional random oscillations, like the two on the plateau of the wave in Fig. A-8, usually arise from transient disturbances and can be ignored. They are most common at fairly negative potentials and especially when hydrogen is being evolved at the surface of the dropping electrode. In some cases they may reflect the effects of fluctuations of line voltage on the balancing mechanism of the

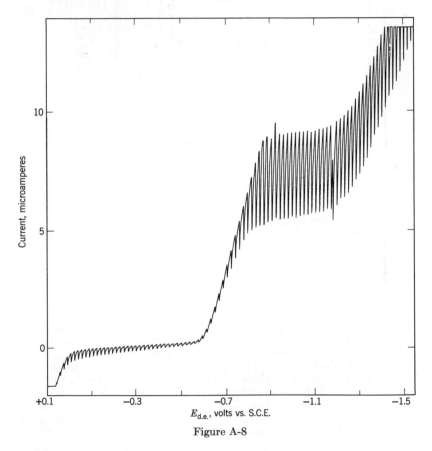

Figure A-8

recorder, and when such fluctuations are known to be severe it may be advantageous to operate the polarograph from a fast-response constant-voltage transformer.

E. Measure the half-wave potential and the value of $E_{3/4} - E_{1/4}$. These should be -0.642 v. vs. S.C.E. and -28 mv., respectively.

1. If the half-wave potential differs appreciably from -0.642 v. while $E_{3/4} - E_{1/4}$ is very nearly -28 mv., check the potential of the reference electrode and the initial potential provided by the polarograph.

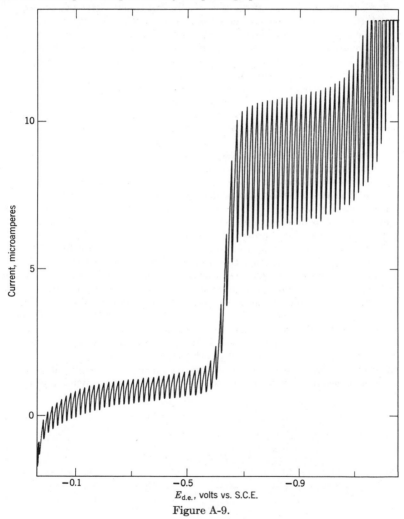

Figure A-9.

2. If the half-wave potential is slightly more negative than -0.642 v. while the value of $E_{3/4} - E_{1/4}$ is slightly more negative than -28 mv., make sure that correction for iR drop through the polarograph has been properly applied. If it has, or

3. If the half-wave potential is considerably more negative than -0.642 v. and the value of $E_{3/4} - E_{1/4}$ is considerably more negative than -28 mv.,

a. Make sure that the potential of the reference electrode is not appreciably altered by the flow of currents as large as 10 or 20 μamps. through it.

b. Check the resistances of the cell and the cell circuit of the polarograph. A high series resistance produces the effects shown in Fig. A-8: the rising part of the wave is drawn out and nearly linear, and the final current rise not only begins at a more negative potential than it should but also has almost exactly the same slope as the rising part of the wave. Figure A-8 was obtained with a resistance of 50,000 ohms in the cell circuit, and thus represents a rather extreme case. As the cell resistance decreases the polarogram becomes less and less easily distinguishable from Fig. A-1. Smaller cell resistances may be identified by seeking a variation of half-wave potential with the concentration of cadmium ion, as described on page 70, or by constructing a plot of $E_{d.e.}$ versus log $i/(i_d - i)$, which will resemble Figure 4.5a if the cell resistance is appreciable.

4. Discrepancies between the observed and expected values may also be produced by traces of electroactive and surface-active impurities.

F. Observe the current at -0.3 v. vs. S.C.E. It should be slightly negative and the widths of the oscillations should decrease appreciably as the foot of the wave is approached: these points are most clearly illustrated by Fig. A-5(a). If the current at -0.3 v. is positive and if the widths of the oscillations in this region are practically independent of potential, as in Fig. A-9, the solution is contaminated with an easily reducible impurity, probably oxygen. This can usually be removed by longer deaeration (note that these observations do not constitute a sensitive test for oxygen in the gas stream); if it cannot, there may be a leak in the gas line or it may be necessary to use purer gas or to introduce a purification train, especially in trace analysis and other work with very dilute solutions or solutions giving anodic waves. Oxygen may be entering the cell while the polarogram is being recorded; this can be checked by recording a current–time curve at -0.3 v., beginning immediately after the flow of inert gas through the solution is stopped. The behavior shown by Fig. A-9 is also produced by mercury(I) compounds adsorbed onto the cell walls during earlier experiments or formed by air-oxidation of metallic mercury present in the cell when the cadmium solution is added.

APPENDIX B

POLAROGRAPHIC CHARACTERISTICS OF INORGANIC SUBSTANCES

The tables in this Appendix contain approximately half of the information that is available on the polarographic behaviors of metal ions and other inorganic substances in aqueous supporting electrolytes. Table B-1 includes data on the ions and compounds of non-metallic elements and the ions of the alkali, alkaline earth, and several other metals whose behaviors in complexing media are uninteresting or little known. Table B-2 gives data on other metal ions in a fairly large number of supporting electrolytes containing different complexing agents. Table B-3 is an index intended to facilitate the location of the data given for each of the substances listed in Tables B-1 and B-2.

This is not a complete compilation. It omits non-aqueous media, numerous unusual oxidation states of uncommon elements, many supporting electrolytes that seem unlikely to prove interesting or advantageous in practical work, and many isolated data and data of dubious validity. A more comprehensive collection of reliable data, accompanied by a number of references to the original literature, is given in the *Handbook of Analytical Chemistry*, L. Meites, ed., McGraw-Hill, New York, 1963, pp. 5-53 through 5-103.

Table B-1

Polarographic Characteristics of the Ions and Compounds of Non-metallic Elements and of Some Metal Ions

The first column of this table gives the formula or oxidation state of the electroactive substance. The ions and compounds of different elements are arranged in the alphabetical order of the symbols of the elements; for example, magnesium ion precedes hydrazine because Mg precedes N. The ions and compounds of any one element are arranged in the order of increasing oxidation number of that element; thus hydrazine precedes hydroxylamine because the oxidation number of nitrogen is lower in hydrazine than it is in hydroxylamine.

The second column gives the composition of the supporting electrolyte, including information regarding maximum suppressors. Concentrations of maximum suppressors are given in thousandths of a per cent (mg./100 ml.); thus "0.5

methylene blue" means "0.0005% methylene blue." The symbols "T" and "G" denote Triton X-100 and gelatin, respectively, so that "2T" means "0.002% Triton X-100."

The third column gives the half-wave potential, in volts, versus the saturated calomel electrode. All data in this table pertain to a temperature of 25°C. except as otherwise specified in the seventh column. A half-wave potential enclosed in parentheses is the half-wave potential of an anodic wave. The symbol ">0" means that the wave rises from zero applied e.m.f., as described on page 159. "NR" (not reducible) means that neither a cathodic nor an anodic wave is obtained, while "NO" (not oxidizable) means that no anodic wave is obtained but carries no implication regarding the presence or absence of a cathodic wave. The symbol "i" following a half-wave potential means that the wave is ill-defined: because of either irregularities on the plateau or the proximity of the wave to the final current rise or to a following wave, the accurate measurement of the wave height is virtually impossible. A wave that is ill-defined for any of these reasons except the last one usually prevents the accurate measurement of the height of a subsequent wave due to another substance, even though that substance would give a well-defined wave if it were present alone. The symbol "w", on the other hand, means that the wave is well-defined: its plateau is so long, so regular, and so nearly parallel to the residual-current curve that its height or the height of a subsequent wave can be easily and accurately measured. The symbols "fi" and "fw" mean "fairly ill-defined" and "fairly well-defined", respectively, and represent the subjective judgment of either the original author or the present compiler.

The fourth column gives the value of the diffusion current constant I ($= i_d/Cm^{2/3}t^{1/6}$) in microamperes/millimole/liter/mg.$^{2/3}$ sec.$^{-1/2}$. The symbol "I" means that the wave height decreases on standing, while "D" means that it decreases; in either of these cases the numerical value is necessarily only approximate.

The fifth column gives the value of $E_{3/4} - E_{1/4}$ in millivolts. Some of the values in this column were calculated from the reported slopes of log plots, while others were calculated from the reported values of αn_a for irreversible waves. A value in brackets is the theoretical value for a reversible wave, and the brackets signify that the wave was judged to be reversible by the original author but that a numerical value was not given. Often, for want of quantitative data, the term "irr." is used in this column as a guide to possible wave-separation problems. It signifies that the wave is more drawn out than it would be if it were reversible, and is sometimes preceded by "sl." (slightly) or "v." (very) as a crude qualitative description of its slope.

The sixth column gives the formula or oxidation state of the product of the half-reaction at the dropping electrode, and is also used to identify catalytic waves. Thus, the entry "0" would mean that the reduction or oxidation yielded the elemental state as the chief or only product. Catalytic processes are identified by the symbol "c" and the formula of either the product of the catalytic reaction if it is known with reasonable certainty or, if it is not, the substance that is catalytically reduced. Thus the entry "c H_2" would signify that the wave was due to the catalytic evolution of hydrogen, while "III c $ClO_3^- \rightarrow$" would mean that the reduction of the electroactive substance to the +3 state was accompanied by catalytic reduction of chlorate to an unknown product.

Remarks are given in the seventh column.

In the third through seventh columns, data on multiple waves are denoted by slanting lines between two or more values in the same column. The most positive half-wave potential is always given first in the third column, then the next most positive one, and so on, and the same order is preserved in the columns that follow. For example, the entry

$E_{1/2}$	I	$E_{3/4} - E_{1/4}$	Product
(-0.10) i$/-1.20$ w	$-1.8/3.6$	$-/-50$	VI/III

would mean that there are two waves: an ill-defined anodic wave and a well-defined cathodic one. The anodic wave has a half-wave potential of -0.10 v. vs. S.C.E. and a diffusion current constant of -1.8; the value of $E_{3/4} - E_{1/4}$ is unavailable, but the wave represents oxidation to the $+6$ state. For the cathodic wave $E_{1/2} = -1.20$ v. vs. S.C.E., $I = 3.6$, $E_{3/4} - E_{1/4} = -50$ millivolts, and the reduction proceeds to the $+3$ state.

When multiple waves appear, the values of I given in the fourth column are always for individual waves unless they are followed by the symbol "T". Thus, the entry

$E_{1/2}$	I
-0.80 w$/-1.20$ w	$1.51/1.49$

would mean that the diffusion current constant of the second wave (for which $E_{1/2} = -1.20$ v.) was 1.49 when its diffusion current was measured from the plateau of the first wave. Its total diffusion current constant, obtained by measuring the height of its plateau above the residual-current curve, can be calculated by adding 1.49 to the sum of the values for all of the preceding cathodic waves, and in this case would be $1.49 + 1.51 = 3.00$. When multiple anodic waves appear on a single polarogram, the first anodic wave is the one having the most negative half-wave potential, and is therefore the last anodic wave listed. For example, the entry

$E_{1/2}$	I
$(-0.30)/(-0.60)$	$-3.2/-1.6$

would mean that the total diffusion current constant of the second anodic wave (for which $E_{1/2} = -0.30$ v.) was $-3.2 + (-1.6) = -4.8$.

When two waves are very closely spaced, the height of the first is difficult to measure, and so is the difference between its height and the total height of the wave that follows it. The individual diffusion current constants of both waves are uncertain in such cases, and total diffusion current constants are therefore often given and are identified by the symbol "T." In the entry

$E_{1/2}$	I
-0.80 i$/-1.00$ w	$1.6/3.31$ T

the value 3.31 pertains to the total height of the second wave, measured from the residual-current curve. The individual diffusion current constant of the second wave, measured from the ill-defined plateau of the first wave, would be approximately $3.31 - 1.6 = 1.7$.

TABLE B-1.

Polarographic Characteristics of the Ions and Compounds of Non-metallic Elements and of Some Metal Ions (*continued*)

Substance	Supporting electrolyte	$E_{1/2}$, v. vs. S.C.E.	I	$E_{3/4} - E_{1/4}$, mv.	Product	Remarks
Al(III)	0.1F KCl or LiCl, 10G	−1.70 w	4.63	−44	$Al(OH)_3 + H_2$	
	Alkaline and complexing solutions	NR				
	0.2F NaOAc, pH 4.7, excess Pontachrome Violet SW	−0.53 w	5.09	—	—	For excess dye $E_{1/2}$ = −0.34 v.
	0.6F NaOAc, pH 4.6, excess Superchrome Garnet Y	−0.45 w	—	—	—	For excess dye $E_{1/2}$ = −0.20 v.
BH_4^-	pH >9	(+0.105 − 0.013 pH) w	−26.0	irr.	BO_2^-	fi in $MgCl_2$
Ba^{++}	0.05F $CaCl_2$ or 0.1F Me_4NCl	−1.940 w	3.57	—	0	Preceded by H^+ wave at −1.4 v.
Be^{++}	Pure $BeCl_2$ or $BeSO_4$ solutions	ca. −1.8 fi	—	—	$Be(OH)_2 + H_2(?)$	
Br^-	0.1F KNO_3	(+0.12) w	—	—	Hg_2Br_2	1mM Br^-; adsorption wave at higher concentrations
Br_2	Acidic solutions	>0	—	—	Br^-	
BrO_3^-	0.1F H_2SO_4, 0.2F KNO_3	−0.41 w	—	irr.	Br^-	
	0.1F $CaCl_2$	−1.51 w	—	irr.	Br^-	
	1F $CaCl_2$	−0.94 w	—	irr.	Br^-	
	1F KCl	−1.17 w	—	irr.	Br^-	
	0.1F KOH	ca. −1.7	—	irr.	Br^-	
CN^-	0.1F KOH	(−0.36) w	−3.0	—	$Hg(CN)_2$	1mM CN^-
CNO^-	Alkaline solutions	NR				
CNS^-	0.1F KNO_3	(+0.18)	—	—	$Hg_2(CNS)_2$	1mM CNS^-
	1F $NaClO_4$	(+0.208)	—	−53	$Hg_2(CNS)_2$	1mM CNS^-
C_2N_2	0.1F NaOAc	−1.2/−1.55	−/−I	−/−	CN^-/−	2nd wave due to $CO(NH_2)COOH$ formed by hydrolysis
	Strongly acidic, alkaline, or KCN solutions	NR				
CNBr	0.1F H_2SO_4	−0.26	—	—	$HCN + Br^-$	
	0.18F NH_3 + NH_4Cl, pH 9.0	−0.31	—	—	$HCN + Br^-$	
	1F Me_4NBr	−2.16 fi	—	irr.	HCOOH	
CO_2	Dilute KCl or NaOH	>0	—	—	CO_3^-	
$C_2O_6^-$	0.1F Me_4NCl or Et_4NI	−2.22	3.39	[−28]	CO_3^-	
Ca^{++}	0.1F KNO_3	(+0.25) w	—	—	0	La^{+++} or Ba^{++} suppresses maximum
Cl^-	Acidic solutions	>0	—	—	Hg_2Cl_2	1mM Cl^-; i above 2mM
Cl_2			—	—	Cl^-	

Species	Supporting electrolyte	$E_{1/2}$			Product	Remarks
ClO^-	0.1F KNO_3, pH 9.8	+0.10 w	irr.	—		Cl^-
ClO_2^-	0.1F HOAc, 0.1F NaOAc, pH 4.5	−0.35 w	irr.	—		Cl^-
ClO_3^-	1F NaOH	−1.0	irr.	—		Cl^-
	Neutral or acidic solutions	NR				
	6–12F HCl	>0	—	8 D		Cl^- ; Due to Cl_2
	3F HCl, 0.05M Fe^{++}	>0	—	8.77		Fe^{++} ; Due to Fe^{+++}
ClO_4^-	All supporting electrolytes	NR				
Cs^+	0.1F Et_4NOH	−2.09	—	—		0
Dy^{+++}	0.1F LiCl, pH 3.0, 10G	−1.80 fw/−2.00 i	irr./−	3.67/varies		$Dy(OH)_3 + H_2/Dy(OH)_3 \rightarrow H_2$
F^-	All supporting electrolytes	NR				
$Fe(CN)_6^{-4}$	0.05F H_2SO_4	(+0.28)/(+0.20)/(+0.05)	−/−/−	−/−/−		$Fe(CN)_6^{-3}/-/-$; 1st wave is an adsorption wave
$Fe(CN)_6^{-3}$	0.1F KCl, 9G	>0 w	—	1.79		$Fe(CN)_6^{-4}$
Gd^{+++}	0.1F KCl or LiCl, pH 2.9, 10G	−1.82 fw	irr.	3.7		$Gd(OH)_3 + H_2$
H^+	0.1–0.5F KCl, LiCl, or $NaClO_4$	−1.58 w	−110	5.60		H_2
	10F KCNS	−1.13 w	irr.	—		H_2
Hf(IV)	All supporting electrolytes	NR				
Hg_2^{++}	0.1F HNO_3, 1 tropeolin 00	>0	—	3.68		0
Hg^{++}	$HClO_4$, $NaClO_4$, and many others	>0	—	—		0
	0.1F HNO_3, 1 tropeolin 00	>0	—	3.48		0
	$HClO_4$, $NaClO_4$, KCN, and many others	>0	—	—		0
I^-	0.1F KNO_3	(−0.03) fi	—	—		Hg_2I_2 ; 1mM I^-; w below 0.5mM
IO^-	4F KOH, 0.05F KI	>0	−D	—		I^-
IO_3^-	ca. 0.1F $HClO_4$, pH 0.90	−0.04 w	−125	—		I^-
	0.1F HCl, 0.1F KCl	—	—	12.04		I^-
	0.1F biphthalate, 0.1F KCl, pH 3.2	−0.31	−110	—		I^-
	0.1F acetate, 0.1F KCl, pH 4.9	−0.50	−110	—		I^-
	0.2F phosphate, pH 6.4	−0.79	—	—		I^-
	0.05F $Na_2B_4O_7$, 0.1F KCl, pH 9.2	−1.20	−100	—		I^-
	0.1F NaOH, 0.1F KCl	−1.21	−80	—		I^-
IO_4^-	1F H_2SO_4, 0.16F K_2SO_4, 10G	>0/−0.12	−/ca. −160	−/−		IO_3^-/I^-
K^+	0.1F Et_4NOH in 50% EtOH	−2.10	[−56]	1.69		0
La^{+++}	0.1F LiCl, pH 2.8, 10G	−1.91	—	—		$La(OH)_3 + H_2$
Li^+	0.1F Et_4NOH in 50% EtOH	−2.31	[−56]	1.16		0
Lu^{+++}	0.1F LiCl, pH 2.85, 10G	−1.79	—	—		$Lu(OH)_3 + H_2$
Mg^{++}	0.1F Me_4NCl	−2.3 i	—	—		$0 + H_2$
NH_3	0.1F Me_4NI, 0.05F Me_4NOH, pH 12.7	−2.25	−51	2.48		—

(continued)

TABLE B-1 (continued)

Substance	Supporting electrolyte	$E_{1/2}$, v. vs. S.C.E.	I	$E_{3/4} - E_{1/4}$, mv.	Product	Remarks
NH_4^+	0.1F Me$_4$NBr	−2.21	—	—	$NH_4(Hg)_x$	
$N(CH_3)_4^+$	None	NR				
$N(C_2H_5)_4^+$	Dilute Me$_4$NBr	−2.67	—	—		
$N(n\text{-}C_3H_9)_4^+$	Dilute Me$_4$NBr	−2.57	—	—		
N_2H_4	4F NaOH	(−0.334) w	−6.9		N_2	
	Various buffers, pH 9–13	(+0.590 − 0.063 pH)		+55	N_2	
NH_2OH	1F NaOH	(−0.43) w	—	+55	N_2(?)	
	0.1F KCl, NH$_4$Cl, or tartaric acid	NR		irr.		
N_3^-	0.1F KNO$_3$	(+0.25)	—	—	$Hg_2(N_3)_2$	1mM N_3^-
HN_3	15F H$_2$SO$_4$	−0.68 w	—	−135	—	$n = 1$
NO	Dilute HCl	−0.9	—	—	—	Probably due to HNO$_2$
HNO_2	0.1F H$_2$SO$_4$, 0.2F Na$_2$SO$_4$	−0.98	—	—	—	
	0.1F KCl, 0.01F HCl, 0.2mF UO$_2$(OAc)$_2$	−1.0 w	7.45	ca. −70	U(III), c HNO$_2 \rightarrow$ NH$_2$OH + other products	
NO_3^-	0.1F CeCl$_3$	−1.60 w	ca. 15	−5	NH_4^+ + NH$_2$OH	
	0.04F LaCl$_3$	−1.58 w	—	−5		
	0.1F KCl, 0.01F HCl, 0.2mF UO$_2$(OAc)$_2$	−0.95 w	13.8	ca. −60	U(III), c NO$_3^- \rightarrow$ 75% NH$_2$OH + other products	
Na^+	0.1F Et$_4$NOH in 50% EtOH	−2.07	1.40	[−56]	0	
Nd^{+++}	0.1F LiCl or Me$_4$NI, 0.002F H$_2$SO$_4$, 10G	−1.83	4.4		Nd(OH)$_3$ + H$_2$	
OH^-	0.1F KNO$_3$	(+0.08) w	—	ca. −220	HgO	1mM OH$^-$
H_2O_2	Various buffers, pH 2–10	−0.94 w	—	[+28]/ca. −200 O$_2$/H$_2$O	H$_2$O	
	0.1F NaOH	(−0.18)/−1.0	−/−			
O_2	0.1F KCl or KNO$_3$	−0.05 w/−0.9 w	6.22/6.1	ca. −80/ca. −200	H$_2$O$_2$/H$_2$O	
	7.3F (42%) H$_3$PO$_4$	−0.23/−0.64	−/−		H$_2$O$_2$/H$_2$O	
	Phosphate–citrate buffer, pH 7	−0.02/−1.0	−/−		H$_2$O$_2$/H$_2$O	
	0.1F NaOH	−0.18/−1.0	−/−	[−28]/−	H$_2$O$_2$/H$_2$O	
Pr^{+++}	0.1F LiCl, 10G	−1.80	3.59		Pr(OH)$_3$ + H$_2$	
	0.1F Me$_4$NCl, 10G	−1.86	3.47		Pr(OH)$_3$ + H$_2$	

Species	Supporting electrolyte	$E_{1/2}$	i_d/C	n	Electrode product	Notes
Ra^{++}	Dilute KCl	−1.84 fw	—		0	
Rb^+	0.1F Me$_4$NOH	−2.03	—		0	
S^-	0.1F NaOH or KOH	(−0.76) w	—		HgS	1mM S^-
S	1.2F pyridine, 0.06F HCl in MeOH	(−0.50) w	5.69		H_2S	
$S_2O_3^-$	0.1F KNO$_3$	(−0.14)	—		$Hg(S_2O_3)_2^-$	1mM $S_2O_3^-$
$S_4O_6^-$	Phosphate buffers, pH 1–8, 0.001% quinoline	(−0.26)	—	irr.	$S_2O_3^-$?	
$S_2O_4^-$	0.5F (NH$_4$)$_2$HPO$_4$, 1F NH$_3$, 10G	(−0.43)	−4.09		SO_2^-	
SO_2	0.1F HCl or HNO$_3$	−0.37 w	5.49	ca. −35	H_2SO_2	
SO_3^-	0.05F phosphate, pH 6.0, 0.1F KNO$_3$	−0.68/−1.23	−/−	irr./irr.	$S_2O_4^-/SO_3^-$	
$S_2O_6^-$	0.1F KNO$_3$	(+0.01)	—	—	$Hg(SO_3)_2^-$	No cathodic wave at pH ≥ 7
SO_4^-	0.1F KCl or 0.05F BaCl$_2$	NR				
$S_2O_8^-$	All supporting electrolytes	NR				
	Dilute KCl or NaClO$_4$	>0	—	—	SO_4^-	Broad minimum around −1 v.
Sc^{+++}	0.1F KCl (or LiCl), trace HCl	−1.80	—	irr.	$Sc(OH)_3 + H_2$	
Sm^{+++}	0.1F Me$_4$NI, 0.5mF H$_2$SO$_4$, 10G	−1.80/−1.96	3.85/varies	−/−	?/?	
Sr^{++}	0.1F Et$_4$NI	−2.11	3.46	—	0	
Ta(V)	Strongly alkaline solutions or solutions of hydrochloric, citric, gluconic, lactic, oxalic, or tartaric acid	NR				
Tc(VII)	0.5F KCl, 0.01F HCl, pH 2	−0.14/−0.91/−1.12	11.9/−/−	−/−/−	III/−/−	
	0.15F Na$_2$P$_2$O$_7$, 0.3F NH$_4$OAc, 0.6F HOAc, pH 4.7	−0.47	—	III	V/IV/c	
	0.25F K$_2$SO$_4$, 0.1F KOH, pH 13	−0.81/−1.02/−1.60	6.32/3.50/−	−/−/−		
Th(IV)	1F LiCl, 10G	−1.27	varies	irr.	$c \to H_2$	
	0.1F KNaTart, pH 12.0, 0.5mM Solochrome Violet RS, 0.002% methyl cellulose	−1.07 vs. Hg pool				For excess dye $E_{1/2} = -0.62$ v. vs. Hg pool
Zr(IV)	0.1F KCl, pH 3	−1.65	—	—	$Zr(OH)_x + H_2$ (?)	

TABLE B-2

Polarographic Characteristics of Common Metal Ions in Various Supporting Electrolytes

This table summarizes the polarographic characteristics of a large number of common metal ions in approximately three dozen supporting electrolytes. Preference has been given to supporting electrolytes that have been systematically investigated, because these are by far the most useful in practical analysis. The composition of each supporting electrolyte is given in boldface type across the page. The supporting electrolytes are listed in the alphabetical order of the "principal" complexing agent, so that, for example, solutions containing acetate precede those containing ammonia. Different supporting electrolytes containing the same principal complexing agent are arranged in order of increasing pH value or in order of increasing concentration of that complexing agent.

Under each supporting electrolyte the electroactive substances are arranged in the alphabetical order of their chemical symbols; different ions of the same element are arranged in the order of increasing oxidation number.

A few data are included that were obtained in supporting electrolytes similar to, but not identical with, those listed. Information on the compositions of these media is given in the last column, under "Remarks," and this column also contains information about maximum suppressors in the same form that was employed in Table B-1.

The terms "low solubility" and "limited solubility" are used to aid in the interpretation of the data and to provide warnings of solubility problems that may arise in practical work. The former means that the solubility is less than perhaps $0.02 \mathrm{m}M$; when it accompanies the entry "NR" in the second column it implies that precipitation is so nearly quantitative that no wave has been detected. The latter means that the solubility is less than perhaps $0.5 \mathrm{m}M$.

In all other respects the arrangement of the table and the symbols employed in it are identical with those described in the introduction to Table B-1.

TABLE B-2 (*continued*)

Substance	$E_{1/2}$, v. vs. S.C.E.	I	$E_{3/4} - E_{1/4}$, mv.	Product	Remarks
	2F HOAc, 2F NH₄OAc, 0.01% gelatin				
Ag(I)	>0 w	—	—	0	
As(III)	−0.92 i	—	—	0	
As(V)	NR				
Au(I)	>0	—	—	0	0.2F HOAc, 0.2F NaOAc or NH₄OAc
Au(III)	>0 w	5.8	—	0	
Bi(III)	−0.25	3.5	—	0	
Cd(II)	−0.653	2.3	[−28]	0	
Co(II)	−1.19	—	irr.	0	0.1F NaOAc
Cr(III)	−1.2 i	—	—	II	
Cu(II)	−0.07 w	3.1	—	0	
Fe(II)	NR				
Fe(III)	>0 i	—	—	II	Low solubility
Ga(III)	NR				
In(III)	−0.708 w	3.7	[−19]	0	
Ir(III)	>0 w	0.8 D	—	0	0.1F NaOAc, pH 5
Mn(II)	NR				
Mo(VI)	−0.6i/−1.1i/−1.2i	—	—	?/?/?	
Ni(II)	−1.1 i	—	—	0	
Pb(II)	−0.50 w	2.7	[−28]	0	
Pd(II)	−0.6 i	—	—	0	
Pt(II)	>0	4.0	—	0	
Pt(IV)	>0i/+0.05 w	−/7.6 TD	—	−/0	0.1F NaOAc, pH 5
Rh(III)	>0 w	0.32 I	—	0 ?	0.1F NaOAc, pH 5
Ru(III)	>0 w/−0.8 w	0.8D/—	—	II/0	0.1F NaOAc, pH 5

(*continued*)

TABLE B-2 (continued)

Substance	$E_{1/2}$, v. vs. S.C.E.	I	$E_{3/4} - E_{1/4}$, mv.	Product	Remarks
	2F HOAc, 2F NH$_4$OAc, 0.01% gelatin (continued)				
Sb(III)	−0.40 w/−0.59 w	ca. 2/4.2T	irr./irr.	—/0	
Sn(II)	(−0.16) w/−0.62 w	—/2.6	—/[−28]	IV/0	
Sn(IV)	−1.1 i	—	—	II	
Te(VI)	−1.18	15.4	—	−II	pH 5.6
Ti(IV)	−0.85 i	—	—	III	0.2F HOAc
Tl(I)	−0.47 w	2.3	[−56]	0	
U(IV)	(−0.12) w	−2.17	+35	V + VI	0.2F OAc⁻, pH 5.1
U(VI)	−0.45 w	1.7	[−56]	V	
V(II)	(−0.11) fw/(−0.70) w	−2.27/−1.09	+52/+70	V/III	1F NaOAc, pH 5.4
V(III)	−0.98 fw/−1.25 fw	0.57/0.82	irr./irr.	II/II	VOH⁺⁺/VO⁺
V(IV)	−1.24 fw	—	−60	II	1F NaOAc, pH 4.7
W(VI)	−0.70	small	irr.	?	
Zn(II)	−1.1 w	1.5		0	
	0.5F HOAc, 0.5F NaOAc saturated with phenol				
Ag(I)	>0 w	—	—	0	
As(III)	NR				
As(V)	NR				
Bi(III)	−0.307 w	—	−57	0	
Cd(II)	−0.615 w	—	−40	0	
Cr(III)	−1.18 w	—	−72	II ?	
Cu(II)	−0.035 w	—	−39	0	

Fe(II)	−1.378 w		−61	0
Fe(III)	−0.012 w/−1.380 w	−/−	−70/−65	II/0
In(III)	−1.09 w		−190	0
Mn(II)	−1.493 w		−30	0
Mo(VI)	−0.98 i		−160	III ?
Ni(II)	−1.29 fw		−87	0
Pb(II)	−0.455 w		−31	0
Sb(III)	−0.61 w		−78	0
Sb(V)	NR			
Sn(II)	NR			
Sn(IV)	NR			
Te(VI)	−1.29 w		−56	−II
Tl(I)	−0.458 w		−53	0
U(VI)	−0.438 w/−1.34 i		−65/−71	IV + V/III
V(IV)	−1.26 fw		−65	II	Large maximum at −1.4 v.
W(VI)	NR			
Zn(II)	−1.14 w		−75	0
		1F NH₃, 1F NH₄Cl		
Ag(I)	>0	−/−	−	0
As(III)	−1.41 fw/−1.63 fw	−/−	−110/−50	−/−III
Au(I)	>0		−	−
Au(III)	>0		−	0
Cd(II)	−0.81 w	3.68	−28	0
Co(II)	−1.29 w	−/−	irr.	0
Co(NH₃)₆⁺⁺⁺	−0.28/−1.3	−/−	irr./irr.	II/0	2F NH₃, 2F NH₄Cl
Co(NH₃)₅(H₂O)⁺⁺⁺	−0.54 w/−1.36	1.67/3.40	irr./irr.	II/0	2.5F NH₃, 0.1F NH₄Cl, pH 10.6

(continued)

TABLE B-2 (continued)

1F NH₃, 1F NH₄Cl (continued)

Substance	$E_{1/2}$, v. vs. S.C.E.	I	$E_{3/4} - E_{1/4}$, mv.	Product	Remarks
Cr(II)	(−0.85) w	−1.14	irr.	III	
Cr(III)	−1.43 w/−1.71 fw	−/−	irr./irr.	II/0	4G
Cr(VI)	−0.2 fw/−1.6	−/−	irr./irr.	III/0	
Cu(I)	(−0.22) w/−0.50 w	−/−	[+56/−56]	II/0	
Cu(II)	−0.24 fw/−0.51 w	−/3.75T	[−56/−56]	I/0	10G
Fe(II)	(−0.34)/−1.49 w	−/−	−/irr.	III/0	
Ge(IV)	−1.45/−1.70	−/−	−/−	0/c	0.5F NH₃, 1F NH₄Cl
Ir(III)	NR				
Ir(IV)	NR				
Mn(II)	−1.66 w	—	—	0	
Mo(VI)	−1.71 fw	—	−57	?	
Ni(II)	−1.10 w	3.56	irr.	0	
	−0.92 w	—	irr.	0	0.1F NH₃, 0.1F NH₄Cl
Os(VIII)	>0 fw/−0.24 fi/−1.6	−/6.7T/ca. 13	−/−/−	VI/III + IV/c H₂	
Pb(II)	−0.67 fw	—	—	0	Low solubility
Pd(II)	−0.75 w	3.8	irr.	0	
Pt(II)	NR				
Rh(NH₃)₅Cl⁺⁺	−0.93				
Se(−II)	(±0.0) fi/(−0.84)	−1.1/−4.9	−/−	?/HgSe	
Se(IV)	−1.53 w	11.02	—	Se⁻	
Te(−II)	(−1.1) w	—	—	0	
Te(IV)	−0.67 w	—	—	0	
Te(VI)	−1.21 w	17.5	—	Te⁻	pH 8.0
Tl(I)	−0.48 w	—	−56	0	
U(VI)	−0.8/−1.4	−/−	−/−	V/IV	

	(−0.32) w / −1.28 w −0.96 fw / −1.26 w	−0.94/1.82 1.6/4.72T	irr./irr. irr./irr.	V/II IV/II	SO₃⁼ catalyzes depoly-merization 0.1F NH₃, 0.1F NH₄Cl
V(IV)					
V(V)					
W(VI)	NR.				
Zn(II)	−1.35 w	3.82	ca. −40	0	

2F K₂CO₃, pH ca. 11.0

Ag(I)	>0			0	
As(III)	NR	—	—		
Bi(III)	−0.64	—	—	0	
Cd(II)	−0.74	—	—	0	
Ce(III)	(−0.157) w	−1.67	+56	IV	
Ce(IV)	−0.158 w	1.69	−56	III	
Co(II)	NR				
Cr(III)	NR				
Cr(VI)	−0.47	—	—	III	
Cu(II)	−0.201 w	—	−28	0	1F K₂CO₃, pH 9.5–11
Fe(II)	(−0.53)	—	—	III	
Fe(III)	−0.86	—	—	II	
Ga(III)	NR				
Ge(IV)	−1.44	—	—	—	
In(III)	−1.24	—	—	0	
Mn(II)	(−0.1)	—	—	III	
Mo(VI)	NR				
Ni(II)	−1.2 i	↑	↑	0	
Pb(II)	−0.66	—	—	0	
Sb(III)	−1.1	—	—	0	

(continued)

TABLE B-2 (continued)

Substance	$E_{1/2}$, v. vs. S.C.E.	I	$E_{3/4} - E_{1/4}$, mv.	Product	Remarks
2F K₂CO₃, pH ca. 11.0 (continued)					
Te(VI)	-1.37	16.6	—	Te⁼	pH 8.5
Ti(IV)	-1.5	—	irr.	III	
Tl(I)	-0.47	—	—	0	
U(VI)	-1.01	ca. 1.25	ca. -60	V	
V(II)	$-0.83/-1.45$	$1.5/—$	$—/—$	V/IV	0.5F (NH₄)₂CO₃
	(-0.18) w$/(-0.75)$ w	$-2.97/-1.19$	irr./irr.	V/III	0.5F Na₂CO₃, 0.5F KHCO₃
V(III)	(-0.337) w	-2.80	$+58$	V	0.5F Na₂CO₃, 0.5F KHCO₃
W(VI)	NR	—	—		
Zn(II)	-1.20	—	—	0	
0.1F KCl, LiCl, (CH₃)₄NCl, or NH₄Cl					
Cd(II)	-0.60 w	3.51	-28	0	
Ce(III)	-2.0 i	—	—	?	
Co(II)	-1.20 w	—	irr.	0	5-10G
Co(NH₃)₆⁺⁺⁺	-0.26 w$/-1.20$ w	1.78/3.60	$—/—$	II/0	5G
Cr(II)	(-0.34) w	-1.54	irr.	III	
Cr(III)	-0.61 fw$/-0.85$ w$/-1.47$ w	D/I/—	irr./irr./irr.	II/II/0 + H₂, 10G	
Cr(VI)	$-0.3/-1.0/-1.55/-1.8$	small/5.95T/—	—	VI + III/	
		$—/12.0$T		III/II/0	
Cu(II)	>0 w	3.23	—	0	10G
Eu(III)	-0.69 w	1.5	-64	II	
Fe(II)	-1.3 w	—	irr.	0	
Ga(III)	-1.1 w	—	irr.	0	

In(III)	−0.561 w	—	−19	0	10G
Ni(II)	−1.1 w	3.38	irr.	0	10G
Pb(II)	−0.40 w	3.85	−28	0	
Pt(II)	—	4.10	—	0	
Se(VI)	NR				
Te(VI)	−1.1/−1.45	small/—	−/−	−/−	
Tl(I)	−0.46 w	2.70	−56	0	
Tl(III)	>0 w/−0.46 w	−/−	−/−56	I/0	
U(VI)	−0.185		—	V	pH 5.4
Yb(III)	−1.41 w/−2.0 i	1.66/—	−/−	II/−	pH 4.75
Zn(II)	−0.995 w	3.42	—	0	10G
1F HCl					
As(III)	−0.428 w/−0.67 fi	6.04/5.96	−35/−	0/−III	0.15 methylene blue
As(V)	NR				
Bi(III)	−0.09 w	5.23	[−19]	0	10G
Cd(II)	−0.642 w	3.58	−28	0	10G
Cu(II)	>0 fw/−0.22 w	−/3.39T	−/[−56]	I/0	10G
Fe(III)	>0 w	1.46		II	3F HCl
Ge(II)	(−0.13) fw/−0.42	−/2.20	−/−	IV/0	
In(III)	−0.597 w	—	−19	0	1F KCl
Mo(VI)	−0.261 i/−0.63 w	−/−	−/−	V/III	0.3F HCl
Np(IV)	−0.102 w		−56	III	
Os(VI)	>0 w	4.77	—	III	10G
Pb(II)	−0.435 w	3.86	−28	0	
Ru(III)	−0.28 w	1.76	irr.	II	10G
Ru(IV)	>0 fw/−0.28 fw	1.66/—	−/irr.	III/II	
Sb(III)	−0.15 w	5.57	−19	0	10G

(continued)

TABLE B-2 (*continued*)

Substance	$E_{1/2}$, v. vs. S.C.E.	I	$E_{3/4} - E_{1/4}$, mv.	Product	Remarks
		1F HCl (*continued*)			
Sb(V)	>0 w	—	—	0	1F HCl, 4F KBr
Se(−II)	(−0.1) fw/(−0.49) fw	−1.3/−3.8	—/—	Se?/HgSe	
Se(VI)	NR				
Sn(II)	(−0.1) i/−0.47 w	—/4.07	—/—	IV/0	5–10G
Sn(IV)	−0.25 fw/−0.52 w	2.84/3.49	—/—	II/0	1F HCl, 4F NH₄Cl, 5G
Te(−II)	(−0.73) w	—	+28	0	
Ti(III)	(−0.14) i	—	—	IV	0.01F HCl
Ti(IV)	−0.81 w	1.56	—	III	0.1F HCl, 5G
Tl(I)	−0.475 w	2.63	−58	0	
Tl(III)	>0 w/−0.45 w	3.83/1.89	—/−58	I/0	0.6F HCl
U(III)	(−0.94) w	—	+51	IV	0° C.
U(IV)	−0.89 fw	—	[−56]	III	
U(VI)	−0.18 w/−0.94 fw	1.54/—	—/—	V/III	0.1F HCl
	−0.213 w/−0.9 fi	3.08/—	—/—	IV/III	2F HCl
V(III)	−0.51 w	1.41	−56	II	
V(V)	>0 fw/−0.80 fi	—/—	—/irr.	IV/II	0.1F HCl
		5F CaCl₂			
Cd(II)	−0.80	—	—	0	
Co(II)	−0.822	—	—	0	
Co(NH₃)₆⁺⁺⁺	−0.260/−0.876	—	—	II/0	
Cr(II)	(−0.51) w	−0.47	[+56]	III	Saturated CaCl₂
Cr(III)	−0.51 w	—	ca. −65	II	Saturated CaCl₂, 5G
Cu(II)	>0/−0.33 w	—/—	—/—	I/0	0.1F HCl

		12F HCl*			
Fe(III)	>0/−1.20	−/−	−/−	II/0	pH 3.5
Mn(II)	−1.45	−	−	0	
Ni(II)	−0.56 w	[−28?]	−	0	
Pb(II)	−0.53		−	0	
Ti(III)	(−0.12)	[+56]		IV	Saturated $CaCl_2$
Ti(IV)	−0.12	[−56]		III	Saturated $CaCl_2$
12F HCl*					
Ag(I)	>0		−	0	
As(III)	>0 fw/−0.55 i	3.94/−	−/−	0/−III	
As(V)	>0 fi/−0.52 fw	−/10.7T	−/−	0/−III	
Bi(III)	−0.45	−	−	0	8F HCl
Cd(II)	−0.34		irr.	0	8F HCl
	NR				
Ce(IV)	−0.80		−	III	
Co(II)	>0			0	
Cr(III)	NR			—	On standing → $Cr(H_2O)_4^-Cl_2^+$, $E_{1/2} = -0.6$ v. in 8F HCl
	NR				
Cu(II)	>0/−0.71		−/−	I/0	8F HCl
	>0/−0.42		−/−	I/0	
Fe(II)	NR				
Fe(III)	>0			II	

* In the absence of a maximum suppressor, metal ions having half-wave potentials more positive than −0.5 v. vs. S.C.E. in concentrated hydrochloric acid also give anomalous waves for which $E_{1/2} = -0.62 \pm 0.06$ v.

(continued)

TABLE B-2 (*continued*)

Substance	$E_{1/2}$, v. vs. S.C.E.	I	$E_{3/4} - E_{1/4}$, mv.	Product	Remarks
		12F HCl (*continued*)			
In(III)	−0.772 w	—	−20	0	
Mn(II)	NR				
Mo(VI)	>0	—	—	?	
Nb(V)	−0.40 w	0.82	—	IV	10F HCl in 20% ethylene glycol
Ni(II)	−0.80	—	—	0	
	−0.67	—	irr.	0	8F HCl
Os(VI)	>0 w	ca. 4.1	—	III	9F HCl
Os(VIII)	>0 w	11.8	—	III	
Pb(II)	−0.90	—	—	0	
	−0.62	—	—	0	8F HCl
Sb(III)	−0.224 w	—	[−19]	0	4F HCl, 30° C.
Sb(V)	>0 fw/−0.24	3.03/—	—/—	III/0	8F HCl
Sn(II)	−0.83	—	−28	0	2T
Sn(IV)	−0.50 fw/−0.83	—/—	irr./−28	II/0	2T
Ti(IV)	>0	—	→	III	8F HCl
Tl(I)	NR				
	−0.67	—	—	0	
U(VI)	>0	—	—	IV	8F HCl
V(II)	(−0.538) w	—	+52	III	
V(III)	−0.526 w	—	−57	II	
V(IV)	>0/−0.75	—/—	—/—	III/II	

Ion					
W(III)	NR (−0.53) (−0.56) w	—	—	IV	Green Yellow Red
W(V)	−0.56 w	−1.10	—	IV	
W(VI)	>0 fw/−0.55 w NR	2.53	−28	III(red) V/III(red)	8F HCl
Zn(II)	NR	1.31/2.51	—/—		
Saturated citric acid (H₃Cit)					
Ag(I)	>0 w	—	—	0	
As(III)	−0.58 i/−0.73 i/−1.02 i	—/—/—	—/—/—	0/−III	1st wave is adsorption wave
As(V)	NR				
Bi(III)	−0.025 w	—	−45	0	
Cd(II)	−0.514 w	—	−28	0	
Ce(III)	NR				
Ce(IV)	NR				
Co(II)	NR				
Cr(III)	−0.78 i	—	−59	II	
Cr(VI)	>0 w	—	—	III	Reduced by H₃Cit
Cu(II)	+0.03 w	—	−60	0	
Fe(II)	NR				
Fe(III)	+0.23 w	—	−56	II	
In(III)	−0.540 w	—	−78	0	
Mn(II)	NR				
Mo(VI)	+0.038 w/−0.44 w	—/—	—/−76	V/III	2F H₃Cit
Nb(V)	−0.86 w	—	—	IV	
Ni(II)	−0.98 i	—	−70	0	

(continued)

TABLE B-2 (continued)

Substance	$E_{1/2}$, v. vs. S.C.E.	I	$E_{3/4} - E_{1/4}$, mv.	Product	Remarks
	Saturated citric acid (H₃Cit) (continued)				
Pb(II)	−0.358 w	—	−28	0	
Sb(III)	−0.38 w	—	−63	0	
Sb(V)	NR				
Sn(II)	(−0.05) fw/−0.40 w	—/—	+28/−28	IV/0	
Sn(IV)	NR				
Te(IV)	−0.05/−0.4	−/5.72T	−/−	0/0	1st wave is adsorption wave
Te(VI)	NR				
Ti(IV)	−0.37	—	−56	III	0.2F H₃Cit
Tl(I)	−0.442 w	—	−56	0	
U(VI)	−0.122 w	—	−63	IV ?	
V(II)	(−0.570) w	—	+55	III	
V(III)	−0.571 w	—	−56	II	
V(IV)	−0.67/−1.05 i	small/−	−/−	−/II	
V(V)	+0.11 w/−0.63 fi	−/−	−56/irr.	IV/II	
W(VI)	NR				
Zn(II)	−0.930 fi	—	−28	0	
	0.25F citrate (Cit) buffer, pH 3–4				
As(III)	−0.75	—	—	0 ?	
Bi(III)	−0.19 w	—	—	0	
Cd(II)	−0.611 w	—	−27	0	0.5F K₃Cit, pH 3
Co(II)	NR				
Cu(II)	−0.111 w	—	−28	0	1F Na₃Cit, pH 4.1

			0.1F (NH₄)₃Cit, pH 6.1		
Fe(II)	(−0.05)	—	—	III	
Fe(III)	−0.05	—	—	II	
Mn(II)	NR				
Mo(VI)	−0.28/−0.66	—/	—/	V/III	1F Na₃Cit, pH 3.0
Nb(V)	−0.95 fw		−60	IV	
Ni(II)	NR	0.81D(slow)		0	
Pb(II)	−0.43 w	—/	—/	0	
Sb(III)	−0.64 w	—/—	—/—		
Sn(II)	(−0.21) w/−0.54 w			IV/0	
Sn(IV)	NR				
Te(−II)	(−0.95)				
Ti(IV)	−0.73 fw	—	—	III	0.25F (NH₄)₃Cit, pH 5
Tl(I)	−0.48		−56	0	0.5F Cit, pH 3.3, 3G
	−0.35				1F Na₃Cit, pH 3.0
U(VI)	−0.65 w			IV	50% (NH₄)₂HCit, pH 4–5
					1F K₃Cit, 0.1F Al₂(SO₄)₃, pH 4.5
					1F Na₃Cit, pH 3.0
W(VI)	NR			0	
Zn(II)	−1.04 w				
Ag(I)	>0 i			0	Large maximum
As(III)	−1.46 i		−150	−III	Large maximum
As(V)	NR				
Bi(III)	−0.31 w		−25	0	
Cd(II)	−0.700 w		−28	0	
Co(II)	NR				

(continued)

TABLE B-2 (continued)

Substance	$E_{1/2}$, v. vs. S.C.E.	I	$E_{3/4} - E_{1/4}$, mv.	Product	Remarks
		0.1F (NH₄)₃ Cit, pH 6.1 (continued)			
Cr(II)	(−1.0) i	—	—	III	
Cr(III)	−1.15 fi	small	−110	II	
Cr(VI)	>0/−0.383 w	−/−	−/−55	VI + III/III	
Cu(II)	−0.170 w	—	−23	0	
Fe(II)	(−0.183) w	−0.8	+57	III	
Fe(III)	−0.225 w	1.24	−75	II	
In(III)	NR				
Mn(II)	−1.615 w	—	−52	0	
Mo(VI)	−1.011 w	—	−130	?	
	−0.93 w	3.6	irr.	IV?	1F Na₃Cit, pH 7
Ni(II)	NR				
Pb(II)	−0.542 w	—	−27	0	
Sb(III)	−0.77 w/−1.12 w/−1.50 i	−/−/−	−54/−110/−	−/−/0	
Sb(V)	−1.56 i	small	−76	0	
Sn(II)	(−0.406) w/−0.662 w	−/−	+36/−38	IV/0	
Sn(IV)	−1.0	small			
Te(VI)	−1.237 w	—	−73	−II	
Ti(IV)	−0.9 w	1.02	—	III	
Tl(I)	−0.510 w	—	−58	0	
U(VI)	−0.415 fi	—	−35	V + IV	
V(II)	(+0.1) i/(−0.04) i/(−1.17) w	−/−/−0.87	−/−/+56	V/IV/III	0.4F Na₃Cit, pH 5.5–6, 5G
V(IV)	−0.44/−1.48 i	small/—	−/−120	−/II	1F Na₃Cit, pH 7
V(V)	>0 w/−1.53 i	−/−	−/−190	IV/II	
W(VI)	NR				
Yb(III)	−1.50 i	—	—	c	
Zn(II)	−1.37 i	—	−165	0	

0.1F NH₃, 0.1F (NH₄)₃Cit, pH 8.5

Substance					Remarks
Ag(I)	>0 w	—	—	0	Large maximum
As(III)	−1.63 fw	—	−57	−III	
As(V)	NR				
Bi(III)	−0.435 w	—	−45	0	Maximum at −1.3 v.
Cd(II)	−0.706 w	—	−42	0	
Ce(IV)	>0 w	—	—	III	
Co(II)	−1.39 fw/−1.7	—/small	−82/—	0/?	
Co(III)	−0.356/−1.519	1.23/2.43	—/—	II/0	0.5F K₃Cit
Co(NH₃)₆⁺⁺⁺	NR				Low solubility
Cr(III)	NR				
Cr(VI)	−0.235 fw/−1.8 i	—/—	−75/—	III/0	
Cu(II)	−0.165 fi/−0.340 w	—/—	−58/−58	I/0	
Fe(II)	(−0.438) w/−1.63 i	—/—	+35/—	III/0	
Fe(III)	−0.457 w/−0.935 w/−1.61 i	—/—/—	−58/—/—	—/II/0	Maximum on anodic wave
In(III)	−1.35 i	small	−145	—	
Mn(II)	−1.62 i	—	−71	0	
Mo(VI)	−1.26 fw/−1.70 i	—/—	−120/—	V/IV?	
Ni(II)	−1.09 i/−1.39 fw	—/—	−82/−105	—/0	
Pb(II)	−0.528 w	—	−28	0	
Sb(III)	−0.972 w/−1.79 i	—/—	−115/—	0/−III	
Sb(V)	NR		—/—		2T
Sn(II)	(−0.470) w/−0.752 w	—/—	+13/−57	IV/0	Curves change slightly as solutions age
Sn(IV)	NR				
Te(VI)	−1.296 w	—	−73	−II	
Tl(I)	−0.447 w	—	−58	0	
U(VI)	−0.585 i/−1.065 w	small/—	−49/−130	VI+V/IV	
V(IV)	(−0.05) i/−1.48 fw	—/—	—/−170	V/II	
V(V)	−0.27 i/−1.36 w	—/—	−51/−100	IV/III	
W(VI)	−1.59 i	large	−53	c	
Yb(III)	NR				
Zn(II)	−1.236 w	—	−50	0	2T

(continued)

TABLE B-2 (continued)

Substance	$E_{1/2}$, v. vs. S.C.E.	I	$E_{3/4} - E_{1/4}$, mv.	Product	Remarks
		1F KCN			
Au(I)	-1.46 fw	—	—	0	0.1F KCN
Au(III)	$>0/-1.4$	—/—	—/—	I/0	0.1F KCN
Cd(II)	-1.18 w	—	irr.	0	
Co(I)	NR				
Co(II)	-1.3 w	—	irr.	I	
Co(H$_2$O)(CN)$_5$$^=$	-1.45 w	—	irr.	I	
Co(CN)$_6$$^{-3}$	NR				
Cr(II)	$(-1.05)/(-1.38)$	varies/—	$-/+58$	$-$/III	
Cr(CN)$_6$$^{-3}$	-1.383	-1.55	—	II	
Cu(II)	NR				
Ga(III)	-1.29 i	—	—	0	
Ir(III)	NR				
Ir(IV)	NR				
Mn(I)	(-1.364) w	-1.6	$+56$	II	
Mn(II)	-1.364 w	1.6	-56	I	
Mn(III)	>0 w$/-1.36$ w	$1.68/1.70$	$-/-56$	II/I	
Ni(I)	(-0.80) w	—	irr.	II	
Ni(II)	-1.36	—	—	—	1F KCN, 0.1F KCl, 10G
Os(VI)	>0 i$/-0.81$ w	$5.3/1.7$	$-/-69$	III/II	0.1F KCN
Os(VIII)					Reduced by KCN to Os(VI), q.v.
Pb(II)	-0.72 w	—	—	0	
Pd(II)	-1.77	—	$[-28]$	0	
	NR				
Pt(II)	NR				0.1F KCN

Substance					Comments
Rh(III)	−1.47	—	—	irr.	II
Ru(H₂O)Cl₅⁼	NR				
RuCl₆⁼	NR				
Sb(III)	−1.11	—	—	—	0
Te(VI)	−1.36	—	—	—	—
Tl(I)	>0 w	—	—	—	0
V(III)	−1.17 fw/−1.77 i	0.71/0.62	irr./−53	−/II	
W(VI)	NR				
Zn(II)	NR				

10F NaCN, 1F NaOH

Substance					Comments
Ag(I)	>0 w	—	—	0	
As(III)	>0/−1.40 w	small/small	−/−42	0/−III	
As(V)	NR				
Bi(III)	>0 w	—	—	0	
Cd(II)	−1.216 w	—	−33	0	Low solubility
Ce(IV)	NR				
Co(II)	−1.24 w	small	−130	I	May be double wave
Cr(III)	NR.				
Cr(VI)	>0 w	—	—	III	
Cu(II)	NR				
Fe(II)	NR				
Fe(III)	>0 i	small	—		
Mn(II)	−1.243 w	—	−51	I	
Mo(VI)	NR				
Ni(II)	−1.346 w	large	−36	c?	
Pb(II)	>0 w	—	—	0	

(continued)

TABLE B-2 (*continued*)

Substance	$E_{1/2}$, v. vs. S.C.E.	I	$E_{3/4} - E_{1/4}$, mv.	Product	Remarks
10F NaCN, 1F NaOH (*continued*)					
Sb(III)	>0 w	—	—	0	2T
Sb(V)	NR				
Sn(II)	NR				
Sn(IV)	NR				
Te(IV)	>0 fw/−1.15 i/−1.21 w	—/—/—	—/−48/−26	—/—/0	
Te(VI)	−1.53 i	—	−95	?	
U(VI)	NR				
V(II)	NR				
V(IV)	−1.45 i	—	−115	III?	
V(V)	−1.62 i	—	−105	II?	
Yb(III)	NR				
Zn(II)	NR				
0.5F ethylenediamine (en), 0.5F K$_3$PO$_4$					
Ag(I)	>0	—	—	0	
As(III)	NR				
Bi(III)	—	—/—	—/—	—/—	Low solubility
Cd(II)	−0.95 w	—	—	0	
Co(II)	(−0.46) w	—	[+56]	III	0.1F en, 0.1F KNO$_3$
Co(III)	−0.70	—	—	III	
Cr(III)	NR.				
Cr(VI)	>0/−1.11	—/—	—/—	—/—	
Cu(II)	−0.60 w	—	[−28]	0	
Fe(III)	−0.59	—	—	II	
In(III)	−1.18	—	—	—	

Ion					
Mn(II)	—	—	—	—	Low solubility
Mo(VI)	NR	—	—	—	
Ni(II)	—1.46	—	—	—	
Pb(II)	—0.71	—	—	—	
Sb(III)	—1.07	—	—	—	
Se(VI)	NR	—	—	—	
Sn(IV)	NR	—	—	—	
Te(VI)	—1.85	—	irr.	—	
Ti(IV)	—1.6	—	—	0	
Tl(I)	—0.54	—	—	II?	
V(V)	—1.75	—	—	—	
W(VI)	NR	—	—	—	
Zn(II)	—1.42	—	—	0	

0.05F ethylenediaminetetraacetate (EDTA), 0.8F HOAc, pH ca. 2

Ion					
As(III)	ca. —0.5	—	—93	0	
Bi(III)	—0.50 w	—	—	—	
Cd(II)	—0.65 fi/—0.85 w	—/—	—/—	0/0	$Cd^{++}/Cd(EDTA)^{=}$
Co(II)	NR	—	—	—	
Co(III)	>0 w	—	—	II	0.3F EDTA, 0.3F pyridine (py), 0.3F (pyH)Cl
Cu(II)	—0.17 w	—1.45	—60	0	
Fe(II)	(—0.12) w	—	+56	III	0.04–0.4F EDTA, pH 4
Fe(III)	—0.12	—	[—56]	II	
Mn(II)	NR	—	—	—	
Mo(VI)	—0.63	—	—	—	01.F EDTA, 0.1F HOAc, 0.1F NH₄OAc

(continued)

TABLE B-2 (continued)

Substance	$E_{1/2}$, v. vs. S.C.E.	I	$E_{3/4} - E_{1/4}$, mv.	Product	Remarks
0.05F ethylenediaminetetraacetate (EDTA), 0.8F HOAc, pH ca. 2 (continued)					
Nb(V)	−0.700 w/−1.1 i/−1.4 i	—/—/—	−58/—/—	IV/III/II	0.1F EDTA, 0.33F K$_2$SO$_4$, 0.1F NaOAc, 0.4F HOAc, pH 4.0. Boiling with EDTA → a stable complex.
Ni(II)	NR				
Pb(II)	−0.75 w	—	−125	0	
Sb(III)	−0.62 w	—	−81	0	
Sn(II)	ca. −0.7	—	—	0	
Ta(V)	ca. −1.2	—	—	—	Same medium as Nb(V) above
Ti(III)	(−0.22)	—	+58	IV	pH 1.0–2.5
Ti(IV)	−0.22	—	−56	III	pH 1.0–2.5
Tl(I)	−0.50	—	−100	0	
U(VI)	−0.25 w	—	−78	V?	
W(VI)	NR				
Zn(II)	NR	—	—	—	0.1F EDTA, pH 5
0.1F ethylenediaminetetraacetate (EDTA), 0.8F NaOAc, pH ca. 7					
As(III)	ca. −1.0	—	—	—	
Bi(III)	−0.66 w	—	—	0	
Cd(II)	−1.27 i	—	—	0	
Co(II)	NR				
Cu(II)	−0.31 w	2.83	−57	0	
	−0.41 w		−28	0	0.25F EDTA, pH 7

Eu(III)	−1.17	1.3	−58	II	0.1F EDTA, pH 6–8
Fe(III)	−0.15	1.46	—	II	0.1F EDTA, pH 6–8
Ge(IV)	−1.30 w	—	—	—	
Mn(II)	NR	—	—	—	1F NaClO$_4$, 0.1F EDTA, pH 5.5
Mo(VI)	−0.82	—	—	—	
Ni(II)	NR	—	—	0	
Pb(II)	−1.37 fi	—	—	0	
Sb(III)	−0.79 w	—	—	0	
Sn(II)	−1.26	—	—	0	
Tl(I)	−0.50 w	—	−89	V	
U(VI)	−0.37 w	—	−55	V	
	−0.35	1.75	ca. −60	V	1F NaClO$_4$, 0.1F EDTA, pH 5.5
V(II)	(−1.27) w	−1.10	+58	III	0.1F EDTA, pH < 8.3
V(III)	−1.27 w	1.20	−58	II	0.1F EDTA, pH 5–8.5
V(V)	−1.37 w	—	—	—	0.02F EDTA, 0.2F KCN
Zn(II)	NR				
0.05F glutamic acid, 0.2F NaClO$_4$, 0.2F borate buffer, pH 9.5					
Ag(I)	>0	—	—	0	
As(III)	−1.60 i	—	—	—	
Bi(III)	—	—	—	—	Low solubility
Cd(II)	−0.84	—	—	0	
Ce(III) or (IV)	—	—	—	—	Low solubility
Co(II)	(−0.068) w/−1.34	—/—	+58/—	III/0	
Co(III)	−0.084/−1.34 ?	—/—	−60/—	II/0	
Cr(III)	NR				
Cr(VI)	−0.31/−0.97	—/—	—/—	—/—	
Cu(II)	−0.226 w	—	[−56]	0	0.04F K glutamate, 0.06F KH$_2$PO$_4$, pH 7.6

(continued)

TABLE B-2 (continued)

Substance	$E_{1/2}$, v. vs. S.C.E.	I	$E_{3/4} - E_{1/4}$, mv.	Product	Remarks
0.05F glutamic acid, 0.2F NaClO$_4$, 0.2F borate buffer, pH 9.5 (continued)					
Fe(III)	—	—	—	—	Low solubility
In(III)	—	—	—	—	Low solubility
Mn(II)	−1.53			—	
Mo(VI)	NR				
Ni(II)	−1.24/−1.55			—	
Pb(II)	—			—	Low solubility
Te(VI)	−1.35			—	
Tl(I)	−0.45			—	
U(VI)	NR				
V(IV)	(−0.11)/−1.25/−1.64	−/−/−	−/−/−	V/−/−	
V(V)	−0.44/−1.32	−/−	−/−	IV/−	
W(VI)	NR				
Zn(II)	−1.28	—	—	0	
Saturated hydrazine dihydrochloride					
Ag(I)	>0 w	−/−	—	0	
As(III)	−0.192 w/−0.575 fw	−/−	irr./−6	0/−III	
As(V)	NR				
Bi(III)	−0.197 w		−16	0	
Cd(II)	−0.729 fw		−27	0	
Ce(III)	NR				
Ce(IV)	NR				Reduced by $N_2H_4 \cdot 2HCl$
Co(II)	NR				
Cr(III)	NR				

Cr(VI)	−0.590 fi	—/—	−70	III?	
Cu(II)	>0 w / −0.326 w	—/—	−/−45	I/0	
Fe(II)	NR			II	
Fe(III)	>0 w	—/—	—	−/0	
In(III)	−0.648 w / −0.91 fw	—/—	−25/−53		
Mn(II)	NR				
Mo(V)	>0 w / −0.435 w	—/—	−/−83	IV/III	
Mo(VI)					Reduced by $N_2H_4 \cdot 2HCl$ to Mo(V), q.v.
Ni(II)	NR			0	
Pb(II)	−0.544 w	—/—	−29	III/0	
Sb(V)	>0 i / −0.21 w	small/—	−/−51	−/0	
Sn(II)	−0.25 fw / −0.53 w	—/—	−83/−28	II/0	
Sn(IV)	−0.214 w / −0.527 w	—/—	−76/−25	—/0	
Te(VI)	−0.75 w	small		—	Final current rise begins early
Tl(I)	−0.562 w	—/—	−57	0	
U(VI)	−0.16 w / −0.885 w	—/—	−/−	IV?/III	
V(II)	(−0.457) w	—	+55	III	
V(III)	−0.462 w	—	−59	II	
V(IV)	−0.99 i		irr.	II	
V(V)	−0.5 i / −0.9 i	small/—	−/irr.	−/II	2T
W(VI)	NR				
Zn(II)	−0.983 i	—	irr.	0	Low solubility

(continued)

TABLE B-2 (continued)

Substance	$E_{1/2}$, v. vs. S.C.E.	I	$E_{3/4} - E_{1/4}$, mv.	Product	Remarks
	1F N_2H_4, 1F NH_3, 1F NH_4Cl				
Ag(I)	>0 w			0	2T
As(III)	$-1.11/-1.30$ fw$/-1.56$ fi	small$/—/—$	$-63/—/-54$	$0/0/-$III?	2T; 2nd and 3rd waves have large maxima
As(V)	NR				
Bi(III)	-1.54 i	—	irr.	0	2T
Cd(II)	-0.823 fi	—	-26	0	
Ce(III)	NR				
Ce(IV)					Reduced by N_2H_4 to Ce(III), q.v.
Co(II)	-1.29 i		ca. -50	0	
Cr(III)	-1.402 w$/-1.7$ i	$—/—$	$-58/—$	II/0	Limited solubility
Cr(VI)					Reduced by N_2H_4 to Cr(III), q.v.
Cu(I)					
Cu(II)	-0.521 fw	—	-60	0	Reduced by N_2H_4 to Cu(I), q.v.
Fe(II)	-1.47 fw	$—/—$	-39	0	2T
Fe(III)	-1.09 w$/-1.48$ w		irr.$/-38$	II/0	2T; limited solubility
In(III)	-0.90 fw	—	irr.	—	Limited solubility
Mn(II)	-1.12 fi	—	-31	0	
Mo(VI)	-1.72 i	—	-45	V	
Ni(II)	-1.08 fw	—	-31	0	
Pb(II)	$-0.42/-0.51$ fi	small$/—$	irr.$/-29$	$—/0$	
Sb(III)	-0.74 fw$/-1.6$ i	$—/—$	$-45/—$	$0/—$	
Sb(V)	NR				

Ion					Supporting electrolyte / Notes
Sn(II)	(−0.634) w / −0.773 w / −1.62 i	−/−/—	irr./−29/—	IV/0/—	Limited solubility
Sn(IV)	−1.13 i / −1.35 i	−/—	irr./irr.	II/0	
Te(IV)	−0.714 w	—	−57	0	Large maximum at −1.2 v. Reduced by N_2H_4 to Te(IV), q.v.
Te(VI)					
Tl(I)	−0.487 fw	—	−55	0	
U(VI)	NR				Low solubility
V(IV)	−1.21 fw / −1.49 i	small/small	irr./irr.	III?/II?	
V(V)	−1.15 w	—	irr.	?	
W(VI)	NR				
Zn(II)	−1.330 fw	—	−27	0	
			1F NaOH		
As(III)	(−0.26) w	−3.82	—	V	0.5F KOH, 2 thymol-phthalein
	(−)/ca. −1.92	−/14.4		−/−III	0.1F LiCl, 0.01F LiOH, 30°C.
As(V)	NR				
Au(III)	−0.2/−0.4/−1.1	−/D/I	−/−/irr.	−/−/—	2F KOH
Bi(III)	−0.6	—	—	0	Low solubility
Cd(II)	−0.783 w	—	−38	0	Low solubility
Co(II)	−1.46 w	—	−90	0	Limited solubility
Cr(III)	−1.94 i	—		0	Limited solubility
Cr(VI)	−0.85	5.72	irr.	III	
Cu(II)	−0.410	2.91	irr.	0	Limited solubility
Fe(II)	(−0.9)	—	[+56]	III	Low solubility
Fe(III)	−1.12 w / −1.74	−/—	−/—	II/0	3F KOH, 3% mannitol

(continued)

TABLE B-2 (continued)

Substance	$E_{1/2}$, v. vs. S.C.E.	I	$E_{3/4} - E_{1/4}$, mv.	Product	Remarks
	1F NaOH (continued)				
In(III)	−1.09	—	—	0	
Mn(II)	−1.70	—	—	—	
Mo(V) or (VI)	NR				
Os(VI)	−0.605 w/−1.54 fw	2.69/2.16	−78/−81	IV + V/III	5T
Os(VIII)	>0 w/−0.63 w/−1.53 w	3.2/—/—	—/—/—	VI/IV/III	
Pb(II)	−0.755 w	3.39	−28	0	10G
Pd(II)	−1.41	—	—	—	2F NaOH
Sb(III)	(−0.45) fw/−1.15	—/6.0	—/—	V/0	1F KOH
Sb(V)	NR				
Se(−II)	(−0.94)/(−1.02)	−1.83/−1.95	—/—	HgSe/Se$_2^-$	
Se(IV) or (VI)	NR				
Sn(II)	(−0.73) w/−1.22 w	−3.45/3.45	—/—	IV/0	10G
Sn(IV)	NR				
Te(−II)	(−0.4)/(−1.2) w	—/−3.5	—/—	IV/0	With <0.5mM Te$^-$
Te(IV)	−1.1/−1.19	small/9.75T	—/—	—/−II	3G
Te(VI)				−II	
Tl(I)	−1.57	—	—	0	
V(IV)	−0.48	—	[−56]	V	
V(V)	(−0.432) w	−1.47D	irr.		
W(VI)	ca. −1.8 i		irr.	—	
	NR				
Zn(II)	−1.53 w	3.14	[−28]	0	10G

	10F NaOH				
Ag(I)	>0	—	—	0	Limited solubility
As(III)	(−0.337) fw	—	+38	V	
As(V)	NR				2T
Bi(III)	−0.670 w	—	−25	0	
Cd(II)	−0.913 fi	—	−25	0	Large maximum
Ce(IV)					Low solubility
Co(II)	−1.58 fw	—/—	−51	0	
Co(NH$_3$)$_6$$^{+++}$	−0.35/−1.54	—/—	—/—	II/0	
Cr(III)	−1.08 i	—	irr.	II	
Cr(VI)	−0.837 w	—	−50	III	
Cu(II)	−0.547 w	—	−38	0	2T
Fe(II)	(−1.050)/−1.67	—/—	+58/irr.	III/0	Limited solubility
Fe(III)	−1.055	—	−58	II	Limited solubility
In(III)	−1.38 fw	—	irr.	—	
Mn(II)	(−0.477)w	—	irr.	III	Limited solubility
Mo(VI)	NR				
Ni(II)	NR				
Os(VI)	−0.601 w/−1.513 fw	1.06/0.39	−27/−45	IV/III	9.4F NaOH
Os(VIII)	>0 w/−0.61 w/−1.51 w	1.32/—/—	—/—/—	VI/IV/III	2T
Pb(II)	−0.825 w	—	−28	0	
Pb(IV)	>0 w/−0.78 w	small/—	—/—	—/0	1st wave is kinetic; 5F NaOH
Sb(III)	(−0.573) w/−1.246 w	—/—	+41/−57	V/0	
Sb(V)	NR				
Sn(II)	(−1.144) w/−1.1980 w	—/—	+22/−20	IV/0	Both waves have large maxima
Sn(IV)	NR				

(continued)

TABLE B-2 (continued)

Substance	$E_{1/2}$, v. vs. S.C.E.	I	$E_{3/4} - E_{1/4}$, mv.	Product	Remarks
10F NaOH (continued)					
Te(VI)	NR				
Tl(I)	−0.458 w	—	−57	0	2T
U(VI)	−0.95 w	—	—	V?	Limited solubility
V(IV)	(−0.558) w	—	ca. −75	V	
V(V)	NR				
W(VI)	NR				
Zn(II)	−1.607 fw	—	−50	0	
Saturated hydroxylamine hydrochloride					
Ag(I)	>0 w	—	—	0	4T
As(III)	−0.52 fw/−0.73 fw/−0.94 i	—/—/—	−58/−25/−90	0/−III/c?	4T
As(V)	NR				
Bi(III)	−0.178 w	—	−18	0	
Cd(II)	−0.714 w	—	−30	0	
Ce(IV)	NR				Reduced by NH₂OH·HCl to Ce(III)
Co(II)	NR				
Cr(III)	−0.81 i	—	−90	II	
Cr(VI)	−0.58 i	small	−135	?	
Cu(I)	−0.335 w	—	−53	0	
Cu(II)					Reduced by NH₂OH·HCl to Cu(I), q.v.
Fe(II)	NR				
Fe(III)					Reduced by NH₂OH·HCl to Fe(II), q.v.

In(III)	−0.617	—	−20	0	
Mn(II)	NR				
Mo(VI)	−0.178 fw	large	−140	c	
Ni(II)	−0.67 i	—	−130	0	
Pb(II)	−0.538 w	—	−29	0	
Sb(III)	−0.187 w	—	−18	0	
Sb(V)	−0.18 i/−0.37	small/—	−22/−105	—/—	
Sn(II)	−0.517 w	—/—	−27	0	
Sn(IV)	−0.16 w/−0.51 w	—/—	−59/−21	II/0	6T
Ti(IV)	−0.8 i/−1.16 i	large/large	—/−39	c/c	
U(VI)	>0 fw/−0.59 i/−0.89 i	—/small/—	—/−130/−70	V + IV/IV/III	
V(IV)	−0.78 i	—	−160	II	
V(V)	−0.47 w	—	−150	II	
W(VI)	−0.28 i/−0.49 i	—/large	−52/−85	III/c	
Yb(III)	NR				
Zn(II)	−1.05 i	—	−35	0	

Saturated malonic acid (H$_2$Mal)

As(III)	−0.70 fi	—	irr.	0	May be double wave
As(V)	NR				
Bi(III)	+0.010 w	—	—	0	2T, large maximum
Cd(II)	−0.519 w	—	−27	0	
Ce(III)	NR				
Ce(IV)					Reduced by malonic acid to Ce(III), q.v.

(continued)

TABLE B-2 (continued)

Substance	$E_{1/2}$, v. vs. S.C.E.	I	$E_{3/4} - E_{1/4}$, mv.	Product	Remarks
		Saturated malonic acid (H_2Mal) (continued)			
Cr(III)	−0.85 i	small	—	II	
Cr(VI)	>0 w	—	—	III	Large maximum
Cu(II)	+0.081 w	—	−45	0	
Fe(II)	NR				
Fe(III)	+0.202 w	—	−59	II	2T
In(III)	−0.50 i /−0.61 fi	—/—	−26/−56	—/0	
Mn(II)	NR				
Mo(VI)	+0.073 w /−0.228 w	—/—	irr./−50	V/III	
Ni(II)	−0.97 i	—	irr.	0	
Pb(II)	−0.375 w	—	−29	0	
Sb(III)	−0.118 w	—	−25	0	
Sb(V)	NR				
Sn(II)	(+0.015) fw /−0.397 w	—/—	+36/−29	IV/0	
Sn(IV)	NR				
Te(VI)	—	—	—	—	Final current rise begins early
Tl(I)	−0.440 w	—/—	−58	0	
U(VI)	−0.12 w /−1.1 i	—/—	−57/irr.	IV?/—	
	(−0.53)w	—		III	
V(II)					
V(IV)	−0.64/−1.08 i	small/—	—/—	—/II	
V(V)	>0 fw /−0.67	—/—	—/—	IV/II?	
W(VI)	—	—	—	—	Final current rise begins early
Zn(II)	−0.94 i	—	—	0	

0.1F NH₃, 0.1F (NH₄)₂Mal

Ag(I)	>0 w	—	—	0	2T
As(III)	−1.63 i	—	−82	−III	2T
As(V)	NR				
Bi(III)	NR				Low solubility
Cd(II)	−0.676 w	—	−28	0	
Ce(IV)	NR				Low solubility
Co(II)	−1.217 w	—	−49	0	
Cr(III)	NR				Low solubility
Cr(VI)	−0.189 fi/−1.70 fi	—/—	−68/−61	III/0	2T/5G
Cu(II)	−0.096 i/−0.307 w	—/—	−46/−60	I/0	5T
Fe(II)	(−0.282) w/−1.434 w	—/—	+51/−32	III/0	
Fe(III)	NR				Low solubility
In(III)	NR				Low solubility
Mn(II)	−1.535 w	—	−35	0	
Mo(VI)	−1.667 w	—	−52	?	5G
Ni(II)	−0.983	—	−75	0	2T
Pb(II)	−0.457 w	—	−30	0	Limited solubility
Sb(III)	−0.670 w	—	−110	0	
Sb(V)	NR				
Sn(IV)	NR				
Te(VI)	−1.29 w	—	−105	−II	5G
Tl(I)	−0.464 w	—	−52	0	
U(VI)	−0.509 w	—	−66	V?	Limited solubility
V(IV)	(−0.25) i/(−0.46)/−1.32 i	—/small/—	+36,/—/−82	V/—/II	
V(V)	−0.39/−1.03 i/−1.29 i	small/—/—	—/−115/−100	—/IV/II	
W(VI)	−1.59 i	large	−83	c	5G
Yb(III)	−1.72 i	—	−89	II	
Zn(II)	−1.138 w	—	−48	0	5G

(continued)

TABLE B-2 (continued)

Substance	$E_{1/2}$, v. vs. S.C.E.	I	$E_{3/4} - E_{1/4}$, mv.	Product	Remarks
		0.25F Na₂C₂O₄, pH 3–4			
As(III)	-0.79	—	—	$-$III	
Bi(III)	—	—	—	—	Low solubility
Cd(II)	-0.63	—	—	0	
Co(III)	>0 w	1.38	—	II	1F K₂C₂O₄, 0.35F HOAc, 0.2F NH₄OAc, 20G
Cr(III)	$-0.90/-1.15$	D/I	$-/-$	II/II	0.1F K₂C₂O₄, pH 5.1, 10G
Cu(II)	-0.15 w	—	-28	0	
	-0.272 w	—	-28	0	
Fe(II)	(-0.23) w	-1.37	[+56]	III	1F K₂C₂O₄, pH 5–10
Fe(III)	-0.23 w	1.50	[-56]	II	
Ge(IV)	NR				
Mn(II)	NR				0.3F (NH₄)₂C₂O₄
Mn(III)	>0 w	1.40D	—	II	Same medium as Co(III) above
Nb(V)	-1.53 fi	—	—	IV	0.1F C₂O₄⁼, pH 1–5.5
Ni(II)	NR				0.3F (NH₄)₂C₂O₄
Pb(II)	-0.50	—	—	—	
	-0.581 w	—	-28	0	1F K₂C₂O₄, pH 7–10.5
Sb(III)	-0.51	—	irr.	—	
	-1.16 i	—		—	pH ca. 7
Sn(II)	ca. -0.7				
Ti(III)	(-0.30) w	-1.60	[+56]	IV	0.2F H₂C₂O₄, pH 1
Ti(IV)	-0.37 w	—	—	III	
	-0.28 w	-1.75	[-56]	III	0.2F H₂C₂O₄, pH 0.5
Tl(I)	-0.46	—	—	0	

Ion					Remarks
U(VI)	-0.13	3.2	—	IV	$0.5F\ H_2C_2O_4$, pH 4.5
V(II)	$(\pm0.0)\ i/(-1.136)\ w$	$-/-1.4D$	$-/+56$	$-III$	$1F\ K_2C_2O_4$, pH 4.5
V(III)	$(-0.1)\ i/-1.136\ fi$	$-/1.95$	$-/-57$	$-/II$	$1F\ K_2C_2O_4$, pH 4.5–6.5
V(V)	$>0\ w/-1.33\ w$	$1.86/3.74$	$-/\text{irr.}$	IV/II	$1F\ K_2C_2O_4$, pH 4.6
Zn(II)	$-1.3\ w$	—	—	0	$0.3F\ (NH_4)_2C_2O_4$

$0.1F\ NH_3,\ 0.1F\ (NH_4)_2C_2O_4$

Ion					Remarks
Ag(I)	$>0\ w$	—	—	0	4T
As(III)	$-1.7\ fi$	—	—	$-III$	
As(V)	NR	—	—	—	
Bi(III)	-0.36	—	—	0	Low solubility
Cd(II)	$-0.705\ w$	—	-57	0	
Ce(IV)	NR	—	—	—	Low solubility
Co(II)	$-1.314\ w$	—	-81	0	
Cr(III)	$-1.64\ i$	small	irr.	0?	Limited solubility
Cr(VI)	$-0.237\ w/-1.7\ fi$	$-/-$	$-55/-$	III/0?	
Cu(II)	$-0.176\ w/-0.379\ w$	$-/-$	$-50/-62$	I/0	
Fe(II)	$(-0.286)\ w/-1.56\ w$	$-/-$	$+59/-68$	III/0	4T
Fe(III)	NR	small	—	—	Low solubility
In(III)	-0.91	small	-115	—	
Mn(II)	$-1.599\ fw$	—	-37	0	
Mo(VI)	$-1.66\ i$	—	-53	—	
Ni(II)	$-1.073\ fw$	—	-97	0	
Pb(II)	$-0.532\ w$	—	-25	0	
Sb(III)	$(-0.2)\ i/-0.80\ w/$	$-/-/$	$-/-30/-$	V/$-$/$-$	
	$-0.93\ w/-1.8\ i$	$-/-$	$-61/-$	0/$-III$?	
Sb(V)	NR				

(continued)

TABLE B-2 (continued)

Substance	$E_{1/2}$, v. vs. S.C.E.	I	$E_{3/4} - E_{1/4}$, mv.	Product	Remarks
0.1F NH₃, 0.1F (NH₄)₂ C₂O₄ (continued)					
Sn(II)	$-1.12/-1.465$ fw	small/—	$-47/-65$	$-/—$	
Sn(IV)	-1.51 i$/-1.75$ i	—/large	$-51/-76$	0/c?	Maximum at -1.2 v.
Te(IV)	-0.704 w	—	-58	0	
Te(VI)	-1.34 w	—	-71	$-$II	
Ti(III)	NR	—	—	—	Low solubility
Tl(I)	-0.473 w	—	-59	0	
U(VI)	-0.498 w	—	-63	V	
V(IV)	(-0.272) fw$/-0.99/-1.32$	$-/$small$/—$	$+89/-/-74$	V$/-/$II	
W(VI)	-1.63 fi	large	-54	c	
Yb(III)	NR	—	—	—	
Zn(II)	-1.243 w	—	-45	0	4T
0.1F HClO₄ or NaClO₄					
Ag(I)	>0 w	2.4	—	0	3T
As(III)	-0.7 i$/-1.0$ fi	$-/$8.8T	$-/—$	$-/—$	1F HNO₃, 10G
As(V)	NR	—	—	—	6F HClO₄
Bi(III)	$+0.022$	4.59	—	0	0.7F HClO₄
	-0.01	—	—	0	1F HNO₃, 10G
Cd(II)	-0.59	3.06	[-28]	0	1F HNO₃, 10G
Ce(IV)	>0	—	—	III	0.1–3F HClO₄
Cr(III)	-0.91 w$/-1.47$ w	$-/—$	$-/—$	II/0	0.1F NH₄ClO₄, 10G
	$-/—$	1.46/>2.92	$-/—$	II/0 + H₂	0.5F NaClO₄, 5G
Fe(II)	-1.46 w	—	irr.	0	1F NH₄ClO₄
Fe(III)	>0 w	—	—	II	Dilute HClO₄
In(III)	-0.573 w	—	-20	0	0.1F HClO₄

Ion	$E_{1/2}$	I			Medium
Mo(VI)	−0.55 w	large	—	IIIc ClO$_4$→	0.4F HClO$_4$
Nb(V)	−0.76	—	—	c NO$_3$→	0.9F HNO$_3$
Ni(II)	−1.013 w	3.3	−69	0	0.1F NaClO$_4$
	−1.010 w	1.5	−62	—	1F NaClO$_4$
	−0.877 w	1.2	−73		8F NaClO$_4$
Np(IV)	−0.102 w	1.43	ca. −75	III	1F HClO$_4$
Os(VIII)	>0 w / −0.45	10.0/—	—/—	Os$_2$O$_3$/—	1F HClO$_4$; 2nd wave is adsorption wave
Pb(II)	−0.38 w	—	[−28]	0	1F HClO$_4$, 5G
	−0.405	3.67	[−28]	0	1F HNO$_3$, 10G
Re(III)	−0.28/−0.46	—/—	irr./irr.	II/0	2F HClO$_4$
Re(VII)	−0.38	6.7		c H$^+$→	4F HClO$_4$
Ru(IV)	>0/+0.20/−0.34	0.91/0.62/1.46	—/—/[−56?]	III/III/II	1F HClO$_4$
Sb(III)	−0.30 w	5.10	ca. −70	0	1F HNO$_3$, 10G
Sb(V)	NR			—	
Sn(II)	(+0.136)/−0.43	—/—	irr./[−28]	IV/0	6F HClO$_4$
	−0.44 w	4.02	—	0	1F HClO$_4$
Sn(IV)	NR				
Tl(I)	−0.46 w	2.74	−56	0	1F HNO$_3$, 10G
	−0.48 w	2.70	−56	0	1F HClO$_4$ or NaClO$_4$
U(III)	(−0.87)	−1.5	[+56]	IV	1F HClO$_4$
U(IV)	−0.86	1.57	irr.	III	0.1F HClO$_4$
U(V)	(−0.18)	−1.57	[+56]	VI	0.01F HClO$_4$, 0.5F NaClO$_4$
U(VI)	−0.18 w	1.57	[−56]	V	0.01F HClO$_4$, 0.5F NaClO$_4$
V(III)	(−0.508) w	1.41	−56	II	1F HClO$_4$ or 0.5F H$_2$SO$_4$
V(IV)	−0.85 fw	3.2	irr.	II	0.05F H$_2$SO$_4$, 5G
Zn(II)	−1.00	—	—	0	1F NaClO$_4$

(continued)

TABLE B-2 (continued)

$7.3F$ (42%) H_3PO_4

Substance	$E_{1/2}$, v. vs. S.C.E.	I	$E_{3/4} - E_{1/4}$, mv.	Product	Remarks
As(III)	-0.46 w/-0.71 i	$-/-$	irr./$-$	$0/-$III	
As(V)	NR				
Bi(III)	-0.15 w	—	—	0	Limited solubility
Cd(II)	-0.77 w	—	-28	0	
Ce(III)	NR				
Ce(IV)	>0	—	—	III	
Co(II)	-1.20 i	—	irr.	0	
Cr(III)	-1.02 fw	—	irr.	II	
Cr(VI)	>0 fi	—	—	III	
Cu(II)	-0.087 w	—	-29	0	
Fe(II)	NR				
Fe(III)	$(-0.395$)w	-1.25	[$+56$]	III	$0.05F$ $Na_4P_2O_7$, $0.05F$ $Na_2B_4O_7$
Mn(II)	$+0.056$ w	—	-60	II	Saturated $K_4P_2O_7$, pH 7–14.5
	NR	—	—	—	$0.4F$ $K_4P_2O_7$, pH 2.3, 20 agar
Mn(III)	NO				
	>0 w	1.17D	—	II	1st wave is doublet
Mo(VI)	±0.0 i/-0.49 w	$-/-$	$-/-$	$-/-$	
Ni(II)	-1.18 i	—	—	0	
Os(VIII)	>0 w	6.4	—	Os_2O_3	i above 0.1 mM Os(VIII)
Pb(II)	-0.534 w	—	-27	0	$0.1F$ $Na_4P_2O_7$, pH 10
Pt(IV)	-0.69	2.57	[-28]	0	$0.045F$ Na_2HPO_4, $0.004F$ citrate, pH 7.0, 12G
	>0 fw	7.65	—	0	

					Remarks
Sb(III)	−0.29 w	—	—	0	
Sb(V)	NR		irr.	0	Minimum at −0.9 v.
Sn(II)	−0.58 fw	small	irr.	0	
Sn(IV)	−0.65 i			—	2T, large maximum
Te(VI)	−0.87 i		—	—	
Tl(I)	−0.63 w	−/−	−57	0	
U(VI)	−0.12/−0.58	−/−	−/−	−/−	
V(II)	(−0.728) w		+97	III	
V(III)	−0.738 i		−59	II	
V(IV)	−0.6 i/−0.93 i	small/—	−/irr.	−/II	
W(VI)	−0.59 w	1.47	—	V	
Zn(II)	−1.13 fi		ca. −50	0	
0.1F KH phthalate					
Bi(III)	−0.23 w	—	[−19]	0	
Co(II)	−1.24	—	irr.	0	
Cu(II)	−0.10 w	—	[−28]	0	
Fe(II)	NR	—		—	
Ni(II)	−1.14	—	irr.	0	
Pb(II)	−0.40	−/−	[−28]	0	
Sn(II)	(−0.89) fi/−1.18 fw		+45/−37	IV/0	1F K$_2$ phthalate, 1F KOH
Ti(IV)	−0.93		irr.	III	1F K$_2$ phthalate, 1F KOH; Saturated phthalic acid
V(II)	(−0.15) fw/(−0.84) w	−1.75/−1.78	+65/+74	IV/III	Saturated KH phthalate, pH 5.2
V(III)	(−0.10) w/−0.88 fw	−1.13/1.22	+85/−150	IV/II	Saturated KH phthalate, pH 5.2
Zn(II)	−1.01	—	[−28]	0	

(continued)

TABLE B-2 (continued)

Substance	$E_{1/2}$, v. vs. S.C.E.	I	$E_{3/4} - E_{1/4}$, mv.	Product	Remarks
	0.1F pyridine (py), 0.1F pyridinium chloride (pyHCl)				
Ag(I)	>0 i	—	—	0	
As(III)	−0.90 i/−1.05 i	−/−	−64/−95	−/−	
As(V)	NR				
Bi(III)	−1.00 i		irr.	0	Low solubility
Cd(II)	−0.617 w		−29	0	
Co(II)	−1.050		−31	0	
Co(III)	>0		—	II	2T
					0.3F py, 0.3F pyHCl, 0.3F EDTA
Cr(III)	−0.99 fi		irr.	II	
Cr(VI)	>0 w/−1.20 fw	−/−	−/−	III/II	2T
Cu(II)	>0 w/−0.219 w	−/−	−/−	I/0	2T
Fe(II)	NR				
Fe(III)	NR			—	Low solubility
In(III)	NR				
IrCl$_6^{-3}$	NR			—	1F py, 1F KCl
IrCl$_6^-$	NR			—	1F py, 1F KCl
Mn(II)	NR				
Mo(VI)	−0.237 fw/−0.680 w	small/—	−/irr.	−/−	2T
Ni(II)	−0.751 w/−1.16 w	2.6/small	−29/irr.	0/−	
Pb(II)	−0.398 w		−27	0	
Pd(II)	−0.31		[−28]	0	
PtCl$_4^-$	NR				1F py, 1F KCl
Rh(III)	−0.414 w			II	1F py, 1F KCl
Ru(H$_2$O)Cl$_5^=$	NR			—	1F py, 1F KCl
RuCl$_6^=$	NR			—	1F py, 1F KCl

Ion					
Sb(III)	-0.47 i	—	irr.	—	Limited solubility
Sb(V)	NR				
Sn(II)	-1.12 fw	—	irr.	0	
Sn(IV)	NR				
Te(VI)	NR				
Tl(I)	-0.451	—	-59	0	
U(VI)	-0.23 fw/-0.45 w/-0.98 fw	—/—/—	—/—/irr.	V/IV/III	
V(IV)	-0.87 fw	—	irr.	—	
V(V)	-0.11 fw/-0.43 w/-0.77 w	—/—/—	irr./irr./irr.	IV/—/II	2T
W(VI)	NR				
Zn(II)	-1.032 fw	—	-29	0	
0.1F NH_3, 0.1F $(NH_4)_2$Tart					
Ag(I)	>0	—	—	0	
As(III)	-1.57 i	22.8	-71	-III	
As(V)	NR				
Bi(III)	-0.543 w	4.23	-66	0	
Cd(II)	-0.727 w	3.40	-36	0	
Ce(IV)	-0.17/-1.02	1.18/1.74	-170/-300	III/—	1st wave may be doublet
Co(II)	-1.225 w	1.88	-43	0	1T
Cr(III)	NR		—	—	Low solubility
Cr(VI)	-0.244 fw	6.23	-43	III	
Cu(II)	-0.147 fi/-0.382 w	1.9/2.2	-61/-77	I/0	1T
Fe(II)	(-0.469) w/-1.418 w	-1.11/0.93	+118/-37	III/0	
Fe(III)	-0.829 i/-1.416 w	1.25/2.69	-145/-28	II/0	
In(III)	-1.16 w	1.28	-150	—	
Mn(II)	-1.528 w	2.10	-35	0	
Mo(VI)	NR				

(continued)

TABLE B-2 (continued)

Substance	$E_{1/2}$, v. vs. S.C.E.	I	$E_{3/4} - E_{1/4}$, mv.	Product	Remarks
0.1F NH$_3$, 0.1F (NH$_4$)$_2$Tart (continued)					
Ni(II)	−0.960 w	3.16	−52	0	1T
Os(VIII)	−0.26 w / −1.51 i	1.5/66	−34/−94	VI/c	1T
Pb(II)	−0.541 w	2.67	−26	0	1T
Ru(IV)	−1.58	17	−74	c	
Sb(III)	−0.95 i	3.74	−110	0	1T
Sb(V)	−1.72 i	—	−64	—	Low solubility
Sn(II)	(−0.534) w / −0.769 w	−2.54/3.02	+42/−22	IV/0	1T
Sn(IV)	NR				
Te(IV)	−0.705 fw	6.39	−74	0	Maximum at −1.26 v.
Te(VI)	−1.51 i	10.1	−125	−II	1T
Tl(I)	−0.468 w	2.21	−57	0	
U(VI)	−0.661 w / −1.08 i	1.52/1.02	−38/−180	V/IV?	
V(IV)	(−0.21) i / −1.58 i	−0.95/1.17	+68/−92	V/III	
V(V)	−0.26/−0.98 fw/−1.58 i	small/1.58/3.2T	−/−190/−160	−/IV/III	
W(VI)	−1.63 i	20.3	−33	c	
Yb(III)	NR				
Zn(II)	−1.204 w	3.32	−40	0	1T
0.25F Na$_2$Tart, 2.0F NaOH					
As(III)	(−0.310) w	ca. −2.9	+38	V	
As(V)	NR				
Bi(III)	−0.961 w	—	−81	0	
Cd(II)	−0.856 w	—	−26	0	

Ce(III)	(−0.30)i (−0.162)w	— —	+91 +56	IV IV	1F KNaTart, 2F K_2CO_3
Ce(IV)	−0.3i/−0.7i/−1.0i/−1.3i	—/—/—/—	−100/−100/ −100/−100	—/—/—/—	1F KNaTart, 2F K_2CO_3
Co(II)	−0.165 w	—	−56	III	
Cr(III)	−1.65 i	—	−80	0	
Cr(VI)	NR		−92	III	
Cu(II)	−0.913 w −0.52 w		−40	0	
Fe(II)	(−1.00)w/−1.38 i	—/—	+58/−135	III/0	
Fe(III)	1.00 w/−1.38 i	—/—	−58/−135	II/0	
Mn(II)	(−0.46)w/−1.82 i	−0.95/—	+46/−40	III/0	
Mo(VI)	NR				
Ni(II)	NR				
Pb(II)	−0.827 w −0.70 w	2.4	−35 [−28]	0 0	0.25F Na_2Tart, 0.1F NaOH, 10G
Sb(III)	(−0.389)w/−1.332 w (−0.30)/−1.3	—/— −2.60/3.5	+45/−55 —/—	V/0 V/0	0.25F Na_2Tart, 0.1F NaOH, 10G
Sb(V)	NR		+56/−62	IV/0	2T
Sn(II)	(−1.01)w/−1.19 w	—/—	−43	0	
Sn(IV)	NR				
Te(IV)	−1.39 w		−59	0	
Te(VI)	NR		−66		
Tl(I)	−0.52 w		+115		2T
U(VI)	−0.87 w		−100	V	Limited solubility
V(IV)	(−0.41)i			IV	
V(V)	−1.86 i				
W(VI)	NR				
Zn(II)	−1.521		−51	0	

(continued)

TABLE B-2 (continued)

Substance	$E_{1/2}$, v. vs. S.C.E.	I	$E_{3/4} - E_{1/4}$, mv.	Product	Remarks
		1F KSCN			
Au(I)	>0	—	—	0	0.1F KSCN or NH$_4$SCN
Bi(III)	>0 w	—	—	0	10G
Cd(II)	−0.651 fw/−1.27 i	—/—	−26/—	0/—	
Ce(IV)		—		?	
Co(II)	−0.53 w	—	−50	0	
Cr(II)	−1.084 fi	−1.64		III	
Cr(III)	(−0.80)	—	−170	II	
	−1.05 fw				
Cr(SCN)$_6^{-3}$	−0.823 w	—	irr.	II	
Cu(II)	>0 w/−0.535 w	D/—	—/−46	I/0	2T
Fe(II)	−1.5 i	—	—	—	
Fe(III)	>0 w	—	—	II	2T
In(III)	−0.72 fw/−1.73 fw	—/—	−22/−63	—/—	
Ir(III) or (IV)	NR	—	—		
Mn(II)	−1.540	—	−36	0	
Mo(VI)	NR				
Ni(II)	−0.685 fw	3.59	−34	0	2T
Pb(II)	−0.445	—	−29	0	0.1F KSCN or NH$_4$SCN
Pd(II)	>0	—	—	0	
Rh(III)	−0.39	—	—	0?	
Ru(H$_2$O)Cl$_5^=$	NR				
RuCl$_6^=$	NR				
Sb(III)	>0 w	—	—	0	2T
Sn(II)	−0.46 i	—	—	0	Limited solubility

					2T
Te(VI)	−1.10 fi/−1.46 w	small/—	—/irr.	—/—	
Ti(III)	(−0.46)	—	[+56]	IV	0.1F KSCN
Ti(IV)	−0.46	—	[−56]	III	0.1F KSCN
Tl(I)	−0.522 w/−1.07 i	—/—	−57/irr.	0/—	
U(VI)	−0.26 w/−1.32 fw		−59/—	V/IV	
V(II)	(−0.47)	−2.04	+67	III	1F NH$_4$SCN
V(III)	−0.46	1.78	−58	II	1F NH$_4$SCN
W(VI)	NR				
Zn(II)	−1.055 fw	—	−29	0	

0.3F triethanolamine, 0.1F NaOH

Bi(III)	−0.74	—	—	0	
Cd(II)	−0.82	—	—	0	
Cu(II)	−0.53	—	—	0	
Fe(III)	−1.01	—	—	II	
Mn(II)	(−0.5)/−1.61	—/—	—/—	III/0	0.6F triethanolamine, 0.54F NaOH
Mn(III)	−0.500 w/−1.7 w	1.25/—	−60/ca. −35	II/0	
Ni(II)	−1.40	—	—	0	I decreases on heating
Pb(II)	−0.88	—	ca. −80	0	
Zn(II)	−1.02 w	2.82	—	0	0.6F triethanolamine, 0.54F NaOH
Zn(II)	−1.57	—	—	0	

TABLE B-3

Index to Data on the Polarographic Characteristics of Inorganic Substances

This index is given to permit the easy location of the data given in Tables B-1 and B-2 for any particular electroactive substance.

The electroactive substances appearing in those Tables are listed below in the alphabetical order of their chemical symbols and in order of increasing oxidation number. For each substance there is given the number of every page on which any information about its polarographic characteristics appears.

Substance	Page numbers
Ag(I)	623, 624, 625, 627, 631, 633, 635, 637, 639, 640, 643, 644, 646, 649, 650, 653, 655, 656, 660, 661
Al(III)	618
As(III)	623, 624, 625, 627, 629, 631, 633, 634, 635, 637, 639, 640, 641, 642, 643, 644, 646, 647, 649, 650, 651, 653, 654, 655, 656, 658, 660, 661, 662
As(V)	623, 624, 629, 631, 633, 635, 637, 639, 644, 646, 647, 649, 650, 651, 653, 655, 656, 658, 660, 661, 662
Au(I)	623, 625, 638, 664
Au(III)	623, 625, 638, 647
BH_4^-	618
Ba^{++}	618
Be^{++}	618
Bi(III)	623, 624, 627, 629, 631, 633, 634, 635, 637, 639, 640, 641, 642, 643, 644, 646, 647, 649, 650, 651, 653, 654, 655, 656, 658, 659, 660, 661, 662, 664, 665
Br^-	618
Br_2	618
BrO_3^-	618
CN^-	618
CNO^-	618
CNS^-	618
C_2N_2	618
CNBr	618
CO_2	618
$C_2O_6^-$	618
Ca^{++}	618
Cd(II)	623, 624, 625, 627, 628, 629, 630, 631, 633, 634, 635, 637, 638, 639, 640, 641, 642, 643, 644, 646, 647, 649, 650, 651, 653, 654, 655, 656, 658, 660, 661, 662, 664, 665
Ce(III)	627, 628, 633, 643, 644, 646, 651, 658, 663
Ce(IV)	627, 631, 633, 637, 639, 643, 644, 646, 649, 650, 651, 653, 655, 656, 658, 661, 663, 664

(continued)

TABLE B-3 *(continued)*

Substance	Page numbers
Cl^-	618
Cl_2	618, 619
ClO^-	619
ClO_2^-	619
ClO_3^-	619
ClO_4^-	619, 657
Co(I)	638
Co(II)	623, 625, 627, 628, 630, 631, 633, 634, 635, 637, 638, 639, 640, 641, 642, 643, 644, 646, 647, 649, 650, 653, 655, 658, 659, 660, 661, 663, 664
Co(III)	625, 628, 630, 637, 638, 640, 641, 643, 649, 654, 660
Cr(II)	626, 628, 630, 636, 638, 647, 664
Cr(III)	623, 624, 626, 627, 628, 630, 631, 633, 636, 637, 638, 639, 640, 643, 644, 646, 649, 650, 652, 653, 654, 655, 656, 658, 660, 661, 663, 664
Cr(VI)	626, 627, 628, 633, 636, 637, 639, 640, 643, 645, 646, 647, 649, 650, 652, 653, 655, 658, 660, 661, 663
Cs^+	619
Cu(I)	626, 646, 650
Cu(II)	623, 624, 626, 627, 628, 629, 630, 631, 633, 634, 636, 637, 638, 639, 640, 641, 642, 643, 645, 646, 647, 649, 650, 652, 653, 654, 655, 658, 659, 660, 661, 663, 664, 665
Dy(III)	619
Eu(III)	628, 643
F^-	619
Fe(II)	623, 625, 626, 627, 628, 631, 633, 635, 636, 637, 639, 641, 645, 646, 647, 649, 650, 652, 653, 654, 655, 656, 658, 659, 660, 661, 663, 664
$Fe(CN)_6^{-4}$	619
Fe(III)	619, 623, 625, 627, 629, 631, 633, 635, 636, 637, 639, 640, 641, 643, 644, 645, 646, 647, 649, 650, 652, 653, 654, 655, 656, 658, 660, 661, 663, 664, 665
$Fe(CN)_6^{-3}$	619
Ga(III)	623, 627, 628, 638
Gd(III)	619
Ge(II)	629
Ge(IV)	626, 627, 643, 654
H^+	619
Hf(IV)	619
Hg(I)	619
Hg(II)	619
I^-	619
IO^-	619
IO_3^-	619

(continued)

TABLE B-3 (*continued*)

(*continued*)

TABLE B-3 (*continued*)

Substance	Page numbers
Os(VI)	629, 632, 638, 648, 649
Os(VIII)	626, 632, 638, 648, 649, 657, 658, 662
Pb(II)	623, 625, 626, 627, 629, 631, 632, 634, 635, 636, 637, 638, 639, 641, 642, 643, 644, 645, 646, 648, 649, 651, 652, 653, 654, 655, 657, 658, 659, 660, 662, 663, 664, 665
Pb(IV)	649
Pd(II)	623, 626, 638, 648, 660, 664
Pr(III)	620
Pt(II)	623, 626, 629, 638, 660
Pt(IV)	623, 658
Ra^{++}	621
Rb^+	621
Re(III)	657
Re(VII)	657
Rh(III)	623, 626, 639, 660, 664
Ru(III)	623, 629, 639, 660, 664
Ru(IV)	629, 639, 657, 660, 662, 664
S^-	621
S	621
SCN^-	618
$S_2O_3^-$	621
$S_4O_6^-$	621
$S_2O_4^-$	621
SO_2	621
SO_3^-	621
$S_2O_6^-$	621
SO_4^-	621
$S_2O_8^-$	621
Sb(III)	624, 625, 627, 629, 632, 634, 635, 636, 637, 639, 640, 641, 642, 643, 646, 648, 649, 651, 652, 653, 654, 655, 657, 659, 661, 662, 663, 664
Sb(V)	625, 630, 632, 634, 636, 637, 640, 645, 646, 648, 649, 651, 652, 653, 655, 657, 659, 661, 662, 663
Sc(III)	621
Se(−II)	626, 630, 648
Se(IV)	626, 648
Se(VI)	629, 630, 641, 648
Sm(III)	621
Sn(II)	624, 625, 630, 632, 634, 635, 636, 637, 640, 642, 643, 645, 647, 648, 649, 651, 652, 654, 656, 657, 659, 661, 662, 663, 664
Sn(IV)	624, 625, 630, 632, 634, 635, 636, 637, 640, 641, 645, 647, 648, 649, 651, 652, 653, 656, 657, 659, 661, 662, 663
Sr^{++}	621

(*continued*)

TABLE B-3 *(continued)*

POLAROGRAPHIC CHARACTERISTICS OF ORGANIC SUBSTANCES

This Appendix consists of a single table containing selected data on the polarographic behaviors of approximately 600 representative organic compounds. Of necessity it is considerably less complete than Appendix B. Many pages would be needed even to list all of the organic compounds that have been investigated polarographically. For most of these, data have been obtained at many pH values; some have been studied in many different buffers and solvents; and some behave in fashions much too complex to be accurately described within the limitations imposed by a tabular form.

For one or another of these reasons, many compounds for which data are available have had to be omitted altogether, while for most of those that are included only a fraction of the data could be given. Nevertheless, an attempt has been made to include enough compounds to illustrate the behavior of each of the important polarographically active functional groups, and to include enough data on each compound to provide a fair description of what is known about its properties.

The first column of the table gives the names of the compounds in alphabetical order. For the most part the nomenclature is that employed in the original literature, although a number of changes have been made to facilitate surveys of the behaviors of closely related compounds. For example, it has seemed better to identify nicotinic and isonicotinic acids as pyridine-3- and -4-carboxylic acids than to separate them by 15 pages, and similarly it seemed better to translate acetoin into 3-hydroxy-2-butanone than to separate it from 1-hydroxy-2-butanone.

The second column gives the composition of the supporting electrolyte, with the aid of the following abbreviations:

BR   Britton–Robinson buffers   McIl   McIlvaine buffers
Cit   citrate   PW   Prideaux-Ward buffers
CL   Clark and Lubs buffers   V   veronal buffers

Quaternary ammonium ions are identified by using conventional abbreviations (Me = methyl, Et = ethyl, n-Bu = n-butyl, etc.) for alkyl groups. The entry "0.5F Na$_2$HPO$_4$–NaH$_2$PO$_4$" means that the buffer contained a total of 0.5 mole per liter of phosphate, the ratio of concentrations of the two salts being such as to yield the pH specified in the following column. The entry "0.5F Na$_2$HPO$_4$ + NaH$_2$PO$_4$," on the other hand, means that the buffer contained 0.5 mole per liter of the monohydrogen phosphate together with enough of the dihydrogen phosphate to yield the stated pH. Maximum suppressors are identified, and their concentrations are given, in the same way as in Tables B-1 and -2. Ionic strengths are given wherever possible unless they are defined by the stated composition of the supporting electrolyte. The solution is understood to be aqueous unless this column contains a slanted line followed by the composition of a non-aqueous solvent. For example, "0.1F LiCl" means 0.1F aqueous lithium chloride; "0.1F LiCl/50% EtOH" means 0.1F lithium chloride in 50% (v/v) ethanol, the remainder of the solvent being water; "0.1F LiCl/EtOH" means 0.1F lithium chloride in anhydrous ethanol; and "0.1F LiCl/C$_6$H$_6$–MeOH (1:1)" means 0.1F lithium chloride in a solvent containing equal proportions (by volume) of benzene and methanol. Non-aqueous solvents are identified by the following symbols:

diox	1,4-dioxane	Me$_2$CO	acetone
DMF	N,N-dimethylformamide	MeOH	methanol
EtOH	ethanol	Me$_2$SO	dimethylsulfoxide
MeCN	acetonitrile	i-PrOH	isopropanol

The third column gives the pH. In work with mixtures of water with non-aqueous solvents, most workers have reported the pH values of their aqueous buffers before addition of the non-aqueous solvent. Others, however, have measured and reported the pH values of the mixtures, and these values are denoted by the symbol "m."

The fourth column gives the half-wave potential, almost always referred to the aqueous saturated calomel electrode, although a few values referred to internal mercury pool electrodes are included and are identified by the symbol "(Hg)". Here and in the columns that follow, data on multiple waves are given in the same way as in Tables B-1 and -2. Half-wave potentials in parentheses are for anodic waves. All values have been rounded off to two decimal places: the half-wave potentials of irreversible waves depend on the drop time, and nearly every wave mentioned in this table is irreversible, but there is hardly a case anywhere in the literature of organic polarography in which an author reporting a half-wave potential to three decimal places has accompanied it by the value of t used to obtain it.

The fifth column gives the diffusion current constant, $i_d/Cm^{2/3}t^{1/6}$. The sixth gives the value of n. The seventh gives the value of αn_a or, by the abbreviation "rev." indicates that the wave is believed to be reversible. If the wave is anodic, the value given in this column is for the anodic parameter $(1 - \alpha)n_a$. The eighth column gives the formula of the product, usually in an abbreviated form to save space. For example, the reduction product of stilbene is given as "—CH_2CH_2—", whose translation into "1,2-diphenylethane" is left to the user. Remarks are given in the ninth column.

Compound	Supporting electrolyte and solvent	pH	$E_{1/2}$, volts vs. S.C.E.	I	n	αn_a	Product	Remarks
Acenaphthene	0.175F (n-Bu)₄NI/75% diox	—	-2.57	—	2	—	—	
Acetaldehyde	HOAc–LiOAc	6.8	-1.89	—	2	—	-CH₂OH	
	0.1F LiOH	—	-1.89	—	2	—	-CH₂OH	
bromo-	Various buffers	2.4	-0.34	—	2	—	Br⁻	
		8.5	-0.40	—	2	—	Br⁻	
		9.8	-1.58/-1.82	—/—	2/2	—/—	Br⁻/-CH₂OH	
		13.0	-1.67/-1.89	—/—	2/2	—/—	Br⁻/-CH₂OH	
chloro-	1F NH₄Cl + NH₃	8.4	-1.06/-1.66	—/—	2/2	—/—	Cl⁻/-CH₂OH	
	0.08F Na₂B₄O₇, 0.8F KCl	9.2	-1.07/-1.78	—/—	2/2	—/—	Cl⁻/-CH₂OH	
dichloro-	1F NH₄Cl + NH₃	8.4	-1.03/-1.67	—/—	4/2	—/—	2 Cl⁻/-CH₂OH	
	0.08F Na₂B₄O₇, 0.8F KCl	9.2	-1.03/ca. -1.8 i	—/—	4/2	—/—	2 Cl⁻/-CH₂OH	
imine	2F NH₃, 2F NH₄Cl	—	-1.36	—	2	—	-CH₂NH₂	
trichloro-, hydrate	1F NH₄Cl + NH₃	8.4	-1.35/-1.66	—/small	6/2	—/—	3 Cl⁻/-CH₂OH	
	0.08F Na₂B₄O₇, 0.32F KCl	9.2	-1.43	3.7	—	ca. 0.3		Partly kinetic
Acetamide, chloro-	0.1F KCl/50% EtOH	—	-1.57	—	2	—	Cl⁻	
oxime	BR/25% EtOH	4	-1.08	—	2	—	-CHNHOH(?)	$\Delta E_{1/2}/\Delta pH = -24$ mv. (pH 2.5-5)
trichloro-, oxime	BR/25% EtOH	4	-0.59	—	2	—	—	$\Delta E_{1/2}/\Delta pH = -54$ mv. (pH 2-5)
Acetanilide, p-chloro-	0.1F Et₄NI/DMF	—	ca. -2.6	3.49	2	0.46	Cl⁻	30°
Acethydroxamic acid	0.1F NaOH	13	(-0.28)/-0.47/-1.27	—/—/—	—/—/—	—/—/—	—/—/—	
Acetic acid	0.05F Me₄NI	—	ca. -1.8	—	1	—	H₂ (+ OAc⁻)	$E_{1/2}$ varies with concn.
bromo-	LiOAc–HOAc + LiBr, μ = 0.2	<3	-0.66	—	2	—	Br⁻	0°
		>7	-1.43	—	2	—	Br⁻	0°
chloro-	0.05F Me₄NI	—	ca. -1.7	—	1	—	H₂	$E_{1/2}$ varies with concn.
dichloro-	0.5F NH₄Cl + NH₃	7-10	-1.55	—	2	—	Cl⁻	

Substance	Medium	pH	E		n		Product
iodo-	0.1F HCl	1.1	−0.17	—	2		I⁻
	0.05F NaOH	12.5	−0.68	—	2	—	I⁻
mercapto-	0.27F Na₂CO₃, 0.07F Me₄NBr/20% i-PrOH	11.3	−0.89	—	2	—	I⁻
	0.2F HOAc, 0.2F NaOAc	4.6	(+0.23)/(−0.26)	—	1-/−1	−/−	—/HgSR
	0.05F NaH₂PO₄, 0.05F Na₂HPO₄	6.8	(−0.38)	—	−1	—	HgSR
	0.2F NH₄Cl, 1F NH₃	—	(−0.56)	—	−1	—	HgSR
trichloro-	0.5F NH₄Cl + NH₃	7-10	−0.84/−1.55	−/−	2/2	−/−	Cl⁻/Cl⁻
	1F NH₄Cl, 2.5F NH₃, 2F KCl	—	−0.73/−1.65	−/−	2/2	−/−	Cl⁻/Cl⁻
trifluoro-	"normal polarographic conditions"	—	NR	—	—	—	—
Acetone	0.05F Et₄NI/75% diox	—	−2.46	—	—	—	=CHOH
	0.05F (n-Bu)₄NCl/90% EtOH	—	−2.57	—	2	—	—
betainylhydrazone	BR	8.2	−1.52	—	2	ca. 1.0	Br⁻
bromo-	OAc⁻ buffer, μ = 0.5	4.6	−0.34	3.3	2	—	—
chloro-	OAc⁻ buffer, μ = 0.5	4.6	−1.15	2.9	2	—	Cl⁻
	V	7	−1.60	—	—	—	—
1,3-dihydroxy-		11	−1.66	—	—	—	—
hydrazone	0.1F KOH	—	(−0.09)	—	—	—	CH₂=C(OHg)—(?)
	1F KOH	—	(−0.15)	—	—	—	—
hydrazone	0.1F NH₄·H₂SO₄, 0.05F H₂SO₄, 0.001F HCl	—	−1.1/−1.4	—	2(?)/—	ca. 0.6/—	=CHNH—(?)/—
	0.025F H₂SO₄/10% Me₂CO, 4T	—	−1.24	3.28	2	—	=CHNH— 30°
imine	2F NH₃, 2F NH₄Cl	—	−1.48	—	2	—	=CHNH₂
iodo-	OAc⁻ buffer, μ = 0.5	4.6	−0.14	3.3	2	—	I⁻
pentabromo-	NH₄⁺-NH₃ buffers	8.2-9.5	−0.12/−0.48/−1.22	—	−/−/−	−/−/−	—/—/—
	PO₄⁻³ buffers	10.5-12.5	−0.15/−0.54/−1.37	—	−/−/−	−/−/−	—/—/—
Acetophenone	0.1F (n-Bu)₄NI, 0.01F Et₄NI/DMF	—	−1.99/−2.46	2.6/2.4	1/1	—/—	monoanion/dianion
	McIl/10% EtOH, μ = 0.45	4.0	−1.23	1.4	1	—	pinacol
		7.1	−1.49	3.2	2	—	carbinol
		9.4	−1.49	3.6	2	—	carbinol

(continued)

Compound	Supporting electrolyte and solvent	pH	$E_{1/2}$, volts vs. S.C.E.	I	n	αn_a	Product	Remarks
Acetophenone (Continued)	Various buffers/50% EtOH	1.3	-1.11	—	1	—	pinacol	
		4.9	-1.31	—	1	—	pinacol	
		7.0	-1.56	—	—	—	chiefly carbinol	
		11.3	-1.60	—	2	—	carbinol	
4-bromo-	McIl/10% EtOH, $\mu = 0.45$	4.0	-1.16/-1.28	1.6/1.6	—/—	—/—	—/—	0°
		7.1	-1.34	2.9	—	—	—	
		9.4	-1.43	3.8	—	—	—	0°
ω-bromo-	McIl/10% EtOH, $\mu = 0.45$	4.8	-0.04/-1.29	1.5/1.1	—/—	—/—	—/—	
		7.1	-0.16/-1.3/-1.43	0.9/small/1.8	—/—/—	—/—/—	—/—/—	
4-chloro-	McIl/10% EtOH, $\mu = 0.45$	4.8	-1.20/-1.31	1.4/1.4	—/—	—/—	—/—	
		5.7	-1.30	2.8	—	—	—	
		9.4	-1.46	3.3	—	—	—	
ω-chloro-	McIl/10% EtOH, $\mu = 0.45$	4.0	-0.58/-1.26	2.7/2.1	—/—	—/—	—/—	
		7.1	-0.54/-1.45	2.9/4.0	—/—	—/—	—/—	
		9.4	-0.55/-1.50	2.7/3.9	—/—	—/—	—/—	
2,4-dihydroxy-	0.1F NH$_4$Cl/50% EtOH	—	-1.49	—	—	—	—	
2,4-dimethoxy-	0.1F NH$_4$Cl/50% EtOH	—	-1.48	—	—	—	—	
ω-fluoro-	McIl/10% EtOH, $\mu = 0.45$	2.2	-0.64/-1.12	3.1/1.4	2/1	—/—	F⁻/pinacol	
		4.0	-0.85/-1.25	3.1/1.4	2/1	—/—	F⁻/pinacol	
		7.1	-1.02/-1.47	3.1/3	2/2	—/—	F⁻/carbinol	
		12	-1.01/-1.59	3.1/2.6	2/—	—/—	F⁻/chiefly carbinol	
2-hydroxy-	0.1F NH$_4$Cl/50% EtOH	—	-1.36	—	—	—	—	
4-hydroxy-	0.1F NH$_4$Cl/50% EtOH	—	-1.45	—	—	—	—	
2-methoxy-	0.1F NH$_4$Cl/50% EtOH	—	-1.37	—	—	—	—	
4-methoxy-	0.1F NH$_4$Cl/50% EtOH	—	-1.43	—	—	—	—	
ω-piperidino-, methiodide	BR, 15G	3.3	-0.80/ca. -1.2	—/—	2/1	—/—	CH$_3$N=/pinacol	
		6.4	-0.90/ca. -1.35	—/—	2/—	—/—	CH$_3$N=/pinacol + carbinol	
		9-10	-0.99/ca. -1.5	—/—	2/2	—/—	CH$_3$N=/carbinol	
Acetylene	0.05F Et$_4$NBr/75% diox	—	NR	—	—	—	—	
diphenyl-	0.175F (n-Bu)$_4$NI/75% diox	—	-2.19	4.16	4	ca. 1.0	—CH$_2$CH$_2$—	
phenyl-	0.175F (n-Bu)$_4$NI/75% diox	—	-2.37	5.10	4	ca. 1.0	—CH$_2$CH$_3$	

Substance	Medium	pH	$E_{1/2}$		n		Substituent
Acetylenedicarboxylic acid	HCl + KCl	0.5	−0.56	7.1	3	—	
diethyl ester	HCl + KCl	1.5	−0.48/−0.63	4.3/4.3	2/2	−/−	rac-α,α'-Me$_2$ succinic acid; Et$_2$ fumarate/Et$_2$ succinate
Acridine	PO$_4^{-3}$ buffer/50% EtOH	8.3	−0.79/−1.45	−/−	1/1	−/−	
1-amino-	PO$_4^{-3}$ buffer/50% EtOH	7.0	−0.65/−1.22	−/−	1/1	−/−	
2-amino-	PO$_4^{-3}$ buffer/50% EtOH	7.0	−0.72/−1.23	−/−	1/1	−/−	
3-amino-	PO$_4^{-3}$ buffer/50% EtOH	7.0	−0.76/−1.35	−/−	1/1	−/−	
4-amino-	PO$_4^{-3}$ buffer/50% EtOH	7.0	−0.75/−1.35	−/−	1/1	−/−	
9-amino-	PO$_4^{-3}$ buffer/50% EtOH	10.4	−1.21/−1.61	−/−	1/1	−/−	
3,6-diamino-	PO$_4^{-3}$ buffer/50% EtOH	7.0	−1.01/−1.36	−/−	1/1	−/−	
3,7-diamino-	PO$_4^{-3}$ buffer/50% EtOH	7.0	−0.84/−1.25	−/−	1/1	−/−	
Acrolein	Various buffers	4.8	−0.83(Hg)	—	2	—	CH$_3$CH$_2$—
		5.8	−0.98(Hg)	—	2	—	CH$_3$CH$_2$—
		8.7–11.0	−1.04/−1.44(Hg)	−/−	2/2	−/−	CH$_3$CH$_2$—/—CH$_2$OH
2,3-dihydroxy-	BR	1.8	(+0.23)	▪	—	—	
		10.7	(−0.18)	—	—	—	
Acrylamide	0.05F Me$_4$NI/30% EtOH	—	−1.91	3.49	—	—	
2-chloro-	0.12F HCl/10% EtOH	—	−1.05	4.93	—	0.69	
	0.05F Me$_4$NI/30% EtOH	—	−1.69/−1.91	3.36/3.16	2/2	0.91/—	Cl⁻/CH$_3$CH$_2$—
Acrylic acid, n-butyl ester	0.2F NH$_4$Cl, 0.2F NH$_3$/10% EtOH	—	−1.59	4.03	—	—	
ethyl ester	0.01F LiCl/20% EtOH	—	−1.95	—	—	—	
	0.05F Me$_4$NI/30% EtOH	—	−1.82	—	—	—	
Acrylonitrile	0.05F Me$_4$NI/30% EtOH	—	−1.96	—	—	—	CH$_3$CH$_2$—
2-chloro-	0.05F Me$_4$NI/30% EtOH	—	−1.53/−1.95	−/−	2/2	−/−	Cl⁻/CH$_3$CH$_2$—
Adenine	McIl, $\mu = 0.5$	1.2–5.5	−0.975–0.090 pH	10.2	6	—	
		≥ 6.5	NR				
Adenosine	HClO$_4$ + KClO$_4$	2.2	−1.13	—	—	—	
Adenylic acid	HClO$_4$ + KClO$_4$	2.2	−1.13	—	—	—	
Adrenaline	PO$_4^{-3}$ buffers	1.8	(+0.19)	—	—	—	
		7.0	(−0.09)	—	—	—	
Adrenochrome	BR	4.5	−0.08	—	2	rev.	
		8.3	−0.29	—	2	rev.	

(continued)

Compound	Supporting electrolyte and solvent	pH	$E_{1/2}$, volts vs. S.C.E.	I	n	αr_a	Product	Remarks
Alloxan	BR	1.8	+0.11	—	—	—	—	
		10.7	−0.29	—	—	—	—	
n-Amyl hydroperoxide	0.3F LiCl/C₆H₆-MeOH (1:1)	—	−0.20	—	2	—	—	
Androstane-3,17-dione	0.05F (n-Bu)₄NCl/90% EtOH	—	−2.38	—	4	—	—CH₂OH	
Aniline, 2-iodo-	0.01F Et₄NBr/67% EtOH	—	−1.56	—	2	—	I⁻	
3-iodo-	0.01F Et₄NBr/67% EtOH	—	−1.66	—	2	—	I⁻	
4-iodo-	0.01F Et₄NBr/67% EtOH	—	−1.72	—	2	—	I⁻	
Anthracene	0.175F (n-Bu)₄NI/75% diox	—	−1.94	—	2	—	9,10-dihydroanthracene	
	0.1F (n-Bu)₄NBr/MeCN	—	−1.48/−2.06(Hg)	3.14/1.89	—/—	—/—	—/—	
9-nitro-	Glycine buffer/55% EtOH	2	−0.21	—	4	—	—NHOH	
Anthraquinone	0.1F Et₄NI/DMF	—	−0.83/−1.46	1.76/1.62	1/1	—/—	monoanion/dianion	
	1F LiCl/DMF	—	−0.85/−1.11	1.3/0.86	1/—	—/—	monoanion/dianion (?)	
	OAc⁻ buffer/40% diox	7.4m	−0.54	—	2	rev.	9,10-diol	
1,2-dihydroxy-	Saturated KCl + HCl/ca. 70% EtOH	1.25	−0.18	—	2	rev.	9,10-diol	
	Saturated KCl + HCl/ca. 70% EtOH	1.25	−0.26	—	2	—	9,10-diol	
-3-sulfonic acid	PO₄⁻³ buffer/1% EtOH	7	−0.55	—	2	—	9,10-diol	
1,3-dihydroxy-	Saturated KCl + HCl/ca. 70% EtOH	1.25	−0.25	—	2	—	9,10-diol	
-1,5-disulfonic acid	PO₄⁻³ buffer/1% EtOH	7	−0.61	—	2	—	9,10-diol	
-2,6-disulfonic acid	PO₄⁻³ buffer/1% EtOH	7	−0.44	—	2	—	9,10-diol	
1-hydroxy-	Saturated KCl + HCl/ca. 70% EtOH	1.25	−0.21	—	2	rev.	9,10-diol	
2-hydroxy-	Saturated KCl + HCl/ca. 70% EtOH	1.25	−0.22	—	2	rev.	9,10-diol	
1-methoxy-	Saturated KCl + HCl/ca. 70% EtOH	1.25	−0.12	—	2	rev.	9,10-diol	
2-methoxy-	Saturated KCl + HCl/ca. 70% EtOH	1.25	−0.20	—	2	rev.	9,10-diol	
1-nitro-	BR	7.0	−0.11	—	—	—	—	
oxime	OAc⁻ buffer/40% diox	5.6	−0.57	—	—	—	—	
	BO₂⁻ buffer/40% diox	10.0	−0.74/−0.99	—/—	—/—	—/—	—/—	
-1-sulfonic acid	PO₄⁻³ buffer/1% EtOH	7.0	−0.58	—	2	—	9,10-diol	
-2-sulfonic acid	PO₄⁻³ buffer/1% EtOH	7.0	−0.48	—	2	—	9,10-diol	
1,2,4-trihydroxy-	OAc⁻ buffer/40% diox	7.4 (m?)	−0.70	—	2	rev.	9,10-diol	

Compound	Medium	pH	$E_{1/2}$		n	Notes/products
Anthrone	OAc⁻ buffer/40% diox	5.6	-0.87/-1.01	-/-	-/-	-/-
		7.4	-0.85	-	1	-
		6.8	-0.99	-	1	-
	PO₄⁻³ buffer/40% diox	2.0	-0.99	-	1	-
	Various buffers/50% EtOH	3.6	-1.03/-1.22	-/-	-/-	-/-
		7.8	-1.26	-	1	-
		12.6	-1.31	-	1	-
Ascorbic acid	BR	1.8	(+0.22)	ca. -3.0	-2	quasi-rev. dehydroascorbic acid
dehydro-		10.7	(-0.19)	ca. -3.0	-2	quasi-rev. dehydroascorbic acid
Aurin	Various buffers	0-10	NR	-	-	-
-tricarboxylic acid	-/30% EtOH	7	-0.76/-1.20	-	-	60°
	-/30% EtOH	7	-0.77/-1.23	-	-	60°
Azobenzene	Various buffers	2.8	-0.11	-	2	rev. -NHNH-
		12.5	-0.72	-	2	rev. -NHNH-
4,4'-dihydroxy-	BO₂⁻ buffer/50% EtOH	9.2	(+0.21)	-	-	-
4-dimethylamino-	0.1F HClO₄/50% EtOH	1.5m	+0.13/ca. -0.7	4.60/ca. 21.5	4/c→H₂	RNH₂ + R'NH₂
	0.1F NaOH/50% EtOH	13.5m	-0.88	2.26	2	-NHNH-
Azoxybenzene	PO₄⁻³ buffer/20% EtOH	6.3	-0.63	-	4	-NHNH-
Azulene	0.175F (n-Bu)₄NI/75% diox	—	-1.64/-2.30/-2.55	-/-/-	1/3/2	rev./-/-/-
Barbituric acid	Various buffers	3-10	NR	-	-	-
5,5-diethyl-	BO₂⁻ buffer	9.3	(+0.04)	-	-	Hg salt
Benzalacetone	Various buffers/50% EtOH, 10G	1.3	-0.72	-	1	bimolecular ketone
		4.9	-0.96	-	-	-
		7.2	-1.11/-1.29	-	-	-CH₂CH₂-
		8.6	-1.27	-	2	-CH₂CH₂-
		11.3	-1.32	-	2	-
Benzalacetophenone	Various buffers/50% EtOH, 10G	1.3	-0.53/-0.96	-/-	1/1	bimolecular ketone/-CH₂CH₂-
		7.2	-0.89/-1.09	-/-	-/-	tone/-CH₂CH₂-
		11.3	-1.15/-1.64	-/-	2/2	-CH₂CH₂-/carbinol

(continued)

Compound	Supporting electrolyte and solvent	pH	$E_{1/2}$, volts vs. S.C.E.	I	n	αn_a	Product	Remarks
Benzalacetophenone (Continued)	Me_4NOAc-HOAc buffers/50% i-PrOH	7.5m	−0.93/−1.12/−1.60	—/—/—	1/1/1	—/—/—	bimolecular ketone/ $-CH_2CH_2-$/pinacol	
2′,4-dihydroxy-	Me_4NOAc-HOAc buffer/50% i-PrOH	9.6m	−1.10/−1.63	—/—	2/1	—/—	$-CH_2CH_2-$/pinacol	
		7.5m	−1.11/−1.24/−1.55	—/—/—	1/1/1	—/—/—	bimolecular ketone/ $-CH_2CH_2-$/pinacol	
4′,4-dihydroxy-	Me_4NOAc-HOAc buffer/50% i-PrOH	7.5m	−1.10/−1.24/−1.72	—/—/—	1/1/1	—/—/—	bimolecular ketone/ $-CH_2CH_2-$/pinacol	
2′-hydroxy-	Me_4NOAc-HOAc buffer/50% i-PrOH	7.5m	−0.98/−1.20/−1.58	—/—/—	1/1/1	—/—/—	bimolecular ketone/ $-CH_2CH_2-$/pinacol	
4′-hydroxy-	Me_4NOAc-HOAc buffer/50% i-PrOH	7.5m	−1.13/−1.79	—/—	2/1	—/—	$-CH_2CH_2-$/pinacol	
Benzaldehyde	0.1F Et_4NI/DMF	—	−1.80/−2.35	2.3/?	—/—	—/—	—/—	
	0.03F $Me_4NH_2PO_4$, 0.07F $(Me_4N)_2$-HPO_4/50% diox							
	BR/50% EtOH	1.3	−1.46	2.12			$-CHOH-CHOH-$	
		4.9	−0.98		1		$-CHOH-CHOH-$	
			−1.21		1		$-CHOH-CHOH-$	
		7.0	−1.33/−1.44	—/—	1/1	—/—	$-CHOH-CHOH-$/$-CH_2OH$	
		11.1	−1.51		2		$-CH_2OH$	
2-amino-	0.2F NaOAc-HOAc/60% EtOH	3.2	−1.09	—	1	—	$-CHOH-CHOH-$	
3-amino-	0.2F NaOAc-HOAc/60% EtOH	3.2	−1.03	—	1	—	$-CHOH-CHOH-$	
4-amino-	—/5% MeOH	3.2	−1.15	—	1	—	$-CHOH-CHOH-$	
4-cyano-		0	−0.68	—	1	—	$-CHOH-CHOH-$	Extrapolated value
2-hydroxy-	BR/50% EtOH	1.8	−1.02	—		—	$-CHOH-CHOH-$	
		6.8	−1.35	—		—	$-CHOH-CHOH-$	
		12.0	−1.63	—	2	—	$-CH_2OH$	
oxime	PO_4^{-3} buffer	5.4	−0.98	—		—		
4-hydroxy-	BR/50% EtOH	1.8	−1.16	—		—		
		6.8	−1.45	—		—		
		12.0	−1.85	—		—		
imine	2F NH_3, 2F NH_4Cl	—	−1.04	—	2	—	$=CHNH_2$	
2-iodo-	0.2F NaOAc-HOAc/60% EtOH	3.2	−0.91	—		—	$-CHOH-CHOH-$ (?)	
3-iodo-	0.2F NaOAc-HOAc/60% EtOH	3.2	−0.95	—		—	$-CHOH-CHOH-$ (?)	
4-iodo-	0.2F NaOAc-HOAc/60% EtOH	3.2	−0.98	—		—	$-CHOH-CHOH-$ (?)	

Substance	Supporting electrolyte	pH	$E_{1/2}$ (v)	i_d	n	Products
2-methoxy-	BR/50% EtOH	1.8	−1.03	—	—	—
		6.8	−1.49	—	—	—
		12.0	−1.53	—	—	—
4-methoxy-	BR/50% EtOH	1.8	−1.17	—	—	—
		6.8	−1.47	—	—	—
		12.0	−1.60	—	—	—
oxime	Various buffers/50% EtOH	1.3	−0.96	—	—	—
		4.9	−1.18	—	—	—
1,2-Benzanthracene	0.175F (n-Bu)$_4$NI/75% diox	—	−2.03/−2.54	—/—	2/2	—/—
Benzanthrone	0.05F H$_2$SO$_4$/75% MeOH	—	−0.92	3.28	—	—
Benzene, bromo-	0.2F (n-Bu)$_4$NI/DMF	—	−2.38	—	—	—
	0.05F Et$_4$NBr/75% diox	—	−2.32	—	—	—
2-chloro-	0.2F (n-Bu)$_4$NI/DMF	—	−1.94/−2.55	4.50/1.44	—/—	—/—
3-chloro-	0.2F (n-Bu)$_4$NI/DMF	—	−2.02/−2.57	3.32/2.83	—/—	—/—
4-chloro-	0.2F (n-Bu)$_4$NI/DMF	—	−2.14/−2.55	3.09/2.61	—/—	—/—
chloro-	0.1F Et$_4$NI/DMF	—	−2.58	—	—	—
	0.2F (n-Bu)$_4$NI/DMF	—	−2.54	2.95	—	—
	0.05F Et$_4$NBr/75% diox	—	NR	—	—	—
m-dibromo-	0.2F (n-Bu)$_4$NI/DMF	—	−1.94/−2.42	3.79/2.68	—/—	—/—
o-dibromo-	0.2F (n-Bu)$_4$NI/DMF	—	−1.83	6.53	—	—
p-dibromo-	0.05F Et$_4$NBr/75% diox	—	−2.07/−2.55	3.02/3.49	—/—	Cl−
m-dichloro-	0.05F Et$_4$NBr/75% diox	—	−2.48	—	—	Cl−
o-dichloro-	0.05F Et$_4$NBr/75% diox	—	−2.51	—	2	Cl−
p-dichloro-	0.05F Et$_4$NBr/75% diox	—	−2.49	—	2	Cl−
1,2-dihydroxy-	Various buffers	3.7	(+0.36)	—	−2	o-benzoquinone
		9.7	(+0.01)	—	−2	o-benzoquinone
1,3-dihydroxy-	Various buffers		NR	—	—	—
2,4-dinitro-	Various buffers	2.0	−0.14/−0.26	—/—	6/6	—/—
		8.0	−0.55/−0.80	—/—	6/6	—/—
		10.0	−0.97i/−1.20i	—/—	6/6	—/—
4,6-dinitro-	Various buffers	2.0	−0.09/−0.27	—/—	6/6	—/—
		8.0	−0.40/−0.74	—/—	6/6	—/—
		10.0	−0.73i/−1.04i	—/—	6/6	—/—

(continued)

Compound	Supporting electrolyte and solvent	pH	$E_{1/2}$, volts vs. S.C.E.	I	n	αn_a	Product	Remarks
Benzene (*Continued*)								
m-diiodo-	0.01F Et₄NBr/67% EtOH	—	-1.38	—	—	—	—	
o-diiodo-	0.01F Et₄NBr/67% EtOH	—	-1.23	—	—	—	—	
p-diiodo-	0.01F Et₄NBr/67% EtOH	—	-1.46	—	—	—	—	
m-dinitro-	KCl–HCl/10% EtOH, 10G	0.5	-0.03/-0.12/—i	—/—/—	4/4/4	—/—/—	—/—/—	
	Phthalate buffer/10% EtOH, 10G	3.0	-0.20/-0.35/—i	—/—/—	4/4/2	—/—/—	—/—/—	
	BO₂⁻ buffer/10% EtOH, 10G	9.2	-0.38/-0.74	—/—	4/4	—/—	—/—	
o-dinitro-	KCl–HCl/10% EtOH, 10G	0.5	-0.01/-0.16	—/—	4/8	—/—	—/—	
	Phthalate buffer/10% EtOH, 10G	3.0	-0.18/-0.41	—/—	4/8	—/—	—/—	
	BO₂⁻ buffer/10% EtOH, 10G	9.2	-0.38/-0.74	—/—	4/6	—/—	—/—	
p-dinitro-	KCl–HCl/10% EtOH, 10G	0.5	-0.01/-0.18	—/—	4/8	—/—	—/—	
	Phthalate buffer/10% EtOH, 10G	3.0	-0.14/-0.40	—/—	4/8	—/—	—/—	
	BO₂⁻ buffer/10% EtOH, 10G	9.2	-0.34/-0.80/—i	—/—/—	4/4/4	—/—/—	—/—/—	
iodo-	0.05F Et₄NBr/75% diox	—	-1.62	—	2	—	I⁻	
3-bromo-	0.01F Et₄NBr/67% EtOH	—	-1.13	—	—	—	—	
3-chloro-	0.01F Et₄NBr/67% EtOH	—	-1.45	—	—	—	—	
nitro-	Various buffers/10% EtOH, 10G	1.0	-0.22/-0.68	5.90/1.95	4/2	—/—	—NHOH/—NH₂	αn_a at pH 2.5
		3.0	-0.34/-0.86	5.35/2.15	4/2	0.79/—	—NHOH/—NH₂	
		6.0	-0.54	—	4	—	—NHOH	
		12.0	-0.83	—	4	0.67/—	—NHOH	αn_a at pH 9.2
2-amino-	0.2F NaOAc + HCl/60% EtOH	3.2	-0.53	—	—/—	—/—	—/—	
3-amino-	BR	1.8	-0.12/-0.53	—/—	—/—	—/—	—/—	
		4.3	-0.23/-0.76	—/—				
		7.2	-0.47	—	—	—	—	
		9.2	-0.65	—	—	—	—	
	0.2F NaOAc + HCl/60% EtOH	3.2	-0.46	—	—	—	—	
4-amino-	Various buffers	1–9	-0.24 − 0.061 pH	—	6	—	—NH₂	
2-chloro-	0.2F NaOAc + HCl/60% EtOH	3.2	-0.59	—	—	—	—	
	Various buffers/50% EtOH	2.7	-0.64	—	—	—	—	
		7.4	-0.91	—	—	—	—	
		11.7	-1.07	—	—	—	—	
3-chloro-	Various buffers/50% EtOH	2.7	-0.53	—	—	—	—	
		7.4	-0.86	—	—	—	—	
		11.7	-1.05	—	—	—	—	

Substance	Supporting electrolyte	pH	$E_{1/2}$		n		Products
4-chloro-	Various buffers/50% EtOH	2.7	-0.59	—	—	—	—
		7.4	-0.87	—	—	—	—
		11.7	-1.15	—	—	—	—
2,3-dihydroxy-	McIl	2.1	-0.16	—	6	—	—NH₂
	BO₂⁻ buffers	8.0	-0.49	—	6	—	—NH₂
		10–11.5	-0.73	—	6	—	—NH₂
2,6-dihydroxy-	McIl	2.0	-0.21	—	6	—	—NH₂
	BO₂⁻ buffers	9.2	-0.61	—	6	—	—NH₂
		10.0	-0.72	—	6	—	—NH₂
3,4-dihydroxy-	McIl	2.1	-0.34	—	6	—	—NH₂
	BO₂⁻ buffers	8.0	-0.65	—	6	—	—NH₂
		10.1	-0.84/-1.32	—/—	2/4	—	—NO/—NH₂
2-methoxy-	Various buffers / 10% EtOH	2.0	-0.29/-0.58	—/—	4/2	—	—NHOH/—NH₂
		4.0	-0.46	—	4	—	—NHOH
		8.0	-0.68	—	4	—	—NHOH
		12.0	-0.80	—	4	—	—NHOH
3-methoxy-	Various buffers/10% EtOH	2.0	-0.28/-0.69	—/—	4/2	—	—NHOH/—NH₂
		4.0	-0.41/-0.93	—/—	4/2	—	—NHOH/—NH₂
		8.0	-0.63	—	4	—	—NHOH
		12.0	-0.76	—	4	—	—NHOH
4-methoxy-	Various buffers/10% EtOH	2.0	-0.35/-0.64	—/—	4/2	—	—NHOH/—NH₂
		4.0	-0.46/-0.84	—/—	4/2	—	—NHOH/—NH₂
		8.0	-0.72	—	4	—	—NHOH
		12.0	-0.86	—	4	—	—NHOH
nitroso-	McIl/10% EtOH, 5G	2	>0/-0.71ƒ	—/—	2/2	—/—	—NHOH/—NH₂
		>4	+0.33 - 0.061 pH	—	2	—	—NHOH
1,3,5-trihydroxy-	Various buffers	—	NR				
1,3,5-trinitro-	KCl–HCl/10% EtOH, 10G	0.5	+0.04/-0.01/	—/—	4/4/	—/—	-/-/-/-
			-0.06/—i			—/—	-/-/-/-
	Phthalate buffer/10% EtOH, 10G	3.0	-0.12/-0.20/	—/—	4/4/	—/—	-/-/-/-
			-0.30/—i		4/2/	—/—	-/-/-/-
	BO₂⁻ buffer/10% EtOH, 10G	9.2	-0.34/-0.48/-0.65	—/—	4/4/4	—/—	-/-/-/-
Benzenediazonium chloride	CL	0	-0.18/-0.67	—/—	—/—	—/—	-/-
		6.0	+0.05/-0.05/-0.92	—/—	—/—	—/—	-/-
		9.9	-0.20/-0.97	—/—	—/—	—/—	-/-

(continued)

Compound	Supporting electrolyte and solvent	pH	$E_{1/2}$, volts vs. S.C.E.	I	n	αn_a	Product	Remarks
Benzenephosphonic acid,								
2- or 4-bromo-	McII (pH 2.2) or BO_2^- (pH 10) buffer	—	NR					
2-nitro-	McII, 10G	2.3	−0.21	—	—	—	—	
	NaH_2PO_4–Na_2HPO_4, 10G	6.9	−0.55	—	—	—	—	
	BO_2^- buffer, 10G	10.0	−0.73	—	—	—	—	
3-nitro-	McII, 10G	2.3	−0.23	—	—	—	—	
	NaH_2PO_4–Na_2HPO_4, 10G	6.9	−0.64	—	—	—	—	
	BO_2^- buffer, 10G	10.0	−0.77	—	—	—	—	
4-nitro-	McII, 10G	2.3	−0.24	—	—	—	—	
	NaH_2PO_4–Na_2HPO_4, 10G	6.9	−0.63	—	—	—	—	
	BO_2^- buffer, 10G	10.0	−0.75	—	—	—	—	
Benzil	Various buffers/50% EtOH, 10G	1.3	−0.27	—	2	—	benzoin	
		7.2	−0.64	—	2	—	benzoin	
		8.6	−0.72	—	2	—	benzoin	
		11.3	−0.75	—	2	—	benzoin	
	BO_2^- buffers	9–10	NR	—				
p-Benzohydroquinone	$0.1F$ Et_4NClO_4/Me_2SO	—	NO					
	$0.1F$ PO_4^{-3} buffer	7.0	(+0.04)	—	−2	rev.	quinone	
Benzoic acid	$0.1F$ Et_4NI/50% diox	—	−1.87	—	1	—	H_2 (+ —COO^-)	$E_{1/2}$ varies with concn.
3,4-dihydroxy-	PO_4^{-3} buffers	2.9	(+0.45)	—	—	—	—	
		9.4	(+0.19)	—	—	—	—	
2-iodo-	$0.5F$ NH_4Cl + NH_3	8.8	−1.41	—	2	—	I^-	
3-iodo-	$0.5F$ NH_4Cl + NH_3	8.8	−1.46	—	2	—	I^-	
4-iodo-	$0.5F$ NH_4Cl + NH_3	8.8	−1.44	—	2	—	I^-	
3,4,5-trihydroxy-	PO_4^{-3} buffers	8.8	(+0.14)	—	—	—	—	
		11.2	(−0.04)	—	—	—	—	
Benzoin	BR/50% EtOH	1.3	−0.90	—	2	—	hydrobenzoin	
		7.0	−1.39	—	2	—	hydrobenzoin	
		11.6	−1.53	—	2	—	hydrobenzoin	

Substance	Medium	pH	E		n	rev.	products
Benzophenone	0.1F Et4NI/DMF	—	-1.72/-1.99	1.7/1.52	1/1	—/—	—/—
	Various buffers/50% EtOH	1.3	-0.91	—	1	—	benzpinacol
		3.0	-1.05/-1.24	—/	1/1	—/—	pinacol/benzhydrol
		4.9	-1.14	—	2	—	carbinol
		8.5	-1.31	—	2	—	carbinol
		11.3	-1.38	—	2	—	carbinol
4-chloro-	Various buffers/25% EtOH	1.1	-0.89	—	1	—	pinacol
		2.7	-0.93/-1.15	—/	1/1	—/—	pinacol/carbinol
		5.6	-1.26	—	2	—	carbinol
		7.5	-1.36/-1.61	—/	2/—	—/—	carbinol/—
		9.6	-1.45/-1.74	—/	2/—	—/—	carbinol/—
		11.2	-1.49/-1.77	—/	2/—	—/—	carbinol/—
oxime	OAc--PO4-3-BO2- buffers + KCl/25% EtOH, μ = 0.33	2	-0.68	4.8	—/	0.21	—/
o-Benzoquinone	BR	9.5	-1.23/-1.65	0.6/3.6	2	—/0.13	pyrocatechol
p-Benzoquinone	0.1F Et4NClO4/Me2SO	5.0	+0.29	—/	1/1	rev./irr.	—/
	0.1F PO4-3 buffer	7.0	-0.40/-1.24	—/	2	rev.	hydroquinone
2,6-dimethoxy-	PO4-3 buffer	7.0	+0.04	—	2	rev.	hydroquinone
2,5-dimethyl-	0.1F HOAc, 0.1F NaOAc/50% MeOH	5.4m	-0.13	—	2	rev.	hydroquinone
2,6-dimethyl-	OAc- buffer/75% EtOH	6.2m	+0.04	—	2	rev.	hydroquinone
2-methoxy-	PO4-3 buffer	7.0	+0.04	—	2	rev.	hydroquinone
2-methyl-	OAc- buffer/75% EtOH	6.2m	-0.04	—	2	rev.	hydroquinone
tetramethyl-	OAc- buffer/75% EtOH	6.2m	+0.05	—	2	rev.	hydroquinone
2,3,5-trimethyl-	OAc- buffer/75% EtOH	6.2m	-0.14; -0.07	—	2	rev.	hydroquinone
Benzoyl peroxide	0.3F LiCl/C6H6-MeOH (1:1)	—	±0.00	3.0	2	—	benzoic acid
Benpinacol	0.12F NaOH	—	(-0.58)	—	-2	0.50	benzophenone
2,2'-Bi(pyrazolanthronyl)	0.65F NaOH/50% EtOH, 5G	—	-0.87	—	2	—	—
Bromoform	0.05F Et4NBr/75% diox	—	-0.64/-1.51	—	2/4	—	Br-/2 Br-
1,3-Butadiene	0.05F Et4NBr/75% diox	0.6	-2.59	—	—	—	—
1,3-Butadione, 1-phenyl-	Various buffers	10	-1.06; ca. -1.6	—	—	—	—
Butadiyne	0.05F Et4NBr/75% diox	—	-2.27	—	—	—	—

(continued)

Compound	Supporting electrolyte and solvent	pH	$E_{1/2}$, volts vs. S.C.E.	I	n	αn_a	Product	Remarks
n-Butane, 1-bromo-	0.05F Et₄NBr/75% diox	—	−2.23	—	—	—	—	
1-iodo-	0.05F Et₄NBr/75% diox	—	−2.27	—	—	—	—	
1-nitro-	0.1F Na₂HPO₄ + H₃PO₄, 0.5F KCl	5.0	−0.73	—	4	—	—NHOH	
		7.0	−0.83	—	4	—	—NHOH	
			−1.22	—	4	—	—NHOH	
2-nitro-	0.3F LiCl/C₆H₆–MeOH (1:1)	5.0	−0.79	—	4	—	—NHOH	
	0.1F Na₂HPO₄ + H₃Cit, 0.5F KCl	7.0	−0.85	—	4	—	—NHOH	
	0.3F LiCl/C₆H₆–MeOH (1:1)		−1.31	—	4	—	—NHOH	
2,3-Butanedione	Various buffers	1.8–9.1	−0.30 – −0.065 pH	—	—	—	—	
dioxime	0.1F HCl/15% EtOH		−0.42	—	—	—	—	
	0.1F HCl/15% EtOH		−0.81	11.5	8	—	diamine	
	same, after aging		−0.54	6.2	8	0.53		
	0.1F NH₄Cl, 0.1F NH₃/15% EtOH PO₄⁻³ or BO₂⁻ buffers, pH > 8, or NaOH solutions/15% EtOH		−1.56	—	—	—		
imine			NR					
1-Butanol, 2-nitro-	2F NH₃, 2F NH₄Cl		−0.58	—	—	—		
	McII	2.0	−0.63	—	—	—		
		7.0	−0.82	—	—	—		
	BO₂⁻ buffer	10.0	−0.92	—	—	—		
2-Butanol, 1-nitro-	McII	2.0	−0.52	—	—	—		
		7.0	−0.81	—	—	—		
	BO₂⁻ buffer	10.0	−0.85	—	—	—		
2-Butanone	0.025F MeNI		−2.2	—	—	—		
betainylhydrazone	0.05F (n-Bu)₄NCl/90% EtOH		−2.59	—	2	—	=CHOH	
	BR	8.2	−1.52	—	2	1.0		
1-chloro-	BO₂⁻ buffer	10	−1.10	—	—	—		
3-chloro-	BO₂⁻ buffer	10	−1.06	—	—	—		
1-hydroxy-	0.1F KCl		−1.79	—	—	—		
3-hydroxy-	0.05F (n-Bu)₄NCl/90% EtOH		−2.45	—	4(?)	—	2-butanol (?)	

Substance	Supporting electrolyte	pH	$E_{1/2}$		n		Products
1-Butene, 2-nitro-	0.1F Na$_2$HPO$_4$ + H$_3$Cit, 0.5F KCl	5.0	-0.35	—	—	—	—/—
		7.0	-0.46	—	—	—	—
1-Buten-3-one	0.1F OAc$^-$, BO$_2^-$, or PO$_4^{-3}$ buffers, 0.5F KCl/10% EtOH	2–12	-0.89–0.061 pH/-1.52	—/—	—/—	—/—	—/—
1-Buten-3-yne	0.05F Et$_4$NBr/75% diox	—	$-2.40/-2.58$	—/—	—/—	—/—	—/—
tert-Butyl hydroperoxide	0.3F H$_2$SO$_4$/5% EtOH	—	-0.31	—	2	—	tert-butanol
	0.3F LiCl/C$_6$H$_6$–MeOH (1:1)	5.8	-1.00	—	—	—	—
i-Butyraldehyde hydrazone	0.2F Me$_4$NOH/50% EtOH	—	-1.91 (Hg)	—	—	—	—
n-Butyraldehyde	0.1F N$_2$H$_4$, H$_2$SO$_4$, 0.05F H$_2$SO$_4$, 0.001F HCl	—	$-0.9/-1.4$	—	—/—	ca. 0.6/—	—/—
2-bromo-	0.2F Me$_4$NOH/50% EtOH	—	-1.90 (Hg)	—	—	—	Br$^-$
	Li$^+$-salt buffers/50% diox	6	-1.23	—	—	—	Br$^-$/—CH$_2$OH
n-Butyric acid, 2-bromo-	0.5F KCl + HCl	11	$-1.26/-1.90$	—	2/2	—/	Br$^-$/—
	0.5F NaOAc + HOAc	2.0	-0.37	—	2	0.55	Br$^-$
	0.5F NH$_4$Cl + NH$_3$	5.2	-0.81	—	2	—	Br$^-$
		8.2	-1.15	—	2	0.28	Br$^-$
Carbon tetrachloride	0.175F (n-Bu)$_4$NBr/DMF	—	$-0.25/-1.49/-2.17$ (Hg)	5.79/ 1.42/1.92	—/—/—	—/—/—	—/—/—
	0.05F Et$_4$NBr/75% diox	—	$-0.78/-1.71$	—	2/2	—/—	Cl$^-$/Cl$^-$
	0.05F Me$_4$NBr/0–20% MeOH	—	$-0.40/—$	—	2/2	—/—	Cl$^-$/Cl$^-$
	0.05F Me$_4$NBr/50% MeOH	—	$-0.58/—$	—	2/2	—/—	Cl$^-$/Cl$^-$
	0.05F Me$_4$NBr/67% MeOH	—	$-0.70/—$	—	2/2	—/—	Cl$^-$/Cl$^-$
	0.05F Me$_4$NBr/100% MeOH	—	$-0.89/—$	—	2/2	—/—	Cl$^-$/Cl$^-$
	0.05F LiCl, LiOH, LiNO$_3$, or NH$_4$Cl/20% MeOH	—	$-0.35/—$	—	2/2	—/—	Cl$^-$/Cl$^-$
	0.05F KSCN/20% MeOH	—	$-0.44/—$	—	2/2	—/—	Cl$^-$/Cl$^-$
	0.05F KI or Me$_4$NI/20% MeOH	—	$-0.53/—$	—	2/2	—/—	Cl$^-$/Cl$^-$
	0.05F LiCl, LiNO$_3$, LiBr, or KI/100% MeOH	—	$-1.09/—$	—	2/2	—/—	Cl$^-$/Cl$^-$
Chloramine-T	0.025F K$_2$SO$_4$	2.2	-0.13	—	—	—	—
Chloramphenicol	BR	2.2	$-0.35/-1.05$	—	—/—	—/—	—/—
		10.1	-0.75	—	—	—	—
Chloroform	0.175F (n-Bu)$_4$NBr/DMF	—	$-1.45/-2.14$ (Hg)	3.18/3.24	2/2	—/—	Cl$^-$/Cl$^-$
	0.05F Et$_4$NBr/75% diox	—	$-1.67/—$(?)	—/—	2/(2)	—/—	Cl$^-$/(Cl$^-$)
	0.1F Me$_4$NBr/67% MeOH	—	-1.70	—	2	—	Cl$^-$

(continued)

Compound	Supporting electrolyte and solvent	pH	$E_{1/2}$, volts vs. S.C.E.	I	n	αn_a	Product	Remarks
p-Chloromercuribenzoic acid	BR, 0.1F KCl	9	−0.28	—	—	—	—	
Chlorotriethyllead	1F KCl	—	−0.68	—	1	—	(Et₃Pb)₂	
Cholestan-3-one	0.05F (n-Bu)₄NCl/90% EtOH	—	−2.28	—	2	—	—	
Cinchonidine	OAc⁻ buffer	3	−0.90	—	—	—	—	
Cinchonine	OAc⁻ buffer	3	−0.90	—	—	—	—	
Cinnamic acid	1F HCl	—	ca. −1.0	—	—	—	—	
	Et₄NOH/50% EtOH	—	−1.95	—	—	—	—	
4-methoxy-	Et₄NOH/50% EtOH	—	−2.00	—	—	—	—	
Citrinin	Buffer/75% EtOH	2.0	−0.81	—	—	—	—	
Colchiceine	Various buffers/50% EtOH	1.8	−0.96	—	1	—	—	
		6.8	−1.42	—	—	—	—	
		12.0	−1.78	—	—	—	—	
Colchicine	Various buffers	1.8	−0.96	—	1	—	—	
		6.8	−1.40	—	—	—	—	
		12.0	−1.42	—	2	—	—	
Cortisone	0.1F HOAc, 0.1F NaOAc/50% MeOH	—	−1.36	—	2	—	—	
Cotarnoline	BR	4	−0.92	—	2	—	—	
		8	−1.19	—	2	—	—	
Crotonaldehyde	Various buffers	1-11	−0.83 − 0.06 pH	1.50	1	—	—	
Crotonic acid	0.1F LiOH	—	−2.05	—	—	—	—	
	0.05F Et₄NBr/75% diox	—	−1.94	—	—	—	—	
Cumene hydroperoxide	0.05F Et₄NBr/75% diox	—	−0.88	—	—	—	—	
Cyclobutane, bromo-	0.3F LiCl/C₆H₆-MeOH (1:1)	—	−2.36	—	—	—	—	
	0.01F Et₄NBr/DMF	—	−2.29	—	—	—	—	
Cyclohexane, bromo-1,2,3,4,5,6-hexachloro-, α isomer	0.06F KI/50% EtOH	—	NR	—	—	—	—	
	0.1F Et₄NI/80% EtOH	—	−1.98	—	—	—	—	
β isomer	0.06F KI/50% EtOH	—	NR	—	—	—	—	
	0.1F Et₄NI/80% EtOH	—	−2.11	—	—	—	—	
γ isomer	0.06F KI/50% EtOH	—	−1.35 i	—	—	—	—	
	0.1F Et₄NI/80% EtOH	—	−1.57	—	—	—	—	

Substance	Supporting electrolyte	pH	$E_{1/2}$, volts	I	n	I	Products	Remarks
Cyclohexanone	0.05F Et$_4$NI/75% diox	—	-2.45	—	—	—	—	—
	0.05F (n-Bu)$_4$NCl/90% EtOH	—	-2.40	—	2	—	—	—
betainylhydrazone	BR	8.2	-1.47	—	2	1.0	—	—
2-chloro-	0.5F OAc⁻ or PO$_4^{-3}$ buffer	4.6–10.5	-0.98	1.9	2	0.3	Cl⁻	$\Delta E_{1/2}/\Delta$pH = ca. -80 mv. I at pH 7
	0.5F NH$_4$Cl + NH$_3$	9.5	-1.02/-1.66	—/—	2/2	—/—	Cl⁻/=CHNH$_2$	—
	0.1F Me$_4$NCl	—	-0.97	1.13	—	0.26	—	—
	0.1F (n-Bu)$_4$NBr/DMF	—	-1.83	0.62	—	0.31	—	—
cis-4-tert-butyl-	0.1F (n-Bu)$_4$NBr/DMF	—	-2.00	0.43	—	0.45	—	—
trans-4-tert-butyl-	0.1F (n-Bu)$_4$NBr/DMF	—	-1.86	0.50	—	0.26	—	—
imine	2.5F NH$_3$, 1.25F (NH$_4$)$_2$SO$_4$	9.3	-1.50	—	2	—	=CHNH$_2$	—
2-Cyclohexenone	0.1F NH$_4$Cl	—	-1.55 (Hg)	—	2	—	—	—
Cycloöctatetraene	0.1F Me$_4$NOH/50% EtOH	—	-1.51	—	2	—	—	—
Cyclopentadienone, tetraphenyl-	0.1F Et$_4$NI/DMF	—	-0.33/-0.89 (Hg)	2.2/1.7	1/1	—/—	—/—CH—CH	—
Cyclopentane, bromo-	0.01F Et$_4$NBr/DMF	—	-2.19	—	—	—	—	—
Cyclopentanone betainylhydrazone	BR	8.2	-1.54	—	2	1.0	—	—
Cysteine	0.1F HClO$_4$	—	(-0.05)	-1.61	-1	—	RSHg	—
	0.1F NaOH	—	(-0.59)	ca. -1.45	-1	—	RSHg	—
Cystine	0.1F HCl, 2.4×10^{-5} M thymol	—	-0.38	2.80	2	0.45	cysteine	—
	0.1F NaOH	—	-1.36	—	—	—	—	—
DL-Cystine, α-methyl-	1F HCl, 0.002% (1.3×10^{-5} M) thymol	—	-0.32	—	—	—	—	—
	0.1F HCl, 0.002% thymol	—	-0.56	1.86	—	irr.	—	$E_{1/2}$ at 20°, I at 25°
	0.2F KH phthalate + NaOH, 0.002% thymol	4.0 (?)	-0.81	—	—	—	—	—
Dibenzyl disulfide	0.025F (n-Bu)$_4$NOH/40% MeOH-40% i-PrOH	—	-1.42	—	—	—	toluenethiol	—
2,6-Dibromophenolindophenol	PO$_4^{-3}$ buffer	6.7	±0.00	—	2	—	—	—
Dichlorodiethyltin	1F KCl	—	-0.57	—	—	—	Et$_2$Sn	—
2,6-Dichlorophenolindophenol	PO$_4^{-3}$ buffer	6.7	+0.03	—	—	—	—	—

(continued)

Compound	Supporting electrolyte and solvent	pH	$E_{1/2}$, volts vs. S.C.E.	I	n	αn_a	Product	Remarks
Diethyl disulfide	0.025F (n-Bu)$_4$NOH/40% MeOH-40% i-PrOH	—	−1.78	—	2	—	ethanethiol	
Diethyl sulfone	0.1F Et$_4$NI/50% EtOH	—	NR	—	—	—	—	
Diethyldithiocarbamate	0.05F Na$_2$B$_4$O$_7$, 0.05F KNO$_3$	9.1	(−0.40)/(−0.67)	—/—	1T/1	—	RSHg/RSHg	Wave at −0.67 v. is adsorption wave
Dilauroyl peroxide	0.3F LiCl/C$_6$H$_6$–MeOH (1:1)	—	−0.09	—	2	—	—	
Diphenyl	0.1F Et$_4$NI/DMF	—	−2.57	3.7	2	—	—	
	0.175F (n-Bu)$_4$NI/75% diox	—	−2.70	—	2	—	—	
4-bromo	0.05F (n-Bu)$_4$NI/75% tetrahydrofuran	—	−2.4 (Hg)	18 (?)	—	—	—	
	0.05F (n-Bu)$_4$NI/75% tetrahydrofuran	—	−1.5/−2.4 (Hg)	4/15 (?)	—	—	—	
2-iodo-	0.01F Et$_4$NBr/67% EtOH	—	−1.48	—	—	—	—	
3-iodo-	0.01F Et$_4$NBr/67% EtOH	—	−1.56	—	—	—	—	
4-iodo-	0.01F Et$_4$NBr/67% EtOH	—	−1.59	—	—	—	—	
2-nitro-	Glycine buffer/55% EtOH	2	−0.27	—	4	—	−NHOH	$\Delta E_{1/2}/\Delta \mathrm{pH} = -85$ mv.
4-nitro-	Glycine buffer/55% EtOH	2	−0.21	—	4	—	−NHOH	$\Delta E_{1/2}/\Delta \mathrm{pH} = -82$ mv.
Diphenyl disulfide	0.025F (n-Bu)$_4$NOH/40% MeOH-40% i-PrOH	—	−0.65	—	2	—	benzenethiol	
Diphenyl disulfone	0.1F Et$_4$NI/10% EtOH	—	−0.70	—	—	—	—	
Diphenyl sulfone	0.1F Me$_4$NBr/50% EtOH	—	−2.04	2.65	2	0.80	C$_6$H$_6$ + C$_6$H$_5$SO$_2^-$	
	0.1F Et$_4$NI/50% EtOH	—	−2.15/−2.6	—/—	2/c?	—/—	—/—	
Diphenyl sulfoxide	0.1F Me$_4$NBr/50% EtOH	—	−2.07	2.54	2	0.71	(C$_6$H$_5$)$_2$S	
	0.1F Et$_4$NI/50% EtOH	—	−2.20/−2.62	—/—	2/c?	—/—	—/—	
Diphenylcarbazide	0.1F NH$_3$ + NH$_4$Cl/10% EtOH	10.0	(−0.13) f/(−0.30) i	—/—	—/—	—/—	—/—	
Diphenylcarbazone	0.1F NH$_3$ + NH$_4$Cl/10% EtOH	10.0	(−0.14) i/−0.34 w	—/—	—/—	—/—	—/—	
Diphenyliodonium ion	MeI, μ = 1.0, 20G	2.2	−0.20/−0.86	—/—	1/1	rev./	ϕI/ϕH + ϕI	
		6	−0.20/−1.08/−1.56	—/—/—	1/1/2	rev./	ϕ_2I/ϕH + ϕI/I$^-$	
	0.1F H$_3$PO$_4$ + Et$_4$NOH/50% EtOH, 20G	8.6	−0.20/−1.14/−1.64	—/—/—	1/1/2	rev./ 0.53/0.56	ϕI/ϕH + ϕI/I$^-$	
Diphenylmercury	Buffers/50% EtOH	—	NR					

Substance	Medium	pH	$E_{1/2}$				Products
Estrone-16β-ol	0.05F (n-Bu)₄NCl/90% EtOH	—	-2.09/-2.46	—/	—/	—/	—/—
Ethane, bromo-	0.01F Et₄NBr/DMF	—	-2.13		—		Br⁻
chloro-	0.05F Et₄NBr/75% diox	—	-2.08		2		
1,2-dihromo-	0.05F Et₄NBr/75% diox	—	NR		—		
1-chloro-	3F NaOAc/80% HOAc	—	-0.85		—		—
1,2-dichloro-	3F NaOAc/80% HOAc	—	-0.55		—		—
1,1,2-trichloro-	3F NaOAc/80% HOAc	—	-0.05		—		—
1,1-dinitro-	Various buffers	2.0	-0.33/-0.81/-1.15i	5.29/3.85/—	—/6T/—	—/—/—	—/—C(NH₂)=NOH/—
		6.0	-0.58	10.3	6	—/	—C(NH₂)=NOH
		10	-0.73/-1.39	5.38/5.38	—/	—/	—/—C(NH₂)=NOH
iodo-	0.05F Et₄NBr/75% diox	—	-1.67	—	2		I⁻
mercapto-	0.01F H₂SO₄	—	(+0.02)	—	—		EtSHg
nitro-	BR/3% MeOH	1.8	-0.73		4		—NHOH
		4.6	-0.83		4		—NHOH
		11.6	-0.97		4		—NHOH
1,1,2,2-tetrabromo-	0.3F LiCl/C₆H₆-MeOH (1:1)	—	-1.16		—		—NHOH
1,1,1-trichloro-	3F NaOAc/80% HOAc	—	-0.30				—
2,2-di-4-bromo-phenyl-	0.01F Me₄NBr/80% EtOH	—	-0.86		1		—
2,2-di-4-chloro-phenyl-	0.01F Me₄NBr/80% EtOH	—	-0.88		1		—
2,2-diphenyl-	0.01F Me₄NBr/80% EtOH	—	-0.97		1-2		—
2,2-di-4-tolyl-	0.01F Me₄NBr/80% EtOH	—	-0.95		1-2		—
1,1,1-trinitro-	Various buffers	2.0	±0.0/-0.2/-0.9	3.5/9/6.5	2/6/	—/—/—	—CH(NO₂)₂ + NO₂⁻/
		6.0	±0.0/-0.6	3.5/9	2/6	—/	—C(NHOH)=NOH/NO₂⁻→ / NO₂⁻/—C(NHOH)=NOH/NOH
		10	±0.0/-0.8/-1.4	3.5/4.5/5	2/—/10T	—/—/—	NO₂⁻/—/—C(NH₂)=NOH
Ethanenitrolic acid	0.1F NaOH	—	-0.82/-1.36i	—/—	—/—/—	—/	—/—
Ethanethiosulfuric acid, 2-amino-	0.1F HCl, 0.9F KCl	1.1	-1.06		2	—	RS⁻ + SO₃⁻
	0.1F NHCl, 0.1F NH₃	9.2	-1.14	3.8	2	0.43	RS⁻ + SO₃⁻

(continued)

Compound	Supporting electrolyte and solvent	pH	$E_{1/2}$, volts vs. S.C.E.	I	n	αn_a	Product	Remarks
Ethylene								
bromo-	0.05F Et$_4$NBr/75% diox	—	NR					
chloro-	0.05F Et$_4$NBr/75% diox	—	−2.47	—	2	—	Br$^-$	
1,2-dibenzoyl- (cis-)	Various buffers/50% EtOH	1.3	−0.30	—	2	—	—CH$_2$CH$_2$—	
		7.2	−0.47/−1.54	—/—	2/2	—/—	—CH$_2$CH$_2$—/carbinol	
		11.3	−0.62/−1.65	—/—	2/2	—/—	—CH$_2$CH$_2$—/carbinol	
(trans-)	Various buffers/50% EtOH	1.3	−0.12	—	2	—	—CH$_2$CH$_2$—	
		7.2	−0.44/−1.5	—/—	2/2	—/—	—CH$_2$CH$_2$—/carbinol	
		11.3	−0.57/−1.53	—/—	2/2	—/—	—CH$_2$CH$_2$—/carbinol	
1,1-dichloro-	0.05F Et$_4$NBr/75% diox	—	ca. −2.4	—	—	varies	—	
1,2-dichloro-	0.05F Et$_4$NBr/75% diox	—	NR					
1,1-diphenyl-	0.2F (n-Bu)$_4$NI/DMF	—	−2.30	3.25	2	varies	—	
	0.2F (n-Bu)$_4$NI/90% DMF	—	−2.24	2.86	2	0.90	—	
	0.175F (n-Bu)$_4$NI/75% diox	—	−2.19	4.74	2	0.74	—CH$_2$CH$_2$—	
	0.1F (n-Bu)$_4$NBr/MeCN	—	−1.92 (Hg)	5.69	—	—	—	
1,2-diphenyl- (cis-)	0.1F (n-Bu)$_4$NBr/MeCN	—	−1.81/−2.11 (Hg)	3.66/1.50	—/—	—/	—/—	
(trans-)	0.2F (n-Bu)$_4$NI/DMF	—	−2.14/−2.50	2.14/1.37	1/1	varies/—	—/—	
	0.2F (n-Bu)$_4$NI/80% DMF	—	−2.13	2.97	2	1.2	—CH$_2$CH$_2$—	
	0.175F (n-Bu)$_4$NI/75% diox	—	−2.20	5.20	2	1.0	—CH$_2$CH$_2$—	
	0.1F (n-Bu)$_4$NBr/MeCN	—	−1.73/−2.06 (Hg)	3.07/1.76	—/—	—/—	—/—	
1,2-di-(4-pyridyl)-	Various buffers/50% EtOH	2.3	−0.60	—	2	—	—CH$_2$CH$_2$—	
		9.6	−1.03	—	2	0.88	—CH$_2$CH$_2$—	
tetrachloro-	0.05F Et$_4$NBr/75% diox	—	−1.88	—			—	
tetracyano-	0.1F LiClO$_4$/MeCN	—	+0.15/−0.56 (vs. S.C.E. in MeCN)	—/—	1/1	—/—	monoanion/dianion	
tetraphenyl-	0.2F (n-Bu)$_4$NI/DMF	—	−2.02	3.04	2	0.92	—	
	0.2F (n-Bu)$_4$NI/80% DMF	—	−1.99	2.06	2	—	—CH$_2$CH$_2$—	
	0.175F (n-Bu)$_4$NI/75% diox	—	−2.05	1.92	2	1.0	—CH$_2$CH$_2$—	
	0.1F (n-Bu)$_4$NBr/MeCN	—	−1.62 (Hg)	4.31	—	—	—	

Substance	Supporting electrolyte	pH	$E_{1/2}$	I	n		Product	Remarks
trichloro-triphenyl-	0.05F Et$_4$NBr/75% diox	—	-2.14	2.61/small	2/—	varies/—	—/—	
	0.2F (n-Bu)$_4$NI/DMF	—	-2.08/—				—	
	0.2F (n-Bu)$_4$NI/80% DMF	—	-2.06	2.14	2	1.1	—	
	0.175F (n-Bu)$_4$NI/75% diox	—	-2.12	1.96	2	1.0	—CH$_2$CH$_2$—	
	0.1F (n-Bu)$_4$NBr/MeCN	—	-1.62 (Hg)	4.84			—	
Ethylmercurithiosal-icylate ion	1F HCl, 10G	—	-0.48				—	
	0.1F NaOH, 10G	—	-0.82				—	
Ethylxanthate ion	0.05F NaOH, 0.1F KCl, 1mM eosin	6.5	(-0.26)	ca. -1.3	—1	—	RSHg	
Ferrocene, nitro-	0.08F PO$_4^{-3}$ buffer, 0.2F KCl	6.2	-0.60	7.7	6	1.21	—NH$_2$	
Flavone	V-OAc$^-$ buffer	6.2	-1.22		2		—	
3-hydroxy-	V-OAc$^-$ buffer		-1.29/-1.45	—/—	1/1	—/—	—/—	
Fluoranthene	0.175F (n-Bu)$_4$NI/75% diox		-1.78/-2.11/—	2.40/1.09/	2/2	1.07/—	—/—	
Fluorene	0.175F (n-Bu)$_4$NI/75% diox		2.63	5.82	4	—	—	
Fluorenone	0.1F KCl + HCl/25% EtOH	1.2	-0.63/-0.87	—/—	1/1	—/—	—/—	
	McIl, 0.1F KCl/25% EtOH	7.8	-0.96/-1.13	—/—	1/1	—/—	—/—	
Fluorescein	Various buffers	2.0	-0.48	—	—	—	—	
		8.5	-0.97	—	—	—	—	
		10.8	-1.20	—	—	—	—	
2,4,5,7-tetrabromo-	0.05F NaOH, 0.1F KCl	—	-1.08/-1.50	—/—	—/—	—/—	—/—	
Formaldehyde	Various buffers	8.0	-1.46	small	2	—	CH$_3$OH	Kinetic wave
		10.7	-1.59	small	2	—	CH$_3$OH	Kinetic wave
		12.7	-1.71	—	2	—	CH$_3$OH	Maximum current at pH 13
Formic acid	0.05F Me$_4$NI	—	ca. -1.8	1	1	—	H$_2$(+HCOO$^-$)	$E_{1/2}$ varies with concn.
Fructose	Ca^{++} or Li$^+$ solutions	7.0	ca. -1.75	—	2(?)	—	—	
Fumaric acid	0.9F KCl + HCl	2.6	-0.79	—	2	ca. 1.0	—CH$_2$CH$_2$—	
	0.9F HOAc + NH$_3$	6.9	-1.48	—	2	ca. 1.0	—CH$_2$CH$_2$—	
	0.9F NH$_4$Cl + NH$_3$	8.4-9.5	-1.58	—	2	ca. 1.0	—CH$_2$CH$_2$—	
	0.9F K$_2$HPO$_4$	8.8	-1.71	—	2	ca. 1.0	—CH$_2$CH$_2$—	
	NH$_4^+$-NH$_3$ buffer/10% EtOH	8.2	-1.57	4.1	2	—	—CH$_2$CH$_2$—	

(continued)

Compound	Supporting electrolyte and solvent	pH	$E_{1/2}$, volts vs. S.C.E.	I	n	αn_a	Product	Remarks
Fumaric acid (Continued)								
bromo-	McII	0.5	$-0.41/-0.51$	3.3/3.0	2/2	—	$Br^-/-CH_2CH_2-$	
		3.9	-0.95	5.4	4	—	$Br^- + -CH_2CH_2-$	2°
		8.2–9.7	-1.56	6.3	4	—	$Br^- + -CH_2CH_2-$	2°; compound hydrolyzes
diethyl ester	McII/4% EtOH	0.5	$-0.48/-0.55$	3.1/3.0	2/2	—/—	—/—	2°
		4.1	$-0.70/-0.87$	3.1/2.9	2/2	—/—	—/—	2°
		8.2	$-0.78/-0.97$	—/—	2/2	—/—	—/—	2°; compound hydrolyzes
diethyl ester	$0.9F$ KCl + HCl	2.2	-0.87	—	2	—	$-CH_2CH_2-$	
	$0.9F$ HOAc + NH₃	7.0	-1.03	—	2	—	$-CH_2CH_2-$	
	$0.9F$ NH₄Cl + NH₃	8.7	-1.04	—	2	—	$-CH_2CH_2-$	
	NH₄⁺–NH₃ buffer/10% EtOH	8.2	-1.01	3.7	2	—	$-CH_2CH_2-$	
2-Furaldehyde	Various buffers	1–8	$-0.86 - 0.07$ pH	—	—	—	—	
oxime	$1F$ KCl, $0.04F$ HCl	>10	-1.43	—	—	—	—	
		—	-0.69	—	—	1.5	—	
α-Furildioxime	$8F$ HClO₄	—	$-0.2/-0.5/-0.8$	—/—/—	—/—/—	—/—/—	—/—/—	
	$1F$ KCl, $0.02F$ HCl	—	$-0.47/-0.74$	8.8/1.0	6/2	0.70/1.3	$-CH(NH_2)-$ / $-CH(NHOH)-$	/diamine
	$0.1F$ ammoniacal and other buffers, $1F$ KCl	6.5–10	-1.43 $(=E_{1/2}^0)$	9.4	6	0.3	$-CH(NH_2)-$ / $-CH(NHOH)-$	I in $0.05F$ NH₄Cl, $0.05F$ NH₃, $1F$ KCl
	$0.1F$ Na₂HPO₄, $1F$ KCl	11.0	-1.66 $(=E_{1/2}^0)$	—	6	0.25	$-CH(NH_2)-$ / $-CH(NHOH)-$	
	Buffers containing $1M$ Na⁺ or K⁺	≥12	NR	—	—	—	—	
D-Glucose	PO₄⁻³ buffer	7.0	-1.55	—	—	—	—	Kinetic wave
	$0.002F$ H₃PO₄ + Me₄NOH	8.0	-1.87	—	—	—	—	Kinetic wave
2-deoxy-	$0.002F$ H₃PO₄ + Me₄NOH	8.0	-2.18	—	—	—	—	Kinetic wave
Glyceraldehyde	BR	5	-1.43	—	—	—	—	
		12	-1.63	small	—	—	—	
Glycolaldehyde	—	7.0	-1.50	—	—	—	—	Kinetic wave
	$0.1F$ NaOH	—	-1.69	—	—	—	—	

Substance	Supporting electrolyte	pH	$E_{1/2}$		n		Product	Notes
Glyoxal	—	3.4	-1.41	—	—	—	—	
methyl-	6F H_2SO_4	—	-0.22	—	—	—	—	
	Na_2HPO_4–Na_3PO_4 buffer	10.8	-0.68	—	—	—	—	
Guanidine, 1,3-dihydroxy-	—	12	-0.39	2.99	—	—	—	
nitro-	BR (0.1F), 0.001% methyl red	2.4	$-0.73/-1.13$	5.28/4.67	6	—/—	—NH₂	
		4.9	-1.26	10.09	—	—	—	
		11.8	-1.15	8.92	5(?)	—	—	
nitroso-	BR (0.1F), 0.001% methyl red	2.4	$-0.73/-1.15$	7.82/0.66	—/—	—/—	—/—	
		4.9	$-0.89/-1.28$	3.98/3.38	—/—	—/—	—/—	
		11.7	-1.12	5.17	3(?)	—	—	
n-Heptanoic acid, 2-bromo-	0.5F KCl + HCl	1.9	-0.22	—	2	0.80	Br⁻	
	0.5F NaOAc + HOAc	5.4	-0.44	—	2	—	Br⁻	
	0.5F NH_4Cl + NH_3	8.8	-0.63	—	2	0.34	Br⁻	
2,4-Hexadienal	Various buffers	1–11	$-0.60 - 0.06$ pH/-1.57	1.40/—	1/—	—/—	—/—	Second wave only at pH 7–9
Hexaethyldilead	0.3F LiCl/C_6H_6–MeOH (1:1)	—	(-0.24)	-2.91	—	—	—	
2,5-Hexanedione	Various buffers	—	NR	—	—	—	—	
n-Hexanoic acid, 2-bromo-	0.5F KCl + HCl	1.9	-0.27	—	2	0.77	Br⁻	
	0.5F NaOAc + HOAc	5.4	-0.54	—	2	—	Br⁻	
	0.5F NH_4Cl + NH_3	8.1	-0.81	—	2	0.26	Br⁻	
n-Hexyl hydroperoxide	0.3F LiCl/C_6H_6–MeOH (1:1)	—	-0.12	—	2	—	n-hexanol	
Hydrazobenzene	0.1F NH_3 + NH_4Cl/10% EtOH	10.0	(-0.45)	—	−2	rev.	—N=N—	
Hypoxanthine	NaOAc–HOAc buffer	5.7	-1.61 i	2.75	2	—	—	
Iodoform	0.05F Et_4NBr/75% diox	—	$-0.49/-1.09/-1.50$	—/—	2/2/2	—/—	I⁻/I⁻/I⁻	
α-Ionone	0.1F Et_4NI/80% EtOH	—	$-1.59/-2.08$	—/—	—/—	—/—	—/—	
β-Ionone	0.1F Et_4NI/80% EtOH	—	$-1.46/-1.82$	—/—	1/—	—/—	—/—	
Isoamylxanthate ion	0.05F NaOH, 0.1F KCl, 1mM eosin	—	(-0.38)	ca. -1.2	−1	—	RSHg	
Isoflavone, 7-hydroxy-7-methoxy-	BR	6.2	-1.47 fw	—	2	—	—	
Isophthalaldehyde	BR	6.2	-1.43 fw	—	2	—	—	Extrapolated values
	—/5% MeOH	0	$-0.75/-1.23$	—/—	—/—	—/—	—/—	
Isophthalaldehydic acid	—/5% MeOH	0	$-0.74/-1.23$	—/—	—/—	—/—	—/—	Extrapolated values
Δ^4-3-Ketosteroids	0.1F (n-Bu)₄NI, 0.01F Et_4NI/DMF	—	-2.17	1.4	1	—	—	

(continued)

Compound	Supporting electrolyte and solvent	pH	$E_{1/2}$, volts vs. S.C.E.	I	n	αn_a	Product	Remarks
Maleic acid	0.9F KCl + HCl	2.4	−0.73/—	—/—	—/—	—/—	—/—	
	0.9F HOAc + NH₃	6.9	−1.27	—	2	ca. 1.0	—CH₂CH₂—	
	0.9F NH₄Cl + NH₃	8.6	−1.37	—	2	ca. 1.0	—CH₂CH₂—	
	0.9F K₂HPO₄	8.7	−1.43	—	2	ca. 1.0	—CH₂CH₂—	
	0.9F NH₄Cl + NH₃	9.6	−1.42	—	2	ca. 1.0	—CH₂CH₂—	
	NH₄⁺–NH₃ buffer/10% EtOH	8.2	−1.35	3.6	2	—	—CH₂CH₂—	I = maleic acid II = fumaric acid III = 1,3-butadiene-1,2,3,4-tetracarboxylic acid IV = succinic acid V=butane-1,2,3,4-tetracarboxylic acid
bromo-	McII	0.5	−0.44/−0.54	5.3/2.9	—/—	—/—	I + II + 35% III/IV + V	
		4.1	−0.80/−0.90	3.7/3.2	—/—	—/—	I + II + 8% III/—	
		8.2	−1.38/−1.56	3.9/3.2	—/—	—/—	II + 10%(IV + V)/IV	
		10.5	−1.49/−1.76	3.3/3.3	2/2	—/—	II/IV	
diethyl ester	McII/4% EtOH	0.5	−0.45/−0.54	3.3/3.2	2/2	—/—	Et₂ fumarate/—CH₂CH₂—	2°
		4.1	−0.74/−0.88	3.0/2.9	2/2	—/—	Et₂ fumarate/—CH₂CH₂—	2°
		8.2	−0.84/−1.01	—/—	2/2	—/—	—/—	2°; compound hydrolyzes
diethyl ester	0.9F KCl + HCl	2.2	−0.75	—	2	—	—CH₂CH₂—	
	0.9F HOAc + NH₃	6.9	−0.97	—	2	—	—CH₂CH₂—	
	0.9F NH₄Cl + NH₃	8.7	−1.05	—	2	—	—CH₂CH₂—	
	NH₄⁺–NH₃ buffer/10% EtOH	8.2	−1.02	3.6	2	—	—CH₂CH₂—	
dihydroxy-	BR	1.8	(+0.06)	—	—	—	—	
		7.8	(−0.16)	—	—	—	—	
Maleimide, N-methyl-	BR/50% EtOH	7.2	−0.78/−1.22	—	1/1	—	—	
N-phenyl-	BR/50% EtOH	7.2	−0.75/−1.10	—	1/1	—	—	
D-Mannose	0.002F H₃PO₄ + Me₄NOH	8.0	−1.91	small	—	—	—	Kinetic wave

Substance	Medium	pH	$E_{1/2}$		n		Product
Mercaptobenzothiazole	BR/25% EtOH	1–7	(+0.13 − 0.055 pH)	—	−1	—	RSHg
Mesityl oxide	Various buffers/50% EtOH, 10G	> 7	(−0.26)	—	−1	—	RSHg
		1.3	−1.01	—	1	—	bimolecular ketone
		4.9	−1.24	—	—	—	—
		7.2	−1.60	—	—	—	—
		11.3	−1.64	—	—	—	—
Mesoxalic acid	Various buffers	—	NR	—	—	—	—
hydrazone	Various buffers	2.6	−0.45	—	—	—	—
		5.3	−0.59	—	—	—	—
oxime	Various buffers	2.8	−0.45	—	—	—	—
		5.6	−0.60	—	—	—	—
Methacrylic acid	$0.1F$ LiCl/50% EtOH	—	−1.65	—	—	—	—
ethyl ester	$0.1F$ LiCl/25% EtOH	—	−1.88	—	—	—	—
methyl ester	$0.1F$ LiCl/30% EtOH	—	−1.96	—	—	—	—
	$0.1F$ $Me(n\text{-}Bu)_3NCl/C_6H_6$-EtOH-$H_2O$ (5.5:1)	·	−2.07	—	—	—	—
Methacrylonitrile	$0.1F$ Me_4NBr	—	−2.07	—	—	—	—
Methane, bromo-	$0.05F$ Et_4NBr/75% diox	—	−1.63	—	2	—	Br⁻
chloro-	$0.05F$ Et_4NBr/75% diox	—	−2.23	—	2	—	Cl⁻
dibenzoyl-	McII/50% EtOH	1.3	−0.59	—	1 (?)	—	pinacol (?)
		4.9	−0.81/−1.21	—/—	—/—	—/—	—/—
		8.6	−1.24/−1.58	—/—	—/—	—/—	—/diol (?)
		11.3	−1.30/−1.62	—/—	—/—	—/—	—/diol (?)
dibromo-	$0.05F$ Et_4NBr/75% diox	—	−1.48	—	4 (?)	—	2 Br⁻ (?)
dichloro-	$0.175F$ $(n\text{-}Bu)_4NBr$/DMF	—	−2.14 (Hg)	6.37	—	—	2 Cl⁻ (?)
diiodo-	$0.05F$ Et_4NBr/75% diox	—	−2.33	—	—	—	2 Cl⁻ (?)
dinitro-	Various buffers	2.0	−1.12/−1.53	—/—	2/2	—/—	I⁻/I⁻
		6.0	−0.28/−0.66/−1.08i	6.54/5.54/—	—/—/—	—/—/—	—/—/—
		10.0	−0.63	12.53	—	—	—
iodo-	$0.05F$ Et_4NBr/75% diox		−0.72/−1.34	2.64/9.14	2	—/—	—/—
			−1.63	—	2	—	I⁻

(continued)

Compound	Supporting electrolyte and solvent	pH	$E_{1/2}$, volts vs. S.C.E.	I	n	αn_a	Product	Remarks
Methane (*Continued*)								
nitro-	BR/3% MeOH	1.8	−0.75	—	4	—	—NHOH	
		4.6	−0.85	—	4	—	—NHOH	
		8–12	−0.90	—	4	—	—NHOH	
	McIl, $\mu = 0.40$/0.5% EtOH	1.0	−0.64	—	4	0.52	—NHOH	
		4.9	−0.77	—	4	0.83	—NHOH	
		8.0	−0.87	—	4	0.97	—NHOH	
tetranitro-	Various buffers/10% EtOH	2.0	+0.06	1.98	—	—	—	⎫ Solutions are unstable and yield subsequent ill-defined waves.
		8.0	+0.06	1.98	—	—	—	⎬
		12.0	−0.16	1.98	—	—	—	⎭
trinitro-	Various buffers	2.0	−0.16	21 (?)	—	—	—	
		6.0	−0.37	21 (?)	—	—	dihydroxyguanidine + NO_2^-	
		10.0	−0.50/—	13/8 (?)	—/—	—/—	—/—	
Methyl phenyl sulfone	0.1F Me₄NBr/50% EtOH	—	−2.14	2.55	2	0.94	$C_6H_5SO_2^-$ + CH_4	
Methyl phenyl sulfoxide	0.1F Me₄NBr/50% EtOH	—	−2.18	2.61	2	0.66	$C_6H_5SCH_3$	
Muconic acid	0.1F NaOAc + HCl	4.5	−0.93	—	—	—	—	
1-Naphthaldehyde	BR/50% EtOH	1.8	−0.98	—	—	—	—	
		6.8	−1.35	—	—	—	—	
		12.0	−1.82	—	—	—	—	
4-methoxy-	BR/50% EtOH	1.8	−1.02	—	—	—	—	
		6.8	−1.40	—	—	—	—	
		12.0	−1.51	—	—	—	—	
Naphthalene	0.1F Et₄NI/DMF	—	−2.48	ca. 2.3	—	—	—	
	0.175F (n-Bu)₄NI/75% diox	—	−2.47	3.02	2	—	1,4-dihydronaphthalene	
	0.05F (n-Bu)₄NI/75% tetrahydrofuran	—	−2.3 (Hg)	14 (?)	—	—	—	
1-bromo-	0.05F Et₄NBr/75% diox	—	−1.96/−2.38	—/—	2/2	—/—	Br⁻/1,4-dihydronaphthalene	
1-chloro-	0.05F Et₄NBr/75% diox	—	−2.10/−2.38	—/—	2/2	—/—	Cl⁻/1,4-dihydronaphthalene	
1,2-dihydro-	0.175F (n-Bu)₄NI/75% diox	—	−2.57	—	2	—	tetralin	

1,2-dinitro-	Various buffers	2.1	−0.12/−0.38	−/−	4/8	−/−	−/−
		6.4	−0.30/−0.62	−/−	4/8	−/−	−/−
		9.4	−0.42/−1.06	−/−	4/8	−/−	−/−
1,3-dinitro-	Various buffers	2.1	−0.16/−0.27/−0.93	−/−/−	4/4/4	−/−/−	−/−/−
		6.4	−0.33/−0.50/−1.45	−/−/−	4/4/−	−/−/−	−/−/−
		9.4	−0.52/−0.76	−/−	4/4	−/−	−/−
1,4-dinitro-	Various buffers	2.1	−0.06/−0.36	−/−	4/8	−/−	−/−
		6.4	−0.29/−0.62	−/−	4/8	−/−	−/−
		9.4	−0.36/−0.93/−1.32	−/−/−	4/−/12T	−/−/−	−/−/−
		11.0	−0.39/−1.49	−/−	2/10	−/−	−/−
1,8-dinitro-	Various buffers	2.1	−0.26/−0.69	−/−	10/2	−/−	naphthodihydropyrazole/—
		6.4	−0.48/−1.23	−/−	8/4	−/−	naphthopyrazole/—
		9.4	−0.64/—	−/−	8/−	−/−	naphthopyrazole/—
		11.0	−0.72/—	−/−	8/−	−/−	naphthopyrazole/—
1-iodo-	0.01F Et4NBr/67% EtOH	—	−1.50	—	2	—	I⁻
2-iodo-	0.01F Et4NBr/67% EtOH	—	−1.56	—	2	—	I⁻
1-nitro-	Various buffers	2.1	−0.30/−0.65	−/−	4/2	−/−	−NHOH/−NH2
		6.4	−0.49/—	−/−	4/−	—	−NHOH/—
		9.4	−0.70	—	4	—	−NHOH
		11.0	−0.82	—	4	—	−NHOH
2-nitro-	Various buffers	2.1	−0.30/−0.72	−/−	4/2	−/−	−NHOH/−NH2
		6.4	−0.49	—	4	—	−NHOH
		11.0	−0.82	—	4	—	−NHOH
1-nitroso-	Various buffers/20% MeOH	5-11	+0.24 − 0.053 pH	—	—	—	—
1-Naphthol, 2-methyl-4-amino- (Vitamin K5)	BR	7	(−0.15)	—	−2	—	naphthoquinoneimine
2-Naphthol, 1-nitroso-	OAc⁻ buffer	4.1	−0.01	—	—	—	—
	CL	9.9	−0.33	—	—	—	—
1-phenylazo-, -3,6-disulfonic acid	BR	2.6	−0.08	—	—	—	—
		5.0	−0.33	—	—	—	—
		8.0	−0.57	—	—	—	—
1,2-Naphthoquinone	BR	4.5	−0.34	—	2	rev. (?)	hydroquinone

(continued)

Compound	Supporting electrolyte and solvent	pH	$E_{1/2}$, volts vs. S.C.E.	I	n	αn_α	Product	Remarks
1,4-Naphthoquinone	PO_4^{-3} buffers	3	+0.12	—	2	rev.	hydroquinone	
		7	−0.13	—	2	rev.	hydroquinone	
2,3-dimethyl-	0.1F HOAc, 0.1F NaOAc/50% MeOH	5.4	−0.21	—	2	rev.	hydroquinone	
2-methyl-	BR	2.3	+0.02	—	2	rev.	hydroquinone	
		6.3	−0.22	—	2	rev.	hydroquinone	
		12.0	−0.47	—	2	rev. (?)	hydroquinone	
3-phytyl-	dilute KCl/i-PrOH	—	−0.54	—	2	—	hydroquinone	
1-Naphthylamine, 4-(p-bromophenylazo)-	0.1F NaHSO$_4$, 0.1F Na$_2$SO$_4$/50% EtOH, 0.02% polyvinyl alcohol	2.0	−0.04	—	2	—	—NHNH—	
	0.05F NaOH, 0.05F KCl/50% EtOH, 0.02% polyvinyl alcohol	12.7	−0.79	—	2	—	—NHNH—	
4-(p-methoxyphenylazo)-	0.1F NaHSO$_4$, 0.01F Na$_2$SO$_4$/50% EtOH, 0.02% polyvinyl alcohol	2.0	−0.05	—	2	—	—NHNH—	
	0.05F NaOH, 0.05F KCl/50% EtOH, 0.02% polyvinyl alcohol	12.7	−0.87	—	2	—	—NHNH—	
4-phenylazo-	0.1F NaHSO$_4$, 0.01F Na$_2$SO$_4$/50% EtOH, 0.02% polyvinyl alcohol	2.0	−0.03	—	2	—	—NHNH—	
	0.05F NaOH, 0.05F KCl/50% EtOH, 0.02% polyvinyl alcohol	12.7	−0.81	—	2	—	—NHNH—	
1-Naphthylhydroxylamine, N-nitroso-, NH$_4^+$ salt	McII, $\mu = 1$	2	−0.64	—	6	—	I → III	I = ArN(OH)N=O; II = ArN$^+$(O$^-$)=NOH; III = ArNHNH$_2$; IV = anion of II; V = naphthalene
		6	−1.18	—	6	—	II → III	
		8	−1.55/−1.82	−/−	6/−	−/−	II → III/ IV → V	
Neutral Red	Various buffers	10–12	−1.82	—	4	rev.	—NH—C=C—NH—	
		0.1–10	−0.06 − 0.072 pH	—	2			
Ninhydrin	BR	2.5	−0.67/−0.83/−0.95	−/−/−	−/−/−	−/−/−	−/−/−	
		4.5	−0.73/−1.01	−/−	−/−	−/−	−/−	
		7.0	−0.82/−1.22	−/−	−/−	−/−	−/−	
		9.2	−1.35	—	—	—	—	
Nitric acid, cyclohexyl ester	0.5F LiCl/14% EtOH, 10G		−0.63	—	—	—	—	
ethyl ester	0.5F LiCl/14% EtOH, 10G		−0.82	—	—	—	—	
n-hexyl ester	0.5F LiCl/14% EtOH, 10G		−0.54	—	—	—	—	

Substance	Supporting electrolyte	pH	$E_{1/2}$		n		Product / Remarks
Nitroglycerin	0.5F Me$_4$NCl/EtOH–Me$_2$CO–H$_2$O (11:2:7), 0.001% methyl red	—	−0.77	—	—	—	—
n-Octanoic acid, 2-bromo-	0.5F KCl + HCl	1.9	−0.16	—	2	0.80	Br$^-$
	0.5F NaOAc + HOAc	5.4	−0.38	—	2	—	Br$^-$
	0.5F NH$_4$Cl + NH$_3$	8.8	−0.58	—	2	0.54	Br$^-$
2,4,6-Octatrienal	Various buffers	1–11	−0.45 − 0.06pH/−1.37	1.38/—	1/—	—/—	Second wave only at pH 8–9
n-Octyl hydroperoxide	0.3F LiCl/C$_6$H$_6$–MeOH (1:1)	—	−0.02	—	2	—	n-octanol
Oxalic acid	OAc$^-$ buffers	5.5–6	−1.77	—	—	—	Reduction of HC$_2$O$_4^-$
Parabanic acid	OAc$^-$ buffers, $\mu = 0.5$	4.0	−0.75	3.6	2	1.08	5-hydroxyhydantoin
		5.6	−0.84	—	2	0.97	5-hydroxyhydantoin
	BR	1.9	−0.65	—	—	—	—
		6.8	−0.94	—	—	—	—
Pantothenic acid	0.1F Me$_4$NBr	—	−1.94	—	—	—	—
Penicillic acid	OAc$^-$ buffer	4.7	−0.69	—	—	—	—
Pentaerythritol tetranitrate	0.7F NH$_4$NO$_3$, 0.07F KNO$_3$/30% pyridine	—	ca. −0.27 (Hg)	—	—	—	—
trinitrate	0.5F Me$_4$NCl/EtOH–Me$_2$CO–H$_2$O (11:2:7) 0.001% methyl red	—	−0.81	—	—	—	—
Pentane, 1-bromo-	0.01F Et$_4$NBr/DMF	—	−2.26	—	—	—	—
2,4-Pentanedione	Various buffers	—	NR	—	—	—	—
n-Pentanoic acid, 2-bromo-	0.5F KCl + HCl	2.0	−0.30	—	2	0.54	Br$^-$
	0.5F NaOAc + HOAc	5.1	−0.64	—	2	—	Br$^-$
	0.5F NH$_4$Cl + NH$_3$	8.2	−1.01	—	2	0.27	Br$^-$
Per-n-decanoic acid, $tert$-butyl ester	0.3F LiCl/C$_6$H$_6$–MeOH (1:1)	—	−0.90	—	—	—	—
Phenanthrene	0.175F (n-Bu)$_4$NI/75% diox	—	−2.46/−2.68	—/—	2/2	—	9,10-dihydrophenanthrene/—
9,10-dihydro-1,10-Phenanthroline,	0.175F (n-Bu)$_4$NI/75% diox	—	−2.62	—	2	—	—
5-nitro-	Glycine buffer/55% EtOH	2	+0.02	—	4	—	—NHOH $\Delta E_{1/2}/\Delta$pH = −75 mv.
Phenazine	PO$_4^{-3}$–Cit buffer, $\mu = 0.5$	7.0	−0.36	—	2	—	5,10-dihydrophenazine

(continued)

Compound	Supporting electrolyte and solvent	pH	$E_{1/2}$, volts vs. S.C.E.	I	n	αn_a	Product	Remarks
Phenol, 4-amino-	BR	6.3	(+0.14)	—	—	—	—	
		12.0	(−0.16)	—	—	—	—	
2,6-diethyl-	10% HOAc/40% EtOH	—	(+0.24)	—	—	—	—	
2,4-dinitro-	PO_4^-[a]–OAc–BO_2^-–HCl mixtures/8% EtOH	2.0	−0.14/−0.32/−i	—/—/—	4/4/4	—/—/—	—/—/—	$E_{1/2}$ varies with pH
		6.0	−0.42/−0.69	—/—	4/6	—/—	—/—	$E_{1/2}$ varies with pH
		10.0	−0.66/−0.96/−i	—/—/—	4/4/2	—/—/—	—/—/—	$E_{1/2}$ varies with pH
		11.9	−0.83/−0.99/−1.63	—/—/—	4/4/2	—/—/—	—/—/—	
2,6-dinitro-	PO_4^-[a]–OAc–BO_2^-–HCl mixtures/8% EtOH	2.0	−0.09/−0.24/−i	—/—/—	4/6/2	—/—/—	—/—/—	
		6.0	−0.40/−0.54	—/—	4/6	—/—	—/—	
		10.0	−0.62/−0.80	—/—	4/6	—/—	—/—	
		11.9	−0.83/−0.97	—/—	4/6	—/—	—/—	
2-iodo-	0.01F Et$_4$NBr/67% EtOH	—	−1.49	—	2	—	I⁻	$E_{1/2}$ varies with pH
3-iodo-	0.01F Et$_4$NBr/67% EtOH	—	−1.62	—	2	—	I⁻	$E_{1/2}$ varies with pH
4-iodo-	0.01F Et$_4$NBr/67% EtOH	—	−1.69	—	2	—	I⁻	$E_{1/2}$ varies with pH
2-nitro-	NaCl–HCl/10% EtOH, 5G	1.0	−0.19/−0.64	—/—	4/2	—/—	−NHOH/−NH$_2$	} 0.5mM 2-nitrophenol
	McIl/10% EtOH, 5G	3.0	−0.31/−0.77	—/—	4/2	—/—	−NHOH/−NH$_2$	
	Na$_2$HPO$_4$–NaOH/10% EtOH, 5G	12	−0.90	—	6	—	−NH$_2$	
3-nitro-	NaCl–HCl/10% EtOH, 5G	1.0	−0.19/−0.69	—/—	4/2	—/—	−NHOH/−NH$_2$	} 0.5mM 3-nitrophenol
	McIl/10% EtOH, 5G	3.0	−0.31/−0.89	—/—	4/2	—/—	−NHOH/−NH$_2$	
	Glycine–NaOH/10% EtOH, 5G	6.0	−0.50	—	4	—	−NHOH	
	Na$_2$HPO$_4$–NaOH/10% EtOH, 5G	10	−0.80	—	4	—	−NHOH	
		12	−0.94/−1.15	—/—	1/3 (?)	—/—	—/—	
4-nitro-	NaCl–HCl/10% EtOH, 5G	1.0	−0.26/−0.78	—/—	4/2	—/—	−NHOH/−NH$_2$	} 0.5mM 4-nitrophenol
	McIl/10% EtOH, 5G	3.0	−0.41/−0.86	—/—	4/2	—/—	−NHOH/−NH$_2$	
		6.0	−0.62	—	6	—	−NH$_2$	
	Glycine–NaOH/10% EtOH, 5G	8.0	−0.81/−1.26	—/—	—/—	—/—	—/—	
	Na$_2$HPO$_4$–NaOH/10% EtOH, 5G	10	−0.98/−1.28	—/—	2/4	—/—	—/—	
		12	−0.98/−1.56	—/—	2/4	—/—	—/—	

Substance	Supporting electrolyte	pH	$E_{1/2}$			Product / Remarks
4-nitroso-	$0.2F\ H_3PO_4,\ 0.02F\ NaH_2PO_4 + KNO_3,\ \mu = 0.3/20\%\ EtOH,\ 5G$	1.7	+0.15/−0.75	—/—	—/—	
	$0.1F\ KOAc,\ 0.1F\ HOAc + KNO_3,\ \mu = 0.3/20\%\ EtOH,\ 5G$	4.9	−0.08/−1.20	—/—	—/4T	
	$0.1F\ NaH_2PO_4,\ 0.1F\ Na_2HPO_4/20\%\ EtOH,\ 5G$	7.0	−0.21	—	—	
	$0.1F\ Na_2HPO_4,\ 0.01F\ Na_3PO_4 + KNO_3,\ \mu = 0.3/20\%\ EtOH,\ 5G$	10.7	−0.51	—	4	
2,4,6-trinitro-	$1F\ HCl$	—	> 0	27	18	s-triaminophenol
Phenolphthalein	Various buffers/25% EtOH, 0.001% basic fuchsin	0–10	−0.54 − 0.046 pH	2.76	2	phenolphthalin
Phenyl isothiocyanate	Buffers/—% MeOH	2.2	−0.99/−1.11	—/—	—/4T	$\phi NH_2 + HCHO + H_2S$
		9.1	−1.18	—	2	$\phi NHCH{=}S$
o-Phenylenediamine	$1F\ OAc^-$ buffer, $3mM\ Ni^{++},\ 6mM\ Ca^{++}$	—	−0.75	—	—	Ni — Catalytic; m- and p-isomers in 10-fold excess do not interfere
Phenylglyoxylic acid	McII	2.2	−0.49	—/—	—/—	
		6	−0.87/−1.25	—/—	—/—	
		7.6	−0.96/−1.23	—/—	—/—	
		9.2	−1.24	—	—	
		9.3	−0.80	—	2	${=}CHNH_2$
imine	$2F\ NH_3,\ 1F\,(NH_4)_2SO_4$	2	(+0.19)	—	2	
		—	—/(−0.37)	—/	—/	
Phenylhydrazine	McII	2		0.95	−4	30°
	$0.1F\ NaOH$	—		/1.0	−/−4T	30°
(as acetone phenylhydrazone)	$0.025F\ H_2SO_4/10\%\ Me_2CO,\ 4T$			3.36	−2	−NH₂
		2	−1.21			
Phenylhydroxylamine	McII/10% EtOH, 5G	4–10	(+0.33 − 0.061 pH)		−2	−NO
		2	−0.68			
N-nitroso-, NH₄⁺ salt	$McI,\ \mu = 1.0$	2	−0.68	—	6	I → III
		4	−0.78/−1.01	—/—	—/6T	I → III/
		6	−1.25	—	6	II → III
		8	−1.42	—	6	II → III
		10	−1.4/−1.85	—/—	6/—	II → III/ ; IV → V
		12	−1.85	—	4	IV → V

$$I = \phi N(OH)N{=}O$$
$$II = \phi N^+(O^-){=}NOH$$
$$III = \phi NHNH_2$$
$$IV = \text{anion of II}$$
$$V = \phi H$$

(continued)

Compound	Supporting electrolyte and solvent	pH	$E_{1/2}$, volts vs. S.C.E.	I	n	αn_a	Product	Remarks
Phenylmercuric borate	0.05F OAc⁻ buffer, 0.1F KCl	4.7	−0.12/−0.86	—/—	1/1	—/—	φHg·/φH	
	0.05F PO₄⁻³ buffer, 0.1F KCl	7.0	−0.12/−1.02	—/—	1/1	—/—	φHg·/φH	
Phthalaldehyde	Various buffers	3.1	−0.64/−1.07	—/—	—/—	—/—	—/—	
		7.3	−0.89/−1.29	—/—	—/—	—/—	—/—	
		11.6	−1.03/−1.46	—/—	—/—	—/—	—/—	
Phthalaldehydic acid	0.1F H₃PO₄, 0.17F Me₄NOH/50% diox	—	−1.38	2.41	—/—	—	—	
methyl ester	0.1F H₃PO₄, 0.17F Me₄NOH/50% diox	—	−1.21	2.23	—	—	—	
Phthalic acid								
diethyl ester	0.1F Me₄NCl/75% EtOH	—	−1.87	4.64	—	—	—	
diphenyl ester	0.1F Me₄NCl/75% EtOH	—	−1.65	4.47	—	—	—	
Phthalide	0.2F H₃PO₄, 0.3F Me₄NOH, 0.08F Me₄NI/50% diox	—	−2.05	—	—	—	—	
Picrolonic acid	OAc⁻ buffer	3.7	−0.29/−0.71	—/—	—/—	—/—	—/—	
Prednisone	0.1F NaOAc, 0.1F HOAc/50% MeOH	—	−1.20	—		—	—	
Pregnane-3,11,20-trione	0.05F (n-Bu)₄NCl/90% EtOH	—	−2.41	—	6	—	—	
Pregnenolone	0.05F (n-Bu)₄NCl/90% EtOH	—	−2.44	—	2	—	—	
Progesterone	BR/50% EtOH	6.0	−1.36	—	—	—	—	
Propadiene	0.05F Et₄NBr/75% diox	—	−2.29	—	—	—	—	
Propane, 1-bromo-	0.01F Et₄NBr/DMF	—	−2.20	—	—	—	—	
1,3-dinitro-	0.3F LiCl/C₆H₆-MeOH (1:1)	—	−1.16	—	—	—	—	
2,2-dinitro-	0.3F LiCl/C₆H₆-MeOH (1:1)	—	−0.86	—	—	—	—	
1-nitro-	BR/3% MeOH	1.8	−0.69	—	4	—	—NHOH	
		4.6	−0.84	—	4	—	—NHOH	
		8.0	−0.91	—	4	—	—NHOH	
	0.3F LiCl/C₆H₆-MeOH (1:1)	—	−1.16	—	4	—	—NHOH	
2-nitro-	McII	2.1	−0.49	—	4	—	—NHOH	
		5.1	−0.81	—	4	—	—NHOH	
	Glycocoll buffers	8.0	−0.94	—	4	—	—NHOH	
		10.9	−0.98	—	4	—	—NHOH	
	0.3F LiCl/C₆H₆-MeOH (1:1)	—	−1.31	—	4	—	—NHOH	

Propene, 3-bromo-	0.05F Et₄NBr/75% diox	—	−1.29	—	2	—	Br⁻
3-chloro-	0.05F Et₄NBr/75% diox	—	−1.91	—	2	—	Cl⁻
3-iodo-	0.05F Et₄NBr/75% diox	—	−0.23/−1.16	—/—	—/—	—/—	—/—
Propiolonitrile	0.05F Me₄NI/30% EtOH	—	−1.10/−1.94	—/—	2/2	—/—	acrylonitrile/EtCN
	0.1F HClO₄/30% EtOH	—	−1.05	—	2	—	acrylonitrile
Propionaldehyde	0.1F LiOH	—	−1.92	—	2	—	n-propanol
Propionic acid, 2-bromo-	0.5F KCl + HCl	2.0	−0.39	—	2	0.44	Br⁻
	0.5F NaOAc + HOAc	5.2	−0.89	—	2	—	Br⁻
	0.5F NH₄Cl + NH₃	8.2	−1.14	—	2	0.33	Br⁻
3-nitro-	0.1F HCl	—	−0.57	—	—	0.60	—
	0.1F HOAc, 0.1F NaOAc	4.8	−0.78	7.23	—	—	—
	0.1F NaOH	—	NR	—	—	—	—
Propionitrile, 2,3-dichloro-	0.05F Me₄NI/30% EtOH	—	−0.88/−1.55/−1.95	—/—/—	2/2/2	—/—/—	2-chloroacrylonitrile/acrylonitrile/EtCN
2,2,3-trichloro-	0.05F Me₄NI/30% EtOH	—	−0.47/−1.52/−1.96	—/—	4/2/2	—/—/—	2-chloroacrylonitrile + 2 Cl⁻/acrylonitrile/EtCN
Pseudoionone	0.1F Et₄NI/80% EtOH	—	−1.36/−1.77	—/—	1/—	—/—	—/—
Peridine, 2-amino-4,6-dihydroxy-	0.1F Li₂B₄O₇	9.1	−0.80	—	2	—	—
	0.1F PO₄⁻³ buffer	11.3	−1.12	—	2	—	—
7-methyl-	ca. 1F H₂SO₄	0	−0.41	—	2	—	—
	BR	5	−0.73	—	2	—	—
		10	−1.02	—	2	—	—
		12	−1.22	—	2	—	—
2-amino-4-hydroxy-6-methyl-	ca. 1F H₂SO₄	0	−0.15	—	2	—	5,8-dihydro-
	BR	12	−1.15	—	2	—	5,8-dihydro-
Pteroylglutamic acid	BR	1.8	−0.37	—	—	—	—
		11.2	−0.89	—	—	—	—
	0.1F NH₄Cl, 0.1F NH₃, 0.1F Me₄NCl, 0.001% methyl red	—	−0.98	—/—	—	—	—
Purine	0.5F KCl + HCl	1.8	−0.84/−1.10	—	2/2	—/—	—/—
	0.25F NaOAc + HOAc	4.7	−1.08/−1.29	3.59/6.09	2/2	—/—	—/—
	dilute KCl, NH₃ buffers, or NaOH solutions	≥ 6.2	NR				

(continued)

Compound	Supporting electrolyte and solvent	pH	$E_{1/2}$, volts vs. S.C.E.	I	n	αn_a	Product	Remarks
Pyrazine, 2,5-dimethyl-	$1F\ PO_4^{-3}$ buffer	3.1	−0.61/—/—	3.46/—/—	2/—/—	—/—/—	—/—/—	
2-methyl-	$1F\ PO_4^{-3}$ buffer, 4G	3.1	−0.58/—/—	3.73/—/—	2/—/—	—/—/—	—/—/—	
tetramethyl-	$1F\ PO_4^{-3}$ buffer, 4G	3.1	−0.66/—/—	3.26/—/—	2/—/—	1.2/—/—	—/—/—	2nd and 3rd waves are small kinetic waves
		6.9	−0.98/−1.25/−1.45	—/—/—	—/—/—	—/—/—	—/—/—	
Pyrazolanthrone	$0.65F$ NaOH/50% EtOH, 5G	—	−1.20	—	2	—	—	
Pyrene	$0.175F\ (n\text{-}Bu)_4NI$/75% diox	—	−2.11/−2.43/−2.66	—/—/—	2/2/4	—/—/—	—/—/—	
Pyridine	PO_4^{-3}–Cit buffer, $\mu = 0.5$	7.0	−1.75	—	c	—	—	
3-acetyl-	BR	2	−0.72/−0.87	—/—	—/2T	—/—	—/H_2	1st wave is adsorption wave
-2-carboxylic acid	$0.1F$ HCl	6	−1.07	—	2	—	—	
	Buffers	10	−1.40	—	2	—	—	
-3-carboxylic acid	$0.1F$ HCl	—	−0.89	—	—	—	—	
		5.0	−1.17	—	—	—	—	
		9.0	−1.50	—	—	—	—	
	$0.6F\ Na_2B_4O_7$	—	−1.08	—	—	—	—	
amide	$0.1F\ Na_2B_4O_7$	8-9	−1.66	—	2	—	—	
	$0.1F$ NaOH	8.7	−1.56	—	2	—	—	
		—	−1.74	—	—	—	—	
-4-carboxylic acid	$0.1F$ HCl	—	−0.80	—	—	—	—	
	PO_4^{-3}–Cit buffer, $\mu = 0.5$	7.0	−1.19/−1.56/−1.74	—/—/—	—/—/—	—/—/—	—/—/—	
1-oxide	PO_4^{-3}–Cit buffer, $\mu = 0.5$	7.0	−1.21/−1.39/−1.76small/—/—	—/—/—	—/—/—	—/—/—	—/—/—	
2-cyano-	BR	2	−1.22	—	4 (?)	—	—	
		10	−1.70	—	2 (?)	—	—	
4-cyano-	BR	2	−0.64	—	4	—	—	
		10.5	−1.32	—	2	—	—	
-2,3-dicarboxylic acid	$0.1F$ HCl	—	−0.78	—	—	—	—	
-2,4-dicarboxylic acid	$0.1F$ HCl	—	−0.66	—	—	—	—	
-3,4-dicarboxylic acid	$0.1F$ HCl	—	−0.61	—	—	—	—	

Substance	Medium	pH	E	pK	n			Notes
-3,5-dicarboxylic acid	0.1F HCl	—	-1.10	—	—	—	—	
2-nitro-	V-OAc⁻ buffer/50% EtOH, 5G	4.0	-0.32/-1.3	—/—	4/2	—/—	-NHOH/-NH₂	
3-nitro-	V-OAc⁻ buffer/50% EtOH, 5G	4.0	-0.37/-1.3	—/—	4/2	—/—	-NHOH/-NH₂	
4-nitro-	V-OAc⁻ buffer/50% EtOH, 5G	4.0	-0.16/-1.4	—/—	—/—	—/—	—/—	
	PO₄⁻²-Cit buffer, μ = 0.5	7.0	-0.28/-1.34	—/—	—/—	—/—	—/—	
	PO₄⁻²-Cit buffer, μ = 0.5	7.0	-1.41/-1.73	—/—	—/—	—/—	—/—	
1-oxide	0.1F Me₄NBr	—	-1.8/-1.95	—/—	—/—	—/—	—/—	
Pyridoxin	0.5F KCl + HCl	0.5	-0.63	2.14	1	—	—	
Pyrimidine	0.25F NaOAc + HOAc	3.7	-0.97/-1.23	1.82/2.25	1/1	—/—	—/—	
	0.25F NH₄Cl + NH₄	9.2	-1.54	8.6	4	—	—	
	0.2F KCl + NaOH	13.1	-1.84	6.04	4	—	—	
2-amino-	McIl + KCl, μ = 0.45	2.1	-0.79	2.14	1	—	—	
	0.25F NH₄Cl + NH₃	4.8	-1.01/-1.37	2.25/2.22	1/1	—/—	—/—	
	Various buffers	9.2	-1.44	4.31	2	—	—	
2,6-dimethyl-4-hydroxy-	McIl	2-8	-1.13 - 0.073 pH	6.8	—	—	—	*I* at pH 2-5
4-methyl-	McIl + KCl, μ = 0.45	0.5-13	NR	—	1	—	—	
		2.1	-0.90	1.98	1	—	—	
		5.0	-1.12/-1.47	2.05/1.49	1/1	—/—	—/—	
	0.25F NH₄Cl + NH₃	9.2	-1.60	4.15	2	—	—	
2,4-dihydroxy-5-methyl-	McIl	0.5-13	NR	—	1	—	—	*I* at pH 2-8
2-hydroxy-4-amino-	Various buffers	2-12	-0.53 - 0.078 pH	2.06	1	—	—	
	0.5F NaOAc + HOAc	3.7-5.7	-1.12 - 0.075 pH	4.9	—	—	—	
Pyrogallol	BR	3.1	(+0.35)	—	—	—	—	
		6.5	(+0.14)	—	—	—	—	
		9.5	(+0.13)	—	—	—	—	
γ-Pyrone	0.2F H₃Cit, 0.2F Na₂HPO₄/50% MeOH	7.0	-1.66	—	2	—	—	
	0.05F HCl	—	-0.97	—	2	—	—	
thia- (=C—S—C=)	0.2F H₃Cit, 0.2F Na₂HPO₄/50% MeOH	7.0	-1.37	—	2	—	—	
	0.05F HCl	—	-0.89	—	—	—	—	
thio- (C=S)	0.2F H₃Cit, 0.2F Na₂HPO₄/50% MeOH MeOH	7.0	-1.29	—	6	—	—	

(continued)

Compound	Supporting electrolyte and solvent	pH	$E_{1/2}$, volts vs. S.C.E.	I	n	αn_a	Product	Remarks
Pyrrole, 3-iodo-	0.01F Et$_4$NBr/67% EtOH	—	−1.60	—	2	—/	I-	
tetraiodo-	0.01F Et$_4$NBr/67% EtOH	—	−0.74/−0.90/	—/—/	2/2/	—/—/—/	I-/I-/I-/ (?)	
			−1.10/−1.60		2/2 (?)	—/—		
Quinidine	OAc$^-$ buffer	3	−1.00	—		—	—	
Quinine	OAc$^-$ buffer	3	−1.00	—		—	—	
Quinoline, -2-aldehyde	BO$_2^-$ buffer, μ = 0.1/50% EtOH	11.6	−0.89/−1.54	1.49/0.73	1/—	0.87/—	−N=C(CHOH)$_2$C=N−	
8-hydroxy-	OAc$^-$ buffers	3.0	−0.89/−1.08 i	small/—	—/2T	—/—/	—/—/	
		6.5	−0.99		4			
6-nitro-	BO$_2^-$ buffer	10	−1.48/−1.8	—/—/	1/—	rev.(?)/	—/—/	$\Delta E_{1/2}/\Delta$pH = −72 mv.
	Glycine buffer/55% EtOH	2	−0.14	—	4	—	−NHOH	
8-nitro-	Glycine buffer/55% EtOH	2	−0.04	—	4	—	−NHOH	$\Delta E_{1/2}/\Delta$pH = −76 mv.
Quinolinium ethiodide	Various buffers/43% EtOH	5-10	−0.85	1.64	—	—	—	With 0.08mM compound; $E_{1/2}$ varies with concn
Quinoxaline	PO$_4$-a-Cit buffer, μ = 0.5	7.0	−0.66/−1.52 i	—/—/	2/c	—/—/	1,4-dihydro-/H$_2$	
	CL, μ = 0.05, 10G	1.9	−0.34/−0.86	3.82/0.65	2/c	—/—/	1,4-dihydro-/H$_2$	
		4.0	−0.49/−1.01	3.63/1.28	2/c	—/—/	1,4-dihydro-/H$_2$	
		6.0	−0.62/−1.06	3.54/0.14	2/c	—/—/	1,4-dihydro-/H$_2$	
		9.0	−0.80	3.77	2	—	1,4-dihydro-	
	0.2F KH$_2$PO$_4$, 0.02F KCl	8.0	−0.75	3.71	2	—	1,4-dihydro-	
6-amino-	0.2F KH$_2$PO$_4$, 0.02F KCl	8.0	−0.80	—	2	—	—	
6-bromo-	0.2F KH$_2$PO$_4$, 0.02F KCl	8.0	−0.71	—	2	—	—	
6-chloro-	0.2F KH$_2$PO$_4$, 0.02F KCl	8.0	−0.71	—	2	—	—	
-1,4-dioxide	PO$_4$-a-Cit buffer, μ = 0.5	7.0	−0.52/−0.68/−1.53 i	—/—/	4/2/c	—/—/—/	quinoxaline/1,4-dihydro-/H$_2$	
6-methoxy-	0.2F KH$_2$PO$_4$, 0.02F KCl	8.0	−0.77	—	2	—	—	
-1-oxide	PO$_4$-a-Cit buffer, μ = 0.5	7.0	−0.52/−0.68/−1.52 i	—/—/	2/2/c	—/—/—/	quinoxaline/1,4-dihydro-/H$_2$	
RDX	0.7F NH$_4$NO$_3$, 0.07F KNO$_3$/30% pyridine	—	ca. −0.85 (Hg)	—	—	—	—	

Substance	Medium	pH	$E_{1/2}$		n		Remarks
Rhizopterin	0.1F Li$_2$B$_4$O$_7$	9.1	−0.84	—	—	—	
Riboflavin	BR	1.8	−0.16	—	2	—	
		12.0	−0.64	—	2	—	
D-Ribose	PO$_4^{-3}$ buffer	7.0	−1.77	—	—	—	Kinetic wave
Semicarbazide (as acetone semicarbazone)	0.025F H$_2$SO$_4$/10% Me$_2$CO, 4T	—	−1.27	3.29	2	—	—CH$_2$NH$_2$— 30°
Streptomycin	0.3F Me$_4$NOH	—	−1.45 (Hg)	—	—	—	14°
Styrene	0.2F (n-Bu)$_4$NI/DMF	—	−2.45	4.56	2	varies	
	0.2F (n-Bu)$_4$NI/90% DMF	—	−2.35	3.54	2	—	—CH$_2$CH$_3$
	0.175F (n-Bu)$_4$NI/75% diox	—	−2.35	2.88	2	1.1	
	0.1F Me(n-Bu)$_3$NCl/C$_6$H$_6$–EtOH–H$_2$O (5.5:1)	—	−2.42	—	2	—	—CH$_2$CH$_2$—
β-methyl-	0.175F (n-Bu)NI/75% diox	—	−2.54	2.64	2	1.0	—CH$_2$CH$_2$—
Succinic acid, bromo-	MeII	1.0	−0.25	3.5	2	—	Br⁻
		4.1	−0.50	3.4	2	—	Br⁻
		8.2	−1.09	3.1	2	—	Br⁻
		9.4	−1.11	3.1	2	—	Br⁻
meso-2,3-dibromo-	0.9F KCl + HCl	2.0	−0.06/−0.72	—/—	2/2	—/—	—/—
	0.9F NaOAc + HOAc	4.0	−0.23/−0.89	—/—	2/2	—/—	—/—
	0.9F NH$_4$Cl + NH$_3$	8–9	−0.55/−1.57	—/—	2/2	—/—	fumaric acid/succinic acid
Terephthalaldehyde	—/5% MeOH	0	−0.68	—	—	—	Extrapolated value
Terephthalaldehydic acid	—/5% MeOH	0	−0.67	—	—	—	Extrapolated value
Testosterone	BR/50% EtOH	6.0	−1.38	—	—	—	
Δ1-dehydro-	BR/50% EtOH	6.0	−1.23	—	—	—	
Thiazolaldehyde	PW	2	−0.40	—	—	—	
		9.1	−0.84	—	—	—	
Thiobenzamide	1F KCl + HCl/40% EtOH, 8G	0.3	−0.89	—	2	—	φCHO (after slow hydrolysis)
	PO$_4^{-3}$-Cit buffer, 1F KCl/50% EtOH	7.4	−1.58	—	4	—	φCH$_2$OH
	0.1F NaOH, 1F KCl/40% EtOH, 8G	—	(−0.50)/−1.67	—/—	−2/ca. 2	—/—	HgS + φCN/complex mixture
Thiophene, 2-nitro-	Glycine buffer/55% EtOH	2	−0.25	—	4	—	—NHOH $\Delta E_{1/2}/\Delta$pH = −67 mv.

(continued)

Compound	Supporting electrolyte and solvent	pH	$E_{1/2}$, volts vs. S.C.E.	I	n	αn_a	Product	Remarks
Thiourea	$0.05F$ H_2SO_4	—	(‐+0.02)	—	−2	rev.	$Hg(tu)_{2-4}^{++}$	With 1mM thiourea
Thioxanthone, 1-amino-4-methyl-	OAc⁻ buffer/50% EtOH	4.6	−1.19	—	—	—	—	
	BO_2^- buffer/50% EtOH	8.5	−1.36/—i	—/—	—/—	—/—	—/—	
Thyroxine	$0.25F$ Na_2CO_3, $0.07F$ Me_4NBr or 0.05 F Et_4NBr/40% EtOH or 20% i-PrOH, 50G	—	−1.20/1.42/−1.70	—/—/—	—/—/8T	—/—/—	—/—/—	
α-Tocopherolquinone	OAc⁻ buffer/75% EtOH	6.2	−0.16	—	2	rev.	hydroquinone	
Toluene, α-chloro-	$0.05F$ Et_4NBr/75% diox	—	−1.94	—	2	—	Cl⁻	
α,α-dichloro-	$0.05F$ Et_4NBr/75% diox	—	−1.81	—	4 (?)	—	2 Cl⁻ (?)	
2,3-dinitro-	KCl–HCl	0.5	−0.03/−0.22	—/—	4/8	—/—	—/—	
	Phthalate buffer	3.0	−0.23/−0.50	—/—	4/8	—/—	—/—	
	BO_2^- buffer	9.2	−0.45/−0.81	—/—	4/6	—/—	—/—	
2,4-dinitro-	KCl–HCl	0.5	−0.05/−0.14/—i	—/—/—	4/4/4	—/—/—	—/—/—	
	Phthalate buffer	3.0	−0.22/−0.36/—i	—/—/—	4/4/4	—/—/—	—/—/—	
	BO_2^- buffer	9.2	−0.50/−0.70	—/—	4/4	—/—	—/—	
2,6-dinitro-	KCl–HCl	0.5	−0.0/−0.19/—i	—/—/—	4/4/4	—/—/—	—/—/—	
	Phthalate buffer	3.0	−0.29/−0.44/—i	—/—/—	4/4/4	—/—/—	—/—/—	
	BO_2^- buffer	9.2	−0.55/−0.74	—/—	4/4	—/—	—/—	
3,4-dinitro-	KCl–HCl	0.5	−0.03/−0.21	—/—	4/8	—/—	—/—	
	Phthalate buffer	3.0	−0.22/−0.46	—/—	4/8	—/—	—/—	
	BO_2^- buffer	9.2	−0.42/−0.79	—/—	4/6	—/—	—/—	
2-nitro-	KCl–HCl	0.5	−0.22/—i	—/—	4/2	—/—	—NHOH/—NH₂
	Phthalate buffer	3.0	−0.44/—i	—	4/2	—/—	—NHOH/—NH₂
	BO_2^- buffer	9.2	−0.75	—	4	—	—NHOH	
3-nitro-	KCl–HCl	0.5	−0.15/—i	—/—	4/2	—/—	—NHOH/—NH₂
	Phthalate buffer	3.0	−0.37/—i	—/—	4/2	—/—	—NHOH/—NH₂
	BO_2^- buffer	9.2	−0.71	—	4	—	—NHOH	
4-nitro-	KCl–HCl	0.5	−0.10/—i	—	4/2	—/—	—NHOH/—NH₂
	Phthalate buffer	3.0	−0.35/—i	—/—	4/2	—/—	—NHOH/—NH₂
	BO_2^- buffer	9.2	−0.69	—	4	—	—NHOH	

Compound	Supporting electrolyte	pH	$E_{1/2}$		n	Product	Remarks
α,α,α-trichloro-2,4,6-trinitro-	0.05F Et₄NBr/75% diox	—	-0.68/-1.65/-2.00	—/—/	2/2/2	—/—/	At higher concns. several adsorption waves and a possibly catalytic wave appear.
	KCl-HCl	0.5	-0.01/-0.08/-	—/—/	4/4/	—/—/—/ Cl⁻/Cl⁻/Cl⁻	
	Phthalate buffer	3.0	0.14/—i	—/—i	4/—	—/—/	
			-0.14/-0.24/		4/4/	—/—/	
			-0.36/—i		4/—	—/—	
	BO₂⁻ buffer	9.2	-0.40/-0.55/-0.73	—/—/	4/4/4	—/—/—/	
	0.02F Na₂B₄O₇, 0.02F Na₂SO₃/20% Me₂CO	—	-0.51 w/-0.65i/-1.05i	—/—/	—/—/—	—/—/—/	
Triethyllead chloride	0.3F LiCl/C₆H₆-MeOH (1:1)	—	-0.98 w/ca. -1.32fw	2.49/ca. 2.5	—/	—/	
Triphenylmethyl	0.175F (n-Bu)₄NI/75% diox	—	-1.05/-1.72/-2.00	2/—/	4/—/	—/—/—/	
Tropolone	0.025F KH₂(C₂O₄)₂, 0.1F KCl	2.2	-1.02	—	1	—	
	0.025F NaOAc–HOAc, 0.1F KCl	4.7	-1.20	—	1	—	
	0.025F PO₄–Cit buffers, 0.1F KCl	6–8	-1.21/-1.50	—	—/	—/	
	0.025F NaHCO₃–Na₂CO₃, 0.1F KCl	10	-1.65	—	—	—	
Tropylium ion	BR	< 4.6	-0.27	—	1	— ditropyl	
		6.6	-0.34	—	1	— ditropyl	
Vanillin	McII	2.2	-1.01	—	—	—	
		5.0	-1.16/-1.32	—/	—/	—/	
		8.0	-1.47	—	—	—	
		12.0	-1.67	—	—	—	
Vitamin B₁	0.1F KCl	—	-1.25	—	—	—	
	PO₄⁻³ buffer	5.9	ca. -1.9	—	c	—	
	Buffer	7.2	-1.3	—	—	H₂	
Vitamin B₁₂	0.1F KCN	—	-1.33	—	2	Co(I)	
	0.1F K₂SO₄	—	-1.11	—	—	—	
2,6-Xylenol, 4-nitro-	H₂SO₄–HOAc–H₂O (6:1:3)	—	-0.27	3.24	4	—NHOH	vs. Hg/Hg₂SO₄ (s) electrode in same solvent
4-nitroso-	H₂SO₄–HOAc–H₂O (5:1:4)	—	> 0	1.66	2	—NHOH	
	PO₄⁻³ buffer	7.0	-1.50	—	—	—	Kinetic wave
D-Xylose	0.002F H₃PO₄ + Me₄NOH	8.0	-2.05 (?)	—	—	—	Kinetic wave

AUTHOR INDEX*

A

Adams, R. N., 149, **200**, 231 (refs. *42, 44*), **265**, 412, 415, 417 (ref. *10*), 421 (ref. *53*), 425 (ref. *53*), 426, 428, 432, 443, 444 (refs. *94, 95*), 449 (ref. *101*), 459 (ref. *101*), **461–463**, 546 (ref. *113*), 563 (ref. *151*), **596, 597**

Airey, L., 120 (ref. *41*), 122 (ref. *41*), **199**, 379 (ref. *45*), **410**, 573 (ref. *178*), 577 (ref. *190*), **598**

Alberts, G. S., 522 (ref. *37*), **594**

Albright, C. H., 261, **266**

Alimarin, I. P., 500 (ref. *34*), **508**

Ammann, R., 530 (ref. *54*), **594**

Anderegg, G., 276 (refs. *12, 14*), **301**

Andersen, D. L., 268 (ref. *1*), **300**

Annino, R., 72 (ref. *27*), **93**

Anson, F. C., 432, 434 (ref. *71*), 438 (refs. *78, 83, 84*), **463**, 551 (ref. *135*), 553 (ref. *135*), 569 (ref. *171*), 571 (ref. *171*), **596, 597**

Antweiler, H. J., 124 (ref. *59*), **200**, 312, **331**

Ariel, M., 546 (refs. *116, 117, 120a*), **596**

Arthur, P., 72 (refs. *23, 26*), **93**, 451 (ref. *104*), **464**

Asada, K., 109 (ref. *10*), **198**

Atta, R. E. van, 258 (ref. *64*), 259 (ref. *64*, **266**, 363 (ref. *26*), **409**

Auerbach, C., 196 (ref. *127*), **202**

Ayabe, Y., 253 (ref. *56*), **266**, 415 (ref. *13*), **461**

Azim, S., 421 (ref. *52*), **462**

B

Babkin, G. N., 545 (ref. *103*), **595**

Ball, R. G., 420 (ref. *23*), **461**, 546 (ref. *114*), **596**

Bannister, L. C., 539 (ref. *81*), **595**

Bard, A. J., 86 (ref. *62*), **94**, 438 (ref. *82*), **463**, 488 (ref. *8*), **507**, 516 (ref. *6*), 521 (ref. *21a*), 522 (refs. *29–31*), 543 (ref. *88b*), 562 (ref. *148*), 563, 566, 569 (ref. *172*), 571 (ref. *172*), **593, 595, 597**

Barendrecht, E., 544, **595**

Barker, G. C., 75 (ref. *55*), **93**, 103 (ref. *3*), 121 (ref. *47*), 122 (ref. *47*), **198, 199**, 257 (ref. *63*), **266**, 420 (refs. *27, 31*), **461**, 589 (refs. *243, 248*), 590 (ref. *257*), 592 (ref. *257*), **600**

Bauer, H. H., 231 (refs. *33, 34*), **265**, 588 (refs. *227–229*), 589, **599, 600**

Bauman, R. P., 346, **409**

Baumann, F., 431 (ref. *67*), 432 (ref. *67*), 437 (ref. *67*), **462**

Bawden, A. T., 506 (ref. *50*), **509**

Baxter, R. A., 72 (ref. *28*), **93**

Bearman, R. J., 149 (ref. *75*), **200**

Becker, E. I., 237 (ref. *46*), 264 (ref. *46*), **266**

Beckmann, P., 73 (ref. *42*), **93**

Beecher, H. K., 73 (ref. *32*), **93**

Beilby, A. L., 439 (ref. *89*), 442, **463**

Belyavskaya, V. B., 543 (ref. *88*), 546 (ref. *88*), **595**

Benesch, R., 189 (ref. *122*), **201**

Benesch, R. E., 189 (ref. *122*), **201**

Bennett, C. E., 521 (ref. *23*), **593**

Berg, H., 537 (ref. *70*), **594**

Bergmeyer, H. U., 362 (ref. *22*), **409**

Berka, A., 502 (ref. *46*), **508**

Berman, D. A., 573 (ref. *181*), **598**

Berzins, T., 250 (ref. *52*), **266**, 286 (ref. *28*), **301**, 418 (ref. *17*), 420 (ref. *17*), **461**, 557 (ref. *140*), 559 (ref. *144*),

SUBJECT INDEX

A

"Absolute" method, 391
Acetaldehyde, indirect methods based on, 362, 370
Acids, attack on agar by, 388
See also Hydrogen ion.
Acrylic plastics, cells made from, 446, 450
Activation energy, in electron-transfer processes, 233
Activity coefficients, in assessment of reversibility, 230
in studies of complex ions, 268
Additivity of currents, 189
Adsorption, onto cell walls, 446
onto electrode surfaces, in a.-c. polarography, 589
in chronopotentiometry, 566
effects on current density, 327
effects on current–drop age curves, 121, 124
effects on drop time, 197
effects on electrokinetic parameters, 245, 323
effects on maxima, 314, 318
effects on solid-electrode voltammograms, 435
effects on transfer of concentration polarization, 124
effects on $\varkappa$, 190
in oscillopolarography, 589
stripping analysis in study of, 539
specific, 255
effects of, 264, 285
Adsorption analysis, 329
Adsorption waves, 187
behavior at hanging mercury drop electrode, 459
heights of, 177
equation for, 187

variation with height of mercury column, 188
identification of, 188
mixtures of substances yielding, 192
variations of i_l/C for, 127
Agar, as maximum suppressor, 319
salt bridges made with, effect of anhydrous solvents on, 340
preparation and storage of, 63
substances attacking, 388
Air, capillary characteristics in, 134
removal of. *See* Deaeration.
Alcohols, as solvents, 141, 337, 339
Aldehydes, analysis of mixtures of, 367
determination of, by amperometric titration, 481
by differential volatilization, 370
by indirect method, 363
masking of, 348, 349
Aldoses, kinetic waves of, 176
α, definition of, 235
range of values of, 245
αn_a, effects of, on half-wave potential–σ correlations, 287
on peak currents, 415
on variation of half-wave potential with t, 229, 242
evaluation of, by chronopotentiometry, 559
correction for double-layer effects in, 260
by polarography, 236, 242
interpretation of, 246
range of values of, 229
for related compounds, 287
tables of, 253, 671
variations of, 248, 260, 263
log-plot criterion of reversibility and, 263
Alternating current, in polarographic circuits, 86, 381